Introduction to

ORGANIC

CHEMISTRY

D. C. HEATH AND COMPANY BOSTON

LIBRARY OF CONGRESS CATALOG NUMBER: 57–6310

PREFACE

This book takes the place of *Organic Chemistry, Abridged Edition* (1944) and *Textbook of Organic Chemistry* (1950). It is given a different name because it departs considerably from the predecessors in scope and organization.

The twenty-eight chapters of Part I develop the essential principles of organic chemistry in a way calculated to best fit the needs of the modern student. Early history that is no longer particularly informative or inspiring is by-passed for a direct approach to the science of today. Tables of physical constants and other elaborations that are appropriate enough in a reference book are omitted. On the other hand, basic theory is not only retained but expanded, and each new concept is developed at the place where it is first applicable. Thus in the chapter on alkenes, development of the idea of geometrical isomerism from the orbital theory approach permits consideration of the steric course of additions to alkenes and alkynes along with the other facts and interpretations and obviates backtracking at a later date. A section on dienes at the end of the same chapter provides occasion for introduction of resonance and for expansion of orbital theory and is followed by an interpretation of the aromaticity of benzene. Examples of aromatic substitution and of the reduction of nitrobenzene are also included in the early part of the book, partly to give greater flexibility to the laboratory schedule. The main discussion of aromatic structure and substitution (Chapter 18) is thereby simplified, and it is further shortened by omission of most of the historically interesting but no longer pertinent preresonance controversies.

Part I includes about all the facts and theories a student can be expected to assimilate in a one-year course. Study aids include chapter summaries, problems at the end of most chapters with answers at the back of the book, review problems at the end of Chapter 11, and marginal captions to supplement side and center headings. Cross references are given in the decimal system: 10.5 = Chapter 10, section 5.

Part II is a new feature. Entitled "Applications to Research," it demonstrates how reactions and principles learned in the student's systematic study are applied in research. The student here gets some idea of the way in which problems originate, of the techniques by which they are solved, and of the extensive experimentation that is usually involved. Brief biographies indicate where and by whom the work was done. Procedure for utilization of Part II will vary with the individual teacher. Some may wish to incorporate part of the material into lectures; some may care to recommend it for reading.

PREFACE

Teaching conformational analysis to a large class demonstrated the effectiveness of visual aids in making the concepts clear and prompted preparation of the photographs of Barton and Stuart models. Lantern slides of paired photographs and projection formulas, as well as slides of some other illustrations from the book and of portraits of prominent chemists, are available from Wilkens-Anderson Co., Chicago.

Louis F. Fieser
Mary Fieser

CONTENTS

PART 1

PART 2

PART I

STRUCTURES OF CARBON COMPOUNDS

Because carbon is in the middle of the periodic table and a member of the first group of elements, it forms compounds with other elements by a process different from that of electron transfer, by which inorganic compounds are formed. Sodium transfers its external valence electron

$$\overset{.}{Na} \overset{\frown}{+} \overset{.}{\underset{..}{Cl}}: \longrightarrow \overset{+}{Na} + :\overset{..}{\underset{..}{Cl}}:^{-}$$

donor   acceptor

Electron transfer

C

to an acceptor because it thereby acquires the stable state of the noble gas neon; chlorine functions as acceptor because incorporation of one more electron into its valence shell of seven gives the stable electron octet characteristic of argon. Loss of an electron converts sodium atom into sodium ion, and gain of an electron by the chlorine atom produces chloride ion, and hence electron transfer results in a typically ionic inorganic compound. **Carbon,** with four valence electrons, has no more tendency to lose than to gain electrons and **tends to resist acquisition of either a positive or negative charge.** Lead, a higher member of group IV, also has four external electrons, but these are so far removed from the atomic nucleus because of the intervening electron shells that the attraction by the nucleus is weak enough to permit electron transfer to form Pb^{++}. In carbon, the valence electrons are so close to the nucleus that the attractive force opposes charge separation.

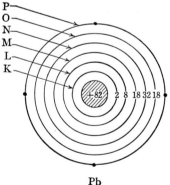

Pb

The compounds of carbon, called organic because the first known members were natural products synthesized by plant or animal organisms, are formed by electron sharing. If each of four hydrogen atoms shares its electron (cross) with one of the four valence electrons of carbon (dots), a stable compound results, methane, in which each hydrogen is associated with two electrons, as in helium, and the carbon atom is surrounded

$$\cdot \overset{\cdot}{\underset{\cdot}{C}} \cdot \ + \ 4\overset{x}{H} \ = \ H \overset{H}{\underset{H}{\overset{x}{\underset{x}{C}}}} H$$

Methane

1.2
Organic compounds

by a stable octet, as in neon and argon. No electron transfer is involved, and hence methane is nonionic. The four electrons of carbon can equally well fill the gaps in the electron septets of four chlorine atoms to give another, typically nonionic, organic compound, carbon tetrachloride, in which each of the five atoms

Electron sharing

$$\cdot \overset{\cdot}{\underset{\cdot}{C}} \cdot \ + \ 4 \overset{xx}{\underset{xx}{x}}{Cl}^x \ = \ \overset{\overset{xx}{Cl}^x}{\underset{\underset{xx}{Cl}^x}{\overset{xx}{Cl} \overset{x}{C} \overset{xx}{Cl}^x}}$$

Carbon tetrachloride

concerned is surrounded by an electron octet. Electron sharing between two or more carbons is also possible, as in the combination of two carbon and six hydrogen atoms to form ethane:

$$2 \cdot \overset{\cdot}{\underset{\cdot}{C}} \cdot \ + \ 6\,H\cdot \ = \ H \overset{H}{\underset{H}{:}}C \overset{H}{\underset{H}{:}}C H$$

Ethane

Covalent bond

A bond between atoms consisting of a pair of shared electrons is called a covalent bond. In the hydrocarbon ethane two carbons are linked by a covalent bond, and each carbon it covalently bonded to three hydrogens. Two carbon atoms can also be linked by a double bond, that is, by two pairs of shared electrons, as in ethylene:

Double and triple
bonds

$$2 \cdot \overset{\cdot}{\underset{\cdot}{C}} \cdot \ + \ 4\,H\cdot \ = \ H:C::C:H \atop \quad\; \overset{}{H}\;\;\overset{}{H}$$

Ethylene

Acetylene is a hydrocarbon containing a triple bond, or three pairs of shared electrons:

$$2 \cdot \overset{\cdot}{\underset{\cdot}{C}} \cdot \ + \ 2\,H\cdot \ = \ H:C:::C:H$$

Acetylene

Acetylene is a stable hydrocarbon, since each hydrogen has the helium arrangement and each carbon is associated with eight shared electrons.

Nitrogen, with five valence electrons, forms with hydrogen the covalently bonded compound ammonia:

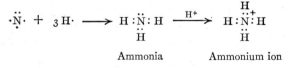

Ammonia   Ammonium ion

In ammonia, unlike methane, the octet surrounding the central atom includes a pair of unshared electrons, and hence ammonia can combine with a proton (hydrogen ion) by sharing the extra electron pair with hydrogen to give an ammonium ion, which carries the charge derived from the proton. Oxygen (6 electrons) forms compounds containing two pairs of unshared electrons, for example water, and water

$$H:\ddot{O}:H \quad + \quad H^+ \quad \longrightarrow \quad H:\overset{..+}{\underset{H}{\ddot{O}}}:H$$

Water   Hydronium ion

likewise combines with a proton to form a hydrated proton or hydronium ion, and this ion or an aggregate is present in an aqueous solution of a mineral acid. Methyl alcohol likewise is capable of combining with a proton by utilization of its unshared electrons. Thus the

$$\overset{H}{\underset{H}{H:\ddot{C}:\ddot{O}:H}} \xrightarrow{H^+} \overset{H}{\underset{H\ H}{H:\ddot{C}:\overset{..}{O}:H}}^+ \qquad \overset{H\ H}{\underset{H}{H:\ddot{C}:\ddot{N}:H}} \xrightarrow{H^+} \overset{H\ H}{\underset{H\ H}{H:\ddot{C}:\ddot{N}:H}}^+$$

Methyl alcohol   Methylamine

oxygen is basic, although not so strongly basic as the nitrogen in ammonia or in methylamine, and oxonium salts are hence not so stable as ammonium salts. Cations such as that from methyl alcohol, however, exist in solution and participate in certain reactions of alcohols.

Electronic formulas are easily derivable for the simple compounds thus far considered because in each case only one structure, or arrangement of atoms, is possible. However, the empirical formula C_2H_6O can be interpreted in terms of two structural formulas, I and II, each of which fulfills electronic requirements for stability. In I the basic

$$\overset{H\ H}{\underset{H\ H}{H:\ddot{C}:\ddot{C}:\ddot{O}:H}} \qquad \overset{H\qquad H}{\underset{H\qquad H}{H:\ddot{C}:\ddot{O}:\ddot{C}:H}}$$

I   II

structural unit is carbon–carbon–oxygen, and in II it is carbon–oxygen–carbon. Two substances of the formula C_2H_6O do indeed exist and are defined as **isomers,** meaning that they are built of the same component parts (Gr. *isos*, same; *meros*, part). How can they be distinguished? Which isomer has the structure I, and which II?

Kekulé Structural Theory. — A principle by which structures can be elucidated experimentally was recognized by the German chemist Kekulé [1] in 1859 and employed by him in an analysis of the known facts that at once brought considerable clarity to a previously highly confused field. This was long before the atom was known to contain a positive nucleus surrounded by electrons, but Kekulé intuitively deduced the idea that elements are joined to one another by a chemical

[1] August Kekulé, 1829–96; b. Darmstadt, Germany; Bonn; *Ber.,* **29,** 1971 (1896); *J. Chem. Soc.,* **73,** 97 (1898)

bond, represented by a line, and for the hydrocarbons mentioned above he wrote the formulas:

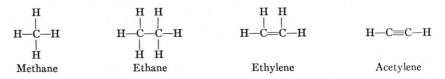

Methane   Ethane   Ethylene   Acetylene

Kekulé bond equivalent to an electron pair

With development of the electronic theory, the Kekulé bond has come to mean a pair of shared electrons. The earlier formulation is still used, with the electronic counterpart implied, because of its simplicity, and it is also abbreviated further by grouping the elements and leaving out some or all Kekulé bonds, as:

CH_4 H_3C—CH_3 or CH_3—CH_3 CH_2=CH_2 HC≡CH

Methane   Ethane   Ethylene   Acetylene

Principle of structure determination

Example

The principle of structure determination introduced by Kekulé and still used involves consideration of all possible structures corresponding to the empirical formula and selection of the one which alone is consistent with the properties and reactions of the compound and (or) with methods for its synthesis. The two isomers of the formula C_2H_6O, mentioned above, can be distinguished by their boiling points, 78° and −25°, and the problem is to identify each isomer with the correct structural formula, I or II, as written above, or the alternatives Ia, IIa:

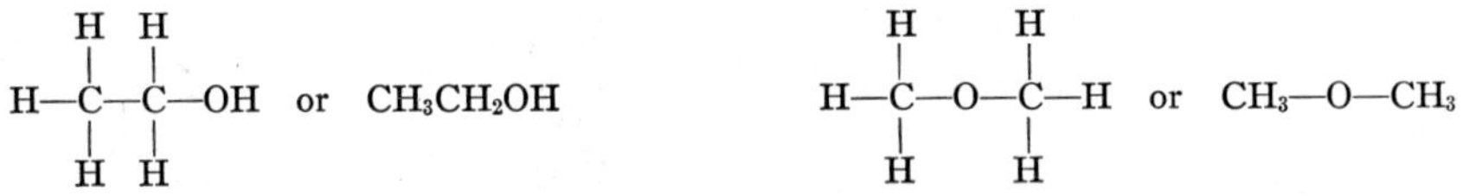

H—C—C—OH or CH_3CH_2OH H—C—O—C—H or CH_3—O—CH_3

Ia   IIa

Chemical properties

Experiment shows that the isomers react in different ways with hydriodic acid, namely:

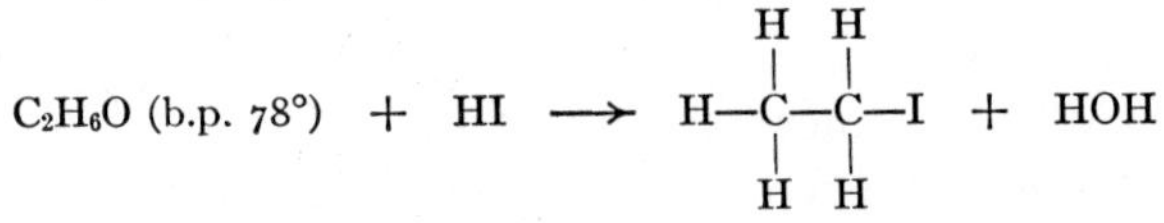

C_2H_6O (b.p. 78°) + HI ⟶ H—C—C—I + HOH

Ethyl iodide

C_2H_6O (b.p. −25°) + 2 HI ⟶ 2 H—C—I + HOH

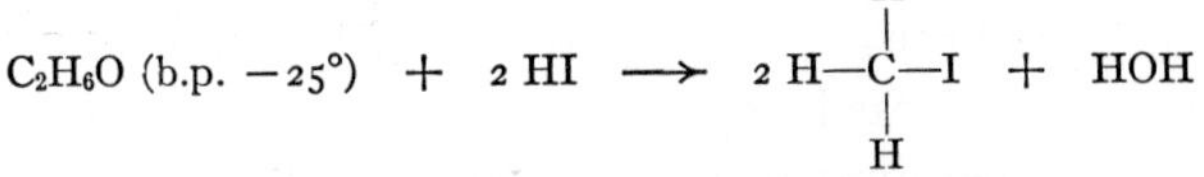

Methyl iodide

The higher boiling isomer reacts with one equivalent of acid to give a molecule each of water and C_2H_5I, for which only one formula is possible, that of ethyl iodide. Iodine, entering the molecule, displaces the OH, or hydroxyl group, which combines with H of HI to form HOH. Structure I (Ia) contains a hydroxyl group whereas II does not, and hence the observation is consistent only with the structure I for the isomer b.p. 78°. The evidence would be incomplete if the behavior of the isomer b.p. −25° were not considered as well. This isomer reacts with hydriodic acid at a higher temperature, consumes two moles of reagent, and gives two moles of methyl iodide and water. This behavior is consistent alone with formula II (IIa), in which two methyl groups are joined through an intervening oxygen. When the central oxygen is abstracted by two hydrogen atoms, the molecule is disrupted and each methyl group left free to combine with iodine:

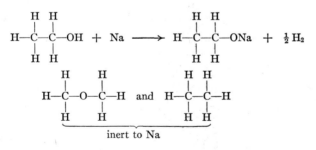

Both reactions with hydriodic acid thus lead to the conclusion that the isomer b.p. 78° is ethyl alcohol, CH_3CH_2OH (I) and the isomer b.p. −25° dimethyl ether, CH_3OCH_3 (II). Confirmatory evidence is that ethyl alcohol reacts with metallic sodium with displacement of one hydrogen by sodium, whereas dimethyl ether is inert to the metal. In structure I one hydrogen is attached to oxygen and therefore is different from the other five, which are linked to carbon; in structure II all six hydrogens are carbon-bonded, like those of ethane, which is inert to sodium. Hence the differing behavior is entirely consistent with the formulas:

$$H-\underset{\underset{H}{|}}{\overset{\overset{H}{|}}{C}}-\underset{\underset{H}{|}}{\overset{\overset{H}{|}}{C}}-OH + Na \longrightarrow H-\underset{\underset{H}{|}}{\overset{\overset{H}{|}}{C}}-\underset{\underset{H}{|}}{\overset{\overset{H}{|}}{C}}-ONa + \tfrac{1}{2}H_2$$

$$H-\underset{\underset{H}{|}}{\overset{\overset{H}{|}}{C}}-O-\underset{\underset{H}{|}}{\overset{\overset{H}{|}}{C}}-H \text{ and } H-\underset{\underset{H}{|}}{\overset{\overset{H}{|}}{C}}-\underset{\underset{H}{|}}{\overset{\overset{H}{|}}{C}}-H$$

inert to Na

Confirmation by synthesis

The structures assigned from chemical properties are further confirmed by the following syntheses:

$$CH_3CH_2I + AgOH \longrightarrow CH_3CH_2OH + AgI$$
$$CH_3ONa + ICH_3 \longrightarrow CH_3OCH_3 + NaI$$

Arrangement of Atoms in Space. — What is the shape of the methane molecule? Is it flat, with all five elements in a plane? Is it

Tetrahedral configuration of carbon

spherical? This question was answered inductively in 1873 in independent papers by van't Hoff [2] and Le Bel,[3] and their inferences were later abundantly confirmed by chemical and physical evidence. The molecule is three-dimensional and symmetrical, with carbon at the center and the four hydrogens attached symmetrically and each equidistant from the others. Thus the carbon atom is tetrahedral; its four valences are directed to the corners of a tetrahedron, as shown in the first model of Fig. 1.1. A more accurate conception of the shape of

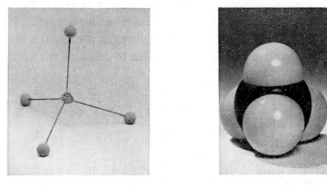

FIG. 1.1.— Methane, Barton and Stuart Models

the molecule is given by the Stuart model, in which the atoms are represented by spheres of appropriate relative diameters and facings on a scale proportional to the actual interatomic distances. Important consequences of the tetrahedral character of carbon are considered in Chapter 12 (Stereochemistry), but the simple basic concept is useful in understanding phenomena to be encountered earlier.

1.5

Classification and Names. — Methyl and ethyl alcohol are the first two members of a large series of alcohols. Methyl and ethyl iodide are members of a series described as **alkyl halides** and symbolized by the formula RX, where X is any halogen and R is any alkyl group, that is, a hydrocarbon group of the type methyl, ethyl, etc. The formula ROH thus designates a type of alcohol exemplified by methyl and ethyl alcohol. The reaction of ethyl alcohol with hydriodic acid is an example of a fairly general reaction formulated as follows:

Type formulas

$$\underset{\text{Alcohol}}{\text{ROH}} \quad + \quad \underset{\text{Hydrogen halide}}{\text{HX}} \quad \longrightarrow \quad \underset{\text{Alkyl halide}}{\text{RX}} \quad + \quad \text{H}_2\text{O}$$

Methane and ethane can be thought of as combinations of the methyl and ethyl group with hydrogen, $CH_3 \cdot H$ and $C_2H_5 \cdot H$, and the general formula for such a hydrocarbon is RH, whence the generic name **alkane**. Ethylene and acetylene are the common names of the first members of series of hydrocarbons characterized by having double

[2] Jacobus Hendricus van't Hoff, 1852–1911; b. Rotterdam, Netherlands; Ph.D. Utrecht; Amsterdam; Nobel Prize 1901; *J. Chem. Soc.*, 1127 (1913)
[3] Joseph Achille Le Bel, 1847–1930, b. Pechelbronn, France; *J. Chem. Soc.*, 2789 (1930)

and triple bonds, respectively, and hence, in a systematic nomenclature worked out at an international congress at Geneva in 1892, these series are designated **alkenes** and **alkynes**. In the Geneva system an alcohol derived from an alkane is designated by changing the name of the parent hydrocarbon from **ane** to **anol**. Thus methyl and ethyl alcohol are called methanol and ethanol.

SUMMARY

Electronic Structures

Neutral character of carbon (top center of periodic table). Resistant to acquisition of positive or negative charge. Formation of stable compounds by electron sharing. Covalent bond a pair of shared electrons. Electronic formulas of methane and carbon tetrachloride.

The double bond (ethylene) and triple bond (acetylene). Ammonia and water, having unshared electrons, can combine with a proton to form cations. Same true of methyl alcohol and methylamine. Oxygen basic but less so than nitrogen.

Determination of Structure

Kekulé bond (1859) the equivalent of a pair of shared electrons. Kekulé structures and their abbreviations.

Method: consider all possible formulas and select the one that accords with properties and (or)

synthesis. Example: isomers of the formula C_2H_6O identified as CH_3CH_2OH and CH_3OCH_3 by results of reactions with HI and with Na; confirmation by synthesis.

Arrangement of Atoms in Space

van't Hoff-Le Bel theory of tetrahedral nature of carbon (1873).

Classification

Geneva nomenclature (1892): alkyl group, R (methyl, ethyl); alkyl halide, RX; alkane, RH (methane, ethane); alkene (double bond,

e.g., ethylene); alkyne (triple bond, e.g., acetylene); alcohols called alkanols (e.g., methanol, ethanol).

PROBLEMS

1. Write electronic formulas for $CHBr_3$, CO_2, HCN.
2. Write Kekulé formulas for hydrazine, N_2H_4 (trivalent nitrogen); formic acid, CH_2O_2; propane, C_3H_8.
3. There are two isomers of the formula $C_2H_4Br_2$ and two of the formula $C_2H_3Br_3$. Write the four structural formulas.
4. The synthesis of ethyl alcohol from C_2H_5I and AgOH proves its structure. Would synthesis of a propyl alcohol from C_3H_7I prove its structure?
5. Two isomers of the formula C_3H_6 exist. What are the structures?
6. The formula $CH_3CH{=}CHCH_3$ represents two isomers. What are they?

READING REFERENCES

F. J. Moore, *A History of Chemistry*, 3rd Ed., 175–246, McGraw-Hill, New York (1939)

J. R. Partington, *A Short History of Chemistry*, 216–239, Macmillan, London (1937)

C. Schorlemmer, *The Rise and Development of Organic Chemistry*, Macmillan, London (1894)

F. R. Japp, "Kekulé Memorial Lecture," *J. Chem. Soc.*, **73**, 97–138 (1898)

G. N. Lewis, "The Atom and the Molecule," *J. Am. Chem. Soc.*, **38**, 762 (1916)

EXPERIMENTATION

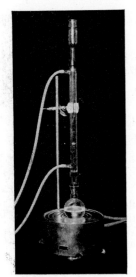

FIG. 2.1.— Reaction
Mixture Heated under
Reflux

2.2
*Factors decreasing
yield*

Reactions of typical inorganic compounds involve interaction of mobile, oppositely charged ions and hence proceed rapidly and quantitatively. Covalent carbon compounds are under no such compulsion to combine from an electrostatic effect, and reaction may depend upon random motion of molecules and chance collisions, some of which are so oriented as to result in reaction. A rise in temperature increases the random motion and hence also the rate of reaction. On the average a $10°$ rise in temperature doubles the reaction rate. If the rate of a given reaction is 1 at $20°$, approximately room temperature in some laboratories, the rate is 128 at $90°$, which is within $1-2°$ of the maximum temperature obtainable by heating a reaction mixture on the steam bath. Hence steam heating is commonly practiced as a safe way to accelerate reactions of flammable organic compounds or of solutions of reactants in flammable organic solvents. The mixture is maintained at a brisk boil in a flask fitted with a vertically mounted condenser which condenses the vapors and returns volatile material to the boiling flask (Fig. 2.1).

Many organic reactions are promoted by catalysts, often a trace of a mineral acid or of an alkali, the function of which is to produce in a neutral organic reactant a few molecules at a time of a transient, ionic species of high enough energy content to serve as intermediate for eventual conversion of starting material into product. Organic compounds as a rule are delicate and easily decomposed. Thus promotion of a reaction by heat or by acid or base catalysis is liable to damage reactants or products, or both, with decrease in yield and formation of brown tars or gums. A further reduction in yield may result from formation of by-products. The reaction of A with B to form C may be accompanied by an inevitable side reaction of A with B to form D. If the main reaction is slow, opportunity is afforded for formation of the by-products AA and BB, or for interaction of either reagents or products with the solvent, the catalyst, or with oxygen of the air.

Several factors thus conspire to decrease the yields of organic reactions, and in a first trial of a new reaction the yield may be discouragingly low. However, various expedients can be explored, such as a change in reaction temperature, use of a different solvent or a milder catalyst, exclusion of air. In the industry, where a difference of a few percent in the yield may spell the success or failure of a process, developmental research teams study exhaustively each reaction involved in the effort to increase the yield. In a multi-step synthesis a loss anywhere along the line hurts because the effect is cumulative. A yield of 80% of the theoretical amount would appear good, but a yield of 80% in each step would, in a two-step synthesis, amount to an overall yield of 64%; in a 10-step synthesis the overall yield would be 10.6%.

Importance of yield

Because a given product is often accompanied in the reaction mixture by by-products of side reactions and by gummy and pigmented substances resulting from decomposition, as well as by solvent and catalyst, a large part of preparative work may involve processing the mixture for separation and purification of the desired product. The problem of separation and purification may be even more difficult in isolation of a natural product from plant or animal tissues, particularly if the substance is present only in minute amount and if, as is often the case, it is accompanied by an array of companions of nearly the same chemical and physical properties.

2.3

Purification.* — Liquid organic compounds, for example hydrocarbons, alcohols, ethers, alkyl halides, can be separated by **distillation** from inorganic material and nonvolatile pigments and other contaminants. The extent to which mixtures can be separated is dependent upon the spread of boiling points, since mixtures of miscible liquids boil at temperatures intermediate between the boiling points of the components. If two liquids differ in boiling point by as much as 20–25°, separation can be accomplished by **fractional distillation,** that is, slow distillation from a boiling flask through a column containing a porous packing and connected to a condenser and receiver (Fig. 2.2). A temperature gradient is established in the column and a part of the vapor condenses and flows back over the packing toward the boiling flask. Heat exchange causes partial condensation of rising vapor and partial vaporization of the more volatile constituents of the liquid, and the vapor eventually rising to the top and passing through the condenser into the receiving flask is highly enriched in the more volatile component. Substances of low volatility can be fractionally

2.4

* See L. F. Fieser, *Experiments in Organic Chemistry*, 3rd Ed., Heath (1955).

distilled in vacuum (1–25 mm.) or in high vacuum (0.01 mm., see Fig. 2.3); gaseous substances, for example methane, ethane, ethylene, can be liquefied under pressure and fractionally distilled at low temperatures.

2.5

Crystallization of solids offers possibilities for differentiation more subtle than those attainable by distillation. The high selectivity is due to the phenomenon of supersaturation; the major component of a mixture often crystallizes in pure form and leaves minor components of even lesser solubility in the mother liquor in supersaturated solution. Extraneous coloring matter in a crude product is removed, prior to crystallization, by stirring a solution of the material with decolorizing carbon, which adsorbs pigments and polymers, filtering the clarified solution, and concentrating the filtrate to a point suitable for crystallization. **Chromatography,** another effective method for selective separations, supplements crystallization because when one of the two methods fails the other is usually effective. A mixture is adsorbed from a solution onto finely divided alumina (Fig. 2.4), and the column is then eluted (washed) with a series of solvents of gradually increasing eluant power, or ability to dislodge adsorbed material. Even closely related substances are adsorbed with different degrees of firmness regardless of their relative solubilities; the least strongly adsorbed components are eluted in early fractions and the most strongly adsorbed substances are recovered from late fractions. A common practice is to crystallize a mixture and isolate such pure components as is possible, and then to chromatograph the residue recovered from the combined mother liquors.

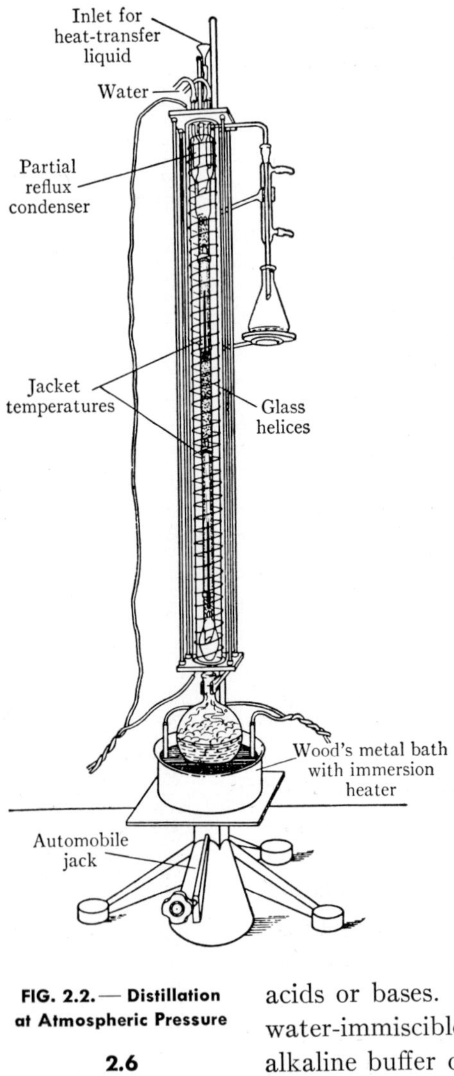

Countercurrent distribution is a powerful tool for effecting separations, particularly of mixtures of acids or bases. When a solution of a mixture of organic acids in a water-immiscible solvent (e.g., ether) is shaken with an aqueous alkaline buffer of suitable pH, the more acidic and more hydrophilic components are preferentially distributed into the water phase as salts and the less acidic and less hydrophilic components concentrate in the ether. The aqueous layer is run out into funnel 2, shaken with a fresh portion of ether, run out into funnel 3, etc. The ethereal solution in funnel 1 is equilibrated with fresh buffer

Inlet for heat-transfer liquid

Water

Partial reflux condenser

Jacket temperatures

Glass helices

Wood's metal bath with immersion heater

Automobile jack

FIG. 2.2.— Distillation at Atmospheric Pressure

2.6

and the aqueous layer run out into funnel 2 and shaken with the ethereal extract which this contains. The efficiency of separation increases with the number of funnels, or plates, used. In the Craig [1]

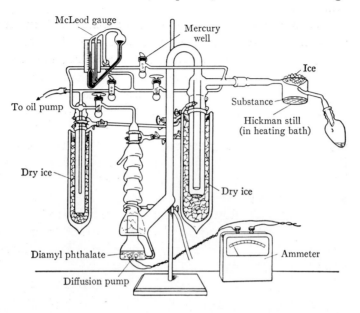

FIG. 2.3. — High-Vacuum Distillation

100-plate countercurrent distribution machine, equilibration is effected simultaneously in 100 small separatory funnels, and transfer of extracts to adjacent funnels is done automatically in all the funnels in one operation.

2.7

Physical Constants. — When a compound has been purified by distillation, citation of the **boiling range** at a given pressure affords some index of purity, since the narrower the range the greater is the homogeneity. This index may be deceptive, since a mixture of two components of the same boiling point is indistinguishable from either component. Hence a second constant, the **refractive index,** should be determined and reported.

A more reliable criterion of both purity and identity is provided by the **melting point,** or melting range of a solid, since substances that are different, even though they have identical melting points, depress each other's melting point. Thus as a substance is purified by one or more of the methods cited above, the melting point becomes progressively higher and sharper, and when it remains constant after attempted further purification the substance is probably pure. The determination is done by scraping a tiny portion of material into a capillary tube (Fig. 2.5), attaching this to the stem of a thermometer

[1] Lyman C. Craig, b. 1906 Palmyra, Ohio; Ph.D. Iowa State College (Hixon), Nat. Res. Fellow Hopkins; Rockefeller Institute

with a rubber band, and heating the bath very slowly until particles of solid begin to melt (t_1) and then until a clear melt results (t_2); the melting point is then t_1-t_2. **Mixed melting point determination** is invaluable for establishing identity or nonidentity of an unknown with a known substance of the same melting point. Small bits of the two samples are mixed with a spatula and scraped into a melting point capillary, which is attached to a thermometer along with tubes of each component. If all three samples melt at the same temperature, the known and unknown are identical; a depression of melting point in the mixture establishes nonidentity.

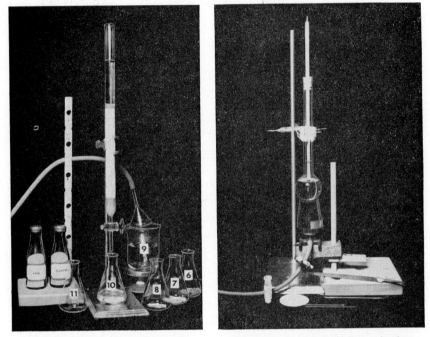

FIG. 2.4.— Elution Chromatography   **FIG. 2.5.— Melting Point Determination**

ANALYSIS

2.8   Once a hitherto unknown compound, natural or synthetic, has been purified until constancy of physical properties indicates that the sample is as pure as it can be obtained, the next step in its characterization is detection of elements present other than carbon, hydrogen, and oxygen by qualitative tests. Fusion of a small sample with sodium converts any nitrogen, halogen, or sulfur present into sodium cyanide, sodium halide, or sodium sulfide, each of which can be detected by color or precipitation tests on portions of an aqueous extract of the cooled melt. The next step is quantitative analysis of the percentage composition. Methods for simultaneous determination of carbon and hydrogen and for determination of nitrogen are described in ensuing sections. Both halogen and sulfur are determined (Carius method) by heating a weighed sample with nitric acid in a sealed tube to oxidize the organic material to carbon dioxide and water and to convert halogen into halide ion or sulfur into sulfate ion. These ions are precipitated and determined as silver halide or as barium sulfate. Methods are available for determination of oxygen but are rarely used; the oxygen content is usually assumed to be the difference between the sum of the percentages of other elements and 100.

Determination of Carbon and Hydrogen. — The method of combustion analysis used for determination of carbon and hydrogen, introduced by Liebig[2] in 1831, involves burning a weighed sample of substance in a stream of oxygen in a glass tube containing a section of red-hot copper oxide as an auxiliary source of oxygen to control the burning and ensure complete combustion, for example:

$$C_2H_6 \;+\; 7\,CuO \;\longrightarrow\; 2\,CO_2 \;+\; 3\,H_2O \;+\; 7\,Cu$$
$$C_4H_{10}O \;+\; 12\,CuO \;\longrightarrow\; 4\,CO_2 \;+\; 5\,H_2O \;+\; 12\,Cu$$

The tube is swept with a slow stream of oxygen, which burns a part of the sample directly and oxidizes metallic copper formed and thus replenishes the original supply of copper oxide. The combustion train shown in Fig. 2.6 is suitable for semimicroanalysis, that is, for analysis of 10–50 mg. samples. The stream of oxygen, which is freed from traces of moisture and carbon dioxide prior to entering the combustion tube, sweeps the products of combustion into a tube of Dehydrite (magnesium perchlorate trihydrate), which absorbs the water formed, and then into a tube of Ascarite (sodium hydroxide on asbestos) to absorb the carbon dioxide. Prior to the analysis each absorption unit is weighed separately and then mounted in position. The sample is weighed into a small platinum boat inserted with a wire hook into a rear position in the combustion tube before this has been heated. The front section, packed with copper oxide wire, is brought to a red glow before introducing the sample. When the boat is in place, burners under the rear part of the tube are lighted progressively, and eventually the whole tube is brought to a dull red heat. Oxygen is passed through the hot tube for a sufficient period to sweep the products of combustion into the absorption train. The presence of nitrogen, halogen, or sulfur in the sample does not interfere with determination of carbon and hydrogen.

At the end of the combustion the absorption tubes are disconnected and weighed; the gain in weight of the Dehydrite tube gives the

[2] Justus von Liebig, 1803–73; b. Darmstadt, Germany; Giessen, München; *Ber.*, **23**, 785 (1890); A. W. v. Hofmann, Faraday Lecture for 1875, "The Life and Work of Liebig," Macmillan, London (1876)

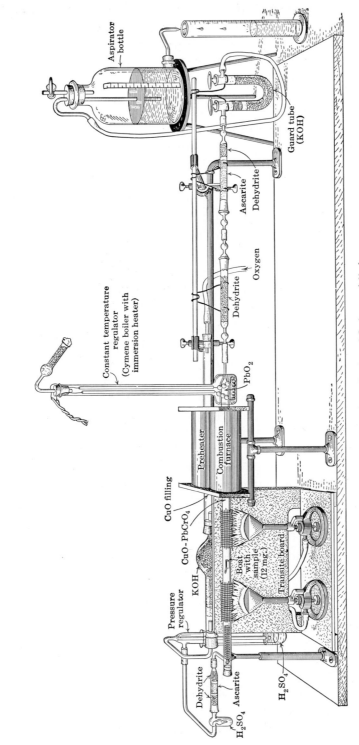

FIG. 2.6. — Semimicrodetermination of Carbon and Hydrogen

Oxygen from a low-pressure tank passes first through a preheater to burn any traces of organic matter, and then through a large tube of solid potassium hydroxide to absorb water and carbon dioxide, and a small unit to condition the gas exactly as it will be discharged from the absorption train. The first tube in this train contains solid Dehydrite (magnesium perchlorate trihydrate) to absorb water, and the second is filled with Ascarite (sodium hydroxide on asbestos) for the absorption of carbon dioxide and with an end section of Dehydrite to maintain the same condition of the gas on exit as on entrance. The oxygen is delivered to the combustion tube at a slight positive pressure and is drawn through the system at an adjustable, measured rate by the aspirator. The combustion furnace and preheater are heated with electric resistance units connected in series. The part of the combustion tube heated in the furnace is filled largely with copper oxide, but contains, at the exit end, a charge of lead chromate to combine with and retain oxides of sulfur. The end section of the tube contains lead peroxide to combine with oxides of nitrogen; this reagent must be maintained at a critical temperature different from that of the furnace, provided by the use of a boiler containing liquid of proper boiling point (cymene, $C_{10}H_{14}$). Silver wool or wire is introduced at the extreme end of the tube to retain halogen.

amount of water produced and that of the Ascarite tube the weight of carbon dioxide. Calculation of the percentage composition then follows from the proportion of hydrogen in water and of carbon in carbon dioxide, using the atomic weights H = 1.008 and C = 12.01:

$$\text{Wt. of hydrogen} = \text{Wt. of water} \times \frac{2.016 \ (H_2)}{18.016 \ (H_2O)}$$

$$\% \ H = \frac{\text{Wt. of hydrogen}}{\text{Wt. of sample}} \times 100$$

$$\text{Wt. of carbon} = \text{Wt. of carbon dioxide} \times \frac{12.01 \ (C)}{44.01 \ (CO_2)}$$

$$\% \ C = \frac{\text{Wt. of carbon}}{\text{Wt. of sample}} \times 100$$

If the percentages of carbon and hydrogen do not add up to 100 and no other element is present, the deficiency is taken as the percentage of oxygen.

For interpretation of results of an analysis in terms of an empirical formula, the first step is to divide the percentage of each element by its atomic weight; the next is to divide the resulting numbers by the smallest one of the group and so ascertain the atomic ratios. An ideal analysis for ethyl alcohol would give 52.14% C and 13.13% H, whence the oxygen content by difference is 34 73%. The calculations are then:

	PERCENT		ATOMIC WEIGHT						ATOMIC RATIO
C	52.14	÷	12.01	=	4.3				2
H	13.13	÷	1.008	=	13.03	$\times$	$\dfrac{1}{2.17}$	=	6
O	34.73	÷	16	=	2.17				1

Ethyl alcohol contains two carbon and six hydrogen atoms for every oxygen atom. A molecule cannot contain less than one of the least abundant species of atom, which in this case is oxygen, but it might contain two or more such atoms. From the analysis alone, ethyl alcohol might be C_2H_6O or $C_4H_{12}O_2$ or $(C_2H_6O)_n$, where n is any integer, for these formulas have the same percentage composition. A choice between the different possibilities is made possible by knowledge of the molecular weight of the compound; even an experimental value recognized as only a rough approximation may suffice. Thus the unit C_2H_6O has the molecular weight (rounded) of 46, and a choice would be required between 46, 92, 138, etc. Molecular weight determinations accurate to no better than 20% and falling in the range from 37 to 55 units would distinguish between the possibilities.

Molecular weight

Because of experimental error associated with an actual analysis, the atomic ratios calculated may deviate appreciably from integral values; therefore careful judgment must be exercised to decide which of possibly two or three of the nearest sets of integral values is the most likely. The best method is to calculate the theoretical percentages of carbon and hydrogen for each formula under consideration and see how closely they correspond to the experimentally determined values. An example for illustration is taken from a series of analyses carried out by Liebig in 1838 and interpreted by him on the basis of the atomic weights accepted at the time. Since the same values figure in the calculation of both the experimental and the theoretical percentages, the inaccuracy in the early atomic weights did not seriously distort the picture, and Liebig usually arrived at formulas that have stood the test of time. In the following example the results are recalculated on the basis of modern atomic weights. Liebig's combustion of a 0.533-g. sample of gallic acid afforded 0.969 g. of carbon dioxide and 0.172 g. of water, and the calculations of the percentage composition and the ratio of carbon, hydrogen, and oxygen are as follows:

	PERCENT		ATOMIC WEIGHT				ATOMIC RATIO
C	49.61	÷	12.01	=	4.13		1.41
H	3.61	÷	1.008	=	3.58 $\times \dfrac{1}{2.92} =$		1.22
O	46.78	÷	16	=	2.92		1

The result indicates that the compound contains approximately 1.4 carbon atoms and 1.2 hydrogen atoms for every oxygen atom. If 2 oxygen atoms were present there would be 2.4 hydrogen atoms, but this figure is too far from an integral value for serious consideration. Multiplication of the atomic ratio values by 3 and by 5, however, gives figures not far from integral, namely $C_{4.2}H_{3.7}O_3$, and $C_{7.1}H_{6.1}O_5$. It would seem possible, then, that the substance is either $C_4H_4O_3$ or $C_7H_6O_5$, or a higher multiple of one of these formulas, and although the second appears to be a better fit than the first, a decision can be made from a comparison of the experimentally determined values for carbon and hydrogen with those calculated for the possible alternative formulas:

	% C	% H
Found.........................	49.61	3.61
Calculated for $C_4H_4O_3$.............	48.01	4.03
Calculated for $C_7H_6O_5$.............	49.42	3.56

The percentage of hydrogen found is in fair agreement with that required for the first formula, but the carbon value is 1.6% too high, and this deviation is considerably greater than the usual experimental error of some 0.3–.4%. The analytical values check very well, however, with the calculated percentages for $C_7H_6O_5$, and hence this minimal formula is correct for gallic acid. Liebig interpreted the analysis in this way and his formula was substantiated in subsequent work.

That Liebig was able to obtain remarkably accurate results with the comparatively crude laboratory equipment and analytical balances of the day is attributable partly to his use of a sample sufficiently large to offset chance error (0.5–.9 g.). Improvements in the instrumental facilities in the ensuing hundred-year period made it possible to reduce the size of the sample to 100–120 mg. and still maintain adequate accuracy. Although this amount would appear to be trivial for an abundantly available material such as sugar, acetic acid, or alcohol, many interesting organic compounds of both natural and synthetic origin have been encountered that, initially at least, were obtainable in only minute amounts. Butenandt's [3] discovery in 1931 of the male sex hormone androsterone, for example, was the result of the processing of 15,000 liters of urine, which afforded a total of 15 mg. of the physiologically active principle. This difficult feat of isolation would have been rather pointless, and might not have been undertaken, had there not been available a modification of Liebig's method of analysis applicable to minute quantities of material. The procedure of microanalysis was introduced in 1911 by the Austrian chemist Pregl,[4] whose own research experience had convinced him of the serious limitations to a method of analysis which may require for a single combustion an amount of sample considerably greater than that which the chemist can secure. With special manipulative techniques, a skilled chemist can carry out a reaction with no more than 5–10 mg. of material and can purify the product for analysis by crystallization or, in some instances, even by distillation. Pregl reinvestigated every detail of the existing analytical method with regard to refinement. The chief determining factor was the accuracy of the balance, and under Pregl's leadership a microbalance was developed with which minute samples can be weighed with extraordinary precision. Microbalances now available, when operated in an air-conditioned room on a vibration-free mounting, can weigh to a precision of about 1 microgram (0.001 mg., or 0.000001 g.). With the aid of a precision instrument and by redesigning the combustion tube, absorption train, and all accessories, Pregl worked out a scheme of microanalysis by which the carbon and hydrogen content of a 3–4 mg. sample of material can be determined accurately. By application of the micro method, which was duly recognized as one of the achievements of modern science by the award to Pregl of the Nobel Prize, Butenandt's 15-mg. sample of androsterone sufficed for two analyses and for preparation and analysis of a derivative. The analytical results, coupled with keen observa-

Microanalysis

[3] Adolf Butenandt, b. 1903 Wesermünde-Lehe, Germany; Ph.D. Göttingen (Windaus); Göttingen, Danzig, KWI Berlin, Tübingen, Munich; Nobel Prize 1939
[4] Fritz Pregl, 1869–1930; b. Laibach, Austria; Ph.D. Graz; Innsbrück, Graz; Nobel Prize 1923; *Ber.*, **64A**, 113 (1931)

tions and inferences, led in 1932 to an initial postulate of the chemical nature of the hormone that proved to be correct.

The semimicro method illustrated in Fig. 2.7 is a compromise requiring less elaborate equipment but employing several of the refinements introduced by Pregl.

2.12
Dumas method

Determination of Nitrogen. — The most widely used method of determining nitrogen in organic compounds was introduced in 1830 by Dumas.[5] The sample is mixed with fine copper oxide and placed in a tube packed with coarse copper oxide. The tube is swept with a stream of carbon dioxide until all air has been displaced, and then gradually brought to a dull red heat, when the sample is oxidized by the copper oxide to carbon dioxide, water, and elementary nitrogen containing oxides of nitrogen. The gaseous products are swept by a slow stream of carbon dioxide over a roll of hot copper gauze at the end of the tube which reduces any oxides of nitrogen to nitrogen. The effluent gas passes into the base of an inverted, graduated glass tube filled with potassium hydroxide solution, which absorbs the carbon dioxide. The volume of the residual nitrogen is measured after adjustment of the pressure to that of the atmosphere with a leveling bulb.

Kjeldahl method

A second method of analysis was introduced in 1883 by Kjeldahl.[6] The sample is digested with concentrated sulfuric acid, usually with addition of an oxidizing agent ($KMnO_4$, $HClO_4$), to decompose the substance and convert the nitrogen into ammonium sulfate. The solution is diluted, excess alkali is added, and the ammonia is distilled with steam into a known amount of standard acid and estimated by titration of the excess acid. The Kjeldahl method is less general than that of Dumas, but it is useful for rapid analysis of compounds of low nitrogen content, for example proteins.

2.13

Molecular Weight Determination. — The molecular weight of a gas or of an easily vaporized substance can be determined by the vapor density method, which consists in weighing a measured volume of the gaseous substance and calculating the number of grams that would occupy a volume of 22.4 liters at standard conditions (N.P.T.). Methods applicable to solid compounds utilize the fact that a dissolved substance raises the boiling point or lowers the freezing point of a solvent to an extent directly dependent on the proportion of the dissolved to the total molecules. These ebullioscopic and cryoscopic methods are widely applicable and are precise. Organic chemists frequently use a rapid, approximate cryoscopic method (Rast), in which the solid substance camphor is used as the solvent and a determination of the lowering of the melting point is made with only a few milligrams

Rast determination

[5] Jean Baptiste André Dumas, 1800–84; b. Alais, France; Paris; *Ber* , **17**, 629 (1884)
[6] Johan Kjeldahl, 1849–1900; b. Seeland, Denmark; Copenhagen

of the mixture and an ordinary thermometer. The method succeeds because the melting or freezing point of camphor is lowered to an extraordinary extent by a small amount of a solute. A rapid boiling

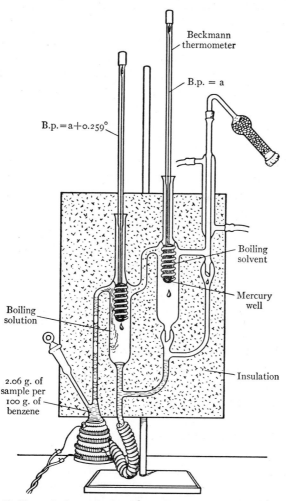

FIG. 2.7. — **Ebullioscopic Determination of the Molecular Weight of a Nonvolatile Solid**
This determination is made by direct measurement of the difference in the boiling point of a solution of the substance in benzene and of pure benzene (Swietoslawski apparatus).

$$\text{Mol. wt.} = \frac{\text{Wt. of sample} \times 1000 \times k}{\text{Wt. of solvent} \times \Delta t}$$

where the constant k is the elevation in boiling point produced by 1 mole of substance in 1000 g. of solvent (for benzene, k = 2.53°), and Δt is the observed elevation in boiling point.

point method which gives reasonably accurate results is illustrated in Fig. 2.7.

Possible and Impossible Formulas. — Since the valence numbers of carbon and oxygen are both even, compounds containing only C,

2.14

H, and O, as well as hydrocarbons, invariably contain an even number of hydrogen atoms. Thus formulas such as C_6H_{11} and $C_7H_7O_5$ are at once recognized as fallacious. Compounds of C, H, and S, or C, H, O, and S, likewise must have an even number of hydrogens; for example, $C_{27}H_{46}O_3S_2$ is possible, $C_{27}H_{47}O_3S_2$ is impossible. Since nitrogen has a valence of three in typical organic substances, compounds containing C, H, O, and one N always have an odd number of hydrogens; if two nitrogens are present, the number of hydrogens is even. In mono and di halogen compounds containing C, H, O, and S, the number of hydrogens is odd and even, respectively.

SUMMARY

Preparation and Purification

Reactions are slow and require promotion by heat or by catalysts to form ionic intermediates. Reaction rate doubles for each 10° rise in temperature.

Yield is lowered by decomposition of sensitive organic compounds and by side-reactions, by-products, gums. Importance of yield, particularly in multi-step syntheses.

Purification an important part of work of preparation. Methods: distillation, fractional distillation, vacuum distillation, crystallization, chromatography, countercurrent distribution.

Physical constants as criteria of purity. Boiling point range and refractive index useful but not conclusive of identity. Melting point affords a better index of purity and mixed melting point determination affords conclusive evidence of identity or nonidentity.

Analysis

Qualitative tests for N, halogen, and sulfur. Carius method for quantitative determination of halogen and sulfur (heating with HNO_3 produces Cl^- and $SO_4^=$).

Determination of C and H (Liebig, 1831): sample burned in oxygen in a tube packed with CuO for auxiliary oxidation; H_2O absorbed in Dehydrite, CO_2 absorbed in Ascarite. Calculation of % C and H from weights of sample, CO_2, H_2O, and factors (C/CO_2, H_2/H_2O). Percentage of oxygen by difference.

Calculation of minimal formula: divide percentage of each element by its atomic weight; divide resulting numbers by smallest one; evaluate possible formulas suggested by calculation of theoretical percentage composition and comparison with found values. Knowledge of molecular weight required for completion of determination of empirical formula.

Microanalysis (Pregl, 1911). Precision determination of C and H with 3–4 mg. sample.

Determination of nitrogen. Dumas method (1830): sample burned on CuO in CO_2 atmosphere; CO_2 absorbed in KOH solution and residual N_2 gas measured. Kjeldahl method (1883): sample digested with H_2SO_4 and an oxidizing agent to convert N into $(NH_4)_2SO_4$; neutralization with NaOH, distillation of liberated NH_3, and titration.

Molecular weight determination: vapor density, freezing point depression, boiling point elevation, Rast cryoscopic method (solid solution in camphor).

Principle of valence balance: even number of hydrogen atoms required for compounds of C, H; C, H, O; C, H, S; C, H, O, S; C, H, N_2; C, H, O, N_2; C, H, O, N_4; C, H, Cl_2; odd numbers for compounds of C, H, N; C, H, O, N; C, H, O, N_3; C, H, Cl; C, H, O, Cl_3.

PROBLEMS

1. A semimicroanalysis of an 11.25-mg. sample of a substance gave 26.99 mg. of CO_2 and 6.77 mg. of H_2O. Calculate the percentage composition.

2. The following two compounds containing only C, H, and O were analyzed and the molecular weights determined, with the results recorded. Calculate the empirical formulas.

   (a) % C = 65.55; 65.25 (b) % C = 70.31; 69.95
       % H = 5.65; 5.35   % H = 4.08; 4.18
       Mol. wt. = 111; 115   Mol. wt. = 185; 187

3. Which of the following formulas represent possible compounds and which are false: $C_{10}H_{22}O$, $C_{20}H_{41}$, $C_{14}H_8O_4$, $C_{21}H_{31}O_3$, $C_{21}H_{31}O_3N$, $C_8H_{14}ON$, $C_{20}H_{32}OSN_2$, $C_{10}H_{20}Br_3$?

4. An analysis of a substance that is a gas at room temperature gave the results 83.06% C, 16.85% H; 1 liter of gas at N.P.T. was found to weigh 3.20 g. What is the most likely empirical formula?

5. A crystalline yellow substance occurring in the grain of certain tropical woods and found to be composed of C, H, and O gave the analysis: C, 74.11%; H, 5.90%. Determinations of the molecular weight by the Rast method gave the results 240 and 255. Calculate the empirical formula and the theoretical percentage composition.

6. A liquid vitamin factor extracted from green plants gave no test for nitrogen or sulfur, and the results of a microanalysis were: 82.64% C, 10.20% H. Calculate the minimal empirical formula.

7. A derivative of morphine contains 72.27% C, 7.13% H, and 4.60% N. No other element except oxygen is present, and the molecular weight is in the range 250–350. Calculate the empirical formula.

8. The determination of molecular weight illustrated in Fig. 2.7 was carried out with benzil, $C_6H_5COCOC_6H_5$. Calculate the result of the determination and compare it with the theoretical value.

CHAPTER

3

ALKANES

3.1 Hydrocarbons of the alkane series are also called saturated hydrocarbons, because the carbon valences are all saturated with hydrogen. They are known further as paraffinic hydrocarbons, because they are characteristically inert and less reactive than the unsaturated alkenes and alkynes (L. *parum affinis*, slight affinity).

Normal Hydrocarbons. — Successive members of the series (Table I) differ in composition by the increment CH_2 and are said to form a homologous series. Thus heptane and octane are homologous hydrocarbons; heptadecane is a higher homolog of methane. The formulas all conform to the type C_nH_{2n+2}. Names of the hydrocarbons beyond butane are derived largely from the Greek numerals.

The hydrocarbons having from one to four carbon atoms are gases,

TABLE I

NORMAL SATURATED HYDROCARBONS

Name	Formula C_nH_{2n+2}	M.P., °C.	B.P., °C.	Sp. Gr. (as liquids)	
Methane	CH_4	−182.6	−161.7	0.4240	gases
Ethane	C_2H_6	−172.0	−88.6	.5462	gases
Propane	C_3H_8	−187.1	−42.2	.5824	gases
n-Butane	C_4H_{10}	−135.0	−0.5	.5788	gases
n-Pentane	C_5H_{12}	−129.7	36.1	.6264	liquids
n-Hexane	C_6H_{14}	−94.0	68.7	.6594	liquids
n-Heptane	C_7H_{16}	−90.5	98.4	.6837	liquids
n-Octane	C_8H_{18}	−56.8	125.6	.7028	liquids
n-Heptadecane	$C_{17}H_{36}$	22.0	303	.7767	liquids
n-Octadecane	$C_{18}H_{38}$	28.0	308	.7767	solids
n-Heptacontane	$C_{70}H_{142}$	105	300 at 0.00001 mm.		solids

the C_5- to C_{17}-homologs are liquids, and the higher members of the series are solids. A similar relationship in a series of progressively increasing molecular weight is found in the halogens: chlorine, bromine, and iodine. The melting points of the hydrocarbons show an initial irregularity but tend to rise steadily as the molecules become larger. The boiling point invariably increases with increasing molecular weight, and the increment is particularly prominent in the first few members of the series, where the increase in molecular weight represents a large proportion of the total. Ethane boils at a temperature 73° higher than methane and has a molecular weight (30) that is 87% greater than that of methane (16). *n*-Octane has a boiling point 27° higher than that of the next lower homolog, and the incre-

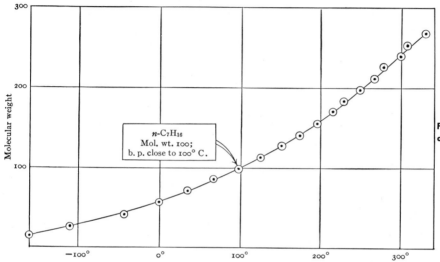

FIG. 3.1. — Boiling Points of Normal Hydrocarbons

ment of 14 units corresponding to CH_2 represents an increase in molecular weight of only 14%. A practical consequence is that lower members of the series are more easily separated by distillation than higher members. The relationship of boiling point to molecular weight is shown in Fig. 3.1. It is useful to remember that the normal alkane (C_7H_{16}) of molecular weight 100 has a boiling point close to 100° (98.4°), for the relationship is that generally found for substances that do not form molecular aggregates.

Rule for unassociated liquids

Specific gravities of the hydrocarbons in the liquid phase are given in the last column of Table I. The hydrocarbons are all lighter than water and, being insoluble, float on water. Methane is less than half as heavy as water; with succeeding members the density increases rapidly for a time and then, in $C_{15}H_{32}$, reaches a limiting value of 0.77–0.78.

Derivatives of Methane. — Since the carbon atom is tetrahedral and the methane molecule symmetrical in space (see 1.4), the four hydrogen atoms are equivalent. Hence only one monochloro deriva-

3.2

tive of methane exists, and there is only one monobromo, monohydroxy, or other monosubstituted derivative. The tetrahedral formula also permits only one dichloromethane, and the Kekulé formulas I and II are thus equivalent representations of a single compound,

$$
\underset{I}{\overset{H}{\underset{Cl}{H-\overset{|}{\underset{|}{C}}-Cl}}} \qquad \underset{II}{\overset{H}{\underset{H}{Cl-\overset{|}{\underset{|}{C}}-Cl}}} \qquad \underset{III}{CH_2Cl_2}
$$

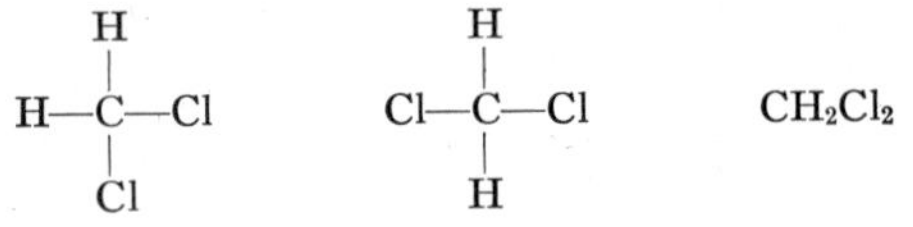

Methylene chloride

called either dichloroethane or, more commonly, methylene chloride, which can also be represented by formula III. The formulas of trichloromethane (chloroform) and of tetrachloromethane (carbon tetrachloride) likewise represent single compounds:

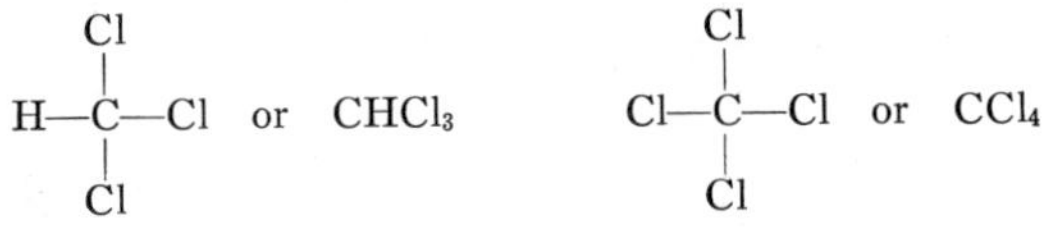

$$
\overset{Cl}{\underset{Cl}{H-\overset{|}{\underset{|}{C}}-Cl}} \quad or \quad CHCl_3 \qquad\qquad \overset{Cl}{\underset{Cl}{Cl-\overset{|}{\underset{|}{C}}-Cl}} \quad or \quad CCl_4
$$

Chloroform   Carbon tetrachloride

3.3   **Derivatives of Ethane.** — In ethane all six hydrogen atoms are identically situated and hence equivalent, and only one monosubstitution product is possible. The monochloro derivative, which can be described as monochloroethane but which is more generally known as ethyl chloride, is represented correctly by any one of the formulas shown, for each conveys the same information.

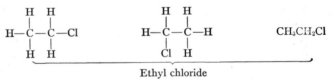

Ethyl chloride

Isomerism becomes possible whenever two substituents are introduced into the ethane molecule, for these can either be located on the same carbon atom or distributed between the two carbon atoms. If two chlorine atoms are linked to one carbon atom, as in the formula below on the left, the compound represented can be distinguished from the isomer on the right by numbering the carbon atoms and

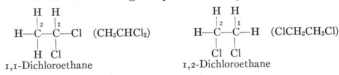

indicating the position of each chlorine atom by citing the number of the carbon atom to which it is joined. In the first compound both chlorines are attached to carbon atom No. 1 (or C_1), and hence the compound is 1,1-dichloroethane. The name 1-dichloroethane is incomplete and therefore incorrect; it would leave unspecified the location of one of the chlorine atoms. The name 1,1-chloroethane is incorrect because it implies 1-monochloroethane. The second dichloroethane is the 1,2-derivative. In this case the molecule is symmetrical and it makes no difference whether the carbon atoms are numbered from right to left, as shown, or in the reverse order. In the case of the isomer, left-to-right counting would give the alternate name, 2,2-dichloroethane, but a choice between the prefixes 1,1- and 2,2- is afforded by the rule that the numbers be kept as low as possible. However a formula is written, one should try all possible methods of counting the carbon atoms and select the name which gives the smallest numbers for the positions of the substituent groups.

Three chlorine atoms or three other substituents can be introduced into the ethane molecule in the following two ways:

$$
\begin{array}{cc}
\underset{\displaystyle\substack{|\\ \text{H}}}{\overset{\displaystyle\substack{\text{H}\\ |}}{\text{H}-\text{C}}} - \underset{\displaystyle\substack{|\\ \text{Cl}}}{\overset{\displaystyle\substack{\text{Cl}\\ |}}{\text{C}}} - \text{Cl} \quad (\text{CH}_3\text{CCl}_3)
\end{array}
$$

1,1,1-Trichloroethane

$$
\begin{array}{cc}
\underset{\displaystyle\substack{|\\ \text{Cl}}}{\overset{\displaystyle\substack{\text{H}\\ |}}{\text{H}-\text{C}}} - \underset{\displaystyle\substack{|\\ \text{Cl}}}{\overset{\displaystyle\substack{\text{H}\\ |}}{\text{C}}} - \text{Cl} \quad (\text{ClCH}_2\text{CHCl}_2)
\end{array}
$$

1,1,2-Trichloroethane

Two isomers

Note that with the second isomer the numbering of the carbon atoms from right to left, as the formula is written, gives smaller numbers (1,1,2-) than the alternate counting (1,2,2-). The two possible types of tetrasubstitution products are illustrated as follows:

$$
\begin{array}{cc}
\text{CH}_2\text{ClCCl}_3 & \text{CHCl}_2\text{CHCl}_2 \\
(1,1,1,2\text{-}) & (1,1,2,2\text{-})
\end{array}
$$

Only one pentachloro and one hexachloro derivative are possible, for the situation is the same as with the penta- and hexahydrogen compounds.

Derivatives of Propane. — The propane molecule presents a different situation because the eight hydrogen atoms are not all similarly located. The six hydrogens attached to the two terminal carbon atoms are equivalent (dotted lines), but the environment is different from that of the two hydrogens located on the central carbon atom. There is thus a differentiation between end and middle positions in the molecule; one result is that two isomeric monosubstitution products are possible, as exemplified by the monochloro derivatives:

3.4

$$
\begin{array}{cc}
\underset{\displaystyle\substack{|\ \ |\ \ |\\ \text{H}\ \ \text{H}\ \ \text{H}}}{\overset{\displaystyle\substack{\text{H}\ \ \text{H}\ \ \text{H}\\ |\ \ |\ \ |}}{\text{H}-\text{C}-\text{C}-\text{C}}}-\text{Cl} \\
(\text{CH}_3\text{CH}_2\text{CH}_2\text{Cl}) \\
\text{1-Chloropropane, or} \\
\textit{n}\text{-propyl chloride}
\end{array}
\qquad
\begin{array}{cc}
\underset{\displaystyle\substack{|\ \ |\ \ |\\ \text{H}\ \ \text{Cl}\ \ \text{H}}}{\overset{\displaystyle\substack{\text{H}\ \ \text{H}\ \ \text{H}\\ |\ \ |\ \ |}}{\text{H}-\text{C}-\text{C}-\text{C}}}-\text{H} \\
(\text{CH}_3\text{CHClCH}_3) \\
\text{2-Chloropropane, or} \\
\text{isopropyl chloride}
\end{array}
$$

Two isomers

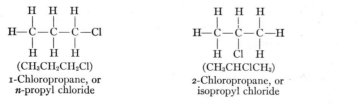

These can be described as the 1-chloro and 2-chloro derivatives of propane but are more commonly called normal (*n*-) propyl chloride and isopropyl chloride. Although there is only one form of a methyl (CH_3—) or ethyl (C_2H_5—) group, the next higher hydrocarbon group can be the *n*-propyl group, $CH_3CH_2CH_2$—, or the isopropyl group, $(CH_3)_2CH$—.

Polysubstitution in propane presents opportunity for isomerism of a still higher degree, as can be seen from the following tabulation.

Dichloropropanes:		Trichloropropanes:	
$CH_3CH_2CHCl_2$	1,1-	$CH_3CH_2CCl_3$	1,1,1-
$CH_3CHClCH_2Cl$	1,2-	$CH_2CHClCHCl_2$	1,1,2-
$ClCH_2CH_2CH_2Cl$	1,3-	$ClCH_2CH_2CHCl_2$	1,1,3-
$CH_3C(Cl_2)CH_3$	2,2-	$CH_3CCl_2CH_2Cl$	1,2,2-
		$ClCH_2CHClCH_2Cl$	1,2,3-

3.5

Butanes. — The formula of ethane can be derived from that of methane by replacing one of the hydrogen atoms by a methyl group, and the propane formula can be built up similarly. This systematic method of derivation serves a useful purpose, for if all possible modes of substitution are considered, no isomers can be missed. Propane has two different types of hydrogen atoms, the type on the ends (*a*) and that in the middle (*b*), and hence in the derivation of the butanes substitution of each by methyl must be tried:

$$\overset{a}{}\ \overset{b}{}\ \overset{a}{}$$
Methyl substitution in propane, $CH_3CH_2CH_3$, gives:

Two butanes

a. $CH_3CH_2CH_2CH_3$
n-Butane
(b.p. −0.5°)

b. CH_3CHCH_3
  |
  CH_3
Isobutane
(b.p. −12°)

Replacement of any one of the terminal hydrogens by a methyl group gives a straight-chain hydrocarbon of the formula C_4H_{10}, namely, normal butane. A similar operation on a centrally located hydrogen affords the isomeric, branched-chain hydrocarbon isobutane. The formula shown can be simplified by pooling the three methyl groups attached to the central carbon atom: $(CH_3)_3CH$. This formula suggests an alternate and descriptive name. The substance is seen to be a derivative of methane in which only one of the original hydrogens remains and the other three have been replaced by methyl groups; isobutane therefore can be named trimethylmethane, just as $CHCl_3$ is described as trichloromethane.

3.6

Pentanes. — Structural formulas of the C_5-hydrocarbons can be derived by the same systematic procedure of making all possible methyl substitutions in both butanes, and the only added operation necessary is to inspect the resulting formulas and eliminate duplicates:

From the butanes,
$$\overset{a}{C}H_3\overset{b}{C}H_2\overset{b}{C}H_2\overset{a}{C}H_3, \qquad \overset{c}{C}H_3\overset{d}{C}H\overset{c}{C}H_3,$$
$$\underset{\underset{c}{CH_3}}{|}$$

are derived:

a. $CH_3CH_2CH_2CH_2CH_3$

b. $CH_3CH_2\underset{\underset{CH_3}{|}}{C}HCH_3$

$\left[\, c.\ CH_3\underset{\underset{CH_3}{|}}{C}HCH_2CH_3 \quad \text{same as } b \,\right]$

d. $CH_3\underset{\underset{CH_3}{|}}{\overset{\overset{CH_3}{|}}{C}}CH_3$

It is seen that the third substitution tried (*c*) gives a formula identical with the second (*b*) and merely written in a different manner. Three distinct formulas remain and, since all possibilities have been investigated, the conclusion is reached that three pentanes can exist. The branched-chain isomers can be represented by simplified formulas and named as derivatives of methane; the three pentanes are as follows:

	B.P.	NAME
$CH_3CH_2CH_2CH_2CH_3$	36.1°	*n*-Pentane
$CH_3CH_2CH(CH_3)_2$	27.9°	Dimethylethylmethane
$(CH_3)_4C$	9.5°	Tetramethylmethane

Naming a compound as a derivative of some simpler parent substance is frequently employed because it affords a convenient method of focusing attention on a special feature of structure. The name tetramethylmethane for the third pentane emphasizes that the substance has a central carbon atom to which four methyl groups are attached. The tabulation of boiling points indicates that this most highly branched isomer is the most volatile of the pentanes and also that dimethylethylmethane has a lower boiling point than the normal, straight-chain hydrocarbon. Comparison of the boiling points of butane and isobutane shows that the branched-chain isomer is the more volatile. This relationship is rather general. On suitable cooling, substances that are gases at ordinary temperatures pass through the liquid to the solid state. Melting points are useful identifying constants, but they usually bear no relationship to the boiling points and often show wider variation from member to member. A frequent relationship is that the more symmetrical isomers tend to have higher melting points. *n*-Pentane melts at −129.7°, dimethylethylmethane at −159.6°, and the symmetrical tetramethylmethane at the much higher temperature of −16.6°. The boiling point is generally correlated closely with the molecular weight, whereas the melting point is sensitive to differences in structure.

Hexanes. — By application of systematic methyl substitution to the three pentanes it can be ascertained that five hexanes should exist. Five, and only five, isomers have been discovered; formulas and physical constants are listed in Table II. The names assigned conform

TABLE II

HEXANES, C_6H_{14}

ISOMER	FORMULA	NAME	M.P., °C.	B.P., °C.
I	$CH_3CH_2CH_2CH_2CH_2CH_3$	n-Hexane	−94.0	68.7
II	$CH_3CH_2CH_2CHCH_3$ | CH_3	2-Methylpentane	−153.7	60.3
III	$CH_3CH_2CHCH_2CH_3$ | CH_3	3-Methylpentane	(−118)	63.3
IV	CH_3 | $CH_3CH_2CCH_3$ | CH_3	2,2-Dimethylbutane	−98.2	49.7
V	$CH_3CH{-}CHCH_3$ | | CH_3 CH_3	2,3-Dimethybutane	−128.8	58.0

to the Geneva system, in which a given compound is regarded as a derivative of that parent hydrocarbon which corresponds to the longest chain of carbon atoms in the molecule. Methyl groups attached to such a chain are substituents, comparable with chlorine atoms. Isomer II has a straight chain of five carbon atoms and is considered to be a pentane with a methyl substituent; since right-to-left counting gives a smaller number than left-to-right, this isomer is 2-methylpentane. It is also proper and for some purposes desirable to employ the methane-derivative system, illustrated in the following list in which simplified formulas are employed:

II	$CH_3CH_2CH_2CH(CH_3)_2$	Dimethyl-n-propylmethane
III	$(CH_3CH_2)_2CHCH_3$	Methyldiethylmethane
IV	$CH_3CH_2C(CH_3)_3$	Trimethylethylmethane
V	$(CH_3)_2CHCH(CH_3)_2$	Dimethylisopropylmethane

Melting points are scattered and irregular in the hexane series. There is less spread in boiling points than in the pentane series of lower molecular weight, and n-hexane is less volatile than the branched-chain isomers.

3.8

Isomers of Higher Hydrocarbons. — Nine isomeric heptanes are demanded by theory and they are all known. It has been ascertained by writing the formulas that 18 octanes and 35 nonanes are possible, and that the number of possible hydrocarbons of the formula $C_{14}H_{30}$ is 1858.

From Alcohols. — Alcohols are one group of available starting materials that can be utilized for synthesis of saturated hydrocarbons. In certain methods the alcohol is first converted into the corresponding halide. As noted in Chapter 1, ethyl alcohol is converted by hydriodic acid into ethyl iodide. The reaction is general and can be used for the preparation of typical halides: methyl, *n*-propyl, and isopropyl

$$CH_3CH_2OH + HI \longrightarrow CH_3CH_2I + H_2O$$
Ethyl iodide

iodide. Hydrobromic acid reacts similarly, for example:

$$\begin{array}{c} CH_3 \\ \diagdown \\ CH_3 \diagup \end{array} CHOH + HBr \longrightarrow \begin{array}{c} CH_3 \\ \diagdown \\ CH_3 \diagup \end{array} CHBr + H_2O$$
Isopropyl bromide

Except in special cases, hydrochloric acid is not reactive enough for practical purposes, but other methods are available for preparing alkyl chlorides.

Wurtz Reaction. — A synthesis of hydrocarbons discovered by Wurtz[1] (1855) consists in treatment of an alkyl halide with metallic sodium, which has a strong affinity for bound halogen and acts on methyl iodide to strip iodine from the molecule and produce sodium iodide. The reaction involves two molecules of methyl iodide and two atoms of sodium:

$$H-\underset{\underset{H}{|}}{\overset{\overset{H}{|}}{C}}+I \ + \ 2Na \ + \ I+\underset{\underset{H}{|}}{\overset{\overset{H}{|}}{C}}-H \longrightarrow H-\underset{\underset{H}{|}}{\overset{\overset{H}{|}}{C}}-\underset{\underset{H}{|}}{\overset{\overset{H}{|}}{C}}-H \ + \ 2NaI$$

Actually, the reaction probably proceeds through formation of methylsodium, which interacts with methyl iodide:

$$CH_3I \xrightarrow{Na} CH_3Na \xrightarrow{CH_3I} CH_3CH_3$$

The Wurtz reaction can be applied generally to the synthesis of hydrocarbons by the joining together of hydrocarbon residues of two molecules of an alkyl halide. With halides of high molecular weight the yields are often good, and the reaction has been serviceable in the synthesis of higher hydrocarbons starting with alcohols found in nature, for example:

$$2 \ n\text{-}C_{16}H_{33}I \xrightarrow[\text{70--80\% yield}]{\text{Mg (ether)}} C_{32}H_{66}$$
Cetyl iodide $\qquad\qquad$ *n*-Dotriacontane

Cetyl iodide (from the alcohol of spermaceti wax) has been converted into the C_{32}-hydrocarbon both by the action of sodium amalgam in alcohol-ether and, as shown in the equation, with use of magnesium.

[1] Adolphe Wurtz, 1817–1884; b. Strasbourg; Giessen, Paris; *Ber.*, **20**, 815 (1887)

A general expression for the Wurtz synthesis is:

$$2\,RX \;+\; 2\,Na \;\longrightarrow\; R{\cdot}R \;+\; 2\,NaX$$
Alkyl halide $\qquad\qquad\qquad$ Alkane

Limitation

It might appear that the synthesis could be varied by use of two different alkyl halides, for example:

$$CH_3CH_2CH_2CH_2I \;+\; ICH_2CH_2CH_3 \xrightarrow{2\,Na} CH_3CH_2CH_2CH_2CH_2CH_2CH_3$$
n-Butyl iodide $\qquad$ *n*-Propyl iodide $\qquad\qquad$ *n*-Heptane

The reaction mixture, however, contains many millions of molecules of each halide, and although some butyl iodide molecules will react with molecules of propyl iodide and yield heptane as pictured, some will combine with each other and produce octane. The total result can be represented as follows:

RX + R'X →
RR', RR, R'R'

$$CH_3CH_2CH_2CH_2I \;+\; CH_3CH_2CH_2I \xrightarrow{2\,Na} \begin{cases} n\text{-}C_6H_{14}, \text{ b.p. } 69° \\ n\text{-}C_7H_{16}, \text{ b.p. } 98° \\ n\text{-}C_8H_{18}, \text{ b.p. } 126° \end{cases}$$

The reaction affords a mixture of three hydrocarbons that do not differ greatly in boiling point, and hence isolation of even a small amount of *n*-heptane in a moderately homogeneous condition would be difficult. It is therefore impracticable to utilize an unsymmetrical Wurtz reaction in synthesis.

3.11

Reduction; the Grignard Reaction. — Alkyl halides in some instances can be reduced directly to hydrocarbons:

$$RX \;+\; 2\,H \text{ (reducing agent)} \;\longrightarrow\; RH \;+\; HX$$

An alternate and generally applicable method utilizes a reactive organometallic compound of a type discovered by Grignard[2] in 1901. Grignard found that methyl iodide, as an example, reacts with metallic magnesium suspended in ether (diethyl ether) to give ether-soluble

Grignard reagent

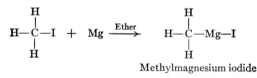

Methylmagnesium iodide

methylmagnesium iodide. The magnesium is employed in the form of thin turnings or granules of the metal, and the ether must be pure and free from traces of moisture. The reaction proceeds satisfactorily with methyl, ethyl, and higher alkyl halides, and can be conducted with a chloride, a bromide, or an iodide. The general formulation is:

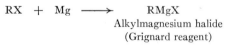

$$RX \;+\; Mg \;\longrightarrow\; RMgX$$
Alkylmagnesium halide
(Grignard reagent)

[2] Victor Grignard, 1871–1935; b. Cherbourg, France; Nancy, Lyon; Nobel Prize 1912; *J. Chem. Soc.*, 171 (1937)

Ether is not merely a convenient solvent but forms a complex (di-etherate) of the composition $RMgX \cdot 2(C_2H_5)_2O$.

Alkylmagnesium halides, or Grignard reagents, are highly reactive and versatile substances capable of entering into many useful reactions. The broad significance of this valuable synthetic tool is reflected in the award to Grignard of the Nobel Prize. The active agent, having a hydrocarbon group and a halogen atom linked to magnesium, is sensitive, but fortunately can be employed for a reaction in the ethereal solution in which it is produced. Conversion into an alkane is accomplished merely by adding slowly to the ethereal solution an equivalent quantity of water. Methylmagnesium iodide gives methane:

$$\underset{\overset{|}{H}}{\overset{\overset{H}{|}}{H-C-MgI}} + HOH \longrightarrow \underset{\overset{|}{H}}{\overset{\overset{H}{|}}{H-C-H}} + HO-Mg-I$$

Methane gas is liberated at once in amount equivalent to the actual Grignard reagent present. Side reactions occur to a slight extent in production of the reagent, but yields in the order of 85–90% are usual, and hence satisfactory overall yields are obtained in the series of reactions:

$$RX \xrightarrow{Mg} RMgX \xrightarrow{HOH} RH + Mg\begin{smallmatrix} X \\ \\ OH \end{smallmatrix}$$

The basic magnesium halide tends to separate from the ether-water mixture as a white precipitate, but can be kept in solution by addition of hydrochloric acid, which forms the normal halide. A solution of mineral acid is often used to effect hydrolytic decomposition of the organometallic halide. Alcohols, organic acids, and any substance containing a hydroxyl group will react as readily as water, for example:

$$CH_3CH_2CH_2MgBr + CH_3OH \longrightarrow CH_3CH_2CH_3 + Mg\begin{smallmatrix} OCH_3 \\ \\ Br \end{smallmatrix}$$

From Acids. — Typical organic acids contain the combination known as the carboxyl group $-C(=O)OH$ as a functional group responsible for the acidity. For convenience in writing this is often abbreviated to $-COOH$ or $-CO_2H$, but such formulas should be read with the understanding that one oxygen is present as a hydroxyl group and the other doubly bound to carbon. Structures and names of typical carboxylic acids and an ester derivative are:

$$\underset{\underset{\overset{|}{H}}{\overset{H}{|}}}{H-C-C}\begin{smallmatrix} O \\ \\ OH \end{smallmatrix} \quad \text{or} \quad CH_3COOH \qquad CH_3CO\overline{[OH + H]}OR \rightleftharpoons CH_3COOR + H_2O$$

Acetic acid   An ester

$$CH_3CH_2COOH \qquad\qquad CH_3CH_2CH_2COOH$$
Propionic acid   *n*-Butyric acid
(cf. propane)   (cf. butane)

The type formula is RCOOH, and the ionization can be represented thus:

$$R-C\overset{O}{\underset{OH}{\big\langle}} \rightleftharpoons R-C\overset{O}{\underset{O^-}{\big\langle}} + H^+$$

In comparison with mineral acids, the organic acids are only weakly acidic, but they react with sodium bicarbonate, as well as with sodium carbonate and sodium hydroxide, and form ionic salts, for example sodium acetate, CH_3COONa.

3.13 **By Decarboxylation.** — One way of converting carboxylic acids into alkanes is pyrolytic elimination of carbon dioxide from the carboxyl group, using a metal salt of the acid. When solid sodium acetate is mixed with sodium hydroxide, or better with the less easily fusible soda lime, and the mixture is heated to a sufficiently high temperature, a breakdown occurs and methane is liberated:

$$CH_3COONa + NaOH \xrightarrow{\text{Fuse}} CH_4 + Na_2CO_3$$

The reaction is somewhat analogous to the thermal decomposition of sodium bicarbonate with loss of carbon dioxide and formation of the more stable sodium carbonate. Sodium carbonate evidently is also more stable than sodium acetate, in combination with alkali. An example of the preparation of a higher hydrocarbon from a natural acid is as follows:

$$\underset{\text{Barium stearate}}{(C_{17}H_{35}COO)_2Ba} \xrightarrow[\text{Dry distillation}]{\text{NaOH, CH}_3\text{ONa}} \underset{n\text{-Heptadecane}}{2\,C_{17}H_{36}}$$

3.14 **Kolbe Synthesis.** — A hydrocarbon synthesis discovered by Kolbe[3] in 1849 consists in electrolysis of an aqueous solution of the salt of an acid. Sodium acetate on electrolysis yields ethane, and the net reaction can be formulated as follows:

$$2\,CH_3COONa + 2\,H_2O \xrightarrow{\text{Electrolysis}} \underbrace{C_2H_6 + 2\,CO_2}_{\text{Anode}} + \underbrace{2\,NaOH + H_2}_{\text{Cathode}}$$

Under the influence of the electric current sodium ions migrate to the cathode, pick up electrons from the inflowing stream, and yield sodium hydroxide and hydrogen. The acetate anion is impelled to the anode, where it gives up the ionic charge and possibly exists in a transient phase as an acetate radical having an odd electron. The radical at once loses carbon dioxide and gives an equally transient

Electrolysis of carboxylate anion

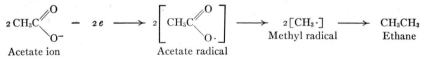

$$\underset{\text{Acetate ion}}{2\,CH_3C\overset{O}{\underset{O^-}{\big\langle}}} - 2e \longrightarrow \underset{\text{Acetate radical}}{2\left[CH_3C\overset{O}{\underset{O\cdot}{\big\langle}}\right]} \longrightarrow \underset{\text{Methyl radical}}{2[CH_3\cdot]} \longrightarrow \underset{\text{Ethane}}{CH_3CH_3}$$

[3] Hermann Kolbe, 1818–84; b. Göttingen; Ph.D. Göttingen; Marburg, Leipzig

trivalent carbon radical, and this finally achieves stabilization by doubling up to form the tetravalent carbon compound ethane.

Sodium propionate on electrolysis affords *n*-butane, and sodium or potassium *n*-butyrate yields *n*-hexane:

$$CH_3CH_2CH_2COOK$$
$$\xrightarrow{\text{Electrolysis}}$$
$$\begin{matrix} CH_3CH_2CH_2 \\ | \\ CH_3CH_2CH_2 \end{matrix}$$

CH₃CH₂CH₂COOK
Potassium *n*-butyrate   *n*-Hexane

CHEMICAL PROPERTIES

3.15

Alkanes, particularly *n*-alkanes, are inert in comparison to alkenes and alkynes, for they are generally resistant to reagents such as strong mineral acids and oxidizing agents, which react readily with unsaturated hydrocarbons. They do, however, enter into certain reactions involving free radical intermediates.

Chlorination. — Methane and chlorine do not react in the dark but react readily on exposure of the mixture to sunlight or to ultraviolet light. The photochemical (light-induced) chlorination involves in the first step substitution of hydrogen by chlorine to give methyl chloride and hydrochloric acid. The reaction does not stop at this initial stage but gives also the higher products, methylene chloride, chloroform, and carbon tetrachloride:

3.16
*Photochemical
chlorination*

$$CH_4 \;+\; Cl_2 \xrightarrow{\text{Light}} HCl \;+\; CH_3Cl \longrightarrow CH_2Cl_2 \longrightarrow CHCl_3 \longrightarrow CCl_4$$

Gives mixtures

Higher substitution products are found in the mixture even though considerable methane is still present, which shows that introduction of chlorine renders the molecule more vulnerable than before to the reagent. Photochemical chlorination is used for the industrial production of mixtures of chlorinated hydrocarbons of use as solvents but is unsatisfactory as a laboratory reaction because it gives mixtures. Bromine reacts with alkanes under photocatalysis in the same way as chlorine but less vigorously. Iodine does not react.

Free radical reaction

Studies of the reaction have led to the conclusion that it proceeds through transient free radicals, which are fragments containing an odd or unpaired electron resulting from breaking of a covalent bond by a process of homolysis in which one electron is retained by each of the atoms forming the bond: $A:B \rightarrow A \cdot + B \cdot$. Such a process requires considerable energy, in this case radiant energy, but a radical is highly reactive because of the tendency of atoms to attain their normal-valence shell. In the photochemical chlorination the chlorine molecule, shown with just the bonding electrons, undergoes homolysis to chlorine radicals, or odd-electron atoms (a), which attack the alkane

Homolysis

(a) $Cl:Cl \longrightarrow Cl \cdot + Cl \cdot$
(b) $Cl \cdot + RH \longrightarrow HCl + R \cdot$
(c) $R \cdot + Cl_2 \longrightarrow RCl + Cl \cdot$

with formation of alkyl radicals (b), which in turn attack chlorine molecules with regeneration of the initiating chlorine radical (c).

The photochemical activation of the reagents can be simulated by use of chemical catalysts, for alkanes have been chlorinated at low temperatures by the action of sulfuryl chloride catalyzed by benzoyl peroxide (Kharasch,[4] 1939):

$$RH \;+\; SO_2Cl_2 \xrightarrow[40-80°]{\text{Peroxide}} RCl \;+\; HCl \;+\; SO_2$$

n-Heptane yields 12.5% of 1-chloroheptane and 76.5% of 2-chloroheptane; *n*-propyl chloride on similar treatment affords 45% of 1,2-dichloropropane and 34% of 1,3-dichloropropane. Benzoyl peroxide functions as a catalyst because it readily decomposes according to equations 1 and 2 to give the phenyl radical, which reacts as in 3 with sulfuryl chloride to give the radical $SO_2Cl\cdot$. The latter radical then initiates a chain reaction involving steps 4–6, in which the radicals

required in the initial step 4 are continually regenerated during the course of transformation of the hydrocarbon into the chloride (5–6). Ideally, a single chain-initiating radical derived from the decomposi-

Chain-initiating reactions
1. $C_6H_5COO{-}OOCC_6H_5 \longrightarrow C_6H_5COO\cdot \;+\; CO_2 \;+\; C_6H_5\cdot$
   Benzoyl peroxide $\qquad$ Benzoate radical $\qquad$ Phenyl radical
2. $C_6H_5COO\cdot \longrightarrow C_6H_5\cdot \;+\; CO_2$
3. $C_6H_5\cdot \;+\; SO_2Cl_2 \longrightarrow C_6H_5Cl \;+\; SO_2Cl\cdot$

Chain reaction
4. $SO_2Cl\cdot \longrightarrow SO_2 \;+\; Cl\cdot$
5. $Cl\cdot \;+\; RH \longrightarrow HCl \;+\; R\cdot$
6. $R\cdot \;+\; SO_2Cl_2 \longrightarrow RCl \;+\; SO_2Cl\cdot$

tion of benzoyl peroxide would suffice for the chlorination, and actually only a catalytic amount of peroxide is required. However, such a reaction is markedly sensitive to traces of impurities that can react with one of the free-radical intermediates and so break the chain.

Cracking. — High temperatures, like photocatalysis and peroxide catalysis, promote production of free radicals. When the vapor of a higher alkane is passed through a hot tube (500–700°), thermal decomposition (pyrolysis), or cracking, occurs with rupture of carbon–carbon linkages and cleavage of the molecule into small fragments.

Cracking of *n*-octane, for example, can involve homolysis of a central bond to produce two C_4-radicals, which by hydrogen exchange can afford the C_4-alkane and the C_4-alkene:

$$C_8H_{18} \longrightarrow 2\,C_4H_9\cdot \longrightarrow \underset{\text{Alkane}}{C_4H_{10}} \;+\; \underset{\text{Alkene}}{C_4H_8}$$

[4] Morris S. Kharasch, b. 1895 Kremenetz, Ukrania; Ph.D. Chicago (Piccard); Nat. Res. Fellow, Chicago; Maryland, Chicago

Rupture at other positions is possible, some carbonization may occur, and elementary hydrogen may result, also through radicals, by rupture of carbon–hydrogen bonds, for example:

$$C_8H_{18} \longrightarrow \begin{cases} C_6H_{14} + C_2H_4 \\ C_4H_{10} + CH_4 + C_2H_4 + C \\ C_8H_{16} + H_2 \end{cases}$$

Although cracking may be complex and give a diversified mixture of products, modern technology has turned it into an extremely useful method of obtaining superior motor fuels and synthetic intermediates.

Oxidation. — The reaction of hydrocarbons with oxygen with output of energy is the basis for use of fractions from petroleum as fuels in internal combustion engines. Cracking to free radicals undoubtedly is involved at the high temperatures of burning, and oxygen itself is a diradical, $\cdot O:O\cdot$. The heat of combustion of methane is 13.14 kg.-cal./g. or 5.57 kg.-cal./ml. *n*-Octane has a higher density and the heat release is 11.43 kg.-cal./g. or 8.03 kg.-cal./ml.

3.19

Free radicals involved

CYCLOALKANES

Hydrocarbons of this series, the first few members of which are shown in the formulas, conform to the type C_nH_{2n}. The boiling points

3.20

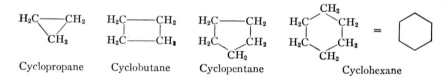

Cyclopropane Cyclobutane Cyclopentane Cyclohexane

are 10–20° higher than those of corresponding alkanes, and the densities are some 20% greater. In chemical properties cyclopentane and cyclohexane are indistinguishable from *n*-pentane and *n*-hexane, respectively. Special properties of the 3- and 4-ring hydrocarbons are discussed in Chapter 13.

SUMMARY

Properties

Boiling points. The normal alkane of molecular weight about 100 (heptane) boils at about 100°. As molecular weight increases, b.p. difference between homologs decreases; only the lower alkanes differ enough in b.p. for easy separation.

Other properties. Nonpolar substances insoluble in the polar solvent water. Neutral: insoluble in aqueous NaOH or in dilute or concentrated H_2SO_4. Lighter than water.

Structure of Alkanes

Methane. Equivalence of the four hydrogen atoms. Only one CH_3Cl (methyl chloride), one CH_2Cl_2 (methylene chloride), one $CHCl_3$ (chloroform), one CCl_4 (carbon tetrachloride).

Ethane. Number of chloro substitution products:. one mono; two di ($1,1$-, $1,2$-); two tri ($1,1,1$-,$1,1,2$-); two tetra ($1,1,1,2$-, $1,1,2,2$-); one penta; one hexa.

Propane. Two types of positions for substitution: central and terminal. n-Propyl chloride and isopropyl chloride. Four dichloropropanes; five trichloropropanes.

n-Butane and i-butane (branched isomer the more volatile). Derivation of formulas from formula of propane by substitution of methyl for hydrogen atoms of the two types represented. Abbreviation of formulas: i-butane = $(CH_3)_3CH$. Naming of compounds as derivatives of methane: $(CH_3)_3CH$ = trimethylmethane.

Pentanes. Derivation of formulas by systematic methyl-substitution in the two butanes. Isomers: n-pentane, $CH_3CH_2CH(CH_3)_2$ = dimethylethylmethane, $(CH_3)_4C$ = tetramethylmethane (most highly branched, is the most volatile, most symmetrical, has the highest m.p.).

Hexanes. Derivation of formulas of the five isomers. Geneva nomenclature: name as derivative of the parent hydrocarbon having the longest straight chain of carbon atoms; positions of substituents indicated by numbers. Example: $CH_3CH_2C(CH_3)_3$ = 2,2-dimethylbutane. Geneva names and methane-derivative names of the five hexanes.

Number of possible isomers: C_8, 18; C_9, 35; C_{14}, 1858.

Synthesis

From an alcohol (ROH) through an alkyl halide (RX). (a) Wurtz reaction (1855): $2 RX + 2 Na \longrightarrow R \cdot R$ (intermediate: RNa); unsatisfactory for unsymmetrical hydrocarbons. (b) Reduction; direct: $RX + 2 H \longrightarrow R \cdot H$; Grignard reaction (1901): $RX + Mg \longrightarrow RMgX$ (as dietherate); $RMgX + H_2O \longrightarrow R \cdot H + Mg(OH)X$.

From an acid (RCO_2H). (a) By decarboxylation: RCOOH (heat with soda lime) $\longrightarrow R \cdot H$. (b) Kolbe electrolysis (1849): $2 RCO_2H \longrightarrow R \cdot R$.

Reactions

Inert (origin of name paraffin). Resistant to mineral acids and oxidizing agents. Realizable reactions require high temperatures, photochemical or peroxide catalysis.

Photochemical chlorination: $CH_4 \longrightarrow$ mixture of CH_3Cl, CH_2Cl_2, $CHCl_3$, CCl_4. Chain reaction initiated by photochemically produced chlorine radicals: $Cl \cdot + RH \longrightarrow HCl + R \cdot$; $R \cdot + Cl_2 \longrightarrow RCl + Cl \cdot$ (attacks another RH). Chlorination with sulfuryl chloride (SO_2Cl_2) catalyzed by benzoyl peroxide. Initiating reaction, e.g.: peroxide $\longrightarrow$ benzoate radical ($C_6H_5COO \cdot$) + phenyl radical ($C_6H_5 \cdot$); $C_6H_5 \cdot + SO_2Cl_2 \longrightarrow C_6H_5Cl + SO_2Cl \cdot$. Chain reaction: $SO_2Cl \cdot \longrightarrow SO_2$ + $Cl \cdot$; $Cl \cdot + RH \longrightarrow HCl + R \cdot$; $R \cdot + SO_2Cl_2 \longrightarrow RCl + SO_2Cl \cdot$; repeats cycle.

Cracking. C_8H_{18} at 600° $\longrightarrow$ smaller molecules, some saturated, some unsaturated (+ carbon). Free-radical reaction.

Oxidation. Combustion is high-temperature free-radical reaction.

Heats of combustion. Among the n-alkanes, methane has the highest fuel value per g. and the C_{16}- and higher hydrocarbons have the highest heat of combustion per ml.

Cycloalkanes boil 10–20° higher than normal alkanes, are denser by 20%.

PROBLEMS

1. Formulate and name all possible dibromo derivatives of isobutane (3 isomers) and of n-butane (6 isomers).
2. Write formulas for all heptanes derived from $CH_3CH(CH_3)CH_2CH_2CH_3$ and name them as derivatives of methane.
3. Write structural formulas for:
   (a) 1-Bromo-2-chlorononane
   (b) 2,2,3-Trichloroheptane
   (c) 2-Hydroxy-2-methylbutane
   (d) Dimethylisopropylmethane
   (e) Tetraethylmethane
   (f) n-Hexylmagnesium iodide

4. Name the following compounds as derivatives of methane:
   (a) CCl_2F_2
   (b) $(CH_3)_2C(CH_2CH_3)_2$
   (c) $(CH_3)_3CCH_2CH_2CH_2CH_3$
   (d) $(CH_3CH_2CH_2)_2CHCH(CH_3)_2$
5. Give Geneva names for:
   (a) $CH_3CH(CH_3)CH_2CH_2CH(CH_3)CH_2CH_3$
   (b) Isobutane
   (c) $CH_3CH_2CH_2CH(C_2H_5)CH_3$
   (d) $(CH_3)_2CHCH(C_2H_5)CH_2CH(CH_3)_2$
6. What octanes can be derived from the heptane $CH_3CH_2CH_2C(CH_3)_3$? Give the Geneva names.

READING REFERENCES

"Definitive Report of the Committee for the Reform of Nomenclature in Organic Chemistry," *J. Chem. Soc.*, 1607 (1931)

E. E. Gilbert, "The Reactive Paraffins," *J. Chem. Educ.*, **18**, 435 (1941)

G. Edgar, G. Calingaert and R. E. Marker, "The Preparation and Properties of the Isomeric Heptanes," *J. Am. Chem. Soc.*, **51**, 1483 (1929)

D. H. Hey and W. A. Waters, "Free Radicals and Homolytic Reactions," *Chemistry of Carbon Compounds* (E. H. Rodd, Ed.), IA, 195–217, Elsevier (1951)

CHAPTER 4

ALKENES

4.1 **Physical properties**

Hydrocarbons of the alkene series have the type formula C_nH_{2n} and are very similar in physical constants to corresponding alkanes, C_nH_{2n+2}. The first few members, exemplified by ethylene and propylene, are gases, and C_5 and higher alkenes are liquids. In contrast to the inert alkanes, they react readily with a variety of reagents without catalysis by light or heat and form products of addition, rather

```
  H  H                                   H   H   H
H:C::C:H   or   CH2=CH2               H:C : C:: C:H   or   CH3CH=CH2
                                         H
```

Ethylene, b.p. −102° Propylene, b.p. −48°

than of substitution. Thus ethylene adds chlorine to form the liquid ethylene dichloride:

Addition reactions

$$CH_2::CH_2 + Cl:Cl \longrightarrow Cl:CH_2:CH_2:Cl$$

Ethylene dichloride, b.p. 84°

The conversion of gaseous hydrocarbons into liquid dihalides led early chemists to describe them as olefins (oil-forming substances), and the terms olefin, olefinic hydrocarbon, olefinic linkage are still used. Common names for the first few members are ethylene, propylene, butylene, and amylene (C_5H_{10}, derived from an amyl alcohol, $C_5H_{11}OH$). Derivative names are sometimes used; thus $(CH_3)_2CHCH{=}CH_2$ is isopropylethylene, and $(CH_3)_2C{=}C(CH_3)_2$ is appropriately described as tetramethylethylene.

Names, common

4.2 **Geneva**

The Geneva name for an ethyl**en**ic hydrocarbon is derived by changing the name of the corresponding paraffin from -**ane** to -**ene**. Ethylene is called ethene and propylene propene. A branched-chain compound is assigned a basic name corresponding to the longest carbon chain, and alkyl groups attached to the chain are considered as substituent groups and their positions indicated by prefix numbers.

The double bond is a functional group, conferring specific reaction functions, particularly additions, and the position of this ene functional group is indicated by a number, usually included at the end of the name, to show the position of the first of the two unsaturated carbons (examples a, b). A hydrocarbon having two double bonds is a diene (c). Where there is a choice in the direction of counting, the func-

(a) $CH_2CH_2CH{=}CH_2$
Butene-1

(b) $CH_3CH{=}CHCH_3$
Butene-2

(c) $CH_2{=}CHCH_2CH{=}CH_2$
Pentadiene-1,4

(d) $CH_3CH_2CH_2CH{=}CHCH_2CH_3$
Heptene-3 (not -4)

(e) $CH_3CH_2C(CH_3){=}CH_2$
2-Methyl-butene-1

(f) $(CH_3)_2CHCH_2CH{=}CHCH_3$
5-Methylhexene-2

tional group number is made as small as possible (d, e). Functional group numbers take precedence over substituent numbers and alone are considered in choosing the direction of counting, as in (f); any doubt that this is a methylhexene and not a dimethylpentene can be dispelled by writing the formula out in full. A formula may be so written that the name is not obvious. For example, (g) has a chain

$$\underset{\text{(g)}}{\overset{\overset{\displaystyle CH_3 \quad\quad CH_3}{|\quad\quad\quad |}}{\underset{|\quad\quad\quad\;\; |}{\underset{CH_2CH_3 \;\; CH_2CH_3}{CH_3CCH{=}CHCCH_3}}}} \quad = \quad \underset{\text{(h)}}{\overset{\overset{\displaystyle CH_3 \quad\quad CH_3}{|\quad\quad\quad |}}{\underset{|\quad\quad\quad\;\; |}{\underset{CH_3 \quad\quad CH_3}{CH_3CH_2CCH{=}CHCCH_2CH_3}}}}$$

of six carbon atoms in a horizontal line but, on counting around the corners, it is seen that a longer chain of eight carbons is present. Therefore the hydrocarbon is 3,3,6,6-tetramethyloctene-4. Rearrangement of the formula as in (h) makes obvious its identity as an octene rather than a hexene.

Alkenes are prepared largely from alcohols which, in the Geneva system, are named by changing the ending -ane to -anol. The -ol functional group is indicated by a terminal number, which again is made as small as possible regardless of the numbers subsequently assigned to substituent groups. Examples:

$CH_3CH_2CH(OH)CH_3$
Butanol-2

$(CH_3)_3CCH_2CH_2OH$
3,3-Dimethylbutanol-1

$HOCH_2CH_2CH_2CH_2OH$
Butanediol-1,4

The basic name should indicate all the functional groups present, that is, it should show that a substance is an ene, a diene, a triene, a diol, an enol, etc. Thus in case the longest carbon chain does not include all functional groups present the rule is to select the next longest chain that includes the maximum number of functional groups.

$$\underset{\text{(i)}}{\underset{CH_2OH}{\underset{|}{CH_3CH_2CHCH_2CH_2CH_3}}} \quad\quad \underset{\text{(j)}}{\underset{CH{=}CH_2}{\underset{|}{CH_3CH_2CH{=}CCH_2CH_3}}}$$

Thus (i) is 2-ethylpentanol-1 and (j) is 3-n-propylhexadiene-1,3.

CHAPTER 4

4.4

From Alcohols. — The most generally useful method of synthesis of alkenes utilizes an alcohol as starting material. The hydroxyl group presents a point of vulnerability, as shown by the reaction with hydrobromic or hydriodic acid already cited, in which the original functional group is replaced by halogen. Conversion of an alcohol into an alkene requires simultaneous elimination of the hydroxyl group with a hydrogen from an adjacent carbon atom. By loss of

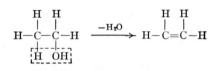

OH from one carbon and of H from another, ethyl alcohol yields ethylene.

Dehydration over alumina

One procedure is catalytic dehydration. The alcohol is distilled through a tube packed with granules of alumina and maintained at a temperature of 350–400° in an electrically heated furnace. The reaction resembles pyrolysis of an alkane, since it involves production of an unsaturated product from a saturated one at an elevated temperature, but the pyrolysis temperature for an alcohol is distinctly lower, and the process is simpler and more uniform. A partial vacuum is sometimes advantageous in providing for removal of the olefin before secondary changes can occur, as in the apparatus shown in Fig. 4.1.

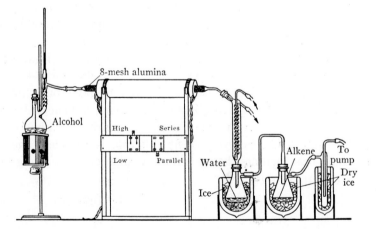

FIG. 4.1. — **Apparatus for Dehydration of an Alcohol over Alumina at Reduced Pressure**

1. $CH_3CH_2OH \xrightarrow[\text{98\%}]{\text{Kaolin or alumina, 350–360°}} CH_2{=}CH_2$

2. $CH_3-\overset{\overset{\displaystyle CH_3}{|}}{\underset{\underset{\displaystyle OH}{|}}{C}}-\overset{\overset{\displaystyle CH_3}{|}}{\underset{\underset{\displaystyle OH}{|}}{C}}-CH_3 \xrightarrow[\text{79–86\%}]{\text{Al}_2\text{O}_3,\ 420\text{–}470°} CH_2{=}\overset{\overset{\displaystyle CH_3}{|}}{C}-\overset{\overset{\displaystyle CH_3}{|}}{C}{=}CH_2$

         Pinacol   2,3-Dimethylbutadiene-1,3

3. $\xrightarrow[\text{89\%}]{\text{Al}_2\text{O}_3,\ 380\text{–}450°}$

       Cyclohexanol   Cyclohexene

Another method of dehydration is the action of sulfuric acid in the temperature range 100–170°. When the acid is added to ethanol gradually with ice cooling, water is eliminated from the two reactants, and ethylsulfuric acid is formed. The reaction proceeds to completion

$$CH_3CH_2O\overline{|H} + HO\overline{|}SO_2OH \underset{\text{Excess H}_2\text{O}}{\overset{\text{concd. H}_2\text{SO}_4}{\rightleftharpoons}} CH_3CH_2OSO_2OH + H_2O$$

                                              Ethylsulfuric
                                                acid

with use of excess concentrated sulfuric acid at 0°, for the acid absorbs the water formed; the process, however, is an equilibrium, and the conversion can be reversed by use of a large excess of water.

Ethylsulfuric acid, an ester in which one of the hydroxylic hydrogens of sulfuric acid is replaced by an ethyl group, is stable at low temperatures but decomposes when heated. At an optimum temperature of 170°, the chief organic product of decomposition is ethylene, formed by loss of the group OSO₂OH from one carbon atom and of hydrogen from the adjacent position to produce sulfuric acid. A side reaction consists in formation of diethyl ether (ordinary ether)

$$H-\overset{\overset{\displaystyle H}{|}}{\underset{\underset{\displaystyle H}{|}}{C}}-\overset{\overset{\displaystyle H}{|}}{\underset{\underset{\displaystyle H}{|}}{C}}\overline{-|OSO_2OH|} \xrightarrow{170°} CH_2{=}CH_2 + HOSO_2OH$$

by the action of alcohol on ethylsulfuric acid. This reaction can be operated for the preparation of ether by adjusting the proportions of

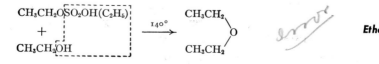

$$\begin{array}{c} CH_3CH_2OSO_2OH(C_2H_5) \\ + \\ CH_3CH_2OH \end{array} \xrightarrow{140°} \begin{array}{c} CH_3CH_2 \\ \diagdown \\ CH_3CH_2 \diagup \end{array}O$$

4.6

The difference in the optimum temperatures for ethylene and ether formation is so slight that each product is an inevitable by-product of the preparation of the other.

Dehydration can be effected with phosphorus pentoxide or with strong acids other than sulfuric. Hydrochloric acid cannot form an intermediate analogous to an alkylsulfuric acid and probably functions as catalyst by protonation of the alcoholic oxygen to form an oxonium ion from which hydronium ion is expelled:

With HCl

$$RCH_2CH_2OH \xrightarrow{\text{H}^+} RCH_2CH_2\overset{+}{\underset{H}{O}}H \xrightarrow{-H_3O^+} RCH=CH_2$$

4.7

Alcohols vary in the ease with which they undergo dehydration to alkenes, those of highly branched-chain structure being particularly susceptible. Alcohols are classified as primary, secondary, or tertiary, according to the number of alkyl groups attached to the carbon atom carrying the hydroxyl group. Tertiary alcohols are dehydrated most

Relative reactivity

RCH₂OH	R₂CHOH	R₃COH
Primary alcohol	Secondary alcohol	Tertiary alcohol

easily, secondary are next, and primary alcohols are least easily converted into alkenes. These differences are illustrated in the accompanying examples. The secondary alcohol shown in example 1 is

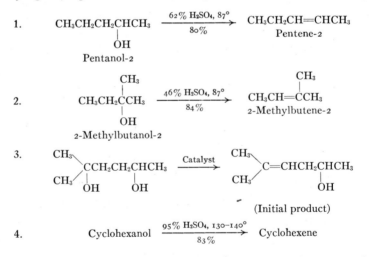

1. $CH_3CH_2CH_2\underset{\underset{OH}{|}}{CH}CH_3 \xrightarrow[80\%]{62\% \text{ H}_2\text{SO}_4,\ 87°} CH_3CH_2CH=CHCH_3$
   Pentanol-2   Pentene-2

2. $CH_3CH_2\underset{\underset{OH}{|}}{\overset{\overset{CH_3}{|}}{C}}CH_3 \xrightarrow[84\%]{46\% \text{ H}_2\text{SO}_4,\ 87°} CH_3CH=\overset{\overset{CH_3}{|}}{C}CH_3$
   2-Methylbutanol-2   2-Methylbutene-2

3. $\underset{CH_3}{\overset{CH_3}{>}}\underset{\underset{OH}{|}}{C}CH_2CH_2\underset{\underset{OH}{|}}{CH}CH_3 \xrightarrow{\text{Catalyst}} \underset{CH_3}{\overset{CH_3}{>}}C=CHCH_2\underset{\underset{OH}{|}}{CH}CH_3$
   (Initial product)

4. Cyclohexanol $\xrightarrow[83\%]{95\% \text{ H}_2\text{SO}_4,\ 130-140°}$ Cyclohexene

dehydrated in 80% yield at the temperature of the steam bath by 62% sulfuric acid, whereas the tertiary alcohol of example 2 affords an olefin in comparable yield at the same temperature by the action of acid of only 46% strength. The case of ethyl alcohol, cited above, is representative of the behavior of a primary alcohol; the best results are obtained with use of 96% (concentrated) sulfuric acid at the higher temperature of 170°. That a tertiary alcohol undergoes dehydration more easily than a secondary alcohol is further demonstrated by the behavior of the dihydroxy compound shown in example 3. This diol contains both a tertiary and a secondary alcoholic group, and on partial dehydration the former is preferentially eliminated. Example 4 shows that cyclohexanol can be dehydrated to cyclohexene by sulfuric acid as well as by the catalytic method cited above, although in slightly lower yield. This dehydration has been accomplished also with potassium bisulfate ($KHSO_4$), phosphoric acid, iodine, and oxalic acid, an organic dibasic acid of acidic strength nearly comparable to that of a mineral acid.

From Alkyl Halides. — The introduction of a double bond can be accomplished by treating an alkyl halide with a basic reagent capable of splitting out the elements of hydrogen halide from adjacent carbon atoms:

$$-\overset{|}{\underset{\underset{H}{|}}{C}}-\overset{|}{\underset{\underset{X}{|}}{C}}-\;+\;\text{Base}\;\longrightarrow\;-\overset{|}{C}=\overset{|}{C}-\;+\;\text{Salt}$$

An acid-binding reagent commonly employed is an alcoholic solution of potassium hydroxide. Aqueous alkali is less suitable because of lack of solubility of the alkyl halide in water; alcohol is a satisfactory solvent for the organic reagent and also dissolves potassium hydroxide. The preparation of an alkene by this method is illustrated by the conversion of both *n*-propyl and isopropyl iodide into propylene; the yield is notably better with the secondary than with the primary iodide

$$\underset{\text{alc. KOH}}{CH_3CH_2CH_2I} \overset{1.}{\underset{36\%}{\big|}} \longrightarrow CH_3CH{=}CH_2 \longleftarrow \underset{\text{alc. KOH}}{\overset{2.}{\underset{94\%}{\big|}}} \overset{\overset{\text{I}}{|}}{CH_3CHCH_3}$$

(temperature in each case, 80–100°). The tertiary iodide shown in example 3 reacts so readily that the alkene is obtained simply by addition of the halide dropwise to boiling water, which retains the hydrogen iodide formed. The order of reactivity of halides of primary, secondary, and tertiary structure is thus the same as that of alcohols.

3.
$$\begin{array}{c}CH_3 \\ {>}C{-}CH_3 \\ CH_3 \;\;\underset{I}{|}\end{array} \xrightarrow{H_2O,\;100°} \begin{array}{c}CH_3 \\ {>}C{=}CH_2 \\ CH_3\end{array}$$
Isobutylene

The method finds little use in the preparation of ethylenic hydrocarbons themselves, for the required alkyl halides are best obtained from the corresponding alcohols and a shorter route from the alcohol to the alkene is direct dehydration. The occasion for introducing a double bond, however, arises in other series; for example, a double bond can be introduced into isobutyric acid by bromination, followed by elimination of hydrogen bromide.

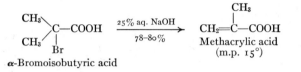

α-Bromoisobutyric acid

4.9

From a *vicinal*-Dihalide. — A compound in which two halogen atoms are situated on adjacent positions in the carbon chain, and are hence in the same vicinity, is described as a vicinal (or *vic-*) dihalide. The halogen atoms in such a compound can be eliminated simultaneously by treatment with bivalent zinc, which can strip off the two

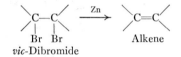

vic-Dibromide

halogen atoms at the same time. The reaction is not of much use in the actual synthesis of alkenes because the required *vic*-dihalides are not sufficiently available, but it is frequently employed in purification

Use in purification   of ethylenic compounds. An alkene can be converted into its bromine-addition product and subsequently regenerated by reduction with zinc dust, with advantages that can be appreciated from an example. A sample of trimethylethylene contaminated with the corresponding saturated hydrocarbon, 2-methylbutane (isopentane), could not be separated from this substance by ordinary distillation because the

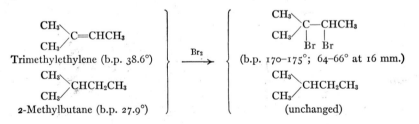

boiling points lie too close together. If the mixture is treated with bromine without undue exposure to light, the alkene reacts selectively and is converted into a derivative heavier by some 160 units of molecular weight and consequently having a very much higher boiling point. Trimethylethylene dibromide boils at a temperature 140–145° higher than 2-methylbutane, and can be separated easily and completely by vacuum distillation. By treatment of the distilled addition product with zinc dust in alcoholic solution, pure trimethylethylene is regenerated. A similar procedure is applicable to the purification of ethylenic substances that are solids.

Nature of the Double Bond. — The properties and reactions of alkenes are best considered in light of some of the concepts of the molecular orbital theory, a theory based upon principles of quantum mechanics by which it is possible to calculate the probable position of an electron in relation to the nucleus. In the case of the hydrogen atom, the region in which the one electron travels is spherically symmetrical and is called a $1s$ orbital (1 = quantum number, s = state). When two hydrogen atoms bond to form a hydrogen molecule, the two $1s$ orbitals coalesce to form a molecular orbital (Fig. 4.2) occupied

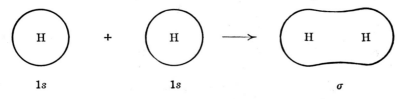

1s   1s σ

FIG. 4.2. — **Atomic and Molecular Orbitals (cross sections)**

by the two electrons and encompassing the two nuclei. This orbital is symmetrical about a line connecting the two nuclei, and hence has the same character as an atomic s orbital and is known as a σ (sigma) molecular orbital. The binding energy of a molecular orbital is highest when the component atomic orbitals overlap to the highest degree, and since two s orbitals overlap efficiently, the σ orbital, or σ bond, of the hydrogen molecule is strong. In methane the four hydrogens are linked to carbon by similarly strong σ bonds and the orbital representation is tetrahedral and similar to the Stuart model, Fig. 1.1. All the covalent bonds of ethane are likewise stable σ bonds.

An atomic orbital of another character, a p type, is involved, with s orbitals, in the compounding of the molecular orbitals of ethylene. In a $2p$ orbital the electron is confined to two merging regions or clouds that, together, form a sort of dumbbell, represented by two balls (Fig. 4.3a) or, in cross section, by a figure eight loop (b). This orbital is not symmetrical but directional, and is oriented along one of three axes. A molecular orbital compounded from two $2p$ atomic orbitals (Fig. 4.4) retains a dumbbell character and consists in one doughnut-like cloud overlying another. It is called a π (pi) molecular orbital and constitutes a π bond. Ethylene contains five σ and one π bonds. In Fig. 4.5 the C—C σ bond is represented by a line; two C—H σ bonds oriented to the front are shown as full lines, and two oriented to the rear and at an angle of $120°$ to the first are shown as dotted lines. The π orbital confining a pair of shared electrons is shown in (a) as a two-doughnut cloud

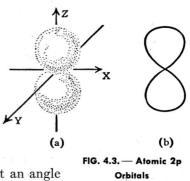

(a)   (b)

FIG. 4.3. — **Atomic 2p Orbitals**

CHAPTER 4

Overlap in π bond

and in (b) by two figure eight loops, corresponding to the original atomic *p* orbitals but with lines joining them to indicate the over-lapping involved in the formation of the molecular π orbital. The concept of a double bond as two pairs of shared electrons is thus

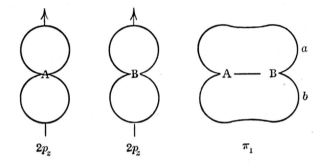

FIG. 4.4.— Formation of a π Molecular Orbital

$$2p_z \qquad 2p_z \qquad \pi_1$$

Double bond contains σ and π electrons

extended in the orbital theory to the concept of two kinds of two-electron bonds: a σ bond, stabilized by efficient overlapping of symmetrical atomic orbitals, and a π bond, compounded with

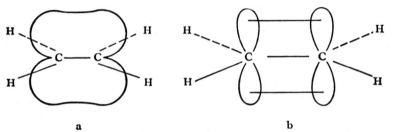

FIG. 4.5.— Ethylene; Cross Sections of π Orbital

a   b

poor overlapping and hence of higher energy content and greater reactivity. The loop representation (Fig. 4.5b) has the advantage of emphasizing the point that π electrons, that is the two electrons occupying the π orbital, retain some of the character of the original *p* orbitals and that the plane of vibration of a π electron is perpendicular to the plane of the σ bond. The reactivity of ethylene in additions is thus attributable to the lack of stability of the π electrons and hence their availability for formation of more stable σ bonds with other atoms. The overlap in formation of the π orbital although weak is

Bond lengths

not without significant consequence. Thus the carbon–carbon bond distance in ethane of 1.54 Å is, in ethylene, shortened to 1.34 Å, evi-dently because the additional π orbital surrounding the two nuclei draws them together more strongly.

4.12

Another consequence of π orbital overlap is stereochemical, that is, concerned with chemistry in space. Atoms connected by a σ bond are free to rotate about this bond, as is demonstrated by the fact that

Geometrical isomerism

1,2-dichloroethane exists in only one stereochemical form and not, for example, in one form in which the chlorine atoms are as close together

46

as possible and in another in which they are maximally separated. In an alkene, however, rotation about the σ bond is restricted by the overlap of *p* orbitals comprising the π bond, and the configuration shown in Fig. 4.4, that is, the arrangement of atoms in space, is relatively rigid. In his paper of 1873, van't Hoff deduced the same configuration from consideration of tetrahedral models and predicted that compounds in which each carbon atom of ethylene is unsymmetrically substituted should exist in two stereochemical forms, or as a pair of geometrical isomers, called *cis* and *trans*:

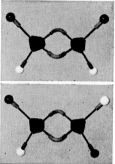

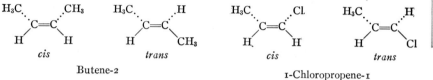

cis   trans   cis   trans

Butene-2   1-Chloropropene-1

The prediction has been abundantly verified and many pairs of *cis-trans* isomers such as those formulated are known.

Bond Polarization. — Since the π electrons of a covalent carbon–carbon double bond lack stability and are in orbitals oriented at right angles to the more stable σ bond, electron displacements are possible in alkenes that have no counterpart in alkanes. Thus a difference in the electron-attracting power of the atoms or groups attached to the two carbon atoms may result in a displacement of the shared electrons in the sense represented in formulas (a) and (b) with curved arrows.

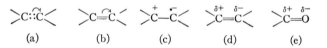

(a)   (b)   (c)   (d)   (e)

No actual charge separation to produce a dipolar ion (c) is implied, but rather an unequal sharing of electrons resulting in a partial polarization in the sense that the carbon atom written to the right has the higher electron density, indicated in formula (d) by the symbol $\delta-$; the other carbon then must have a fractional positive charge of the same magnitude, $\delta+$. Thus formulas (a), (b), and (d) are alternate conventions for representation of a *partially polarized covalent* double bond. A double bond between two unlike atoms, for example the carbon–oxygen double bond of a carbonyl group (C=O), is usually partially polarized, since unlike atoms differ in relative electronegativity. Estimated relative electronegativities are listed in the margin. Oxygen is more electronegative than carbon, and hence the carbonyl group is partially polarized in the sense indicated in formula (e).

Another type of double bond is exemplified by one of two kinds of nitrogen–oxygen linkages in nitric acid. If the usual concept of electron-sharing is applied to the linking together of one atom of

F 4.0	Cl 3.0	S 2.5
O 3.5	Br 2.8	C 2.5
N 3.0	I 2.5	H 2.1

hydrogen (1 *e*), one atom of nitrogen (5 *e*), and three atoms of oxygen (6 *e*), the result (f) is seen to represent an electronically unstable structure because the nitrogen atom is surrounded by ten electrons. It is

$$H:\ddot{O}:N::\ddot{O}: \qquad H:\ddot{O}:\overset{+}{N}:\ddot{\ddot{O}}: \qquad H-O-\overset{+}{N}-\overset{-}{O}$$

$$\underset{:O:}{\overset{::}{}} \qquad \underset{:O:}{\overset{::}{}} \qquad \underset{O}{\overset{\|}{}}$$

(f)   (g)   (h)

thus supposed that two of the four electrons between nitrogen and, say, the oxygen written to the right move into the exclusive sphere of this oxygen atom to give structure (g). In this structure each oxygen and nitrogen atom is surrounded by an electron octet, and the nitrogen and one oxygen atom bear positive and negative charges, since one of the two electrons that was moved from a shared position originally belonged to nitrogen and hence is donated by nitrogen to oxygen. The two atoms concerned are thus linked by the concerted action of a covalent bond and a polar bond, and the combination is defined as a **coordinate covalent bond,** or a **semipolar bond.** Formula (h) is the equivalent counterpart written with Kekulé bonds.

4.15
Formal charge

The doubly bound atoms in an unsymmetrical alkene or in a carbonyl compound are not polarized to anything like the extent that the atoms of sodium chloride are polarized, and the net charges actually are not far from the limiting charge of zero, which is defined as the formal charge. In sodium chloride the formal charge on sodium is +1 and that on chlorine is −1, but there may be a slight electron-sharing to give the bond between the two atoms a minor covalent character, and hence the net charge on each atom approximates but does not quite equal the formal charge. Thus a formula written with either plus and minus charges or with no charges represents an approximation to the actual condition of polarization, which may be intermediate between complete electron transfer and equal sharing.

Calculation
of formal charge

The validity of an electronic formula such as (g) can be tested by conformation of the charge for a given atom to the following equation:

$$F \text{ (formal charge)} = Z - s/2 - p$$

where Z is the positive charge in the kernel (balancing the valence electrons of the atom), s is the number of shared electrons, and p is the number of unshared electrons. Thus for the nitrogen atom in (g), $F = 5 - 8/2 - 0 = +1$; for the charged oxygen atom, $F = 6 - 2/2 - 6 = -1$; for the uncharged oxygen atom, $F = 6 - 4/2 - 4 = 0$.

REACTIONS

4.16

Halogenation. — Ethylene readily adds chlorine or bromine, but not the less reactive iodine. Addition of bromine to a double bond to give a *vic*-dibromide is a general reaction, characteristic of most compounds containing the ethylenic linkage and employed as a test for

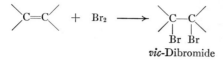

vic-Dibromide

unsaturation. The reaction can be conducted with a solution of bromine in carbon tetrachloride or chloroform, and a positive test is indicated by discharge of the red color due to bromine. Halogenation proceeds readily without illumination or deliberate introduction of a catalyst.

Evidence from studies of rates of reaction shows that addition of halogen to an ethylene is not a simple one-step process involving opening of the double bond with simultaneous affixment of halogen atoms to the adjacent free positions but that the halogen atoms are affixed one at a time, for example by the following mechanism:

1. $>\overset{\downarrow}{C}::C< +\boxed{Br}:Br \longrightarrow >\overset{Br}{\overset{..}{C}}:C< + :\overset{..}{Br}:^- \longrightarrow >\overset{Br}{\overset{..}{C}}:\underset{Br}{C}<$

        (a)   (b)   (c)

Two-step mechanism

In the initial step one bromine atom of the bromine molecule retains the covalent pair of electrons and becomes a bromide ion (b), while the other, defined as an electrophilic agent, accepts a pair of electrons from the double bond and becomes bonded to one of the carbon atoms. One electron of the pair accepted by bromine originally belonged to the second double-bonded carbon atom, and hence this atom acquires a positive charge and the intermediate is a carbonium ion (a). This ion (a) then combines with the bromide ion, which is repelled by the negative bromine atom already present and so approaches on the opposite side with formation of the dibromide (c). In a hydrocarbon such as propylene the reaction product would be the same whether the approach is on the same or opposite side, since there is no restriction to rotation about a single bond and both structures represent one and the same substance. However, in cyclic olefins, where a ring structure imposes restriction to rotation, two dibromides are possible, *cis* and *trans*, and all dibromides investigated have been found to have the *trans* configuration, for example, cyclohexene dibromide. Bromination thus proceeds by *trans*-addition to the double bond.

Electrophilic agent

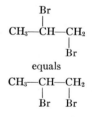

equals

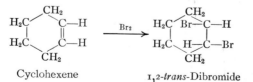

Cyclohexene   1,2-*trans*-Dibromide

trans-Addition

The electronic formula for the intermediate carbonium ion shows that the positively charged carbon atom is surrounded by only six electrons. A carbon atom with only an electron sextet seeks two electrons for completion of the octet. A charge on a carbon atom also represents instability; hence a carbonium ion ordinarily is a highly reactive species of fleeting existence.

$$: \overset{..}{\underset{..}{Br}} :_+$$
$$H : \overset{..}{\underset{..}{C}} : C : H$$
$$\overset{..}{H} \; \overset{..}{H}$$
Carbonium ion

The initial step in bromine addition as formulated in 1 is often represented for convenience as an attack of the alkene by a bromine cation, as in 2, but this should be regarded as an abbreviation of a concept that is expressed more adequately by equation 1. The reaction

Alternate formulation

$$2. \qquad R_2C{=}CR_2' \quad + \quad Br^+ \quad \longrightarrow \quad \overset{Br}{\underset{|}{R_2C}}{-}\overset{+}{C}R_2'$$
$$\qquad\qquad\qquad\qquad\qquad \underset{\text{Bromonium}}{} \qquad\qquad \underset{\text{Carbonium}}{}$$
$$\qquad\qquad\qquad\qquad\qquad \underset{\text{ion}}{} \qquad\qquad\qquad \underset{\text{ion}}{}$$

involves molecular bromine and, if the bromine atom within the dotted lines accepts the pair of electrons from carbon synchronously with separation of the second bromine atom with the pair of bromine-shared electrons, Br^+ may have no actual existence. The symbol Br^+ in equation 2 thus represents merely a possible transient phase of the electrophilic (electron-seeking) agent. If the groups R and R′ attached to the double bond attract electrons from the doubly bound carbons and produce an electron drift away from these centers, combination with positive bromine occurs less readily; if the attached groups are electron-repelling, the process is accelerated. Propylene, with one methyl substituent, adds bromine twice as fast as ethylene, and the rate of bromination of tetramethylethylene (R = R′ = CH_3) is fourteen times that of ethylene. Thus methyl is electron-repelling as compared with hydrogen. The fact that acrylic acid, $CH_2{=}CHCOOH$, reacts very slowly with bromine shows that the carboxyl group is electron-attracting.

*Methyl electron-
repelling*

4.18

Addition of Hydrogen Halides. — Hydrogen halides add to alkenes in such a way that hydrogen becomes affixed to one of the unsaturated carbon atoms and halogen to the other. The order of reactivity of the

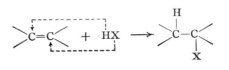

halides is the reverse of that of the corresponding halogens, namely: HI > HBr > HCl. That chlorine has pronounced affinity for other reagents means that the compound which it forms with hydrogen is a comparatively stable one in which the chlorine–hydrogen bond is not easily severed; the relatively inert iodine forms with hydrogen a looser combination in which the constituent elements can part company more readily and enter into either additions or substitutions. Ethylene gas is not absorbed by concentrated hydrochloric acid but reacts with both hydrogen bromide and hydrogen iodide in concentrated aqueous solutions; higher homologs of ethylene are more reactive and usually add hydrogen chloride.

With an unsymmetrical olefin, where two possible modes of addition are available, the reaction ordinarily follows a course defined by an empirical generalization known as the **Markownikoff**[1] **rule,** which states that, in a normal addition, the hydrogen becomes affixed to the carbon carrying the greater number of hydrogen atoms. Propylene adds hydrogen bromide to give isopropyl bromide as the preponderant

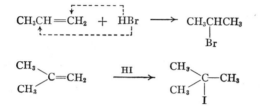

product, accompanied by a few percent of the alternate product *n*-propyl bromide. Isobutylene adds in such a way that the halogen of the hydrogen halide becomes attached to the carbon carrying two methyl groups.

The facts cited find a simple explanation in the theory of the reaction mechanism. Like the addition of bromine, addition of hydrogen halide is a two-step process consisting in electrophilic attack of one carbon atom by a proton with production of an intermediate ion (3).

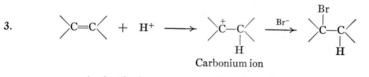

In an unsymmetrical ethylene, say one having the group R on carbon atom C_1 and the group R' on C_2, if one group has a greater tendency to attract or repel electrons than the other a displacement of electrons may occur and determine the mode of addition. Thus if R is more electron-repelling than R', electrons will be displaced away from C_1 and toward C_2, as indicated in formulas 4a and 4b by a curved arrow.

[1] Vladimir W. Markownikoff, 1838–1904; b. Russia; Kasan, Odessa, Moscow; *Ber.*, **38**, 4249 (1905); *J. Chem. Soc.*, **87**, 597 (1905)

The displacement may not reach the complete stage of polarization, pictured in (c), but the tendency is in this direction and C_2 is relatively negative. Since the methyl group of propylene is electron-repelling, as compared with hydrogen, the electron displacement in this case causes the unsubstituted carbon atom to be the more negative of the

5. $CH_3CH{=}CH_2 \xrightarrow{\ H^+\ } CH_3\overset{+}{C}H{-}CH_3 \xrightarrow{\ Br^-\ } CH_3CHCH_3$
                                                                               |
                                                                               Br

pair (5), and hence this is the point of attack by the proton. The addition thus proceeds according to the Markownikoff rule because of the electron displacement produced by the methyl group. The electron-repelling effect of methyl and higher alkyl substituents further accounts for the fact, noted above, that homologs of ethylene add hydrogen halides more readily than ethylene itself does.

4.19

Counter-Markownikoff addition

In 1933 Kharasch discovered that the normal mode of addition of hydrogen bromide frequently can be reversed by a peroxide catalyst. Thus propylene, when treated with hydrogen bromide in the presence of a trace of benzoyl peroxide, yields *n*-propyl bromide. Vinyl bromide under ordinary conditions yields 1,1-dibromoethane, in accordance with the Markownikoff rule, but under the influence of a peroxide affords the 1,2-isomer. Unlike the ordinary reaction, the peroxide-catalyzed addition does not proceed by an ionic mechanism but rather involves free-radical intermediates. Thus factors other than electron

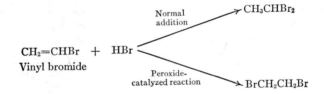

displacements determine the direction of addition. Whereas the addition of hydrogen bromide is usually subject to reversal of direction in the presence of peroxide, most other unsymmetrical reagents (hydrogen chloride, hydrogen iodide, sulfuric acid, hypochlorite) add normally whether a peroxide is present or absent.

4.20

Sulfuric Acid. — Whereas liquid alkanes when shaken with cold, concentrated sulfuric acid are unaffected and separate from the acid in an upper layer, alkenes combine with the acid and dissolve in the acid layer, a differentiation which provides a convenient method of freeing saturated hydrocarbons from traces of unsaturated substances. The reaction with an alkene is an addition, in which a proton from the acid combines with one center of unsaturation and the anion of the acid becomes joined to the other. Ethylene yields ethylsulfuric acid,

also obtainable, as described above, by similar treatment of ethyl
alcohol. Since the latter reaction is reversible, ethylene can be con-

$$CH_2\text{=}CH_2 \; + \; HOSO_2OH \; \xrightarrow{0\text{-}15°} \; CH_3CH_2OSO_2OH$$
Ethylsulfuric acid

verted through formation and hydrolysis of ethylsulfuric acid into
ethyl alcohol. The procedure represents the reverse of reactions

$$CH_2\text{=}CH_2 \; \underset{170°}{\overset{H_2SO_4,\,0\text{-}15°}{\rightleftharpoons}} \; C_2H_5OSO_2OH \; \underset{H_2SO_4,\,0\text{-}15°}{\overset{H_2O}{\rightleftharpoons}} \; C_2H_5OH$$

applicable to the preparation of ethylene, and this example of a complete cyclic process illustrates the importance of temperature and concentration in the course of reactions.

The net result of addition of sulfuric acid to an alkene and hydrolysis of the product is hydration of the double bond, and this reaction is
an important route to alcohols. Sulfuric acid, an unsymmetrical *Direction of addition*
reagent, reacts with an unsymmetrical alkene in accordance with the
Markownikoff rule, that is, the anionic fragment (like Br of HBr)
adds to the carbon poorer in hydrogen. An interesting consequence

$$\underset{CH_3}{\overset{CH_3}{>}}C\text{=}CHCH_3 \; \xrightarrow{HOSO_2OH} \; \underset{CH_3}{\overset{CH_3}{>}}\underset{OSO_2OH}{C}CH_2CH_3$$

of this fact is that primary alcohols can be isomerized to the corresponding secondary alcohols by suitable application of the sulfuric acid reactions, as illustrated for *n*-propyl alcohol.

$$CH_3CH_2CH_2OH \; \xrightarrow{H_2SO_4,\,heat} \; CH_3CH\text{=}CH_2 \; \xrightarrow{H_2SO_4} \; \underset{OSO_2OH}{CH_3CHCH_3} \; \xrightarrow{Hydrol.} \; \underset{OH}{CH_3CHCH_3}$$
n-Propyl alcohol
Isopropyl alcohol

Hypohalite Additions. — Ethylene reacts with an alkaline solution **4.21**
of chlorine to give ethylene chlorohydrin: $ClCH_2CH_2OH$. The reaction was once thought to involve addition of hypochlorous acid, formed
in the equilibrium reaction of chlorine with water. However, kinetic

$$Cl_2 \; + \; HOH \; \underset{}{\overset{OH^-}{\rightleftharpoons}} \; HCl \; + \; HOCl$$

evidence shows that the reaction is a two-step process in which chlorine
cation attacks one of the carbon atoms to produce an ionic intermediate, which in the alkaline medium combines with hydroxide ion.

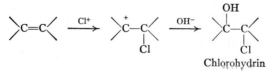

Chlorohydrin

*Mechanism
of addition*

This mechanism explains why in an addition to an unsymmetrical olefin the hydroxyl group, like the bromine of hydrogen bromide, becomes affixed to the carbon poorer in hydrogen. In propylene the displacement produced by the electron-repelling methyl group renders the terminal carbon susceptible to attack by positive chlorine, and the hydroxyl group thus appears on the central carbon atom.

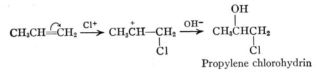

Propylene chlorohydrin

Hypobromous acid adds similarly to give bromohydrins. The halohydrins have certain uses in synthetic operations because they contain two reactive functional groups. Treatment of ethylene chlorohydrin with strong alkali results in elimination of the elements of

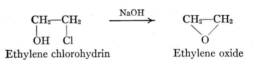

Ethylene chlorohydrin   Ethylene oxide

hydrogen chloride between the two functional groups with production of ethylene oxide. Homologous alkylene oxides are obtainable from the corresponding chlorohydrins; bromohydrins react similarly.

4.22   **Oxidation.** — Alkenes are susceptible to attack by a number of oxidizing agents, one of which, osmium tetroxide, effects hydroxylation of the double bond to give a *vic*-glycol. The initial product, which separates from an ethereal solution of the reactants as a black precipitate, is a cyclic ester, an osmate, such as that from cyclohexene formu-

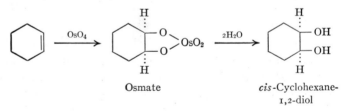

Osmate   *cis*-Cyclohexane-
                          1,2-diol

lated. The ring system of this intermediate is of such a size that only a *cis* linkage is possible, and in consequence the hydroxyl groups formed on hydrolysis of the osmate are *cis* to each other. The formulas are written in conventional abbreviations; in the formula of the diol the hydroxyl groups are joined by full-line bonds to indicate that they project to the front of the molecule (β bonds), and the hydrogens are joined by dotted lines to indicate that their orientation is to the rear (α bonds). That the overall result is a *cis* rather than a usual *trans* addition is a consequence of the nature of the cyclic intermediate. In contrast, oxidation of an alkene with hydrogen peroxide in acetic acid solution and hydrolysis of the product results in *trans*-hydroxylation:

$$-CH=CH- \xrightarrow{H_2O_2,\ H_2O,\ 80-100°;\ NaOH} \begin{array}{c} OH \\ | \\ -CH-CH- \\ | \\ OH \end{array}$$

Potassium permanganate reacts like osmium tetroxide to form a cyclic manganate ester which, however, is hydrolyzed to the *cis*-glycol by water. When the oxidation is done with a solution of potassium permanganate in dry acetone and the manganate ester decomposed with water in the absence of excess oxidizing agent, the *cis*-glycol can be obtained in high yield. When the oxidation is done in neutral or alkaline aqueous solution, the *cis*-glycol liberated from the intermediate ester is in part oxidized to further products by unused reagent. Acids split the ester even more rapidly, and hence in oxidations conducted with acidified permanganate or with chromic acid in acetic acid solution the only isolable products are the end products. A symmetrical alkene of type (a) yields two moles of a single acid, for the limit of

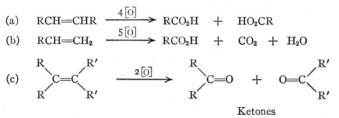

Ketones

oxidation of —C(H)= is —C(OH)=O. If the alkene has a terminal double bond (b), the methylene group is oxidized to carbon dioxide. If both unsaturated carbon atoms are fully substituted by alkyl groups (c), the oxidation products are ketones.

Since exhaustive oxidation cleaves unsaturated centers, it provides an experimental method for location of such centers and hence for determination of structures of unsaturated compounds. Thus the butylene (d) yields a three-carbon acid and carbon dioxide, indicative

(d) $CH_3CH_2CH=CH_2 \longrightarrow CH_3CH_2CO_2H + CO_2$
(e) $CH_3CH=CHCH_3 \longrightarrow 2\ CH_3CO_2H$
(f) $(CH_3)_2C=CH_2 \longrightarrow (CH_3)_2C=O + CO_2$

of the chain CCC=C. Production of a single two-carbon acid identifies the structure (e), and formation, in the last instance, of the three-carbon ketone acetone and carbon dioxide fixes the structure as having a branched chain and a terminal, doubly bound methylene group.

Oxidation with excess permanganate or chromic acid is subject to some limitation, as applied to determination of structure, because it is not entirely selective. Thus primary and secondary alcohols are readily oxidized by the same reagents. A more selective method of characterizing ethylenic compounds is ozonization. Ozone, produced in amounts up to 6–8% by passing a stream of oxygen through a generator in which it is submitted to an electric discharge (Fig. 4.6), adds

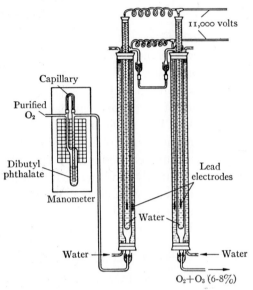

FIG. 4.6.— Ozone Generator with Flow-meter

quantitatively to the double bond of an alkene to give an ozonide. The ozonides usually are not isolated, for they are for the most part

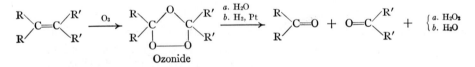

viscous oils or glasses, sometimes of explosive properties, but they can be characterized adequately by identifying the products of their decomposition by water or by catalytic hydrogenation. Ozone is a more specific reagent for the double bond than the above-mentioned oxidizing agents and does not attack alcohols. The normal mode of action involves addition, and is not accompanied by subsequent secondary oxidation. Thus hydrogen atoms attached to the unsaturated centers are undisturbed, and it is possible to isolate reaction products having

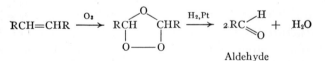

the —CH=O, or aldehyde group; with permanganate, aldehydes are converted into acids.

Another specific reagent is perbenzoic acid, C_6H_5COOOH, which reacts with alkenes to form oxides (Prileschajew, 1909). The reaction is regarded as involving electrophilic attack by OH^+ to give a transient oxonium ion (the three-membered ring is, of necessity, *cis*-linked):

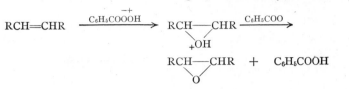

Quantitative determination of the amount of perbenzoic acid consumed affords a means of determining the number of double bonds present in a given substance.

Hydrogenation. — Ethylenic hydrocarbons add hydrogen under the influence of a suitable catalyst, and saturation of a double bond with hydrogen is called catalytic hydrogenation. Ethylene and hydrogen show no tendency to combine in the absence of a catalyst and

$$\text{C=C} + H_2 \xrightarrow{\text{Catalyst}} \underset{H\ \ H}{\text{C}-\text{C}}$$

indeed are products of cracking of ethane at high temperatures. Certain metals in a finely divided condition function as catalysts capable of activating both the olefin and the hydrogen gas to the point of interaction. Combination between the reactants depends upon their adsorption on the active surface of the catalyst, and activity increases with increased surface area. With many alkenes products of *cis* and *trans* addition of hydrogen are indistinguishable, but where there is a difference hydrogenation is found to proceed by *cis* addition, as in

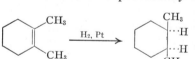

the example of 1,2-dimethylcyclohexene. In the formula of the product the methyl groups are joined by full lines (β) to indicate that they project to the front of the molecule and the hydrogens are joined by dotted lines (α bonds) to indicate their orientation to the rear. *Cis* hydrogenation may be a consequence of formation of a cyclic intermediate involving the catalyst surface.

The most potent catalysts are platinum and palladium oxides prepared (R. Adams [2]) by fusing chloroplatinic acid or palladium chloride with sodium nitrate, digesting the cooled melt with water, and shaking

[2] Roger Adams, b. 1889 Boston; Ph.D. Harvard (Torrey, Richards); Illinois; *The Roger Adams Symposium*, Wiley (1955)

CHAPTER 4

a portion of the brown oxide produced with the substance to be reduced in an apparatus (Fig. 4.7) in which a slight positive pressure of hydrogen is maintained. The oxide first absorbs enough hydrogen to form a very fine, black suspension of the metal, which is the active

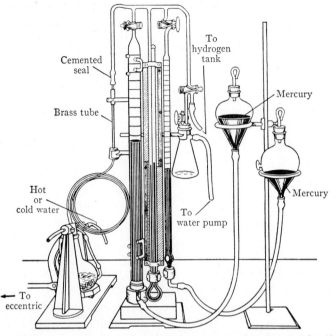

FIG. 4.7. — Apparatus for Catalytic Hydrogenation at Atmospheric Pressure (Hershberg)

Hydrogen, introduced to the shaker flask through a flexible tube, is taken from either the large or the small burette; the volume of reserve gas present at any time is read on the burette after adjusting the appropriate leveling bulb to a point where the mercury is at the same level in the two arms of the central manometer tube.

catalyst. Temperatures of 20–90° usually suffice. Less expensive but also less active base-metal catalysts can be used by operating at high enough temperatures or pressures to compensate for the lesser activity (Ipatieff[3]). A copper-chromium oxide catalyst is used in an electrically heated hydrogenator of special alloy-steel mounted in a mechanical rocker operated at temperatures of 150–250° and pressures of 3000–5000 lbs./sq. in. (Adkins[4]). Raney nickel catalyst (Raney, 1927), made by treating a nickel–aluminum alloy with warm sodium hydroxide solution, which dissolves the aluminum and leaves the nickel as a black pyrophoric suspension, is active enough to promote many hydrogenations at room temperature and at pressures of only 50–100

[3] Vladimir N. Ipatieff, 1867–1952; b. Moscow; St. Petersburg, Northwestern Univ.; *Nature*, **171**, 151 (1953)
[4] Homer Adkins, 1892–1949; b. Newport, Ohio; Ph.D. Ohio State Univ. (Evans); Univ. Wisconsin

lbs./sq. in. In the industry hydrogenations are done in a continuous vapor phase process in which vaporized unsaturated material is passed with hydrogen over a base-metal catalyst (Ni) at temperatures around 300° (Sabatier[5]).

Hydrogenation is applicable to almost all ethylenic compounds, including unsaturated alcohols, acids, etc. The conversion of alkenes into alkanes is an important step in synthesis. An alcohol can be converted into an alkane of the same carbon content via the alkyl halide by methods described in Chapter 3, but an often preferred route is dehydration to the alkene and catalytic hydrogenation, as illustrated in the example (it is immaterial that dehydration gives a mixture of

$$CH_3CH_2CH_2CHCH_2CH_3 \xrightarrow{-H_2O} \begin{cases} CH_3CH_2CH{=}CHCH_2CH_3 \\ CH_3CH_2CH_2CH{=}CHCH_3 \end{cases} \xrightarrow{H_2,\ Pt} CH_3CH_2CH_2CH_2CH_2CH_3$$

$$\underset{\substack{| \\ OH \\ \text{Hexanol-3}}}{} \qquad\qquad\qquad\qquad\qquad\qquad\qquad \underset{n\text{-Hexane}}{}$$

hexene-2 and hexene-3, for they both yield *n*-hexane on hydrogenation).

Quantitative microhydrogenation is used for determination of the number of double bonds in unsaturated compounds. If a hydrocarbon contains x double bonds and the empirical formula is C_nH_m, the number of rings (y) can be calculated from the expression:

$$y = n - m/2 - x + 1$$

Tests for Unsaturation. — One test, decoloration of bromine solution, has been mentioned. Another is decoloration of a solution of permanganate in dilute sulfuric acid; some alcohols are also oxidized by the reagent. A third test, which does not involve a chemical reaction, is formation of a yellow complex of an alkene with liquid tetranitromethane, $C(NO_2)_4$.

Conjugated Dienes; Resonance. — Compounds such as pentadiene-1,4 ($CH_2{=}CHCH_2CH{=}CH_2$) and hexadiene-1,5 ($CH_2{=}CHCH_2$-$CH_2CH{=}CH_2$), in which two equivalent double bonds are separated by one or more saturated carbon atoms, present no novel features and behave in accordance with expectations based on analogy with monoolefins. The two double bonds would be expected to absorb bromine, hydrogen, or hydrogen bromide at the same rate, and such is the case. A different situation is encountered in butadiene-1,3, which has a pair of doubly bonded carbon atoms adjacent to each other. Butadiene is known as a conjugated diene because in characteristic addition reactions the two centers of unsaturation function as a unit rather than as isolated double bonds. When butadiene is treated with

[5] Paul Sabatier, 1854–1941; Ph.D. Paris; Toulouse; Nobel Prize 1912; *J. Am. Chem. Soc.*, **66**, 1615 (1944)

bromine, the first molecular equivalent of reagent is taken up so much more rapidly than the second that a dibromide fraction is easily isolated. The 1,2-dibromide is a minor component of this fraction; the principal component carries bromine atoms not on adjacent carbon atoms but at the terminal positions 1 and 4. The main reaction is thus a 1,4-addition to the conjugated system and involves disappearance of both original double bonds with establishment of a new double bond at the 2,3-position.

1,4-Addition

$$CH_2=CHCH=CH_2 \xrightarrow{Br_2} BrCH_2CH=CHCH_2Br + CH_2=CHCHBrCH_2Br$$

$$\underset{\substack{1,4\text{-addition} \\ (\text{major product})}}{} \qquad \underset{\substack{1,2\text{-addition} \\ (\text{minor product})}}{}$$

The special mode of addition of butadiene is associated with special characteristics of the molecule disclosed by physical measurements. Thermochemical data show that butadiene is significantly more stable, in the sense of having a lower energy content, than dienes with isolated (nonconjugated) double bonds; and electron-diffraction measurements reveal abnormality in bond length, defined as the distance between atomic centers. The normal bond length for the C—C link is 1.54 Å and for the isolated C=C link the distance is 1.34 Å. In butadiene the central bond in the molecule, represented in the ordinary formula as a single link, is found actually to have a bond distance of 1.46 Å, intermediate between a double and a single bond; the two terminal bonds are somewhat longer than an isolated double bond.

Bond shortening

The evidence suggests that the three bonds linking the carbon atoms are neither true double nor true single bonds but have something of an intermediate character.

The resonance theory (Pauling[6]) accounts for the facts cited on the postulate of certain redistributions of electrons. Thus redistribution

Redistribution of electrons

$$CH_2::CH:CH::CH_2 \leftrightarrow CH_2:CH::CH\dot{C}H_2 \leftrightarrow \overset{+}{CH_2}:CH::CH:\overset{-}{CH_2} \leftrightarrow \overset{-}{CH_2}:CH::CH::\overset{+}{CH_2}$$
$$\text{(a)} \qquad\qquad \text{(b)} \qquad\qquad \text{(c)} \qquad\qquad \text{(d)}$$

of the electrons in formula (a) in the directions indicated by the dotted lines (one electron of each double bond moved to the center) would give structure (b), which has a central double bond, two terminal single bonds, and terminal carbon atoms each having an unpaired electron. An electron transfer in (b) from one terminal carbon atom to the other could give a polarized species, (c) or (d), depending upon the direction of transfer. These four structures differ merely in the positions of the electrons. According to the resonance theory, when a substance can have two or more structures that are equivalent or nearly equivalent to one another and that are interconvertible by mere

[6] Linus Pauling, b. 1901 Portland, Oregon; Ph.D. and Nat. Res. Fellow, Calif. Inst. Techn.; Calif. Inst. Techn.; Nobel Prize 1954

redistribution of valence electrons of unsaturated or ionized centers, the actual molecule does not conform to any one of the structures but exists as a resonance hybrid of them all. In the formulation, resonance is indicated by a double-headed arrow. It is sometimes possible to infer that certain structures make greater contributions than others to the average character or ground state of the molecule. A structure that contributes to a minor extent is called an excited structure.

The concept of butadiene as a resonance hybrid of structures formulated as a–d, or as the equivalent a′–d′, explains why the central link-

$$CH_2{=}CHCH{=}CH_2 \longleftrightarrow \dot{C}H_2CH{=}CH\dot{C}H_2 \longleftrightarrow \overset{+}{C}H_2CH{=}CH\overset{-}{C}H_2 \longleftrightarrow \overset{-}{C}H_2CH{=}CH\overset{+}{C}H_2$$
$$\text{(a′)} \qquad\qquad \text{(b′)} \qquad\qquad \text{(c′)} \qquad\qquad \text{(d′)}$$

age partakes of the character of both a single and a double bond. Quantum mechanics calculations have shown that bond shortening is a necessary consequence of such a resonance effect, as is the lengthening of the terminal linkages in consequence of their partial single-bond character.

A further consequence of resonance is dissipation of energy, or thermodynamic stabilization. Conversely, thermodynamic data afford a measure of the magnitude of resonance stabilization. The average heat of hydrogenation of propylene, butene-1, and other olefins having the terminal-bond structure of butadiene is 30.3 kg.-cal./mole. The heats of hydrogenation of the nonconjugated pentadiene-1,4 and hexadiene-1,5, namely 60.8 and 60.5 kg.-cal./mole, are almost exactly twice that of the monoolefins. The value observed for butadiene, however, is only 57.1 kg.-cal./mole, and hence this hydrocarbon has a lower energy content than that corresponding to two isolated double bonds. The difference of 3.5 kg.-cal./mole represents the resonance stabilization, or resonance energy, of butadiene.

Resonance energy
4.31

Any structure contributing to a resonance hybrid may participate in a reaction such as bromination, even an excited structure. If structure (a′) of butadiene is attacked by a bromonium ion, the resulting carbonium ion would be a resonant hybrid of structures (e′) and (f′); attack of the polarized structure (c′) would afford the same hybrid ion. The combination of this hybrid with bromide ion can give either the 1,2- or the 1,4-addition product; the preponderance of the 1,4-product suggests that structure (f′) is the major contributor or the more reactive species of the carbonium ion hybrid.

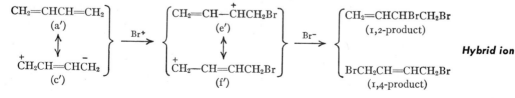

Hybrid ion

Resonance of a further type probably contributes to the stability of ionic intermediates, even those involved in the addition of bromine to monoolefins. Thus the intermediate ion resulting from electrophilic attack of ethylene by bromine is regarded as a resonance hybrid of the carbonium ions (g) and (i) and the bromonium ion (h).

Bromonium ion
intermediate

$$CH_2{=}CH_2 \xrightarrow{\text{Br}^+} \overset{+}{C}H_2{-}CH_2 \longleftrightarrow CH_2{-}CH_2 \longleftrightarrow CH_2{-}\overset{+}{C}H_2$$

$$\underset{(g)}{\overset{|}{Br}} \qquad \underset{(h)}{\overset{|}{Br^+}} \qquad \underset{(i)}{\overset{|}{Br}}$$

4.32

CH$_3$
|
CH$_2$=C—CH=CH$_2$
Isoprene

Polymerization of Dienes; Rubber. — Natural rubber is a polymeric, unsaturated hydrocarbon of the formula $(C_5H_8)_n$. It was available for study to chemists of the early nineteenth century, a time when destructive distillation was a favored technique, and the oil obtained in this way was studied by Dumas, Liebig, Dalton, and Faraday. Finally Greville Williams in 1860 isolated from among the products a low-boiling liquid of the formula C_5H_8, which he named isoprene. The correct structural formula was proposed by Sir William Tilden in 1882. The inference that rubber is a polymer of isoprene units gained credence from experiments of G. Bouchardat (1879), who found that isoprene when shaken with concentrated hydrochloric acid is converted into an elastic mass. Ozonization experiments initiated by Harries (1905–12) and extended by Pummerer (1931) established the structure; the polymer chains are indeed made up of isoprenoid units linked head-to-tail.

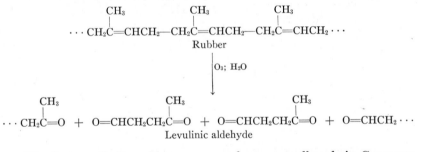

$$\cdots CH_2\underset{\underset{CH_3}{|}}{C}{=}CHCH_2{-}CH_2\underset{\underset{CH_3}{|}}{C}{=}CHCH_2{-}CH_2\underset{\underset{CH_3}{|}}{C}{=}CHCH_2 \cdots$$
Rubber

$\downarrow$ O$_3$; H$_2$O

$$\cdots CH_2\underset{\underset{CH_3}{|}}{C}{=}O \; + \; O{=}CHCH_2CH_2\underset{\underset{CH_3}{|}}{C}{=}O \; + \; O{=}CHCH_2CH_2\underset{\underset{CH_3}{|}}{C}{=}O \; + \; O{=}CHCH_2 \cdots$$
Levulinic aldehyde

Cl
|
CH$_2$=C—CH=CH$_2$
Chloroprene

The first synthetic rubbers were made on a small scale in Germany during World War I, not from isoprene but from 2,3-dimethylbutadiene, readily available from pinacol (4.4), and better rubbers were produced later (1927) by polymerization of butadiene with sodium and called Buna rubbers (butadiene–Natrium). The first American synthetic rubber (1932), neoprene, is made from the monomer chloroprene, prepared from acetylene as described in the next chapter (5.11). It is too expensive for use in tires but has many special uses because of its superior resistance to organic solvents, chemicals, and air oxidation (aging). The preferred method of manufacture is by the technique

of emulsion polymerization, suggested by the fact that natural rubber
latex is a colloidal dispersion of rubber particles in water. The liquid
monomer is dispersed in 2–4 parts of water with the aid of an emulsifying agent (sodium naphthenate) and a protective colloid (gelatin) and
polymerization is maintained at a suitable rate by addition of a suitable
catalyst. The process allows control of the degree of polymerization
and lends itself well to incorporation of modifying agents. The usual
catalyst is benzoyl peroxide, which is effective because it gives rise to
free radicals (3.17) capable of initiating and propagating the following
chain reaction (R· represents a radical):

$$R\cdot \;+\; CH_2\!=\!\overset{\overset{\displaystyle Cl}{\mid}}{C}\!-\!CH\!=\!CH_2 \longrightarrow RCH_2\overset{\overset{\displaystyle Cl}{\mid}}{C}\!=\!CH\dot{C}H_2 \xrightarrow{CH_2=\overset{\overset{\displaystyle Cl}{\mid}}{C}-CH=CH_2}$$

$$RCH_2\overset{\overset{\displaystyle Cl}{\mid}}{C}\!=\!CHCH_2\!-\!CH_2\overset{\overset{\displaystyle Cl}{\mid}}{C}\!=\!CH\dot{C}H_2 \xrightarrow{\;etc.\;} R(CH_2\overset{\overset{\displaystyle Cl}{\mid}}{C}\!=\!CHCH_2)_n \cdots$$

The polymer can be described as resulting from 1,4-addition of diene
units with formation of a new double bond at the 2,3-position. The
head-to-tail arrangement, established by oxidation experiments, is
attributable to electron displacement toward the chlorine atom and
partial charge separation in the direction shown. The radical initiator
attacks at the positive pole, and in the growing chain the carbon
carrying the odd electron attacks a fresh molecule in the same way.
The electron-repelling methyl group of isoprene induces polarization
in the opposite direction, but this polarization likewise leads to a
C_1—C_4 orientation. Whereas the double bonds in natural rubber
have the *cis* configuration, usual methods of polymerization give chiefly
the more stable *trans* products; however, a new process (Ziegler,[7]
1955) involving catalysis by lithium gives *cis*-polyisoprene. Emulsion
polymerization made possible the production of copolymers, for example, the GRS rubber widely used in manufacture of tires. It is a
copolymer of butadiene and styrene, $C_6H_5CH\!=\!CH_2$, of the following
structure:

$$CH_2=\overset{\overset{\displaystyle Cl}{\mid}}{C}-CH=CH_2$$
$$\overset{\overset{\displaystyle Cl}{\mid}}{\overset{\displaystyle \downarrow}{}}$$
$$\overset{+}{C}H_2-\overset{\overset{\displaystyle Cl}{\mid}}{C}=CH-\overset{-}{C}H_2$$

$$\cdots CH_2CH\!=\!CHCH_2\!-\!CH_2CH\!=\!CHCH_2\!-\!CH_2CH\!-\!CH_2CH\!=\!CHCH_2 \cdots$$
$$\underset{\displaystyle C_6H_5}{\overset{\mid}{}}$$

GRS rubber

Benzene. — Benzene is the parent hydrocarbon of a series of compounds called aromatic because some of the first ones known are
natural products having an aromatic fragrance. The formula of benzene, C_6H_6, indicates a high degree of unsaturation, and in the presence of a sufficiently active catalyst the hydrocarbon absorbs three

4.33

[7] Karl Ziegler, b. 1898 Kassel, Germany; Ph.D. Marburg (von Auwers); Heidelberg, Halle; KWI for Coal Research, Mülheim/Ruhr

moles of hydrogen and gives cyclohexane. Kekulé in 1865 proposed for benzene the formula of cyclohexatriene, (a) or (b), but the formula was contested for many years because chemists of the period could not reconcile a formula indicating the presence of three double bonds with the fact that benzene is peculiarly inert in comparison to alkenes and is indifferent to many oxidizing and addition-type reagents to which alkenes are responsive. However, the resonance theory pro-

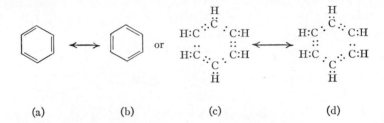

(a)   (b)   (c)   (d)

vides a simple explanation. The two Kekulé forms (a) and (b), or the electronic counterparts (c) and (d), are identical resonance structures which contribute equally to the resonant hybrid. X-ray analysis has shown that the six carbon and six hydrogen atoms all lie in a plane and that the six carbon–carbon bonds all have the identical length 1.40 Å, which is shorter than the average value of 1.46 Å for three nonresonant double and three single bonds. Unlike the case of butadiene, redistribution of electrons in the hybrid does not even require partial bond polarization. Resonance stabilization is much greater in the symmetrical cyclic system, and the resonance energy amounts to 39 kg.-cal., as compared to 3.5 kg.-cal. for butadiene. Thus resonance accounts fully for the stable, inert character often described as aromaticity. A phenyl group, C_6H_5-, is so inert in comparison to alkenes that allylbenzene, $C_6H_5CH_2CH{=}CH_2$, can be put through reactions such as bromine addition to the double bond, oxidation to $C_6H_5CH_2CO_2H$, or hydrogenation to $C_6H_5CH_2CH_2CH_3$ without alteration of the phenyl group. The reactions characteristic of benzene are substitutions, exemplified by nitration and sulfonation; a molecule of water is eliminated between the reactants with substitution of hydrogen by a nitro or a sulfonic acid group.

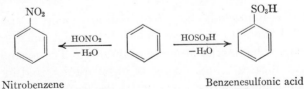

Nitrobenzene   Benzenesulfonic acid

4.34

Orbital Theory. — The theory of molecular orbitals offers useful supplements to the concepts of conjugated and aromatic systems derived from the resonance theory. In butadiene a π molecular orbital is compounded out of four $2p$ orbitals on four adjacent and coplanar carbon atoms, and these orbitals are parallel to one another and at right angles to the common nuclear axis (Fig. 4.8). It will be recalled

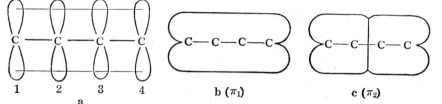

FIG. 4.8.— Butadiene, Carbon Skeleton

(4.10) that the greater the overlap of atomic orbitals the greater is the stability of a molecular orbital. In ethylene two atomic orbitals overlap, but in butadiene it is clear that C_2 and C_3 overlap each other as much as they overlap C_1 and C_4, and hence that stabilization is greater than is possible in two nonconjugated, or isolated, double bonds. The wave functions of all four carbon atoms thus coalesce to form an orbital large enough for the electrons to swarm over the complete molecule instead of moving in localized regions. Resonance energy is thus alternatively described as delocalization or overlap energy.

Stabilization from orbital overlap

It is clear that the stability and other special properties of conjugated systems require coplanarity of the unsaturated centers but not colinearity. Thus one would expect more delocalization and stability in cyclohexatriene (benzene) than in butadiene. A ring of six members is uniquely proportioned for formation of a strongly σ-bonded coplanar

4.35
Benzene

(a) σ Orbitals

π Orbitals

FIG. 4.9.— Orbitals of Benzene

ring (Fig. 4.9a) and the conditions are also ideal for multiple overlapping of p orbitals, as shown schematically in the loop diagram (b). Because the system is cyclic, each p orbital overlaps an orbital on either side of it, with particularly extensive delocalization and consequent high resonance energy. The cloud charge of the π orbital takes on the shape of a pair of doughnuts (c), and all six bonds of benzene are identical and of a unique character.

SUMMARY

Nature of Alkenes

Similar to alkanes in physical properties but much more reactive chemically. Characteristic reactions are additions. Formation of dihalides basis for the name olefin. Common names: ethylene, butylene, propylene, amylene.

Geneva nomenclature: enes and dienes; ols and diols. Terminal number to indicate position of functional group. Precedence over substituent group number. Care in selection of longest chain regardless of how formula is written. Chain selected for basic name must include maximum number of functional groups.

Synthesis

Dehydration of alcohols over alumina. Or with sulfuric acid; participation of $ROSO_2OH$ (an ester); ether a by-product. Dehydration with HCl involves protonation to $R_2CH \cdot CH_2\overset{+}{O}H_2$ and loss of hydronium ion. Order of reactivity in dehydration: $R_3COH > R_2CHOH > RCH_2OH$.

Dehydrohalogenation of alkyl halides. Order of activity also tertiary $>$ secondary $>$ primary. Debromination of a *vic*-diol; use in separations.

Nature of the Double Bond

Orbital theory. Atomic orbitals: s (symmetrical) and p (dumbbell-like). Molecular orbitals: σ (symmetrical, stable) and π (two-doughnut cloud). Ethane contains only σ bonds. Double bond of ethylene composed of one σ two-electron bond and one π two-electron bond of less overlap stabilization and of orbitals at right angle to σ bond. Addition reactions due to availability of π electrons.

Consequences of π orbital overlap: bond shortened to 1.34 Å (ethane: 1.54 Å); restriction of rotation occasioning existence of geometrical isomers, *cis* and *trans*.

Bond polarization. Electron displacement in C::C with partial polarization, represented by curved arrow or by fractional charges (δ^+, δ^-). Unequal sharing of electrons in double bond between elements of different electronegativity, with partial polarization: C relatively positive in carbonyl group (C=O); N relatively positive in N=O. Coordinate covalent bond (semipolar bond in HNO_3). Formal charge; method of calculation.

Reactions

Halogen addition. Relative reactivity of the halogens. Ionic mechanism: electrophilic attack by Br^+ to form carbonium ion, approach of Br^- from opposite side to produce dibromide. Addition to cyclohexene establishes fact of *trans* addition. Relative reactivity of ethylene, propylene, tetramethylethylene establishes electron-releasing character of methyl group. Inference that the carboxyl group is electron-attracting.

Addition of hydrogen halides. Reactivity: $HI > HBr > HCl$; $CH_3CH{=}CH_2 > CH_2{=}CH_2$. Markownikoff rule. Concept of electrophilic attack by H^+ at the more negatively polarized carbon atom; explanation of Markownikoff rule and of relative reactivities.

Peroxide-catalyzed addition of HBr contrary to Markownikoff rule (Kharasch, 1933). Free-radical mechanism. Limitation to HBr-addition.

Addition of sulfuric acid. Solubility in H_2SO_4 distinguishes alkenes from alkanes. Hydrolysis of products to alcohols. Reversibility in the case of ethylene. Markownikoff rule. Isomerization of primary to secondary alcohols.

Hypohalite addition. Ionic mechanism. Direction of addition to unsymmetrical olefins. Ethylene chlorohydrin and ethylene oxide.

Oxidation. Osmium tetroxide adds to give cyclic osmate ester, hydrolyzed to a *cis* glycol. Hydrogen peroxide in acetic acid gives *trans* glycol. Permanganate in acetone gives cyclic ester, hydrolyzed by water to *cis* glycol. Aqueous permanganate in acid solution (or chromic acid) cleaves double bond and gives carboxylic acids, ketones, CO_2. Diagnosis of structure: test for unsaturation, location of a double bond. Ozone ——→ ketones and aldehydes. Perbenzoic acid ——→ oxides.

Hydrogenation. Demonstration of *cis* addition.

Noble metal catalysts: Pt, Pd. Base-metal catalysts: Cu-Cr, Ni, Raney Ni. Use in synthesis of alkanes. Quantitative microhydrogenation; determination of number of double bonds and number of rings.

Tests for unsaturation: Br_2 solution, acid permanganate, tetranitromethane.

Conjugated Systems

Butadiene; conjugated system functions as a unit: 1,4-addition of bromine. Stability as indicated by decreased energy content. Bond distance of central linkage is 1.46 Å, intermediate between C—C link (1.54 Å) and C=C link (1.34 Å).

Resonance theory. Equivalent structures with 2,3-double bond possible by mere redistribution of electrons. Butadiene conceived as resonance hybrid of all contributing structures. Partial double bond character of central link accounts for bond shortening. Resonance dissipates energy, effects stabilization. Resonance stabilization: 3.5 kg.-cal./mole. Mechanism of 1,4-addition to butadiene: formation of an intermediate resonant carbonium ion hybrid; combination with bromide ion.

Rubber, $(C_5H_8)_n$, a polymer of isoprene units linked head-to-tail. Structure by ozonization. Synthetic rubbers from dimethylbutadiene, butadiene, chloroprene (Neoprene). A radical-initiated chain reaction. Polarization in resonance structure determines orientation. New process gives *cis* polymer like natural rubber. Emulsion polymerization used to make copolymers, e.g. from butadiene and styrene.

Benzene, C_6H_6. Hydrogenable (with difficulty) to cyclohexane. Kekulé formula (1865) with three double bonds seemed inconsistent with inert character and failure to enter into alkene additions. This aromaticity explained: benzene a resonant hybrid of two Kekulé forms. All 6 bonds have length of 1.40 Å. Resonance energy: 39 kg.-cal. Phenyl group in $C_6H_5CH=CH_2$ not affected in reactions of terminal ene group. Aromatic substitutions: nitration, sulfonation.

Orbital theory. Overlap of orbitals with delocalization accounts for stability of butadiene. Benzene ideal for stable coplanar σ-bonded structure and for multiple overlap to form stable π orbital.

PROBLEMS

1. Calculate the formal charges on the magnesium and oxygen atoms of the Grignard reagent dietherate (7.34).

2. On the postulate that the sixth valence of sulfur in sulfuric acid is polar, the acid contains a semipolar double bond and has the structure

$$(HO)_2\overset{+}{\underset{\underset{O^-}{|}}{S}}=O.$$

Write the electronic formula and check it by calculation of the formal charges.

3. Give Geneva names for:
   (a) Propylene glycol
   (b) Dimethylisopropylmethane
   (c) Citronellol,

   $CH_3C(CH_3)=CHCH_2CH_2CH(CH_3)CH_2CH_2OH$

   (d) $(CH_3)_2CHCHCH(CH_3)CH_2OH$

   $\qquad\qquad\overset{|}{CH_2CH=CH_2}$

   (e) $CH_3CHCH_2CHCH_2CH_3$

   $\qquad\overset{|}{CH_3CHCH_2CH_2}$

   (f) $(CH_3)_2C=CHCH=C(CH_3)_2$

4. Write formulas for:
   (a) 2-Methyl-3-ethylpentanol-1
   (b) 1,4-Diphenylbutadiene-1,3
   (c) Trimethylethylene
   (d) Butanediol-2,3
   (e) 5-Chloro-4-methylpentene-1
   (f) 1,2-Butylene oxide

5. Give the Geneva names of all alcohols that are monohydroxy derivatives of

   $CH_3CH_2CH_2CHCH_3$

   $\qquad\qquad\overset{|}{CH_2CH_3}$

6. By what methods can each of the following hydrocarbon samples be purified?
   (a) *n*-Hexane, contaminated with hexene-3
   (b) *n*-Hexane, contaminated with hexanol-1
   (c) Hexene-3, contaminated with *n*-hexane

7. In what way can the following isomers be distinguished?

   $CH_3CH_2CH=C(CH_3)_2$

   and $\quad CH_3CH_2C(CH_3)=CHCH_3$

8. A hydrocarbon C_7H_{10} on drastic oxidation gives the products

$$\underset{\underset{\displaystyle CH_3}{|}}{O=C}CH_2\underset{\underset{\displaystyle CH_3}{|}}{C=O}$$

and HOOC—COOH. What is its structure?

9. A pure hydrocarbon of the formula C_6H_{12} decolorizes bromine solution, dissolves in concentrated sulfuric acid, yields *n*-hexane on hydrogenation, and on oxidation with excess potassium permanganate affords a mixture of two acids of the type RCOOH. What is the structure?

10. Devise a method of preparing adipic acid, $HOOC(CH_2)_4COOH$, from cyclohexanol.

11. A hydrocarbon $C_{11}H_{20}$, which on catalytic hydrogenation absorbs two moles of hydrogen, gives on oxidation the products $CH_3CH_2COCH_3$, $HOOCCH_2CH_2COOH$, and CH_3CH_2COOH. What is its structure?

12. (a) A hydrocarbon of the formula $C_{10}H_{14}$ absorbs two moles of hydrogen on catalytic hydrogenation and gives a product inert to acid permanganate. How many rings does it contain?

(b) If a compound with the formula $C_{27}H_{46}$ absorbs just one mole of hydrogen, how many rings are present?

13. A hydrocarbon $C_{10}H_{16}$ absorbs one mole of hydrogen, is known to contain no methyl, ethyl, or other alkyl groups, and on ozonization gives a symmetrical diketone of the formula $C_{10}H_{16}O_2$. What is its structure?

READING REFERENCES

H. Adkins, "Role of the Catalyst," *Ind. Eng. Chem.*, **32**, 1189 (1940)

F. R. Mayo and C. Walling, "The Peroxide Effect in the Addition of Reagents to Unsaturated Compounds and in Rearrangement Reactions," *Chem. Rev.*, **27**, 351 (1940)

L. Pauling, *The Nature of the Chemical Bond*, Cornell University Press, Ithaca (1940)

G. W. Wheland, *Resonance in Organic Chemistry*, Wiley, New York (1955)

C. A. Coulson, "Molecular Orbitals," *Quart. Rev.*, **1**, 144 (1947)

ALKYNES

Alkynes, or acetylenic hydrocarbons, differ little in boiling point and specific gravity from corresponding alkanes. Acetylene itself is noteworthy in that the melting point of the solid, $-81.8°/891$ mm., is very close to the boiling point of the liquid ($-83.4°/760$ mm.). The four atoms of the acetylene molecule lie in a line, and hence no opportunity exists for geometrical isomerism: $H-C\equiv C-H$. The six shared electrons form one σ bond and two π bonds, and the π orbitals are crossed at right angles to each other.

GENERAL METHODS OF PREPARATION

From *vic*-Dihalides. — Hydrocarbon derivatives having halogen atoms in adjacent positions in the chain, or *vic*-dihalides, are readily available by addition of halogens to alkenes and can be converted into acetylenic hydrocarbons through elimination of two molecules of hydrogen halide by treatment with alcoholic potassium hydroxide. Thus one method for introduction of the triple bond is the sequence of reactions:

$$-CH=CH- \xrightarrow{Br_2} \begin{array}{c} -CH-CH- \\ | \quad | \\ Br \quad Br \end{array} \xrightarrow{\text{alc. KOH}} -C\equiv C-$$

When bromine is added to the double bond of propylene and the product is treated with potassium hydroxide in alcohol, the unsaturated hydrocarbon produced is essentially pure methylacetylene. A possible

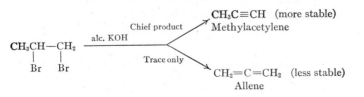

C—C≡C *more stable than* C=C=C

alternative course of the reaction would involve elimination of hydrogen bromide between the 2-bromo atom and a hydrogen of the adjacent methyl group to give allene, $CH_2{=}C{=}CH_2$. This diene, however, appears in no more than traces; allenes are labile and show a marked tendency to rearrange to the more stable acetylenic isomers. A *vic*-dihalide of the type $RCH_2CHBrCHBrCH_2R$ on dehydrohalogenation may afford either the acetylene or the conjugated diene, $RCH{=}CHCH{=}CHR$, or a mixture of both.

5.3

    From *gem*-Dihalides. — An alternate method of introducing a triple bond consists in elimination of two molecules of hydrogen bromide from a substance having two halogens on the same carbon atom, a twinned (L., *gemini*), or *gem*-dihalide:

$$-CH_2{-}CBr_2{-} \quad \xrightarrow{\text{alc. KOH}} \quad -C{\equiv}C-$$

From aldehydes and ketones

gem-Dihalides are obtainable by the action of phosphorus tribromide or trichloride on compounds having oxygen doubly bound to carbon, namely aldehydes, $RCH{=}O$, and ketones, $R_2C{=}O$. Preparative processes are illustrated in the formulas. An alternate procedure for

$$CH_3CH_2C{\Big\langle}{}^{H}_{O} \quad \xrightarrow{PBr_3} \quad CH_3CH_2CHBr_2 \quad \xrightarrow{\text{alc. KOH}} \quad CH_3C{\equiv}CH$$

Propionaldehyde

$$\underset{\underset{O}{\|}}{CH_3CH_2CCH_2CH_3} \quad \xrightarrow{PCl_3} \quad CH_3CH_2CCl_2CH_2CH_3 \quad \xrightarrow{\text{alc. KOH}} \quad CH_3CH_2C{\equiv}CCH_3$$

Diethyl ketone

elimination of hydrogen bromide involving use of sodamide has the advantage that it can be conducted in an anhydrous medium, with avoidance of side reactions:

$$-CH_2CCl_2{-} \; + \; 2\,NaNH_2 \; \longrightarrow \; -C{\equiv}C{-} \; + \; 2\,NaCl \; + \; 2\,NH_3$$

5.4

    By Alkylation of Acetylene. — Acetylene and the monoalkylacetylenes ($RC{\equiv}CH$) are unique among hydrocarbons in that the hydrogen atom attached to triply bound carbon is acidic and is replaceable by metals. In its weakly acidic character, acetylene ($H{-}C{\equiv}CH$) is analogous to hydrogen cyanide ($H{-}C{\equiv}N$). Acetylene when passed into the blue solution of one equivalent of sodium in liquid ammonia is converted into a monosodio derivative; under more drastic conditions a disodio derivative can be produced (acetylene gas over warm

Sodio derivative

$$HC{\equiv}CH \; + \; Na \; \xrightarrow{\text{(liq. NH}_3)} \; HC{\equiv}CNa \; + \; \tfrac{1}{2}H_2$$

Sodium acetylide

sodium). Sodamide is employed for replacement of the lone acetylenic hydrogen of the homologs $RC{\equiv}CH$:

$$RC{\equiv}CH \ + \ NaNH_2 \ \longrightarrow \ RC{\equiv}CNa$$

The sodium compounds are hydrolyzed by water with regeneration of the hydrocarbon: ${\equiv}CNa + HOH \longrightarrow {\equiv}CH + NaOH$. They also enter into a metathetical reaction with methyl iodide and can be used for synthesis of methyl homologs of the original hydrocarbons, thus:

$$HC{\equiv}CNa \ + \ CH_3I \ \longrightarrow \ HC{\equiv}CCH_3$$
$$RC{\equiv}CNa \ + \ CH_3I \ \longrightarrow \ RC{\equiv}CCH_3$$

Another derivative having the same application is the Grignard reagent, obtainable by a replacement reaction: **5.5**

$$\underset{\substack{\text{Acetylenemagnesium} \\ \text{bromide}}}{HC{\equiv}CH \ + \ C_2H_5MgBr \ \longrightarrow \ HC{\equiv}CMgBr} \ + \ C_2H_6$$

Grignard reagent

The Grignard reagent reacts similarly to the sodio derivative with water or with methyl iodide, for example:

$$HC{\equiv}CMgBr \ + \ CH_3I \ \longrightarrow \ HC{\equiv}CCH_3 \ + \ MgBrI$$

With two equivalents of ethylmagnesium bromide acetylene yields the disubstituted derivative $BrMgC{\equiv}CMgBr$.

ACETYLENE

Although alkynes in general are comparatively rare, acetylene itself **5.6** is a key chemical in the synthetic production of a number of strategic materials. This importance is a consequence of unique chemical properties, coupled with the fact that acetylene has long been available from coal, limestone, and water by a process applicable to quantity production. Calcium carbide is first prepared by fusion of coke with *From calcium carbide* quicklime in an electric furnace; the crude product consists of hard gray lumps with a crystalline fracture. When treated with water, it affords acetylene (compare the behavior of the other metal derivatives mentioned above). Probably unsaturation is attained in the

$$\underset{\text{Quicklime}}{CaO} \ + \ \underset{\text{Coke}}{3\,C} \ \xrightarrow{2500-3000°} \ \underset{\text{Calcium carbide}}{CaC_2} \ + \ CO$$

$$CaC_2 \ + \ 2\,H_2O \ \longrightarrow \ Ca(OH)_2 \ + \ HC{\equiv}CH$$

thermal reaction and not in the subsequent low-temperature reaction of calcium carbide with water. Acetylene manufactured by this method has a characteristic odor due to the presence of hydrogen sulfide and phosphine; these contaminants can be removed by passing the gas through a solution of mercuric chloride in dilute hydrochloric acid, and the purified material is practically odorless. Acetylene is also manufactured by cracking methane in an electric arc; the process was introduced in Germany during World War II.

Acetylene burns with a highly luminous flame, probably because at the combustion temperature the hydrocarbon is in part broken down to finely divided carbon particles that become incandescent. Because of this luminosity, acetylene was employed as an illuminating gas prior to the advent of the electric lamp, particularly for transportation vehicles. A few decades ago the usual bicycle lamp was a small acetylene generator consisting of a calcium carbide canister into which water could be dripped as desired through a setscrew valve. It is not feasible to prepare supplies of preformed acetylene for transportation by liquefying the gas under pressure in steel cylinders because in this condition the substance is sensitive to shock and may explode. This instability is associated with the high energy content of acetylene, as shown by a high negative value for the heat of formation:

High energy content

$$2\,C\ +\ H_2\ \longrightarrow\ C_2H_2\ -\ 54.8\ \text{kg.-cal.}$$

The substance is endothermic, in contrast to ethane, for which the heat of formation is positive. A safe method of storage consists in absorbing the gas at a moderate pressure (12 atmospheres) in acetone, which can dissolve 300 times its volume of acetylene. The solution is prepared in a steel cylinder containing asbestos or other porous solid that absorbs the liquid and prevents its slushing about in transit. Preformed acetylene is used as a fuel in welding and cutting of metals. The oxyacetylene flame reaches temperatures as high as 2700°; the high heat value is derived in part from the endothermic character of the hydrocarbon.

Welding torch

REACTIONS

5.7

Electrophilic Additions. — Alkynes, like alkenes, add halogens and hydrogen halides in reactions that initiate in an attack by a positive fragment, or electrophilic agent. For example, acetylene reacts with chlorine, probably by a two-step mechanism (1), to form acetylene dichloride, which, in turn, adds a further mole of reagent to form *s*-tetrachloroethane, a useful solvent. However, a triple bond is less

Halogen

1. $CH\equiv CH \xrightarrow{Cl^+} \overset{+}{C}H=CHCl \xrightarrow{Cl^-} ClCH=CHCl \xrightarrow{Cl_2} Cl_2CHCHCl_2$
   Acetylene dichloride   *s*-Tetrachloroethane

Double vs. triple bond

reactive in electrophilic additions than a double bond, as evidenced by the selective bromination formulated in (2).

2. $CH_2=CHCH_2C\equiv CH \xrightarrow{Br_2} CH_2BrCHBrCH_2C\equiv CH$

Hydrogen halides also add more slowly to triple than to double bonds. The addition proceeds in two stages (3) and, in the absence of a peroxide, the second step follows the Markownikoff rule. Alkynes are

3.　　CH≡CH $\xrightarrow{\text{HI}}$ CH₂=CHI $\xrightarrow{\text{HI}}$ CH₃CHI₂
　　　　　　　　　Vinyl iodide　　　　Ethylidene iodide

much less reactive than alkenes to peracids, which involve attack by OH⁺ (4.26). The triple bond also shows less reactivity than the double bond in chromic acid oxidation, as demonstrated by reaction (4). Also, alkynes do not form colored complexes with tetranitromethane.

4.　　CH≡C(CH₂)₇CH=C(CH₃)₂ $\xrightarrow[40\%]{\text{CrO}_3}$ CH≡C(CH₂)₇CO₂H

Nucleophilic Additions. — Hydrogen cyanide and water are representative reagents capable of adding to acetylene but not to ethylene. Hydrogen cyanide also adds to carbonyl compounds, and the addition involves attack of the positively polarized carbon by cyanide ion, a nucleophilic agent:

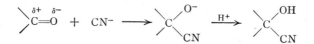

Consequently, the addition of the same reagent to acetylene is formulated similarly, as in (5). The addition product, acrylonitrile, is used

5.　　CH≡CH $\xrightarrow{\text{CN}^-}$ CH=CHCN $\xrightarrow{\text{H}^+}$ CH₂=CHCN
　　　　　　　　　　　　　　　　　　Acrylonitrile

for production of synthetic polymers. Thus a triple bond is less vulnerable to attack by electrophilic agents than a double bond, but more susceptible to nucleophilic attack.

Another nucleophilic addition to alkynes is hydration. Alkenes can be hydrated to alcohols, but only by stepwise addition of sulfuric acid and hydrolysis. Alkynes, however, add water directly under catalysis by hot dilute sulfuric acid containing a little mercuric sulfate. The reaction probably involves a complex of alkyne with catalyst. The initial product from acetylene (6), vinyl alcohol, is not stable and

6. CH≡CH + HOH $\xrightarrow{42\% \text{ H}_2\text{SO}_4,\ \text{HgSO}_4}$ [$\overset{\alpha}{\text{CH}_2}$=$\overset{\beta}{\text{CH}}$—$\overset{\gamma}{\text{OH}}$] ⟶ CH₃—CH=O
　　　　　　　　　　　　　　　　　　　　Vinyl alcohol　　　　　Acetaldehyde
　　　　　　　　　　　　　　　　　　　　(hypothetical)

at once isomerizes to acetaldehyde by migration of hydrogen from oxygen to carbon with simultaneous shift of the double bond. The hypothetical vinyl alcohol is an unstable enol; the same lability or tendency to isomerize is generally characteristic of enols.

The hydrogen atom of the enolic hydroxyl group is attached to the first, or α, atom in a three-atom system in which the β and γ atoms are joined by a double bond. Thus the migration of hydrogen from the α to the γ atom, with movement of the double bond to the α,β-position, is described as an α,γ-shift. Derivatives of vinyl alcohol in which the mobile hydrogen is replaced by alkyl groups or acid residues (acyl groups) exist as chemical entities and do not isomerize.

Acetic acid adds to acetylene in the presence of mercuric salts or acetylsulfuric acid as catalyst to give vinyl acetate, an ester (7). Vinyl

7. $$CH_3-\overset{\overset{\displaystyle O}{\|}}{C}-OH \;+\; CH\equiv CH \;\xrightarrow[80\%]{\text{Acetylsulfuric acid}}\; CH_3-\overset{\overset{\displaystyle O}{\|}}{C}-O-CH=CH_2$$
Vinyl acetate

acetate manufactured by this method is a key material for production of the vinyl resins. The chief technological utilization of the conversion of acetylene into acetaldehyde is the manufacture of acetic acid (8). The acetaldehyde is separated from unchanged acetylene, which

8. $$CH_3-C\overset{\displaystyle H}{\underset{\displaystyle O}{\diagdown}} \xrightarrow{\text{[O]}} CH_3-C\overset{\displaystyle OH}{\underset{\displaystyle O}{\diagdown}}$$
Acetaldehyde   Acetic acid

is recycled, and is oxidized catalytically with air in the presence of manganese acetate. The hydration reaction is applicable to other members of the series; methylacetylene, for example, yields acetone. The initial addition follows the Markownikoff rule (9).

Per Markownikoff rule

9. $$CH_3C\equiv CH \xrightarrow{H_2O,\ \text{catalyst}} \left[\underset{\displaystyle OH}{CH_3C=CH_2} \right] \longrightarrow \underset{\displaystyle O}{CH_3CCH_3}$$
Methylacetylene   Acetone

5.10
Catalytic; cis

Reduction. — The triple bond is sufficiently more reactive than the double bond that selective hydrogenation is feasible and is frequently used in synthesis:

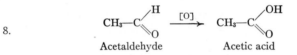

$$RC\equiv C(CH_2)_nCH=CHR' \xrightarrow{2\ H} R\overset{\overset{\displaystyle H\ \ H}{}}{C}=C(CH_2)_nCH=CHR'$$

As in the hydrogenation of olefins, the reaction proceeds by *cis*-addition and gives *cis*-olefins. Alkynes are also reducible chemically, and

Chemical; trans

the products in this case are *trans*-alkenes. The most useful technique is reduction with sodium or lithium in liquid ammonia; since alkenes are inert to this mode of reduction there is no problem of overreduction. The reaction involves nucleophilic attack, and the greater reactivity of the triple bond is in line with observations cited in the preceding section.

Additions of Acetylene. — Some of the special reactions of acetylene involve its functioning as the entity H—A in additions to unsaturated compounds. One is addition of acetylene to itself to form vinylacetylene, a dimerization. This is effected by absorption of

$$HC{\equiv}CH + HC{\equiv}CH \xrightarrow{\text{Cu}_2\text{Cl}_2,\ \text{NH}_4\text{Cl}} CH_2{=}CHC{\equiv}CH$$

Vinylacetylene

acetylene in a solution of cuprous chloride and ammonium chloride in hydrochloric acid. Vinylacetylene is a key intermediate in the production of neoprene rubber (4.32), since on addition of hydrogen

$$\overset{4}{C}H_2{=}\overset{3}{C}H\overset{2}{C}{\equiv}\overset{1}{C}H \xrightarrow[\text{(1,4-addition)}]{\text{HCl}} \overset{\alpha}{C}H_2\overset{\beta}{C}H{=}\overset{\gamma}{C}{=}CH_2 \xrightarrow[\text{(α,γ-shift)}]{\text{Isomerization}} CH_2{=}CHC{=}CH_2$$

(with Cl on the α-carbon on the left, and Cl on the γ-carbon on the right)

chloride it affords chloroprene. The dimerization of acetylene is analogous to the addition of hydrogen cyanide to acetylene (5), and since the structures H—C≡N and H—C≡CH are similar (and the compounds similarly acidic), dimerization probably involves attack by $\bar{\text{C}}{\equiv}\text{CH}$. Another analogy is that both hydrogen cyanide and acetylene add to the carbonyl group (C=O); the hydrocarbon adds as follows:

$$CH{\equiv}CH + H_2C{=}O \longrightarrow CH{\equiv}CCH_2OH$$

Propargyl alcohol

$$O{=}CH_2 + CH{\equiv}CH + CH_2{=}O \longrightarrow HOCH_2C{\equiv}CCH_2OH$$

Butyne-2-diol-1,4

Metal Derivatives. — When acetylene gas is passed into a solution of cuprous ammonium hydroxide, a reddish brown precipitate of cuprous acetylide is produced. Both acetylenic hydrogens are replaced

$$HC{\equiv}CH + 2\ Cu(NH_3)_2OH \longrightarrow CuC{\equiv}CCu + 4\ NH_3 + 2\ H_2O$$

Cuprous acetylide

by univalent copper atoms; an alkyne of the type RC≡CH gives a monocopper derivative. Since the reaction is specific to hydrocarbons containing an acetylenic hydrogen and is not shown by alkanes, alkenes, or alkynes of the type RC≡CR', it is used as a diagnostic test for the unit ≡CH. Silver acetylides are similarly precipitated from an ammoniacal solution of silver nitrate, for example:

$$CH{\equiv}CH \longrightarrow AgC{\equiv}CAg$$

The heavy-metal acetylides differ from light-metal derivatives in that they are not hydrolyzed by water and, in the dry state, are explosive and highly sensitive to shock. Copper acetylide on explosion produces copper and carbon and no gaseous products. An occasional use for the heavy-metal acetylides is in the purification of acetylene or of alkynes of the type $RC\equiv CH$; the metal derivative is precipitated, collected, washed, and treated with dilute hydrochloric acid, or better with aqueous potassium cyanide, with regeneration of the purified alkyne.

SUMMARY

Preparation. From alkenes, via *vic*-dihalides:

$$—CH{=}CH— \longrightarrow$$
$$—CHBrCHBr— \longrightarrow —C{\equiv}C—.$$

From aldehydes or ketones, via *gem*-dihalides:

$$—COCH_2— \longrightarrow —CBr_2CH_2— \longrightarrow —C{\equiv}C—.$$

Alkylation of acetylenes:

$$\equiv CH \longrightarrow \equiv CNa;$$

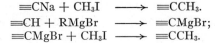

$$\equiv CNa + CH_3I \longrightarrow \equiv CCH_3.$$
$$\equiv CH + RMgBr \longrightarrow \equiv CMgBr;$$
$$\equiv CMgBr + CH_3I \longrightarrow \equiv CCH_3.$$

Acetylene. Manufacture (*a*) coke + lime $\longrightarrow$ calcium carbide; $CaC_2 + H_2O \longrightarrow HC{\equiv}CH$. (*b*) Cracking of methane in electric arc. Special uses: illumination, welding. Absorbed in acetone-saturated asbestos under pressure.

Reactions

Electrophilic additions (less reactive than alkenes): halogens, HX (follows Markownikoff rule); very resistant to attack by peracids ($\overset{+}{O}H$ of $C_6H_5\overset{-\,+}{C}OOH$) and by CrO_3 (selective oxidation of an eneyne).

Nucleophilic (negative fragment) additions (not applicable to alkenes). HCN; attack by $\overset{-}{C}N$, then by H^+. Hydration (Hg^{++} catalysis):

$$—C{\equiv}C— \longrightarrow —CH{=}C(OH)— \longrightarrow$$
$$—CH_2—C({=}O)— \text{ (follows Markownikoff rule).}$$

Partial hydrogenation to *cis*-alkenes. Reduction with Na or Li in liquid NH_3 to *trans*-alkenes.

Additions of acetylene. Self-addition of $HC{\equiv}CH$ (dimerization) to vinylacetylene; reaction with HCl to form chloroprene. Analogy to addition of $HC{\equiv}N$ to $HC{\equiv}CH$; involves nucleophilic attack by $^-C{\equiv}CH$. Addition to carbonyl compounds:

$$\diagup\hspace{-0.6em}\diagdown C{=}O \longrightarrow \diagup\hspace{-0.6em}\diagdown C(OH)C{\equiv}CH.$$

Metal derivatives. $\equiv CH \longrightarrow \equiv CAg$ and $\equiv CCu$. Dry solids explosive. Use in purification of alkynes.

PROBLEMS

1. Indicate methods that could be employed for the following syntheses:
   (*a*) Methylacetylene from acetone
   (*b*) Phenylacetylene from β-phenylethanol, $C_6H_5CH_2CH_2OH$
   (*c*) 4-Methylpentyne-2 from isopropylacetylene
   (*d*) *n*-Butane from acetylene
2. Vinylacetylene can be hydrated under the catalytic influence of a mercuric salt. Predict the structure of the product.

3. A hydrocarbon of the formula C_6H_{10} yields 2-methylpentane on hydrogenation; it combines with the elements of water when treated with mercuric sulfate and dilute sulfuric acid but does not react with ammoniacal cuprous chloride solution. What is the structure?
4. Suggest a method for transforming *trans*-stilbene (I) into *cis*-stilbene (II).

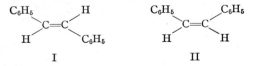

I   II

READING REFERENCE

R. A. Raphael, *Acetylenic Compounds in Organic Syntheses*, Butterworths, London (1955)

PETROLEUM

Natural gas and petroleum, probably formed by decomposition of organic material of marine origin, occur in pockets of the upper strata of the earth entrapped by overlying rock (L. *petra*, rock + *oleum*, oil). When a well is drilled through the cap, oil for a time is forced to the surface until the pressure subsides and then is removed by pump. Natural gas flowing from a well consists largely of methane and gaseous homologs but contains dissolved C_5–C_7 hydrocarbons which are normally liquid and valuable as gasoline components. Consequently the raw gas is passed through an oil scrubber or a compressor for recovery of material known as natural gasoline, which is blended with refinery gasoline to increase volatility. The residual gas is carried by pipeline to industrial areas for use as fuel. Refining of petroleum, a dark, viscous oil, involves distillation into fractions of different boiling ranges and reprocessing of fractions, for example, by extraction of acidic and basic components. Gasoline fractions boil in the range 40–205° (kerosene, b.p. 175–325°).

Natural gasoline

Constituents. — Natural gas, freed of natural gasoline, contains methane and decreasing amounts of C_2–C_4 homologs; gas from specific fields also contains either nitrogen or helium. Since the lower alkanes differ considerably in boiling point from one another and from nitrogen or helium, the components are separated efficiently by liquefaction and fractional distillation under pressure at low temperature. Pure products produced in this way and their boiling points are: methane (−162°), ethane (−89°), propane (−42°), and helium (−269°). The hydrocarbons from this source are converted by selective cracking into unsaturated products useful in industrial syntheses. Further hydrocarbons utilized similarly are obtained by fractionation of natural gasoline, which contains alkanes in the range C_3–C_8; the most useful products are propane, a butane–isobutane fraction, and a frac-

6.2
Hydrocarbons from natural gas

Components separable

Synthetic use

77

tion known as the C_5-cut since the three components are isomers of the formula C_5H_{12}:

$CH_3CH_2CH_2CH_2CH_3$	$(CH_3)_2CHCH_2CH_3$	$C(CH_3)_4$ (minor component)
n-Pentane, b.p. 36°	Isopentane, b.p. 28°	Neopentane, b.p. 9.5°

C_5-cut

6.3

Hydrocarbon fractions from petroleum of boiling range higher than the C_5-cut are extremely complex mixtures. The major components are alkanes, straight-chain and branched. A second group of components, known in petroleum technology as naphthenes, are polyalkyl derivatives of cyclopentane and cyclohexane. A third group, described as aromatics, includes benzene, its methyl derivative toluene ($C_6H_5CH_3$), and other alkyl derivatives of benzene and the related naphthalene, $C_{10}H_8$.

Petroleum also contains from 0.1 to 3% naphthenic acid, a mixture of acids extractable with alkali. A few of countless components of the mixture have been isolated and identified as carboxylic acid derivatives of polyalkyl-substituted cyclopentanes or cyclohexanes. The naphthenic acid mixture thus contains carboxylic acid derivatives of the naphthene constituents. Naphthenic acid extracted from petroleum fractions is converted into water-insoluble salts, or soaps, of lead, cobalt, and copper of value as oxidation catalysts, or driers, for promotion of setting of paints and varnishes. Copper naphthenate is employed for mildewproofing sandbags and rope for use at sea. Napalm, a coprecipitated aluminum soap from naphthenic acid and the fatty acids of coconut oil developed in 1942 (Fieser, Hershberg,[1] *et al.*), was used in World War II for preparation of gasoline gels for incendiary munitions.

Sulfur-containing constituents, present in petroleum to the extent of 0.1–1%, include alkyl mercaptans of the formula RSH, analogs of cycloalkanes, such as pentamethylene sulfide, and analogs of aromatic hydrocarbons, such as thiophene, which is very similar to benzene. Aromatic nitrogen-containing compounds such as pyridine and quino-

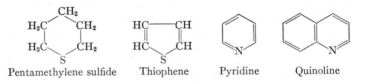

Pentamethylene sulfide   Thiophene   Pyridine   Quinoline

line are also present in traces (e.g., 0.008%) and are extractable with mineral acid.

[1] Emanuel B. Hershberg; b. 1908 Lynn, Mass.; Ph.D. Mass. Inst. Techn. (Huntress); postdoctoral work Zurich (Karrer), Harvard (Fieser); Schering Corp.

Octane Rating. — The knock or ping heard when an automobile engine is accelerated too rapidly is a warning that conditions for efficient performance of the engine with the particular gasoline used have been exceeded. The knocking tendency of a given gasoline is expressed as the octane number, or the performance in a standard one-cylinder test engine in comparison with that of mixtures of two synthetic standard fuels. Isooctane (2,2,4-trimethylpentane), which detonates only at high compression and was superior to any gasoline known in 1927 when the rating was introduced, was assigned the octane rating of 100, and *n*-heptane, which is particularly prone to knocking, was given the rating 0. The octane number of a fuel is the percent of isooctane in a blend with *n*-heptane that has the same knocking characteristics as the fuel under examination. Investigation of pure synthetic hydrocarbons has shown that in the alkane series octane number decreases as the chain is lengthened and increases with chain branching. Alkenes have higher ratings than corresponding alkanes, and the octane number increases as the double bond is shifted to the center of the molecule. Cycloalkanes are less prone to knock than normal alkanes, and aromatic hydrocarbons have exceptionally high octane numbers.

$(CH_3)_3CCH_2CH(CH_3)_2$
Isooctane = 100

n-Heptane = 0

Octane rating and structure

Engine efficiency increases with increased compression ratio, but so does knocking. Straight-run gasolines provided by distillation of petroleum have octane ratings as low as 20 (Michigan field) and, at best, no higher than 75, and hence engines of the nineteen twenties operating on such fuels had compression ratios of only about 4:1. However, technological discoveries have so increased octane ratings as to make possible engines of superior power and mileage of ratios of 8–9:1.

In Diesel engines the air alone is compressed, with the result that the temperature is increased to 290–340°. The fuel is injected almost at the end of the compression stroke and is spontaneously ignited. Diesel fuel need not be volatile, and generally consists of the fraction boiling between kerosene and the heavier lubricating oils. Owing to differences in engine construction, high octane fuels are much less efficient than low ones. The ignition quality is expressed in terms of the cetane number, which refers to a mixture of cetane (*n*-hexadecane, value = 100) and α-methylnaphthalene (value = 0); most automotive Diesel engines require a fuel of cetane number greater than 45; that is, the desirability of hydrocarbons is exactly reversed for the Diesel as compared with the ordinary engine.

6.7

Diesel fuel

Antiknock Compound. — The first major advance in improvement of motor fuels was discovery that knocking can be inhibited by addi-

6.8

tion of certain chemicals, the most important of which is tetraethyllead (TEL), developed by Midgley[2] and Boyd (1922). About 88% of all American gasolines contain tetraethyllead; gasolines leaded to an octane rating of 80 or more are known as Ethyl or premium gasoline. The commercial process consists in interaction of a sodium-lead alloy with ethyl chloride at moderate temperatures and pressures:

Tetraethyllead

$$4\,PbNa\ +\ 4\,C_2H_5Cl\ \longrightarrow\ Pb(C_2H_5)_4\ +\ 4\,NaCl\ +\ 3\,Pb$$

The lead derivative is separated by steam distillation, and the lead sludge is smelted into pig lead.

Ethyl fluid contains not only tetraethyllead (63%), but also ethylene dibromide (26%), ethylene dichloride (9%), and a dye (2%). Ethylene dibromide is an essential constituent since it reacts with the lead oxide produced during combustion to form volatile lead bromide, which is swept from the cylinders in the exhaust gases. The manufacture of large amounts of ethylene dibromide presented a problem, since bromine was not available in sufficient quantity. The difficulty was solved by extraction of bromine from sea water, 7.5 tons of which contain one pound of bromine. An early process, operated on board the S.S. Ethyl, extracted bromine by adding aniline to chlorinated sea water and recovering bromine from the filtered precipitate.

6.9

Gasoline from kerosene

Cracking. — The perfection of practicable processes for controlled pyrolytic decomposition, or cracking, of paraffinic hydrocarbons has had the immensely important result of more than doubling the amount of motor gasoline obtainable from petroleum. The large and relatively nonvolatile hydrocarbons of otherwise practically unutilized fractions can be broken down by thermal treatment into mixtures of smaller molecules having the desired volatility. The cracking of a fraction consisting of higher paraffins gives a mixture of alkanes and olefins; since olefins have advantageous octane ratings, cracked gasolines have superior antiknock characteristics. Several methods of cracking are employed in the industry: thermal cracking (500°, 30 lbs./sq. in.); catalytic cracking (Houdry catalyst: $SiO_2\text{-}Al_2O_3\text{-}MnO$); fluid catalytic process (catalyst: HF); reforming (brief heating at high pressure). Cracked gasolines require protection to prevent oxidation, which initiates polymerization leading to gum formation. The oxidation is a chain reaction and can be inhibited by addition of a small amount of an antioxidant (phenols and aromatic amines).

Studies of the pyrolysis of the gaseous hydrocarbons available from natural gas and natural gasoline have provided information concerning the reactions involved in cracking and have led to develop-

[2] Thomas Midgley, 1889–1944; b. Worthington, Ohio; M. E. Cornell; Ethyl Gasoline Corp.

ment of several synthetic intermediates of great technical importance. Methane is exceptionally stable but decomposes into carbon and hydrogen at temperatures above 1000° (carbon black). Ethane yields ethylene as an initial product of pyrolysis (1), and this olefin can be produced in high yield. The higher alkanes undergo both dehydrogenation and rupture, usually with formation of methane. Propane (2) affords both propylene, by dehydrogenation, and ethylene, by

Petroleum

Production of ethylene and propylene

1. $$CH_3CH_3 \xrightarrow{485°} CH_2{=}CH_2 + H_2$$

2. $$CH_3CH_2CH_3 \xrightarrow{460°} \begin{cases} CH_3CH{=}CH_2 + H_2 \\ \text{(45 parts)} \\ CH_2{=}CH_2 + CH_4 \\ \text{(55 parts)} \end{cases}$$

methane splitting. The branched-chain hydrocarbon isobutane (3) suffers both dehydrogenation and elimination of methane and gives isobutene as the chief product. The isobutane fraction from petro-

3.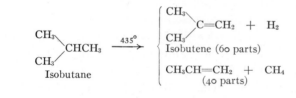

Isobutene by cracking

leum is often considerable and is employed for production of the valuable synthetic intermediate isobutene (isobutylene).

Polymerization of Gaseous Hydrocarbons. — The gaseous hydrocarbons produced in cracking are valuable starting materials for production not only of important chemicals but also of liquid fuels. The first large-scale use involved polymerization of the olefins to a liquid known as polymer gasoline (octane number 78–83). The process of polymerization, usually induced by phosphoric or sulfuric acid (Ipatieff, 1935), is actually one of dimerization. Thus isobutene yields the dimer isooctene, which consists mainly of 2,4,4-trimethylpentene-1 but contains about 20% of 2,4,4-trimethylpentene-2. Both isomers on

6.10

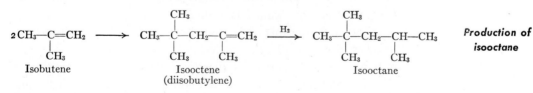

Production of isooctane

hydrogenation yield isooctane. The acid-catalyzed polymerization can be interpreted by the following reaction mechanism: (*a*) a proton attacks the more negative of the two unsaturated carbon atoms to give trimethylcarbonium ion; (*b*) this ion attacks the more negative

(a) $(CH_3)_2C\!=\!CH_2$ $\xrightarrow{\;H^+\;}$ $(CH_3)_2\overset{+}{C}CH_3$ [or $(CH_3)_3\overset{+}{C}$]

(b) $(CH_3)_3C^+$ + $CH_2\!=\!C(CH_3)_2$ $\longrightarrow$ $(CH_3)_3C\!-\!CH_2\overset{+}{C}(CH_3)_2$

(c) $(CH_3)_3CCH_2\overset{+}{C}(CH_3)_2$ $\xrightarrow{\;-H^+\;}$ $(CH_3)_3CCH_2C(CH_3)\!=\!CH_2 + (CH_3)_3CCHC\!=\!CH_3)_2$

center of a second molecule of isobutene; (c) the resulting dimer ion expels a proton to form isooctene.

6.11   Alkylation. — A second reaction of considerable technological importance can be represented as an addition of an alkane to the double bond of an olefin but is usually described as the alkylation of an alkane

Isooctane by a second process

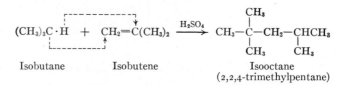

$$\underset{\text{Isobutane}}{(CH_3)_3C\!\cdot\!H} + \underset{\text{Isobutene}}{CH_2\!=\!C(CH_3)_2} \xrightarrow{\;H_2SO_4\;} \underset{\substack{\text{Isooctane}\\ \text{(2,2,4-trimethylpentane)}}}{CH_3\!-\!\underset{\underset{CH_3}{|}}{\overset{\overset{CH_3}{|}}{C}}\!-\!CH_2\!-\!\underset{\underset{CH_3}{|}}{CH}CH_3}$$

with an olefin. The alkylation of isobutane with isobutene gives isooctane, and hence this important hydrocarbon is obtained in one step from the C_4-cut of cracked gasoline, which contains both components. Alkylation can be induced with catalysts (sulfuric acid, boron fluoride, anhydrous hydrogen fluoride, aluminum chloride) or by thermal treatment. The reaction is not limited to isoparaffins or to an olefin of special structure. A mechanism for acid-catalyzed alkylation postulates (a) addition of a proton to the olefin to form a carbonium ion, (b) addition of this ion to another molecule of olefin to form a dimeric

Mechanism

(a) $(CH_3)_2C\!=\!CH_2$ + H^+ $\rightleftharpoons$ $(CH_3)_3\overset{+}{C}$

(b) $(CH_3)_3C^+$ + $CH_2\!=\!C(CH_3)_2$ $\rightleftharpoons$ $(CH_3)_3CCH_2\overset{+}{C}(CH_3)_2$

(c) $(CH_3)_3CCH_2\overset{+}{C}(CH_3)_2$ + $(CH_3)_3CH$ $\longrightarrow$
  $(CH_3)_3CCH_2CH(CH_3)_2$ + $(CH_3)_3C^+$

6.12   carbonium ion, and (c) reaction of this with the alkane to form the final product, with regeneration of the original carbonium ion.

Isomerization. — At the same time that isobutane became a key compound in the manufacture of high-octane fuel, a method for its preparation on a large scale fortunately became available. *n*-Butane occurs in greater concentration than isobutane in both natural and thermally cracked gas. Isobutane has never been detected as a pyrolysis product of butane, and it has been calculated that an equilibrium mixture of the butanes at 527° would contain only 13% of isobutane. The point of equilibrium however is tremendously influenced by the temperature. In the presence of aluminum bromide an equilibrium

$$\underset{\text{Butane}}{CH_3CH_2CH_2CH_3} \rightleftharpoons \underset{\text{Isobutane}}{(CH_3)_3CH}$$

mixture is obtained at 27° that contains 75–80% of isobutane. Isomerization of straight-chain paraffins is important commercially since the octane number is increased considerably with branching. Isomerization undoubtedly occurs during catalytic cracking and reforming, and is partly responsible for the superior quality of the products.

Olefins also can undergo isomerization. In some instances only the double bond is shifted; butene-1, for example, is converted into butene-2 when heated in a quartz tube at 550° (87% conversion):

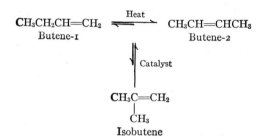

Partial isomerization of the butenes to isobutene can be accomplished by alumina, aluminum sulfate, or phosphoric acid as catalyst.

Aromatization. — Toluene, or methylbenzene, is normally obtained from coal tar, the production of which is geared to coke requirements, and this source is adequate except in time of war. A new process, announced in 1940, is based on the cracking of *n*-heptane. The reaction proceeds through intermediate formation of heptene-1, which is converted into methylcyclohexane by intramolecular alkylation. The reaction is catalyzed by oxides of chromium or molybdenum carried on alumina. Yields are excellent: about 72% in one pass and 90% on recycling.

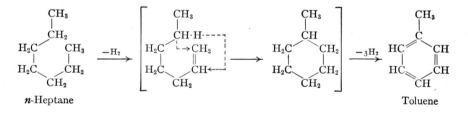

SYNTHETIC FUELS FROM COAL

Bergius Process. — The production of fuels by destructive hydrogenation of coal was developed in Germany during World War I by Bergius. Coal probably is an elaborate network of carbon rings, which are cleaved during the process into fragments that are hydrogenated to open-chain and cyclic hydrocarbons. Powdered coal mixed with heavy tar (bottom of previous operation) is stirred with a tin or lead catalyst and hydrogen at high pressure and temperature (450–490°). The product is separated by distillation into gasoline (b.p. to 200°), gas oil (b.p. 200–300°), and a residue that is recycled with fresh coal. A typical gasoline fraction contains 74% paraffins, 22% aromatics, and 4% olefins. Octane numbers of 75–80 are reported.

SUMMARY

Constituents of Petroleum

Paraffins. Methane, ethane, propane separable from natural gas; natural gasoline affords propane, butanes, and a C_5-cut (chiefly *n*-pentane and isopentane; a little neopentane). Higher fractions are complex mixtures.

Naphthenes (alkylated cycloparaffins).

Aromatics (e.g. benzene, toluene, naphthalene).

Naphthenic acids (carboxylic acid derivatives of naphthenes). Industrial uses of heavy-metal naphthenates.

Sulfur and nitrogen compounds (e.g. mercaptans, thiophene).

Motor Fuels

Octane rating. Higher for branched-chain than for straight-chain paraffins; very high for aromatics.

Cetane rating. Requirements for a Diesel engine the reverse of those for a gasoline motor.

Antiknock compound: tetraethyllead. Preparation. Efficacy. Ethyl fluid; function of ethylene dibromide.

Cracking. Conversion of otherwise practically waste high-boiling fractions into cracked gasoline of favorable octane rating (protection by antioxidants). Ethane ⟶ ethylene. Propane ⟶ propylene + ethylene. *n*-Butane ⟶ butenes + propylene + ethylene. Cracking of the C_5-refinery cut to a C_4-fraction rich in isobutene.

Polymerization. Acid-catalyzed dimerization of an olefin. Isobutene ⟶ isooctene ⟶ isooctane (100-octane); ionic mechanism of the reaction.

Alkylation. Acid-catalyzed addition of an alkane to the double bond of an olefin. Described as alkylation of an alkane with an olefin. Processing of the C_4-cut of cracked gasoline: production of isooctane by alkylation of isobutane with isobutene. Reaction mechanism.

Isomerization (equilibrium). Butane ⟶ isobutane (AlBr$_3$ at 27°). Butene-1 ⟶ butene-2. Butene-1 and butene-2 ⟶ isobutene.

Aromatization. *n*-Heptane (Michigan field; low-octane) ⟶ toluene (required for TNT; high octane).

Synthetic Fuels from Coal

Bergius process. Hydrogenolysis of coal ⟶ gasoline (octane number 75–80).

ALCOHOLS

Alcohols can be regarded either as hydroxyl derivatives of alkanes or as alkyl derivatives of water, and similarities to both parent types

$$R \cdot H \qquad R \cdot OH \qquad H \cdot OH$$
Alkane   Alcohol   Water

exist. The boiling points of methanol ($65°$), ethanol ($78°$), and pro-panol-1 ($97°$) are comparable to the boiling point of water, and these lower alcohols are miscible with water in all proportions. The solu-bilities of the next three higher homologs in 100 g. of water ($20°$) are: n-butyl alcohol, 8.3 g.; n-amyl alcohol (n-$C_5H_{11}OH$), 2.6 g.; n-hexyl alcohol, 1 g. These facts accord with the generalization that like dissolves like. The lower alcohols are like water in that the hydroxyl group comprises a considerable part of the molecule, whereas n-hexyl alcohol, $CH_3CH_2CH_2CH_2CH_2CH_2OH$, is preponderantly hydrocarbon in character; it is only slightly soluble in water, but more soluble in hydrocarbon solvents than methanol.

Solubility in water; like dissolves like

The simpler alcohols are known by both common and Geneva names. One propyl alcohol is primary and the other secondary, and the usual names are as follows:

$$CH_3CH_2CH_2OH \qquad (CH_3)_2CHOH$$
n-Propyl alcohol   Isopropyl alcohol

The structures and common names of the four butyl alcohols are as listed. The prefixes n-, *sec*- (secondary), and t- (tertiary) indicate the

$$CH_3CH_2CH_2CH_2OH \qquad \underset{CH_3}{\overset{CH_3}{\diagdown}}CHCH_2OH \qquad CH_3CH_2\underset{OH}{\overset{}{CH}}CH_3 \qquad CH_3-\underset{CH_3}{\overset{CH_3}{C}}OH$$

n-Butyl alcohol   Isobutyl alcohol   *sec*-Butyl alcohol t-Butyl alcohol

Butyl alcohols

alcohol type. Since two of the isomers are primary, the one of branched chain is called isobutyl alcohol; the amyl and hexyl alcohols that likewise contain the $(CH_3)_2CH-$ group are called isoamyl and isohexyl. Alcohols are also named as derivatives of carbinol (carbon–alcohol), that is, CH_3OH. For example, isobutyl, *sec*-butyl, and *t*-butyl alcohol are called isopropylcarbinol, methylethylcarbinol, and trimethyl-

Carbinol names

carbinol. The system has the advantage of indicating the alcohol type as well as describing the structure. The substance $(C_6H_5)_3COH$ is invariably called triphenylcarbinol. The alcohol of cyclohexane is known by the Geneva name, cyclohexanol; the unsaturated alcohol $CH_2{=}CHCH_2OH$ by the common name, allyl alcohol.

Some common alcohols contain two or more hydroxyl groups, for example:

Polyhydric alcohols

$HOCH_2CH_2OH$	$HO(CH_2)_6OH$	$HOCH_2CH(OH)CH_2OH$
Ethylene glycol	Hexamethylene glycol	Glycerol

These and all other polyhydric alcohols have no more than one hydroxyl group on any one carbon atom, since the *gem*-diol group, $>C(OH)_2$, is ordinarily unstable and loses water to form the carbonyl group, $>C{=}O$.

7.3

Hydrogen Bonding. — Whereas the normal alkane of molecular weight of about 100 boils at a temperature close to 100°, the alcohol $n\text{-}C_6H_{13}OH$, of molecular weight 102 boils at 156°. The relatively low volatility of alcohols is due to the fact that in the liquid state the molecules are associated. Liquid water is also associated, and contrasts with unassociated hydrogen compounds of comparable molecular weight that are gases at ordinary temperature: H_2, H_2S, HCl, NH_3; water vapor is monomeric. The association of alcohol and water molecules is due to hydrogen bonding. The electronic formulation of an alcohol dimer shows that the hydroxylic hydrogen atom of one monomer molecule is attracted by the strongly electronegative oxygen of a second molecule with the result that the hydrogen forms a bridge,

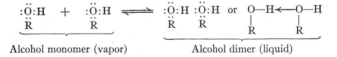

Alcohol monomer (vapor)   Alcohol dimer (liquid)

or hydrogen bond, linking the two oxygen atoms. The bonding of oxygen to hydrogen through an unshared pair of electrons is often represented by an arrow pointing to hydrogen, as in the alternate formula for the alcohol dimer. In electronegativity, defined as the tendency of an atom to gain electrons, fluorine surpasses oxygen and all other atoms, and hydrogen fluoride dimer contains a particularly stable hydrogen bond. That methanol has a lower boiling point (65°) than water even though the molecular weight is greater is because it is not so highly associated as water.

The presence in a compound of an unbonded hydroxyl group can be recognized by an absorption band of characteristic wave length in the infrared spectrum, and the absence of this band is evidence of hydrogen bonding. The high boiling points of water and of alcohols are attributable to the fact that heat energy is required to break the hydrogen bonds. Energy required to dissociate a given covalent bond in a gaseous molecule is the bond energy of that linkage and is accurately determinable (Pauling). From the table of bond energies given at the back of the book it will be seen that the hydrogen bond energy of 5 kg.-cal./mole is distinctly less than the energy of covalent single and double bonds; it is, however, appreciable and significant.

SYNTHESIS

Hydrolysis of Alkyl Halides. — The reaction of an alcohol with a hydrogen halide to give an alkyl halide and water is an equilibrium process and can be conducted in the reverse sense for preparation of an alcohol:

$$RX + HOH \longrightarrow ROH + HX$$

Water alone acts slowly at ordinary temperatures, except upon the particularly reactive tertiary halides, for example *t*-butyl chloride, $(CH_3)_3CCl$, but the hydrolysis can be promoted by a basic reagent to bind the acid produced. Since ethyl, propyl, and higher halides can also yield alkenes when treated with bases, experimental conditions have to be sought by which the hydrolytic reaction gains precedence over elimination of the elements of hydrogen halide from adjacent positions. This requirement is met by use of silver hydroxide, as obtained from a suspension of silver oxide in moist ether.

$$RCH_2I + AgOH \longrightarrow RCH_2OH + AgI$$

This method has limited application because alcohols are usually more accessible than the corresponding alkyl halides.

Hydration of Alkenes. — Conversion of alkenes into alcohols by addition of sulfuric acid to the double bond and hydrolysis of the resulting alkylsulfuric acid has been discussed in Chapter 4. The

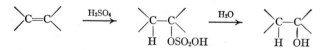

course of addition and, consequently, the structure of the alcohol can be predicted from the electronic concept of the reaction mechanism.

Reduction of Carbonyl Compounds. — Aldehydes and ketones contain the carbonyl group, which, like the ethylenic linkage, can enter into various additions, in some instances with reagents that add to alkenes. Hydrogen adds to both the carbonyl group and the ethylenic double bond, but under different conditions. An aldehyde affords a primary alcohol on reduction; a ketone gives a secondary alcohol.

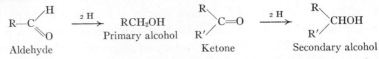

7.7

Ricinoleic acid, castor oil

One application of the method is the preparation of *n*-heptyl alcohol. The starting material, *n*-heptaldehyde, is readily available as one of two useful products resulting from pyrolysis of castor oil, consisting in large part of the glyceride of ricinoleic acid.

$$CH_3(CH_2)_5CH\,CH_2CH{=}CH(CH_2)_7COOH \xrightarrow{\text{Heated in vacuum}}$$
$$\quad\;\; |$$
$$\quad\;\; OH$$

Ricinoleic acid (as glyceride)

$$CH_3(CH_2)_5C\!\!\diagup^{H}_{\diagdown O} \;+\; CH_2{=}CHCH_2(CH_2)_7COOH$$

n-Heptaldehyde   Undecylenic acid

$$CH_3(CH_2)_5CHO \xrightarrow[75-81\%]{\text{Fe, aq. HOAc}} CH_3(CH_2)_5CH_2OH$$
n-Heptaldehyde   *n*-Heptyl alcohol

7.8

Reduction with lithium aluminum hydride

A new route to alcohols was provided by the discovery of the ether-soluble lithium aluminum hydride (Finholt, Bond, and Schlesinger,[1] 1947):

$$4\,LiH \;+\; AlCl_3 \longrightarrow LiAlH_4 \;+\; 3\,LiCl$$

This substance reacts at room temperature with a carbonyl compound to form an alcoholate, which on hydrolysis yields the alcohol (Nystrom and W. G. Brown[2]); the solvent must be free from water or alcohol, both of which liberate hydrogen from the reagent. One

$$4\,R_2C{=}O + LiAlH_4 \longrightarrow (R_2CHO)_4LiAl \xrightarrow{4\,H_2O} 4\,R_2CHOH + LiOH + Al(OH)_3$$

advantage is that the reagent ordinarily does not attack ethylenic bonds. Aldehydes, ketones, and esters can be reduced.

$$CH_3(CH_2)_5CHO \xrightarrow[86\%]{LiAlH_4} CH_3(CH_2)_5CH_2OH$$

$$CH_3CH_2COCH_3 \xrightarrow[80\%]{LiAlH_4} CH_3CH_2CH(OH)CH_3$$

$$CH_3CH{=}CHCHO \xrightarrow[70\%]{LiAlH_4} CH_3CH{=}CHCH_2OH$$
Crotonaldehyde   Crotyl alcohol

$$C_6H_5COOC_2H_5 \xrightarrow[90\%]{LiAlH_4} C_6H_5CH_2OH$$
Ethyl benzoate   Benzyl alcohol

[1] Hermann I. Schlesinger, b. 1882 Minneapolis; Ph.D. Chicago; Chicago
[2] Weldon G. Brown, b. 1908 Saskatoon, Canada; Ph.D. California; Nat. Res. Fellow, Chicago, Berlin, Frankfurt; Chicago

One of the most novel applications of lithium aluminum hydride
is preparation of alcohols by reduction of carboxylic acids, which are
resistant to most other reducing agents:

$$(CH_3)_3CCOOH \xrightarrow[92\%]{LiAlH_4} (CH_3)_3CCH_2OH$$
Trimethylacetic acid   Neopentyl alcohol

$$HOOC(CH_2)_8COOH \xrightarrow[97\%]{LiAlH_4} HOCH_2(CH_2)_8CH_2OH$$
Sebacic acid   Decanediol-1,10

Grignard Synthesis. — The most important method of synthesizing alcohols is a widely variable application of the Grignard reaction.
The essential step consists in addition of an alkylmagnesium halide
to the carbonyl group of a second component, followed by hydrolysis:

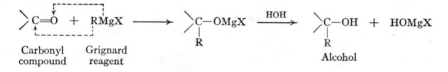

Carbonyl   Grignard   R   Alcohol
compound   reagent

That the MgX-radical becomes affixed to the oxygen atom accords
with the marked affinity of magnesium metal for oxygen (magnesium
incendiaries). The alkyl group of the Grignard reagent becomes linked
to the carbon of the carbonyl group, and in the final product appears
on the carbon carrying the alcoholic hydroxyl group. Alcohols of
all three classes, primary, secondary, and tertiary, can be synthesized
by suitable selection of the carbonyl component. With an aldehyde,
which has one alkyl group initially joined to the carbonyl function,
the Grignard addition results in a secondary alcohol (1). A ketone,

1.

$$R-C{\overset{H}{\underset{O}{}}} \xrightarrow{R'MgX} {\overset{R}{\underset{R'}{}}}CHOMgX \xrightarrow{H_2O} {\overset{R}{\underset{R'}{}}}CHOH$$
          Aldehyde   Secondary alcohol

Example:

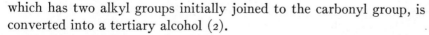

n-Butyraldehyde   Ethylmagnesium   Ethyl-*n*-propylcarbinol
                       iodide   (hexanol-3)

which has two alkyl groups initially joined to the carbonyl group, is
converted into a tertiary alcohol (2).

Tertiary alcohols can be synthesized also by the action of two
molecules of Grignard reagent on an ester. The reaction involves
initial addition to the carbonyl group of the ester to give an intermediate which has two oxygen substituents on the same carbon and

2.

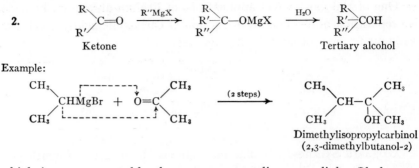

Example:

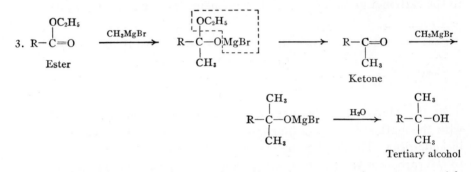

Dimethylisopropylcarbinol
(2,3-dimethylbutanol-2)

which is no more stable than a corresponding *gem*-diol. If, for example, a methyl Grignard reagent acts on an ethyl ester (3), an un-

3.

stable addition product is formed and at once decomposes with elimination of C_2H_5OMgBr and formation of a ketone; this substance then adds a further molecule of Grignard reagent and affords, after hydrolysis, a tertiary alcohol. Whereas in the synthesis from ketones tertiary carbinols having three different constituents can be prepared, the synthesis from esters can be applied only to the preparation of products in which two of the three alkyl groups are identical. Di-

methylisopropylcarbinol, given above as an example of reaction 2, can be prepared alternately by the action of two equivalents of methylmagnesium bromide on methyl isobutyrate, $(CH_3)_2CHCOOCH_3$. Triphenylcarbinol is prepared in a similar reaction from ethyl benzoate, the ethyl ester of the benzene derivative benzoic acid.

$$C_6H_5COOC_2H_5 + 2 C_6H_5MgBr \longrightarrow (C_6H_5)_3COMgBr \xrightarrow[91\%]{H_2O} (C_6H_5)_3COH$$

Ethyl benzoate   Phenylmagnesium   Triphenylcarbinol
bromide

Synthesis of a primary alcohol by the Grignard reaction can be accomplished by employing a carbonyl component having no attached alkyl substituents, namely formaldehyde, $HCH{=}O$. The type reaction (4) is generally applicable, and increases the carbon chain by one unit. A reagent that also gives primary alcohols, and with

4. $RMgX + CH_2=O \longrightarrow RCH_2OMgX \xrightarrow{H_2O} RCH_2OH$

Example:

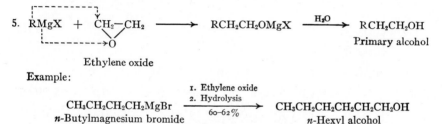

| Cyclohexylmagnesium chloride | | Cyclohexylcarbinol |

which the chain is lengthened by two carbon atoms, is ethylene oxide. This substance possesses reactivity akin to that of formaldehyde, for the three-membered ring tends to open with ease comparable to that noted for the carbonyl group. In the reaction with a Grignard reagent (5) the oxide ring is ruptured and the alkyl group adds to carbon and the magnesium halide group adds to oxygen.

5. $RMgX + CH_2-CH_2 \longrightarrow RCH_2CH_2OMgX \xrightarrow{H_2O} RCH_2CH_2OH$

Ethylene oxide $\qquad\qquad\qquad\qquad$ Primary alcohol

Example:

$$CH_3CH_2CH_2CH_2MgBr \xrightarrow[\substack{60-62\%}]{\substack{1.\ \text{Ethylene oxide} \\ 2.\ \text{Hydrolysis}}} CH_3CH_2CH_2CH_2CH_2CH_2OH$$
n-Butylmagnesium bromide $\qquad\qquad\qquad\qquad$ *n*-Hexyl alcohol

Because of the many variations possible in the type of the carbonyl component or cyclic oxide and in the choice of both specific oxygen-containing compounds and alkylmagnesium halides, the Grignard synthesis provides an invaluable route to alcohols of all types, whose structures can be foretold with assurance from the method of synthesis. When a meticulous technique is employed throughout, including use of pure reagents and dry ether, pure reaction products are obtainable in satisfactory overall yields.

INDUSTRIAL PREPARATION OF ALCOHOLS

Methanol. — Until 1923 methanol was prepared by destructive distillation of wood, which consists of the carbohydrate cellulose, $(C_6H_{10}O_5)_n$, together with some 20–30% of lignin, a polymeric substance containing aromatic rings bearing methoxyl groups (—OCH$_3$). Methanol derived from wood arises from the lignin component. When wood is heated without access of air to temperatures above 250°, it decomposes into charcoal and a volatile fraction that partly condenses on cooling to a liquor, pyroligneous acid, which contains methanol, acetic acid, and traces of acetone. Acetic acid can be neutralized with calcium hydroxide, and methanol separated by distillation. At the present time methanol is made largely synthetically in nearly quantitative yield by hydrogenation of carbon monoxide:

Synthetic

$$2 H_2 + CO \rightleftharpoons CH_3OH$$

Formation of methanol is accompanied by a decrease in volume, and hence pressures of 3000 lbs. per sq. in. are commonly employed to promote the conversion. The usual temperature range is 350–400°. The hydrogenation is catalyzed by chromic oxide in combination with zinc oxide.

7.11

Ethanol. — Ethyl alcohol has been made since antiquity by fermentation of sugar by yeast. Extensive biochemical investigations have established that alcoholic fermentation of a sugar, for example fructose, proceeds by an elaborate cycle, or series of steps, most of which are reversible. The formulation indicates the principal intermediates, but actually the alcoholic components react in the form of

Fermentation of sugar

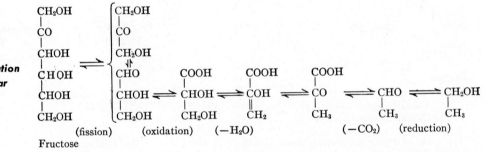

Fructose

phosphoric acid esters formed by reversible interaction with phosphate donor and acceptor substances present in small amounts in yeast. Thus the dihydroxy acid (glyceric acid) appears as the phosphate ester I, which on dehydration affords the phosphate ester II. This is an enol ester, and when it is hydrolyzed to the free enol III the

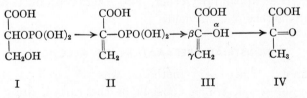

latter at once undergoes α,γ-hydrogen shift (5.9) to form pyruvic acid, IV. Similar shifts are involved in the isomerization of the two three-carbon products of initial fission of the sugar; the formulation below shows the conversion of glyceraldehyde to an enediol by one α,γ-hydrogen shift and the transformation of the intermediate to dihydroxyacetone by another; both reactions are reversible. α,γ-Shifts

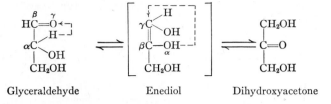

Glyceraldehyde   Enediol   Dihydroxyacetone

occur because hydrogen attached to an α-atom is activated by a β,γ-double bond, and this activation is manifested in another way in the first step of the fermentation cycle, the reversible fission of the six-carbon chain. The reverse reaction, the union of the two three-carbon fragments, involves addition of the ketone component V to the carbonyl group of the aldehyde component VI as shown, and the

$$
\underset{V}{\overset{OH}{\underset{\beta}{CH_2}}-\overset{\gamma O}{\underset{\alpha}{C}}-\overset{OH}{\underset{}{C}}\overset{H}{\underset{H}{}}} \quad + \quad \underset{VI}{O=CHCHOHCH_2OH} \quad \rightleftharpoons \quad \underset{VII}{\overset{OH}{CH_2}-\overset{O}{C}-\overset{OH}{CH}-\overset{OH}{CH}-\overset{OH}{CH}-\overset{OH}{CH_2}}
$$

addition occurs because of β,γ-activation of hydrogen attached to an α-carbon atom.

Yeast also contains a number of enzymes, each of which is a protein capable, under physiological conditions, of promoting some one kind of chemical transformation. Thus an oxidation-reduction step requires a specific enzyme, an oxidoreductase. An oxidation in one phase of the cycle is paired with a reduction in another phase. Thus the elaborate process of fission of the six-carbon chain to two three-carbon components, isomerization of the keto component to the aldehyde, and degradation of this to ethanol and carbon dioxide proceeds without gain or loss of any atoms and corresponds to the extent of 95% or better to the equation: $C_6H_{12}O_6 \longrightarrow 2\ CH_3CH_2OH + 2\ CO_2$. Glycerol is formed in small amounts by reduction of dihydroxyacetone.

A large amount of industrial alcohol is made by fermentation of blackstrap molasses derived from the refining of cane sugar. Ethanol is also made from ethylene, derived from the cracking of petroleum fractions, usually by absorption in sulfuric acid and hydrolysis.

Ordinary commercial alcohol is a constant-boiling mixture of alcohol (95.57% by weight) and water (4.43%), and since this mixture boils at 78.2°, a temperature slightly lower than the boiling point of absolute ethyl alcohol, 78.3°, separation cannot be effected by ordinary distillation. Absolute alcohol can be prepared by chemical methods, for example with use of quicklime, which combines with water but not with alcohol, but it is prepared commercially by azeotropic distillation. When a mixture of 95% alcohol and benzene is distilled, the

From ethane via ethylene

7.12
Absolute alcohol

initial fraction consists of benzene—alcohol—water (64.8°), followed by alcohol—benzene (68.2°), and the final fraction consists of absolute alcohol.

7.13   **Isopropyl Alcohol.** — Isopropyl alcohol is made by high-pressure

$$CH_3COCH_3 \xrightarrow{H_2 \ (Ni)} CH_3CHOHCH_3$$

        Acetone   Isopropyl alcohol

hydrogenation of acetone and by sulfuric acid hydration of propylene (cracking).

7.14   **Butyl Alcohols.** — *n*-Butyl alcohol is made along with acetone by bacterial fermentation of carbohydrates in a process developed by

Weizmann process

Weizmann[3] in 1911 to provide acetone, required for compounding the explosive Cordite; after World War I, the major function of the process was to supply *n*-butyl alcohol, required for quick-drying automobile lacquers. *sec*-Butyl alcohol is made from the mixture of butene-1 and -2 present in the C$_4$-cut of cracked gasoline.

$$\left.\begin{array}{l} CH_3CH{=}CHCH_3 \\ \text{Butene-2} \\ CH_3CH_2CH{=}CH_2 \\ \text{Butene-1} \end{array}\right\} \xrightarrow[80\%]{H_2SO_4,\ H_2O} CH_3CH_2CHOHCH_3$$

                                                   Butanol-2

7.15   **Amyl Alcohols.** — A mixture of amyl alcohols is prepared by chlorination of the C$_5$-cut of natural gasoline, consisting of approximately equal amounts of *n*-pentane and isopentane, and hydrolysis of the mixture of halides. Chlorination is carried out in vapor phase at 200° in the absence of catalysts and in darkness. Hydrolysis by aqueous sodium hydroxide is facilitated by addition of a sodium oleate soap, which provides more intimate contact by emulsifying the two immiscible layers. The alcohol mixture is used as solvent and plasticizer, and for production of the lacquer solvent amyl acetate. The chloride mixture is useful in the preparation of various synthetic products.

7.16   **Ethylene Glycol.** — Ethylene glycol (b.p. 197.5°) is prepared from ethylene chlorohydrin either by hydrolysis with soda or through ethylene oxide. Ethylene oxide is made more usually by direct combina-

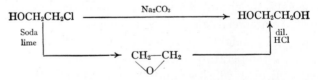

tion of ethylene and oxygen at a high temperature in the presence of silver catalysts. Ethylene glycol is an antifreeze agent (Prestone).

[3] Chaim Weizmann, 1874–1952; b. Russia; Ph.D. Berlin and Freiburg, Switzerland (Bistrzycki); Univ. Manchester, Weizmann Inst. Sci., Israel

A series of useful monoalkyl ethers, marketed under the trade name of Cellosolve, are obtained by alcoholysis of ethylene oxide.

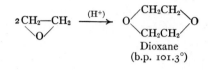

$$CH_2\!\!-\!\!CH_2 + CH_3OH \xrightarrow{\text{(H}_2\text{SO}_4)} HOCH_2CH_2OCH_3$$

Methyl Cellosolve
(b.p. 125°)

The Cellosolves are widely used as solvents in varnishes and lacquers. Dioxane, made by polymerization of the oxide, is an excellent solvent

$$2\,CH_2\!\!-\!\!CH_2 \xrightarrow{\text{(H}^+)} O\!\!<^{\displaystyle CH_2CH_2}_{\displaystyle CH_2CH_2}\!\!>O$$

Dioxane
(b.p. 101.3°)

for many organic compounds and is also completely miscible with water; this property is shown by methyl, ethyl, and even *n*-butyl Cellosolve.

Glycerol. — Glycerol is produced as a by-product in the manufacture of soap in amounts sufficient except in time of war (nitroglycerin). Production was announced in 1938 of synthetic glycerol from petroleum (propylene) by the reactions shown. The first step

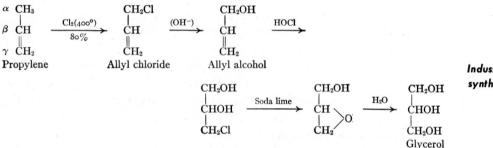

consists in high-temperature substitution by chlorine of a hydrogen on the α-member of an α—β═γ system, and this reaction is a further instance of activation by a β,γ-double bond (7.11). That chlorine does not add to the double bond is because the dichloride is unstable at 400°; high temperatures favor unsaturated systems.

Glycerol (Gr. *glykys*, sweet), a viscous, hygroscopic liquid with a sweet taste, contains both primary and secondary alcoholic groups, and in the reactions with dry hydrogen chloride and with nitric acid, the former type is the more reactive. Oxidation of glycerol under

CH₂Cl		CH₂OH		COOH
CHOH	←HCl	CHOH	→HNO₃	CHOH
CH₂OH		CH₂OH		CH₂OH
α-Monochlorohydrin (with some β-isomer)				Glyceric acid (chief product)

milder conditions, for example with sodium hypobromite, gives an equilibrium mixture of glyceraldehyde and dihydroxyacetone in which the former predominates; these three-carbon compounds are intermediates in the fermentation of sugar (7.11).

REACTIONS OF ALCOHOLS

7.19

With Metals. — When metallic sodium is added cautiously in small pieces to excess methanol, the metal rapidly dissolves, hydrogen is evolved, and there is a considerable heat effect, although not sufficient to cause ignition of hydrogen as in the parallel reaction with water. The resulting solution contains sodium methoxide, CH_3ONa (also called sodium methylate). The substance can be obtained as a dry white solid by preparing a suspension of powdery or granular

$$CH_3OH \quad + \quad Na \quad \longrightarrow \quad CH_3ONa \quad + \quad \tfrac{1}{2} H_2$$
$$\text{Sodium methoxide}$$

sodium in absolute ether and adding in portions one molecular equivalent of methanol. Sodium methoxide and ethoxide are subject to hydrolysis, and with a limited amount of water an equilibrium mixture is obtained. Conversely, a solution prepared from sodium or potassium

$$C_2H_5ONa \quad + \quad H_2O \quad \rightleftharpoons \quad C_2H_5OH \quad + \quad NaOH$$
$$\text{Sodium ethoxide}$$

*Nucleophilic
potency of CH_3O^-*

hydroxide in alcohol contains a certain amount of ethoxide in equilibrium. The reaction of an alkyl halide with alcoholic potassium hydroxide involves attack by the nucleophilic alkoxide ion (RO^-). An alkoxide ion is more nucleophilic than a hydroxide ion because the inductive drift of electrons away from the alkyl group increases the electron density on oxygen: $CH_3{\rightarrow}O^-$.

Higher alcohols react with sodium to give sodium alkoxides, but the reaction proceeds with decreasing readiness as the molecular weight increases; as the hydrocarbon residue increases in size, the functional hydroxyl group responsible for the reaction becomes a minor part of the whole and offers a more elusive target for sodium atoms. Aluminum isopropoxide, $Al[OCH(CH_3)_2]_3$, and aluminum *t*-butoxide, $Al[OC(CH_3)_3]_3$, have specific synthetic uses and are prepared by interaction of the anhydrous alcohol with amalgamated aluminum.

7.20

Reactivity: **t** >
sec > **primary**

Dehydration. — Elimination of water from adjacent positions in an alcohol, either by pyrolysis over alumina or by use of mineral acids, constitutes a valuable path to alkenes. Examples given in Chapter 4 illustrate the generalization that tertiary alcohols suffer dehydration more readily than secondary ones, which in turn react more readily than primary alcohols. These relationships are significant not only in fixing the conditions required to convert a given alcohol into an alkene but also in determining the course of partial dehydration of a polyhydric alcohol. Thus a tertiary alcoholic group usually can be eliminated from a substance having secondary and primary groups without disturbance of these less labile hydroxyls.

A further differentiation can be made with respect to the direction of dehydration when two routes are open. In pentanol-2 hydrogen atoms adjacent to the hydroxylated carbon are available at both positions 1 and 3, but actually the latter hydrogen is utilized almost exclusively, and the chief product of dehydration is pentene-2. An alkene having a terminal double bond (pentene-1) is a less preferred

$$CH_3CH_2CH_2CH(OH)CH_3 \xrightarrow{-H_2O} CH_3CH_2CH=CHCH_3$$
$$\text{Pentanol-2} \qquad\qquad\qquad \text{Pentene-2}$$

product than an isomer with the ethylenic linkage in an interior position (pentene-2). In the case of 2-methylpentanol-3 removal of hydrogen from either of the alternate positions 2 or 4 would give an internal double bond, but nevertheless a definite preference exists,

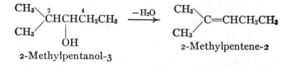

and the chief product is that resulting from abstraction of the hydrogen in the 2-position. The carbon atom at this position is tertiarily substituted and carries but one hydrogen, whereas at the alternate (secondary) position there are two. In the dehydration of pentanol-2 cited above the hydrogen eliminated comes from a secondarily, rather than a primarily substituted carbon atom. These examples are representative and illustrate an empirical rule due to Saytzeff [4] (1875) that, in dehydration of alcohols, hydrogen is eliminated preferentially from the adjacent carbon atom that is poorer in hydrogen.* This relationship means that the tertiarily bound hydrogen of the structure R_3CH is more reactive than the hydrogen of a methylene group, R_2CH_2, and the latter surpasses in reactivity the hydrogen of the primary carbon of a methyl group, RCH_3. The relationship is exactly the same as that noted for the relative reactivities of alkanes in the catalytic addition to ethylenic hydrocarbons (6.11). The Saytzeff rule applies also to the elimination of hydrogen halide from an alkyl halide.

Saytzeff rule (see Matthew)

Rearrangements. — Alcohols having a tertiary carbon atom (i.e. three alkyl substituents) adjacent to that carrying the hydroxyl group

7.21

[4] Alexander M. Saytzeff, 1841–1910; b. Kasan, Russia; stud. Marburg, Paris; Kasan
* Matthew XXV, 29, ". . . but from him that hath not shall be taken away even that which he hath."

when subjected to acid-catalyzed dehydration are prone to undergo a molecular rearrangement of a type clarified by investigations of Wagner[5] and of Meerwein.[6]   For example, methyl-*t*-butylcarbinol (I) gives the normal product *t*-butylethylene (II) on dehydration over alumina (basic), but on dehydration with an acid gives tetramethyl-

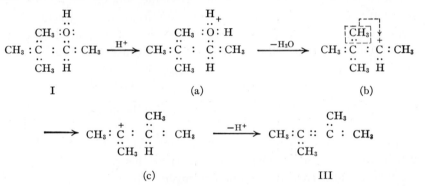

ethylene (III).   This Wagner-Meerwein rearrangement is interpreted as follows.   The oxygen atom of the alcohol I accepts a proton to form the oxonium ion (a), which loses water to form the carbonium ion (b).   This ion is unstable not only because of the presence of an

electron-deficient carbon (electron sextet), but because this carbon is secondary, that is, it has only two electron-releasing alkyl groups to counterbalance the positive charge.   In ion (c) the electron-deficient carbon, being tertiary, is stabilized by three alkyl groups.   The difference in stability thus provides a driving force for rearrangement of (b) into (c), accomplished by migration of a methyl group with the pair of shared electrons.   The tertiary carbonium ion (c) then expels a hydrogen atom and the charge, as a proton, and the electron pair released is utilized for formation of the double bond of III.   Actually, the migration of a methyl group from one carbon atom to the next, (b) → (c), may proceed through a carbonium ion (b′) of intermediate structure:

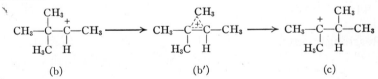

[5] Georg Wagner, b. Russia; Univ. Moscow
[6] Hans Meerwein, b. 1879 Hamburg, Germany; Ph.D. Bonn (Schroeter); Marburg

A related case is that of pinacol (IV), which on dehydration over alumina gives the normal product, 2,3-dimethylbutadiene (4.4), but which on acid-catalyzed dehydration affords pinacolone (V). The

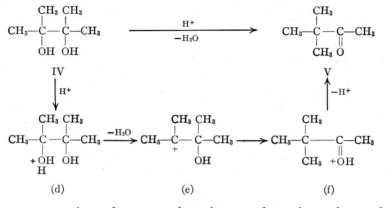

IV   V

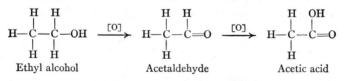

(d)   (e)   (f)

rearrangement is analogous to that above and can be understood as involving formation of the tertiary carbonium ion (e) by elimination of water from the oxonium ion (d), migration of methyl with its electron pair to the electron-deficient carbon of (e) to give the oxonium ion (f), and expulsion of a proton with formation of V.

Oxidation. — Methyl, ethyl, and many higher alcohols are highly susceptible to oxidation by chromic acid, potassium dichromate, or by potassium permanganate. Since methane and ethane are resistant to these reagents, the presence of oxygen in a molecule confers susceptibility to further oxidation. In ethyl alcohol one of the two carbon atoms is linked to oxygen, and hence is already oxidized, while the other is joined to hydrogen and carbon and corresponds to the carbon atoms of the inert ethane; hence oxidizing agents attack the molecule at the former, rather than the latter position. The initial oxidation product is acetaldehyde, which on further oxidation is attacked in the

7.22

Ethyl alcohol   Acetaldehyde   Acetic acid

already oxidized part of the molecule and yields acetic acid as an end product resistant to further attack. An empirical statement of the oxidation is that a hydrogen atom on an oxidized carbon of acetaldehyde becomes converted into a hydroxyl group. That such hydroxylation can occur is demonstrated by the ready oxidation of triphenylmethane to triphenylcarbinol: $(C_6H_5)_3CH \xrightarrow{[O]} (C_6H_5)_3COH$. If, in ethyl alcohol, one of the hydrogen atoms attached to the already oxidized carbon were to become hydroxylated, the product would be

Hydroxylation of oxidized or activated carbon

an unstable *gem*-diol and would lose water to form acetaldehyde. Acetic acid is stable to oxidation, though it contains a highly oxidized

Unstable gem-*diol*

$$CH_3CH_2OH \xrightarrow{[O]} \left[CH_3CH \underset{OH}{\overset{O\!-\!H}{\diagdown}} \right] \xrightarrow{-H_2O} CH_2CH{=}O$$

carbon atom, because this atom carries no hydrogen. Oxidation of methanol may proceed to the stage of formaldehyde through an intermediate *gem*-diol; the next product is formic acid, HCOOH, and this, unlike acetic acid, still possesses a hydrogen atom on the oxidized

$$\underset{\text{Methanol}}{H\!-\!\overset{\displaystyle H}{\underset{\displaystyle H}{C}}\!-\!OH} \xrightarrow{[O]} \left[H\!-\!\overset{\displaystyle OH}{\underset{\displaystyle H}{C}}\!-\!OH \right] \xrightarrow{-H_2O} \underset{\text{Formaldehyde}}{H\!-\!\overset{\displaystyle }{\underset{\displaystyle H}{C}}{=}O} \xrightarrow{[O]}$$

$$\underset{\text{Formic acid}}{H\!-\!\overset{\displaystyle }{\underset{\displaystyle OH}{C}}{=}O} \xrightarrow{[O]} \left[HO\!-\!\overset{\displaystyle }{\underset{\displaystyle OH}{C}}{=}O \right] \xrightarrow{-H_2O} O{=}C{=}O$$

carbon and is oxidized further. Hydroxylation of the specially situated hydrogen would give carbonic acid, an unstable diol which decomposes to carbon dioxide and water.

The behavior of ethyl rather than methyl alcohol is generally typical of primary alcohols, for such alcohols on oxidation yield aldehydes initially and then acids. A secondary alcohol can undergo

Aldehydes and ketones

$$\underset{\text{Primary alcohol}}{RCH_2OH} \xrightarrow{[O]} \underset{\text{Aldehyde}}{RCHO} \xrightarrow{[O]} \underset{\text{Acid}}{RCOOH}$$

hydroxylation of the lone hydrogen on the oxidized carbon followed by loss of water, with production of a ketone, and this product represents a stopping point for normal oxidation. Isopropyl alcohol yields

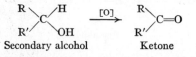

$$\underset{\text{Secondary alcohol}}{\overset{R}{\underset{R'}{\diagup}}C\overset{H}{\underset{OH}{\diagdown}}} \xrightarrow{[O]} \underset{\text{Ketone}}{\overset{R}{\underset{R'}{\diagup}}C{=}O}$$

acetone; diethylcarbinol affords diethyl ketone, $CH_3CH_2COCH_2CH_3$. Acetone is sufficiently resistant to further oxidation to be employed as a solvent in permanganate oxidation of other substances, and ketones are normal end products of oxidation even though, under special conditions, they can undergo oxidative degradation.

t-Alcohols resistant

A tertiary alcohol, R_3COH, contains a hydroxylated carbon atom but this carries no hydrogen, and hence the alcohol should be resistant to oxidation.   Under ordinary conditions of oxidation in a neutral or alkaline medium tertiary alcohols are indeed inert and hence can be distinguished from primary and secondary alcohols (alkaline permanganate test).   Primary and secondary alcohols are capable of oxidation to aldehydes, acids, or ketones, in which the original carbon skeleton is still intact.   The oxidation reaction therefore has diagnostic value, since qualitative tests can distinguish between aldehydes and ketones and identify a carboxylic acid.   An alcohol that on oxidation yields either an aldehyde or an acid of the same carbon chain is a primary alcohol;   one that affords a ketone is a secondary alcohol; and an alcohol that is resistant to attack under neutral conditions must have a tertiary structure.

As noted in Chapter 4, an alkene on oxidation with alkaline permanganate under controlled conditions or on treatment with hydrogen peroxide in acetic acid yields initially a *vic*-glycol, which is readily oxidized further.   A glycol such as II, derived from an alkene (I), offers various possibilities for oxidation.   Two hydrogens on oxidized carbon

$$RCH{=}CHR' \xrightarrow{\text{[O]}} \underset{\substack{\text{II}}}{RCH{-}CHR'} \quad \begin{array}{c} \xrightarrow{\text{KMnO}_4} RCOOH \; + \; HOOCR' \\[2ex] \xrightarrow{\text{Pb(OAc)}_4} RCHO \; + \; OCHR' \end{array}$$

with OH OH on II below the RCH—CHR', and I below the first structure.

atoms are available for hydroxylation, and furthermore a bond extending between two oxidized carbon atoms is subject to oxidative severance.   Thus excess permanganate or dichromate converts the glycol II into a mixture of the acids RCOOH and R'COOH, either by cleavage of the connecting bond and oxidation of the fragments or by oxidation of the secondary alcoholic groups followed by oxidative cleavage.   The selective cleavage of the weakened connecting bond of a *vic*-glycol can be accomplished with either lead tetraacetate in acetic acid solution or with periodic acid in aqueous solution.   With either of these specific reagents the outcome of glycol cleavage can be visualized as fission of the bond between the oxidized carbons and addition of a hydroxyl group to each fragment:

$$\underset{\substack{\text{OH} \;\; \text{OH}}}{RCH{-}CHR} \xrightarrow[\text{Pb(OAc)}_4 \text{ or HIO}_4]{\text{2[OH]}} \left[\underset{\substack{\text{OH}}}{2RCHO{\cdot}H} \right] \longrightarrow 2RCH{=}O$$

$$\underset{\substack{\text{OH} \;\; \text{OH}}}{RCH{-}CR_2} \xrightarrow{\text{2[OH]}} \left[\underset{\substack{\text{OH}}}{RCHOH} + \underset{\substack{\text{OH}}}{HOCR_2} \right] \longrightarrow RCH{=}O \; + \; O{=}CR_2$$

101

An ester is the organic equivalent of an inorganic salt, since it is derived by elimination of water from an acid and an alcohol. The

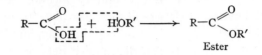

analogy is superficial, since esters are typically organic; they are nonionic and, with the exception of the initial members, sparingly soluble in water. Formation of an ester from the components, known as esterification, can be accomplished by refluxing a mixture of the acid and the alcohol in the presence of a trace of mineral acid as catalyst (method of E. Fischer). The process is an equilibrium, the attainment of which is hastened by a trace of hydrogen ion. Pure acetic acid reacts very slowly with an equivalent amount of pure ethanol to give the ester ethyl acetate, and equilibrium is attained only after a reflux period of several days. If about 3% of dry hydro-

Fischer esterification

$$CH_3C{\overset{O}{\underset{OH}{}}} \ + \ HOCH_2CH_3 \ \overset{[H^+]}{\rightleftarrows} \ CH_3C{\overset{O}{\underset{OCH_2CH_3}{}}} \ + \ H_2O$$

Ethyl acetate

gen chloride, concentrated sulfuric acid, or boron fluoride is added to the original mixture, the same equilibrium can be reached in a few hours. With equivalent quantities of reactants the conversion into the ester amounts to only about two thirds of that theoretically possible before the reverse reaction of hydrolysis is proceeding at the same rate as the esterification reaction and equilibrium is reached. In accordance with the mass-action law the equilibrium is displaced in favor of the ester by an excess of one component, and in practice it is expedient to employ a large excess of alcohol for efficient esterification of a valuable acid.

Esterification of an alcohol with an inorganic acid is favored both by the strongly acidic character of the inorganic component and by the fact that such acids are dehydrating agents. Concentrated sulfuric acid effects complete conversion of an alcohol into an alkylsulfuric

$$ROH \ + \ HOSO_2OH \ \rightleftharpoons \ ROSO_2OH \ + \ H_2O$$
Alkylsulfuric acid

Esters of inorganic acids

$$CH_3CH_2OH \ + \ HONO_2 \ \rightleftharpoons \ CH_3CH_2ONO_2 \ + \ H_2O$$
Ethyl nitrate
(b.p. 87.5°)

$$CH_3CH_2OH \ + \ HONO \ \rightleftharpoons \ CH_3CH_2ONO \ + \ H_2O$$
Ethyl nitrite
(b.p. 17°)

acid because it is highly ionized and absorbs the water formed in esterification. Ethyl alcohol similarly combines with nitric acid and with nitrous acid to form ethyl nitrate and ethyl nitrite, respectively.

Nitroglycerin. — The powerful explosive commonly known as nitroglycerin is more accurately defined as the trinitrate ester of glycerol, or glycerol trinitrate. It is made by cautious addition of anhydrous glycerol to a stirred mixture of concentrated nitric acid and fuming sulfuric acid at a temperature maintained at 10–20° by efficient cooling (exothermic reaction). The nitration is conducted

$$
\begin{array}{llll}
CH_2OH & & & CH_2ONO_2 \\
| & & & | \\
CHOH & + \ 3\ HONO_2 & \xrightarrow[94\%]{H_2SO_4} & CHONO_2 \\
| & & & | \\
CH_2OH & & & CH_2ONO_2 \\
\text{Glycerol} & & & \text{Nitroglycerin}
\end{array}
$$

in lead vessels with cooling coils, and agitation is accomplished with compressed air.

Nitroglycerin is a colorless oily liquid (sp. gr. 1.6) with a sweet burning taste. The substance has some use for treatment of angina pectoris, usually in the form of a dilute alcoholic solution (which can be handled safely if care is taken to prevent evaporation of solvent). The most significant property of the nitrate ester is violent detonation on slight shock. More than enough oxygen is present to convert the carbon and hydrogen into the corresponding oxides, with liberation

$$C_3H_5(ONO_2)_3 \longrightarrow \tfrac{3}{2} N_2 + 3\ CO_2 + \tfrac{5}{2} H_2O + \tfrac{1}{4} O_2$$

High explosive

of elemental nitrogen. The sudden liberation of this large volume of gas in a space initially occupied by the liquid substance gives an explosion wave of enormous pressure. Nitroglycerin was first prepared in 1846, and some years later Alfred Nobel in Sweden undertook its manufacture. The great sensitivity introduced considerable hazard, and the expedient of transporting the product in the frozen condition, in which state nitroglycerin is somewhat less sensitive to shock than in the liquid form, reduced but did not eliminate accidents. The experience, however, provided a clue that materialized in Nobel's discovery in 1866 of the practical explosive dynamite. Kieselguhr, a diatomaceous earth, will absorb up to three times its weight of nitroglycerin and still remain dry; the absorbed nitroglycerin in this solid form retains explosive properties but shows greatly diminished sensitivity. Dynamite is sufficiently insensitive to shock to be shipped with safety, and it is exploded with use of a percussion cap, or detonator, containing mercuric fulminate, $Hg(ONC)_2$, or lead azide, PbN_6.

Dynamite

In 1875 Nobel made the further discovery that guncotton can be gelatinized with nitroglycerin to give a jelly of satisfactory stability and powerful explosive properties. Guncotton looks like ordinary

7.26

cotton and consists of cellulose trinitrate, or nitrocellulose, of the formula $[C_6H_7O_2(ONO_2)_3]_n$; it is a nitric acid ester structurally similar to nitroglycerin, $C_3H_5(ONO_2)_3$, and this similarity accounts for the solubility of the solid of high molecular weight in the liquid ester. Nobel's Blasting Gelatin containing 92% of nitroglycerin and 8% of

Blasting gelatins, propellants

guncotton is one of the most powerful and brisant (shattering) explosives known. By greatly reducing the proportion of nitroglycerin to guncotton, formulations are obtainable of slow-burning characteristics

Cordite

suitable as propellants in shells. Cordite, a superior smokeless powder, has the composition: nitroglycerin, 30%; guncotton, 65%; Vaseline, 5%. With this high proportion of guncotton, gelatinization cannot be accomplished by nitroglycerin alone, and acetone is employed as a mutual solvent adapted to the production of a homogeneous gel. A paste of the ingredients, moistened with the solvent, is incorporated in a kneading machine into a stiff dough that is then extruded through a die in the form of rods or cords (hence Cordite) of various sizes, usually having carefully spaced perforations to provide for even burning from within as well as from without. The cords are cut into lengths and dried thoroughly to evaporate the acetone, the bulk of which is recovered.

7.27   **Pentaerythritol Tetranitrate (PETN)** is a related high explosive prepared by esterification of the alcohol with mixed acid. The substance has considerable brisance, but is more sensitive to shock than

High explosive

$$
\begin{array}{c}
CH_2OH \\
| \\
HOCH_2-C-CH_2OH \\
| \\
CH_2OH \\
\text{Pentaerythritol (m.p. 260°)}
\end{array}
\xrightarrow{HNO_3, H_2SO_4}
\begin{array}{c}
CH_2ONO_2 \\
| \\
O_2NOCH_2-C-CH_2ONO_2 \\
| \\
CH_2ONO_2 \\
\text{PETN (m.p. 138-140°)}
\end{array}
$$

other common high explosives, such as TNT, and usually is detonated by impact of a rifle bullet. The substance is used chiefly in manufacture of detonating fuse (Primacord), a waterproof textile filled with powdered PETN.

ETHERS

7.28   The type formula for an ether can be derived by replacement of the two hydrogens of the water molecule by alkyl groups, but ethers are regarded more appropriately as derivatives of alcohols, from which they usually are prepared. Ethers boil at temperatures much lower

HOH	ROH	ROR′ or R:O:R′
Water	Alcohol	Ether

than the alcohols from which they are derived or than alcohols of similar molecular weight, but the boiling points correspond closely to those of comparably constituted alkanes of similar molecular complexity. Since an oxygen atom (16) is nearly the equivalent of a methylene group (14), it is appropriate to compare diethyl ether (b.p. 34.6°) with *n*-pentane (b.p. 36.1°); methyl *n*-butyl ether (b.p. 70.3°) with *n*-hexane (b.p. 68.7°); or di-*n*-butyl ether (b.p. 140.9°) with *n*-nonane (b.p. 150.7°). Ethers, like alkanes, are unassociated in the liquid form and hence different from the high-boiling, hydrogen-bonded alcohols.

Diethyl ether, known simply as **ether,** is used extensively as a solvent and as an anesthetic. The combination of two hydrocarbon residues linked through an inert oxygen atom confers marked solvent power for organic compounds of most types other than those of a highly hydroxylic character. Ether is an excellent extraction medium because it is a good solvent for organic compounds and dissolves but few inorganic substances, because it is not miscible with water and separates as a discrete upper layer, and because its high volatility (b.p. 34.6°) permits rapid removal from an extract by distillation at a temperature so low as to avoid damage to sensitive substances. Dimethyl ether would not be suitable because it is a gas at room temperature (b.p. −25°), and the higher homologs are less volatile and are not so readily available. Ether falls short of being an ideal extraction solvent because it is not completely insoluble in water; at room temperature ether dissolves 1–1.5% of water and water dissolves 7.5% of ether; hence considerable solvent is lost in extraction operations. The volatile solvent is also highly flammable. Another disadvantageous property is that on standing for some time in contact with air ether is partly oxidized to a nonvolatile peroxide, which is left as a residue on evaporation of the solvent and which may explode violently in a distillation carried to dryness with consequent overheating.

Ether as an Anesthetic. — The safe abolition of pain by inhalation of ether for a period long enough for a surgical operation was first publicly demonstrated by the Boston dentist Morton at the Massachusetts General Hospital in 1846. The term anesthesia (insensibility) was suggested to Morton by Oliver Wendell Holmes. Inhalation of ether vapor produces unconsciousness by depressing activity of the central nervous system. Ethylene, divinyl ether, $(CH_2{=}CH)_2O$, and cyclopropane are also potent anesthetics, but in each case advantages for use in clinical surgery are offset by disadvantages. For example, divinyl ether is about seven times as potent as ether and acts more rapidly, but these advantages are offset by danger of rapidly reaching a too deep plane of anesthesia. Nitrous oxide has found some use in dentistry but not in general surgery, for even undiluted nitrous

Normal b.ps.; unassociated

7.29

Use for extraction; high solvent power; very volatile

Flammable, and forms dangerous peroxide

7.30
Discovery, 1846

Other anesthetics

Nitrous oxide

105

oxide has only a weak depressant action on the central nervous system. Chloroform, formerly employed to some extent as an anesthetic, causes significant liver toxicity and is now little used except in the tropics, where the low boiling point of ether presents difficulties. Ether thus continues to be the safest and the most widely used general anesthetic.

7.31

Preparation of Ethers. — Diethyl ether can be produced from ethanol, either by the sulfuric acid method or by dehydration over aluminum oxide at high pressure and at elevated temperatures. The *Sulfuric acid method* sulfuric acid process consists in heating a mixture of alcohol and sulfuric acid to a temperature of about $140°$, and running in a large additional quantity of alcohol at the rate at which the ether produced distils from the reaction mixture (4.5). The competitive reaction of *Limitation* dehydration of the alcohol to an alkene limits applicability of the method to alcohols that are not easily dehydrated.

7.32

A generally applicable method of preparing either simple or mixed ethers is the **Williamson [7] synthesis,** which involves interaction of a sodium alkoxide with an alkyl halide. A given alcohol can be trans-

$$RONa + R'X \longrightarrow ROR' + NaX$$

formed into the corresponding simple ether by converting one part into the sodio derivative and another into the bromide or iodide, and bringing these two components into reaction with each other. Examples of the preparation of mixed ethers are:

$$CH_3CH_2CH_2ONa + CH_3CH_2I \xrightarrow{70\%} CH_3CH_2CH_2OCH_2CH_3$$
Sodium *n*-propoxide $\qquad\qquad\qquad$ Ethyl *n*-propyl ether

Mixed ethers

$$CH_3CH_2ONa + BrCH_2CH_2CH_2CH_3 \xrightarrow{110°} CH_3CH_2OCH_2CH_2CH_2CH_3$$
$\qquad\qquad\qquad\qquad\qquad\qquad\qquad$ Ethyl *n*-butyl ether

The alkyl halide in the Williamson synthesis can be replaced by a dialkyl sulfate. This method of alkylation has particular importance

Dimethyl sulfate method

$$(CH_3)_2SO_4 + NaOCH_2CH(CH_3)_2 \longrightarrow CH_3OCH_2CH(CH_3)_2 + CH_3NaSO_4$$
$\qquad\qquad\qquad\qquad\qquad\qquad\qquad$ Methyl isobutyl ether

in the aromatic series and is widely employed for preparation of methyl and ethyl ethers of phenols, for example:

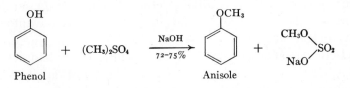

Phenol $\qquad\qquad\qquad\qquad\qquad\qquad\qquad$ Anisole

---

[7] Alexander W. Williamson, 1824–1904; b. Wandsworth, England; Ph.D. Giessen (Liebig); London; *J. Chem. Soc.*, **87**, 605 (1905)

Conversion of an alcohol into an ether is sometimes done to provide temporary protection of the hydroxyl function during an operation at another part of the molecule. A reagent convenient for the purpose is dihydropyran, which reacts with an alcohol under acid

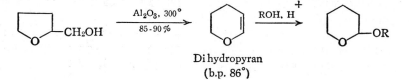

Dihydropyran
(b.p. 86°)

catalysis to give an ether. This ether is stable to oxidation, acylation, Grignard reagents, and bases, and it can be split easily when desired by hydrolysis with dilute acid with regeneration of the hydroxyl group.

Properties of Ethers. — Ethers are inert in comparison with alcohols, and approach alkanes in lack of chemical affinity. They do not react with sodium and are undamaged by treatment at moderate temperatures with strong acids or bases. An ether group is also resistant to attack by chemical oxidizing agents. An alkoxy group likewise is indifferent to a Grignard reagent, and, unlike hydroxyl, does not decompose the reagent with formation of the hydrocarbon. Thus hydroxyl groups are often protected during synthetic operations by methylation.

The ether linkage between hydrocarbon residues can be split fairly readily by halogen acids, particularly hydrogen iodide. Moderate treatment with one equivalent of this reagent brings about hydrolysis of an aliphatic ether to a mixture of alkyl halides and alcohols; if one group attached to oxygen is methyl and the other is a higher radical other than a tertiary group, cleavage chiefly produces methyl

$$CH_3OCH_2CH_2CH_3 \xrightarrow{HI} CH_3I + HOCH_2CH_2CH_3$$

iodide. With excess hydrogen iodide an ether suffers fission to two molecules of alkyl halide:

$$R—O—R' + 2\,HI \longrightarrow RI + R'I + H_2O$$

Hydrobromic acid acts similarly at a higher temperature, and a frequently used method of demethylating nonvolatile methoxy compounds consists in refluxing with constant-boiling hydrobromic acid in acetic acid solution. Such a process is useful for removal of a masking methyl group introduced to provide protection for a reactive hydroxyl group, which then can be regenerated by treatment of the halide with silver hydroxide. The cleavage of methoxy compounds by hydrogen iodide is the basis of the Zeisel method for quantitative determination of the methoxyl content of substances other than mixed ethers of low molecular weight. A weighed sample is boiled with excess hydriodic acid, the volatile methyl iodide formed (b.p. 42.3°) is distilled into an alcoholic solution of silver nitrate, and the resulting precipitate of silver iodide is weighed. The other cleavage product must be relatively nonvolatile. An example is the alkaloidal drug papaverine, which was found by Zeisel determination to contain four methoxyl groups:

$$C_{16}H_9N(OCH_3)_4 \xrightarrow{\text{HI}} C_{16}H_9N(OH)_4 + 4\,CH_3I$$

Papaverine   Nonvolatile residue   Distillate

7.34

Basic Properties. — Ethers are basic in the sense that they are able to combine with strong mineral acids to form oxonium salts, $[R_2OH]^+X^-$, comparable to ammonium salts, $[NH_4]^+X^-$. Thus dimethyl ether combines with hydrogen chloride by attachment of a proton to oxygen by one of the unshared electron pairs to produce a cation that is bound to the chloride ion by electrostatic forces. The

Oxonium salts

$$CH_3{:}\ddot{O}{:} \;\; + \;\; H^+Cl^- \;\longrightarrow\; \left[CH_3{:}\ddot{O}{:}H \atop \;\;\;CH_3 \right]^+ Cl^-$$
$$\overset{\cdot\cdot}{CH_3}$$

Oxonium salt

salt exists only in a strongly acidic medium and is decomposed to the components by water. Ethers dissolve in cold concentrated sulfuric acid owing to formation of oxonium salts, $[R_2OH]^+OSO_2OH^-$, and they are thereby readily distinguishable and separable from paraffinic hydrocarbons and alkyl halides. If the sulfuric acid solution of the oxonium salt is diluted carefully by pouring it slowly on ice, the ether can be liberated in unchanged condition.

Formation of nonpolar complexes of an ether with a Grignard reagent and with substances such as mercuric bromide, magnesium bromide, boron fluoride, or aluminum chloride is best understood in terms of the G. N. Lewis[8] concept of acids and bases. Lewis defined an acid as an electron acceptor and a base as an electron donor. In the formation of an oxonium salt from an ether, the proton of the mineral acid accepts an electron pair from oxygen and thus functions as a Lewis acid; the electron-donating ether is a base. Boron fluoride

Lewis acids and Lewis bases

$$R{:}\ddot{O}{:} \;\; + \;\; H^+ \;\longrightarrow\; \left[R{:}\ddot{O}{:}H \atop \;\;R \right]^+$$
$$\overset{\cdot\cdot}{R}$$

Lewis base   Lewis acid   Oxonium ion

is a Lewis acid because the boron atom, with an original sextet of electrons, can form an octet by accepting electrons; ether serves as an electron donor, or base, and the two reactants form a stable, coor-

[8] Gilbert N. Lewis, 1875–1946; b. Weymouth, Mass.; Ph.D. Harvard; U. California, Berkeley

dinate covalent complex, boron fluoride etherate, which distils without decomposition. Boron fluoride, a gas, is an excellent catalyst for

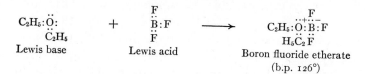

Lewis base   Lewis acid   Boron fluoride etherate
(b.p. 126°)

esterification and acylation and is conveniently employed as the
etherate. An alkylmagnesium halide, $R:Mg:X$, is a Lewis acid, and
the magnesium atom completes its octet by accepting a pair of electrons from each of two ether oxygen atoms to form a dietherate (see
3.11). Neutralization can be regarded as the combination of a proton
(Lewis acid) with hydroxide ion, as Lewis base. The resulting water
molecule has an electronic structure like that of an ether; it is a Lewis

$$R':\overset{..}{\underset{..}{O}}:R'$$
$$R:M\overset{+}{g}:X$$
$$R':\overset{..}{\underset{..}{O}}:R'$$

*Grignard reagent
dietherate*

$$[H:\overset{..}{\underset{..}{O}}:]^- \quad + \quad H^+ \quad \longrightarrow \quad H:\overset{..}{\underset{H}{O}}: \quad \xrightarrow{+\,H^+} \quad \left[H:\overset{..}{\underset{H}{O}}:H\right]^+$$

Lewis base   Lewis acid   Water   Hydronium ion

base and combines with a proton to form a hydronium ion, the active
species in reactions of mineral acids in aqueous solution. The members of an acid-base pair are said to be conjugate with respect to each
other. Thus water is the conjugate acid of the hydroxide ion, and the
hydronium ion is the conjugate acid of water. The ammonium ion
is the conjugate acid of ammonia, a Lewis base comparable to water.

Conjugate acids

PROBLEMS IN SYNTHESIS

Several of the reactions described in this chapter are serviceable
for synthesis of compounds of predictable structure, and the student
should seek to acquire facility in applying the information to the
solution of specific problems in synthesis. Although even a complicated synthesis may be comprehended easily when viewed in a completed form, the working out of an original plan of synthesis is difficult and facility usually comes only with considerable practice.

7.35

A ready grasp of the scope and limitations of the different reactions
and of the types of both the starting materials and products involved
is helpful. In planning syntheses of alcohols, for instance, it is useful
to recall that in the Grignard process formaldehyde and ethylene
oxide give primary alcohols, aldehydes afford secondary alcohols, and
both ketones and esters yield tertiary alcohols. Although the reaction
has wide scope, a limitation is that neither component may contain
functional groups capable of reaction with the reagent. Allyl chloride,
$CH_2{=}CHCH_2Cl$, forms a Grignard reagent satisfactorily, since the
ethylenic linkage is inert to an alkylmagnesium halide, but chloro-

*Scope and limitations
of reactions*

acetone, CH_3COCH_2Cl, possesses a carbonyl group capable of adding RMgX and hence fails to yield a Grignard reagent. Ethylene chlorohydrin similarly is unsuitable for production of a Grignard reagent because the hydroxyl and MgCl groups are incompatible.

Useful generalizations

Generalizations such as the Markownikoff rule are also useful in planning syntheses. The rules pertaining to the relative ease of dehydration of primary, secondary, and tertiary alcohols, and to the direction of dehydration where alternate paths are open are equally applicable to reactions in which an alkene is produced by elimination of HX from an alkyl halide. The course of oxidation of alcohols and of alkenes also can be predicted on the basis of empirical generalizations, and an oxidation reaction may be useful at either an initial or a terminal stage of synthesis. Alcohols can be converted by oxidation into aldehydes, ketones, or acids, which serve as synthetic intermediates. Association of one reaction with another is of further assistance. Dehydration of an alcohol to an alkene can be followed by catalytic hydrogenation to an alkane, and the alcohol required in the first step

Reaction sequences

may be obtainable by a Grignard reaction. A primary alcohol can be oxidized to a carboxylic acid, which can be decarboxylated to an alkane having one carbon atom less than the alcohol. A Grignard synthesis leading to a secondary alcohol also makes available the ketone obtainable from such an alcohol by oxidation. The sulfuric acid hydration of an alkene having the grouping —CH=CH— also provides an alcohol capable of being transformed into a ketone:

$$—CH_2CH(OH)— \longrightarrow —CH_2CO—$$

Specific problems in synthesis usually are attacked advantageously by working back from the final product to available starting materials, rather than by centering attention on starting materials. A

Problem 1

typical requirement would be to synthesize 2-methylbutanol-2, utilizing as starting materials any alcohol having not more than three carbon atoms; this requirement would include the saturated C_1-, C_2-, and C_3-monohydric alcohols, ethylene glycol, and glycerol, but of course these substances constitute potential sources of formaldehyde, acetaldehyde, propionaldehyde, acetone, and formic, acetic, and propionic acid (also the esters of these substances), as well as of allyl alcohol and ethylene oxide (from ethanol, through ethylene and ethylene chlorohydrin). If the suggested process of deductive reasoning is followed, the formula of 2-methylbutanol-2 is first examined. This tertiary alcohol contains the hydroxyl group at a branching point in the carbon chain, as would result from a Grignard synthesis. Tertiary alcohols are obtainable by the action of alkylmagnesium halides on either ketones or esters, and the desired alcohol can evi-

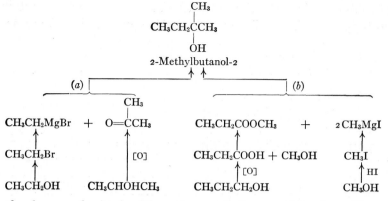

$$
\begin{array}{c}
CH_3 \\
| \\
CH_3CH_2CCH_3 \\
| \\
OH
\end{array}
$$

2-Methylbutanol-2

(a) | (b)

$$CH_3CH_2MgBr \;+\; \overset{CH_3}{\underset{}{O{=}CCH_3}} \qquad CH_3CH_2COOCH_3 \;+\; 2\,CH_3MgI$$

$$CH_3CH_2Br \qquad\qquad [O] \qquad CH_3CH_2COOH + CH_3OH \qquad CH_3I$$

$$CH_3CH_2OH \qquad CH_3CHOHCH_3 \qquad CH_3CH_2CH_2OH \qquad\;\; [O] \qquad CH_3OH \;\; HI$$

dently be synthesized either from ethylmagnesium bromide and acetone (a), or from methyl propionate and a methylmagnesium halide (b). Both sets of intermediates are obtainable from simple C_1- to C_3-alcohols, and hence two satisfactory solutions of the problem are at hand.

Another problem is the synthesis of 3-methylhexene-3 (I) from alcohols having not more than four carbon atoms. Two possible precursors come to mind, one with the hydroxyl at the 3-position (III)

Problem 2

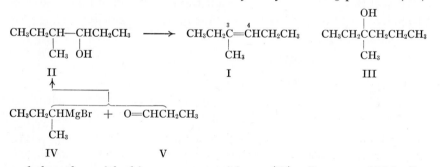

$$CH_3CH_2CH{-}CHCH_2CH_3 \;\longrightarrow\; CH_3CH_2\overset{3}{C}{=}\overset{4}{C}HCH_2CH_3 \qquad CH_3CH_2CCH_2CH_2CH_3$$

$$
\begin{array}{ccc}
\;\;\;| \quad | & | & | \\
CH_3 \; OH & CH_3 & CH_3
\end{array}
$$

$$\text{II} \qquad\qquad\qquad \text{I} \qquad\qquad\qquad \text{III}$$

$$CH_3CH_2CHMgBr \;+\; O{=}CHCH_2CH_3$$
$$| \qquad\qquad\qquad\qquad$$
$$CH_3$$

$$\text{IV} \qquad\qquad\qquad \text{V}$$

and the other with this group at position 4 (II). Structure III is disadvantageous because the hydroxylated carbon atom is flanked on each side by a methylene group (—CH₂—) and dehydration would probably occur to about the same extent in each of the two possible directions. In the alcohol II, however, one carbon adjacent to the hydroxylated carbon carries a lone hydrogen atom whereas the alternate position carries two, and hence, in analogy with known cases, dehydration can be expected to yield the desired alkene I. Synthesis of the intermediate alcohol II can be accomplished by interaction of *sec*-butylmagnesium bromide (IV) with propionaldehyde (V), and these substances in turn are obtainable from *sec*-butyl alcohol and *n*-propyl alcohol, respectively.

The synthesis of 4-methyloctane (VI) from C_1- to C_4-alcohols obviously calls for a process more elaborate than the union of two parts,

Problem 3

for the hydrocarbon contains nine carbon atoms. It could be obtained from the alcohol VII either by dehydration and catalytic hydrogena-

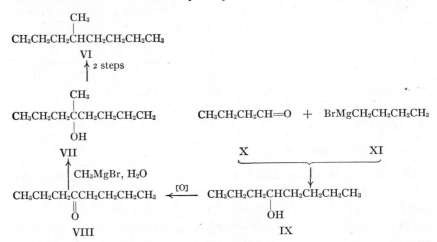

tion or by conversion into the bromide, preparation of the Grignard reagent, and treatment with water. The alcohol VII could be synthesized, in turn, by addition of methyl Grignard reagent to the ketone VIII, and this substance would result from oxidation of the secondary alcohol IX, obtainable by interaction of *n*-butyraldehyde (X) with *n*-butylmagnesium bromide (XI).

SUMMARY

Properties, Structures

Lower members, hydroxylic like water, are soluble in water; solubility decreases as hydrocarbon part becomes dominant.

Common names and carbinol names of the two propyl and four butyl alcohols. Triphenylcarbinol, cyclohexanol, allyl alcohol, ethylene and tetra-methylene glycol, glycerol. *gem*-Diol group unstable.

Hydrogen bonding responsible for association in liquid state and hence for high boiling points. Bond energy of hydrogen bond 5 kg.-cal. (cf. 59 kg.-cal. for C—C).

Synthesis

Hydrolysis of alkyl halides (AgOH).

Hydration of alkenes: addition of $HOSO_2OH$ and hydrolysis of the alkylsulfuric acid.

Reduction of aldehydes and ketones. Example: heptaldehyde, formed with undecylenic acid by pyrolysis of castor oil. Preparation of alcohols by reduction of aldehydes, ketones, esters, and acids with lithium aluminum hydride.

Grignard synthesis: addition of $RMgX$ to carbonyl group, $C=O$ (MgX to oxygen, R to carbon). Aldehyde ——→ *sec*-alcohol. Ketone ——→ *t*-alcohol. Ester ——→ *t*-alcohol of type RR'_2COH. Formaldehyde ——→ primary alcohol (RCH_2OH). Ethylene oxide ——→ primary alcohol (RCH_2CH_2OH).

Industrial Alcohols

Methanol. (*a*) Early process from wood. (*b*) Modern synthesis from CO

Ethanol. (*a*) Fermentation of sugars (enzymes and phosphate donors required; three-carbon intermediates; isomerization of dihydroxyacetone and glyceraldehyde through common enediol). (*b*) From ethylene (cracking of petroleum) by sulfuric acid process (through $ROSO_2OH$). Absolute and 95% alcohol.

Isopropyl alcohol from acetone and from cracked

gasoline. Butyl alcohols by bacterial fermentation of carbohydrates (with acetone) and from petroleum. Amyl alcohols from the C_5-cut of natural gasoline (thermal chlorination and hydrolysis). Ethylene glycol (antifreeze) from ethylene chlorohydrin.

Ethylene oxide from the chlorohydrin or from ethylene. Cellosolves. Dioxane.

Glycerol. By-product of soap manufacture. By thermal chlorination of propylene, etc. Oxidation to glyceraldehyde and dihydroxyacetone.

Reactions

With metals. Preparation of metal alkoxides; decreasing reactivity of higher alcohols. Equilibrium of $RONa + H_2O$. Powerful nucleophilic character of RO^- due to electron-releasing character of alkyl group.

Dehydration. Ease of dehydration: tertiary > secondary > primary. Preferential elimination of H from carbon poor in H (Saytzeff rule).

Wagner-Meerwein rearrangement on acid-catalyzed dehydration of alcohols with OH next to

t-carbon: $R_3CCHOHR$. Production of a secondary carbonium ion having unstable electron sextet, migration of alkyl to give a tertiary carbonium ion, expulsion of proton. Related rearrangement of pinacol to pinacolone.

Oxidation. Interpretation as hydroxylation of H on an oxidized C. Primary alcohol ⟶ aldehyde. Secondary alcohol ⟶ ketone. Comparative stability of acids (except formic) and ketones. Glycol cleavage with HIO_4 or $Pb(OAc)_4$.

Esters

Fischer esterification. Inorganic esters. Nitroglycerin. Nobel's discovery of dynamite (1866) and of blasting gelatin (1875). Solubility of nitro-

cellulose in nitroglycerin (like dissolves like). Cordite. PETN.

Ethers

Unassociated liquids. Ether (diethyl ether) as extraction solvent. Peroxide hazard.

Ether as an anesthetic. Other anesthetics: ethylene, divinyl ether, cyclopropane, nitrous oxide, chloroform.

Preparation. (a) Sulfuric acid method (note limitations). (b) Williamson synthesis: RONa + RX or R_2SO_4. Dihydropyran for protection of alcoholic group.

Properties. Inert to Na, oxidation, RMgX. Cleavage with HI or HBr—HOAc. Zeisel determination of methoxyl.

Basic properties. Formation of basic salts with

strong HCl or H_2SO_4; salts decomposed by water. Electronic structures.

Lewis concept of an acid as an electron acceptor and a base as an electron donor. A proton (Lewis acid) combines with ether (Lewis base). Boron fluoride functions as a Lewis acid to combine with ether and form boron fluoride etherate (distillable; is coordinate covalent complex). Comparable complex: alkylmagnesium halide dietherate. Electronic formulation of the hydronium ion ($H^+ + H_2O$). Conjugate acids.

Suggestions for solution of problems in synthesis.

PROBLEMS

1. Predict the chief products of the following reactions:

   (a) Methyldiethylcarbinol on dehydration
   (b) $(CH_3)_2CHCHBrCH_2CH(CH_3)_2$ + alcoholic KOH
   (c) $(CH_3)_2COHCH_2CH_2CH_2OH$ on partial dehydration (elimination of one molecule of H_2O)
   (d) $CH_3CH_2CH_2COH(CH_3)_2 + K_2Cr_2O_7$ in a hot solution of dilute sulfuric acid

   (e) Cyclohexene, heated in acetic acid with hydrogen peroxide, followed by the addition of lead tetraacetate
   (f) Ethylene oxide + n-amyl alcohol, in the presence of dry hydrogen chloride
   (g) Ethylene oxide + ammonia

2. Indicate Grignard syntheses of the following substances from n-propylmagnesium bromide and any second component desired:

   (a) 2-Methylpentanol-2

(b) 4-Methylheptanol-4

(c) *n*-Butyl alcohol

(d) *n*-Amyl alcohol

(e) Methylethyl-*n*-propylcarbinol

3. Devise syntheses of the following compounds, starting with any alcohols having not more than three carbon atoms and any desired components readily obtainable from these alcohols (the list of available starting materials thus includes C_3-compounds of the types RX, RMgX, RCHO, RCOR, RCO_2H; also ethylene oxide, allyl alcohol):

(a) $(CH_3)_2CHCH_2OH$

(b) $(CH_3)_2C(OH)CH_2CH_3$

(c) $(CH_3CH_2)_3COH$

(d) $CH_3CH_2CH_2CH_2CH_2OH$

(e) 2-Methylbutene-2

(f) 4-Methylpentene-1

(g) 2,3-Dimethylbutene-2

(h) Isobutane

(i) 2-Methylpentane

(j) 2,3,4-Trimethylpentane

4. Give syntheses of the following compounds from the starting materials of (3):

(a) 4-Ethylheptane

(b) 4-Methylpentadiene-1,3

(c) Neopentyl alcohol, $(CH_3)_3CCH_2OH$

5. Devise syntheses of the following compounds starting with alcohols and derived substances having no more than four carbons:

(a) 2,4-Dimethylpentene-2

(b) 3-Methylhexanol-3

(c) 2-Methylhexane

(d) 2,2-Dimethylpentane

6. A hydrocarbon C_5H_{10} yields 2-methylbutane on catalytic hydrogenation and adds HBr to form a compound that on reaction with silver hydroxide affords an alcohol. The latter on oxidation gives a ketone. What is the structure of the hydrocarbon?

7. An alcohol $C_5H_{11}OH$ gives a ketone on oxidation, and when it is dehydrated and the resulting alkene is oxidized, a mixture of a ketone and an acid results. What is the structure of the alcohol?

8. Plan a synthesis of octadiene-2,6 from cyclohexene.

9. How could you distinguish experimentally between the following isomers?

$$\underset{\displaystyle |}{CH_3} \qquad \underset{\displaystyle |}{CH_3}$$
$$HOCH_2CHCH_2CH_2CHCH_2OH$$

$$\underset{\displaystyle |}{CH_3} \; \underset{\displaystyle |}{CH_3}$$
$$HOCH_2CH_2CH—CHCH_2CH_2OH$$

READING REFERENCES

M. L. Huggins, "Hydrogen Bridges in Organic Compounds," *J. Org. Chem.*, **1**, 407 (1936)

R. W. Cairns, "Industrial and Military Explosives," *J. Chem. Educ.*, **19**, 109 (1942)

C. A. Thomas, "Chemicals Derived from Pentanes," *Science of Petroleum*, IV, 2795, Oxford University Press, London (1938)

E. E. Gilbert, "The Unique Chemistry of Castor Oil," *J. Chem. Educ.*, **18**, 338 (1941)

F. C. Whitmore, "The Common Basis of Intramolecular Rearrangements," *J. Am. Chem. Soc.*, **54**, 3274 (1932)

HALOGEN COMPOUNDS

In the series of alkyl halides (Table 1) the boiling point rises with an increase in molecular weight due to the presence of either a heavier halogen atom or a larger alkyl group.   The halide $CH_3(CH_2)_4Cl$

TABLE I

BOILING POINTS OF ALKYL HALIDES, RX

R	CHLORIDE	BROMIDE	IODIDE
Methyl	$-24°$	$5°$	$42°$
Ethyl	$13°$	$38°$	$72°$
n-Propyl	$46°$	$71°$	$102°$

has the molecular weight 106.6 and the boiling point 105.7°; therefore the liquid is unassociated.   Methyl chloride, ethyl chloride, and methyl bromide are gases at laboratory temperature; liquefied methyl chloride is obtainable commercially in steel cylinders and the other two in sealed glass ampules, which are chilled prior to being opened or resealed.   When a small quantity of a methyl or an ethyl halide is required, convenience in measuring may dictate selection of methyl iodide or ethyl bromide, but the chlorides are cheaper and preferable for large-scale operations.   The boiling point of ethyl chloride is such that a fine stream of the liquid sprayed on the skin freezes tissues in a localized area by abstraction of heat required for evaporation. Because of the resulting insensitization to pain, ethyl chloride is used as a local anesthetic for minor operations of short duration.

Alkyl halides are practically insoluble in water and separate from water in layers.   The chlorides are slightly lighter than water, and the bromides and particularly the iodides are very much heavier. Like alkanes, the halogen compounds are insoluble in and inert to cold concentrated sulfuric acid, and extraction with this reagent removes contaminants such as alkenes, alcohols, and ethers.

115

Preparation. — A method applicable to the preparation of many alkyl bromides and iodides consists in treatment of the appropriate alcohol with constant-boiling hydrobromic or hydriodic acid. Hydrochloric acid is not reactive enough, except in the case of alcohols of two structural types, tertiary and β,γ-unsaturated. Both t-butyl and allyl alcohol are convertible into the chlorides by the action of aqueous hydrochloric acid without catalyst and at moderate tempera-

Alcohols of special reactivity

$$(CH_3)_3COH \xrightarrow[94\%]{\text{concd. HCl, } 25°} (CH_3)_3CCl$$
$$\text{t-Butyl alcohol} \qquad\qquad\qquad \text{t-Butyl chloride}$$

$$CH_2{=}CHCH_2OH \xrightarrow{\text{concd. HCl, } 100°} CH_2{=}CHCH_2Cl$$
$$\text{Allyl alcohol} \qquad\qquad\qquad \text{Allyl chloride}$$

tures. t-Butyl chloride can be prepared by merely shaking the alcohol with concentrated hydrochloric acid for a few minutes in a separatory funnel at room temperature. In the second reaction the replacement of hydroxyl by halogen proceeds readily in an aqueous medium under conditions not adequate for addition of hydrogen chloride to the double bond.

Ordinary alkyl chlorides are obtainable by the reaction of an alcohol with phosphorus pentachloride or thionyl chloride ($SOCl_2$). Bro-

$$ROH + PCl_5 \longrightarrow RCl + HCl + POCl_3$$
$$ROH + SOCl_2 \longrightarrow RCl + HCl + SO_2$$

mides can be prepared by reaction either with preformed phosphorus tribromide or with a mixture of red and yellow phosphorus and bro-

$$3\,ROH + PBr_3 \longrightarrow RBr + H_3PO_3$$

mine. Alkyl iodides can be prepared with phosphorus triiodide generated by addition of iodine to a suspension of red phosphorus in the alcohol.

8.3

Reactivity. — The instances already discussed in which alkyl halides react with magnesium (Grignard), sodium (Wurtz), sodium alkoxides (Williamson), alcoholic potassium hydroxide (alkenes), and silver hydroxide (alcohols), illustrate the general reactivity of these substances. Quantitative investigations of relative reactivities have been made by determination of the amount of material entering into a given reaction after varying periods of time (reaction rate). In the series of normal saturated chlorides, bromides, and iodides, the methyl homolog is distinctly more reactive (from 5 to 20 times) than the ethyl and higher halides, and the reactivity remains essentially constant from the ethyl homolog on:

Rule 1

$$CH_3X > C_2H_5X, \; n\text{-}C_3H_7X, \; n\text{-}C_4H_9X, \text{ etc.}$$

A second generalization is that a given iodide is more reactive than the corresponding bromide, which in turn surpasses the chloride:

$$RI > RBr > RCl$$

The differences here are even more pronounced than between a methyl and an ethyl halide and are observable, for example, in the speed of reaction with magnesium in the presence of ether. In the reaction of alkyl chlorides with potassium iodide in acetone solution, $RCl + KI \longrightarrow RI + KCl$, secondary chlorides ($R_2CHCl$) are only about 0.05 as reactive as primary chlorides.

Mechanism of Substitution. — Whereas secondary halides invariably are less reactive in substitution reactions than primary halides, tertiary halides under most conditions are more reactive than secondary or even than primary halides. Hydrolysis of a halide is the counterpart of displacement of the hydroxyl group of an alcohol by halogen, and it was noted above that tertiary alcohols differ from primary and secondary alcohols in the great facility with which they react with hydrochloric acid to yield chlorides. A plausible explanation is afforded by the results of kinetic studies, that is, measurement of reaction rate under standardized conditions and determination of the effect on the rate of varying the concentrations of reactants. In dilute aqueous or alcoholic-aqueous solutions at low concentrations of hydroxide ion alkyl halides undergo hydrolysis rather than elimination of hydrogen halide. In the hydrolysis of methyl, ethyl, and iso-

$$\overline{[HO^- + R]} : Br \longrightarrow HOR + Br^-$$

propyl bromide the reaction rate is increased by an increase in concentration of either OH^- or RBr and hence the key step must involve collisions between molecules of alkyl halide and nucleophilic hydroxide ions. The reaction rate conforms to a physicochemical equation defining bimolecular reactions and hence is described as bimolecular, or as a reaction of the second order. The hydrolysis is thus described as an S_N2 reaction (nucleophilic substitution of second-order kinetics). A generally accepted mechanism advanced by Ingold[1] postulates that the two reactants combine to form an intermediate complex or transition state. The bromine atom of methyl bromide is electronegative and repels the negative hydroxide ion, and the latter attacks the opposite side of the carbon, or the back side. In the transition state the hydroxyl group is partially attached to carbon, the bond to bromine is weakened (dotted lines), and the original charge of the hydroxide ion is distributed evenly between the entering and departing groups;

[1] Christopher Kelk Ingold, b. 1893 Illford, England; D.Sc. London (Thorpe); University College, London

the three hydrogen atoms and the carbon of the methyl group are in a plane at right angles to the line connecting OH and Br. Attack by

S$_N$2 Mechanism:

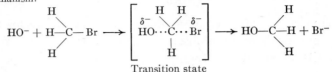

Transition state

hydroxide ion and expulsion of bromide ion from the complex are synchronous processes.

8.5

Reactivity to hydrolytic agents drops markedly in the series methyl, ethyl, and isopropyl bromide, as shown by the following relative reaction rates (80% ethanol at 55°): CH_3Br, 100; CH_3CH_2Br, 8.0; $(CH_3)_2CHBr$, 0.2. This progressive decrease in reactivity is attributable to an inductive effect, an electron displacement that can be represented by an arrow pointing in the direction of the drift of electrons (B→A). In ethyl bromide the electron-releasing methyl joined to the carbon undergoing substitution inhibits attack by hydroxide ion, and in isopropyl bromide the inductive effect of two methyl groups results in still greater impediment to approach of the nucleophilic agent. In tertiary butyl bromide the combined inductive

Inductive effect
of methyl groups

S$_N$2

$$CH_3 \rightarrow CH_2Br \qquad \begin{matrix} CH_3 \\ \\ CH_3 \end{matrix}\!\!\!\diagup\!\!\!\diagdown CHBr$$

effect of three methyl groups completely suppresses the bimolecular reaction and hydrolysis proceeds unimolecularly; that is, the reaction rate is dependent only on the concentration of alkyl bromide and is not increased by an increase in concentration of hydroxide ion. In the unimolecular reaction the rate-determining step is considered to be ionization of the halide to form a carbonium ion, which then com-

S$_N$1 Mechanism:

S$_N$1

$$(CH_3)_3C\!-\!Br \longrightarrow (CH_3)_3C^+ + Br^- \text{ (relatively slow)}$$
$$(CH_3)_3C^+ + OH^- \longrightarrow (CH_3)_3COH \text{ (fast)}$$

bines with hydroxide ion as rapidly as it is formed. Ionization is promoted by the combined electron release of the three alkyl groups.

8.6

Mechanism of HX-Elimination. — In the reaction of an alkyl halide with a solution of potassium hydroxide in ethanol, the conditions favor elimination of HX to form an alkene, rather than hydrolysis. The active agent is the alkoxide ion, $C_2H_5O^-$, a nucleophilic agent more potent than hydroxide ion (7.19), and the concentration of base is much higher than in the hydrolytic reactions discussed above. The reaction is bimolecular and hence involves a two-component transition state; it is termed an E$_2$ reaction (elimination, second order).   Ingold postulates that alkoxide ion approaches a β-hydrogen atom of ethyl bromide and, since it is repelled by negative bromine, attacks from the most distant point possible.   In the

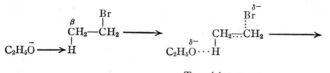

Transition state

$$C_2H_5OH + CH_2{=}CH_2 + Br^-$$

transition state the ethoxyl group is partially joined to the β-hydrogen (dotted line), a double bond has started to form between the two carbon atoms, the bromine atom is loosened from its attachment to carbon, and the charge is distributed between the attacking group and the bromine atom.   In the terminating phase, ethanol separates from one carbon and bromine departs from the other and carries with it the full negative charge.

Allyl-Type Halides. — In a typical replacement reaction allyl chloride, $CH_2{=}CHCH_2Cl$, reacts 79 times as fast as the corresponding saturated chloride, $CH_3CH_2CH_2Cl$.   Allyl bromide and iodide show corresponding enhanced reactivity.   If the double bond is at a site more distant from the halogen atom, as in $CH_2{=}CHCH_2CH_2X$ or $CH_2{=}CHCH_2CH_2CH_2X$, no enhancement in reactivity over that of the corresponding saturated halides is observed.   The activation by a double bond of a halogen atom on an adjacent carbon atom is a further example of a phenomenon encountered with carbonyl compounds (7.11) and in the chlorination of propylene (7.17) and described as β,γ-activation in an α—β=γ system.   In allyl bromide the halogen is attached to the α-atom in such a system (a).   In allyl alcohol (b),

8.7

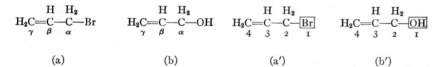

(a)   (b)   (a′)   (b′)

which reacts with hydrochloric acid with unusual ease to give allyl chloride (8.2), the hydroxyl group is in a position to be activated. Where Greek letters are used for another purpose, one alternate method of describing the phenomena is to consider that an atom or group in position 1 of a 1—2—3=4 system is activated by the 3,4-double bond (a′,b′).   Another is to describe the activation as due to a double bond in the allylic position.

An explanation of the enhanced reactivity of allyl compounds is afforded by the resonance theory.   Kinetic studies have shown that

8.8

the hydrolysis of allyl bromide is unimolecular and hence indicate that the rate-controlling step is ionization to a carbonium ion. The allyl ion is a resonance hybrid, and resonance stabilizes this ion and

$$CH_2=CH-CH_2Br \xrightarrow{-Br^-} \underbrace{CH_2=CH-\overset{+}{C}H_2 \longleftrightarrow \overset{+}{C}H_2-CH=CH_2}_{\text{resonance hybrid}}$$

$$\downarrow OH^-$$

$$CH_2=CH-CH_2OH$$

Explanation of reactivity

promotes its formation, and hence promotes hydrolysis. The double bond in the allyl position has an activating effect because it affords opportunity for resonance. In the case of a substituted allyl halide, for example cinnamyl bromide, the two resonance forms are not identical; in one the positive charge is on the α-carbon and in the

$$C_6H_5\overset{\gamma}{C}H=\overset{\beta}{C}H\overset{\alpha}{C}H_2Br \xrightarrow{-Br^-} C_6H_5CH=CH\overset{+}{C}H_2 \longleftrightarrow C_6H_5\overset{+}{C}HCH=CH_2$$

Cinnamyl bromide

other it is on the γ-carbon. Such halides usually react to give both the normal replacement product and the product of allylic rearrangement, in which the entering group is linked to the γ-carbon atom:

Normal and allylic displacements

$$C_6H_5\overset{\gamma}{C}H=\overset{\alpha}{C}HCH_2Br + KOCOCH_3 \longrightarrow$$

C₆H₅CH=CHCH₂OCOCH₃
Cinnamyl acetate

C₆H₅CHCH=CH₂
|
OCOCH₃
Phenylvinylcarbinol acetate

8.9   **Grignard Coupling.** — The reactivity of allyl-type compounds is utilized in a special hydrocarbon synthesis. When an allyl halide is added to an ethereal solution of the Grignard reagent from an ordinary alkyl halide, the hydrocarbon residues couple to give an alkene having a terminal double bond:

Use in synthesis

$$CH_2=CHCH_2X + RMgX \longrightarrow CH_2=CHCH_2R + MgX_2$$

Coupling is sometimes a minor side reaction in the preparation of Grignard reagents, but is practical only for coupling with an allyl group.

8.10   **Allylic Bromination.** — Ziegler (1942) discovered that unsaturated compounds can be brominated in the allyl position at ordinary temperature by use of N-bromosuccinimide; for example, cyclohexene (a) affords 3-bromocyclohexene-1:

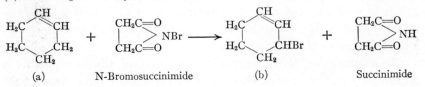

(a)   N-Bromosuccinimide   (b)   Succinimide

The product (b) is useful as an intermediate to cyclohexadiene-1,3, which is formed on dehydrobromination with base. Allylic bromination is promoted by peroxides and by illumination and hence involves free radicals.

Vinyl-Type Halides. — In contrast with allyl bromide, vinyl bromide is peculiarly unreactive. A halogen atom directly attached to an ethylenic carbon atom displays definitely diminished reactivity

CH_2=CHBr
Vinyl bromide

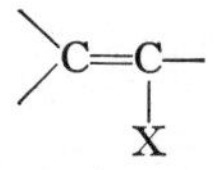

Vinyl halide type

as compared with the halogen of the corresponding saturated alkyl halide. Even vinyl iodide does not react satisfactorily with magnesium to produce a Grignard reagent, and vinylmagnesium halides are ordinarily unavailable. Neoprene rubber (4.32) owes its special stability to the fact that each chlorine atom is linked to a double-bonded carbon.

The inert character of the bromine atom in vinyl bromide (*a*) is interpreted as due to resonance involving the polarized structure (*b*).

Resonance

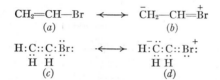

The corresponding electronic formulations are (*c*) and (*d*). In consequence of the resonance effect, bromine is held to carbon by a linkage that has a certain double-bond character and that is therefore shorter (1.86 Å) than the normal C—Br bond (1.91 Å) and less labile.

The diminished reactivity of halides of the vinyl type finds a parallel in the character of halides of the aromatic series, or aryl halides (ArX). In chlorobenzene and bromobenzene the halogen is attached to an unsaturated carbon atom, and the compounds are distinctly less reactive than corresponding alkyl halides but not so inert as vinyl chloride and bromide. Bromobenzene is reactive enough to combine with magnesium to give a Grignard reagent, but chlorobenzene does not react similarly.

Aryl halides

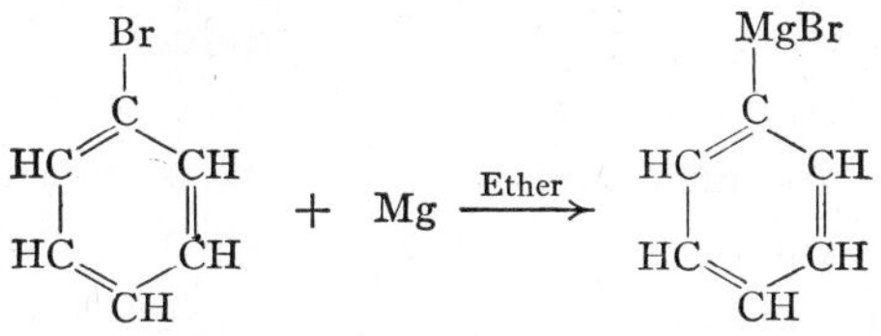

Br
|
C
HC⟍ ⟋CH
| ‖
HC⟍ ⟋CH
CH   + Mg →(Ether)→ MgBr
|
C
HC⟍ ⟋CH
| ‖
HC⟍ ⟋CH
CH

Bromobenzene   Phenylmagnesium bromide

CHAPTER 8

8.12

Methylene chloride (CH_2Cl_2) is a low-boiling liquid heavier than water, and it finds use as an extraction solvent immiscible with water (b.p. 41°, sp. gr. 1.4). It is prepared technically as one product of chlorination of methane.

8.13 **The Haloform Reaction.** — The trihalomethanes, chloroform (b.p. 61°), bromoform (b.p. 150°), and iodoform (m. p. 119°), are obtained easily by a process known as the haloform reaction (chloroform is so named because the structure is derivable from that of formic acid, HCOOH, by replacement of all oxygen substituents by chlorine atoms). This process consists in treatment of acetone with bleaching powder or with a solution of sodium hypochlorite. In the first phase

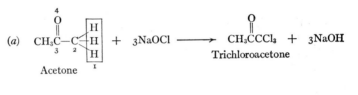

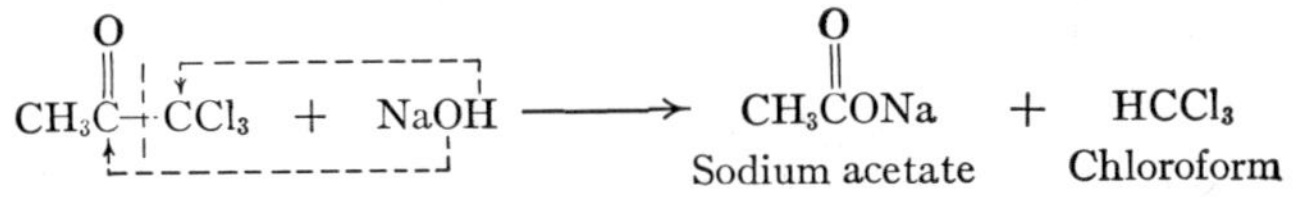

of the reaction (a) one methyl group is fully substituted by chlorine, and in the second (b) alkaline cleavage of the trichloroacetone occurs with production of sodium acetate and chloroform. Since sufficient alkali to bring about the cleavage is produced in the initial chlorination, the reactions proceed together and require a single operation. Both reactions have points in common with phenomena already discussed. The hydrogen atoms in acetone that suffer ready replacement are in a position (1) to be activated by the adjacent carbon–oxygen double bond (3,4). A simple interpretation of the activating effect is that the ketone is in equilibrium with a trace of the enol (c), which adds chlorine to give a transient intermediate that loses hydro-

Mechanism of α-halo substitution

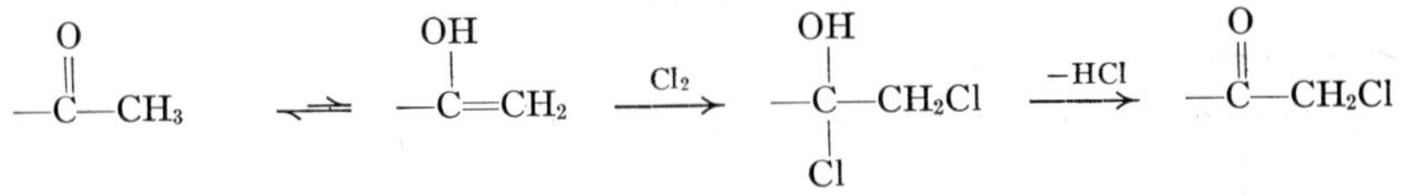

gen chloride and gives the substitution product. After the first halogen has entered the acetone molecule, a choice is open between further substitution in the same methyl group or in the one that is still intact, for both are equally activated by the carbonyl group. Since chlorine is a close neighbor of oxygen in the periodic table, analogy between the process of chlorination and that of oxidation is expected, and it has been noted (7.22) that an already oxidized site in a molecule is more susceptible to further oxidation than unoxidized sites. Thus chlorine is more prone to attack the already partly chlorinated carbon atom than the intact methyl group. The cleavage reaction (b) finds some analogy in the oxidative cleavage of *vic*-glycols (7.23), described as rupture of a weak bond connecting two oxidized carbon atoms. In the present instance the bond between the oxidized and the chlorinated carbon evidently is weak, or labile, and suffers easy rupture.

Chloroform is also obtainable in good yield by the action of hypochlorite on ethyl alcohol, for the reagent has oxidizing properties and acts initially by oxidizing the alcohol to acetaldehyde (d); the reac-

(d) $CH_3CH_2OH + NaOCl \longrightarrow CH_3CHO + NaCl + H_2O$

tions of halogen substitution (e) and cleavage (f) then follow the same course as before:

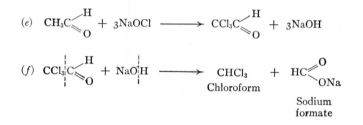

Either acetone or alcohol can be employed satisfactorily for technical production of chloroform; at the end of the reaction the halide is removed by distillation from the alkaline solution of sodium acetate or formate. Sodium hypobromite and hypoiodite react in the same manner and yield bromoform ($CHBr_3$) and iodoform (CHI_3), respectively. The iodoform reaction is particularly well adapted to test purposes because this substance has properties that make it easily recognized and identified. Iodoform is a crystalline yellow solid, m.p. 119°, with a characteristic odor that reveals the presence of traces of the substance; it is sparingly soluble in water and a quantity of only a few milligrams separates in fine yellow crystals from an aqueous medium and can be identified by melting-point and mixed melting-point determinations. One application of the test is in distinguishing ethyl from methyl alcohol; ethyl alcohol gives a positive test, but methyl alcohol is converted into formaldehyde, which cannot afford iodoform, and hence the test is negative.

Iodoform test

Acetaldehyde is the only aldehyde that gives the iodoform test, but all ketones that, like acetone, have at least one methyl radical joined to the carbonyl group yield iodoform on reaction with iodine

123

in sodium hydroxide solution. Thus all methyl ketones give a positive response in the test:

$$RCOCH_3 \xrightarrow{NaOI} RCOCI_3 \xrightarrow{NaOH} RCOONa + CHI_3$$

Secondary alcohols undergo oxidation by sodium hypoiodite to ketones, and those that yield methyl ketones likewise give a positive result:

$$RCHOHCH_3 \xrightarrow{NaOI} RCOCH_3 \xrightarrow{NaOI} CHI_3$$

Generalization

Thus the iodoform reaction is exhibited by acetaldehyde, by methyl ketones, and by such alcohols as can yield acetaldehyde or a methyl ketone on oxidation. The test has important uses in the diagnosis of structure. In the series of isomers pentanol-1 (I), pentanol-2 (II), and pentanol-3 (III), the first substance on oxidation with potassium dichromate gives an aldehyde, and the other two give ketones; the latter two compounds are distinguished by the fact that II yields iodoform on treatment with sodium hypoiodite and III gives a negative test.

$$CH_3CH_2CH_2CH_2CH_2OH \qquad CH_3CH_2CH_2\underset{\underset{OH}{|}}{C}HCH_3 \qquad CH_3CH_2\underset{\underset{OH}{|}}{C}HCH_2CH_3$$
$$II \qquad\qquad III$$

8.14

Carbon tetrachloride is manufactured by chlorination of carbon disulfide, obtained by heating sulfur with coke in an electric furnace; antimony pentachloride is employed as catalyst. Having no hydrogen

$$CS_2 + 3\,Cl_2 \xrightarrow{SbCl_5} CCl_4 + \underset{\substack{Sulfur \\ monochloride}}{S_2Cl_2}$$

Fire extinguisher

atoms, carbon tetrachloride is one of the rare instances of a noncombustible organic compound, and it is used in fire extinguishers (e.g., Pyrene). It has a low boiling point (77°) and volatilizes readily when sprayed on a fire, and the heavy vapor settles over the flame and smothers it by excluding oxygen. It is a powerful solvent for greases and is preferred for use in commercial dry cleaning and as a household cleaning fluid (Carbona) because of the freedom from fire hazard.

8.15

Solvents

Ethylene dichloride, $ClCH_2CH_2Cl$, is made by addition of chlorine to ethylene, and **s-tetrachloroethane,** $Cl_2CHCHCl_2$, is produced by addition of two moles of chlorine to acetylene. The dichloro compound is an excellent extraction solvent of moderate boiling point (84°), and the tetrachloro derivative is a powerful, higher-boiling (146°) solvent. **Ethylidene chloride,** CH_3CHCl_2, can be prepared by the action of phosphorus pentachloride on acetaldehyde and by addition of hydrogen chloride to vinyl chloride.

Dichlorodifluoromethane (b.p. $-30°$) has ideal properties for use as a refrigerant liquid for domestic refrigerators and for air-conditioning units and has been employed widely for this purpose since its introduction (Midgley and Henne,[2] 1930). It is nonflammable, nontoxic, noncorrosive, nearly odorless, and stable up to $550°$. Preparation is accomplished by replacement of two chlorine atoms of carbon tetrachloride by fluorine by the action of antimony trifluoride containing antimony pentahalide as catalyst. The industrial process utilizes liquid hydrogen fluoride as a cheap source of the fluorine substituents and involves continuous regeneration of a small initial batch of antimony trifluoride containing pentahalide:

$$3\ CCl_4\ +\ 2\ SbF_3\ \xrightarrow{(SbCl_5)}\ 3\ CCl_2F_2\ +\ 2\ SbCl_3$$
$$6\ HF\ +\ 2\ SbCl_3\ \longrightarrow\ 2\ SbF_3\ +\ 6\ HCl$$

Teflon, a superior plastic because of its unusual resistance to solvents and to almost all chemicals, is made by polymerization of tetrafluoroethylene:

$$n\ CF_2{=}CF_2\ \longrightarrow\ -(CF_2CF_2)_n-\quad (n = about\ 1000)$$

Polymerization proceeds under the influence of a free-radical initiator $(A\cdot)$ as follows:

$$A\cdot\ +\ CF_2{=}CF_2\ \longrightarrow\ A{-}CF_2\dot{C}F_2$$
$$A{-}CF_2\dot{C}F_2\ +\ CF_2{=}CF_2\ \longrightarrow\ A{-}CF_2CF_2{-}CF_2\dot{C}F_2$$

SUMMARY

Alkyl chlorides have boiling points about the same as those of alkanes of comparable molecular weight; bromides and iodides are progressively less volatile. Lower members liquid at $25°$: CH_3I, CH_3CH_2Br. Ethyl chloride, b.p. $13°$, used for localized anesthesia (freezes tissue by evaporation). Alkyl halides are insoluble in water; bromides and iodides are heavier than water.

Preparation

$ROH + HBr$ or HI. General.

$ROH + HCl$. Usually inapplicable (HCl not reactive enough). Special cases: *t*-butyl alcohol and allyl alcohol react readily with concentrated hydrochloric acid.

PBr_3, PCl_3, PCl_5, P (red) $+ I_2$, $SOCl_2$. General for all types of alcohols.

Reactivity

Type reactions: Mg (Grignard), Na (Wurtz), NaOR (Williamson), alcoholic KOH (alkenes), AgOH (alcohols). Comparison of alkyl groups: CH_3X the most reactive; C_2H_5X, C_3H_7X, etc. about comparable in reactivity. Comparison of halogens: $CH_3I > CH_3Br > CH_3Cl$. Comparison of alkyl types: RCH_2X more reactive than R_2CHX.

Mechanism of substitution. The hydrolysis $CH_3Br + OH^- \longrightarrow CH_3OH$, defined as nucleophilic substitution (S_N), is bimolecular (2nd order,

[2] Albert L. Henne, b. 1901 Brussels, Belgium; Ph.D. Brussels; Ohio State Univ.

S_N2). Postulate of back-side attack by OH⁻ to produce transition complex. Electron-release of methyl explains decreased reactivity of CH_3CH_2Br and $(CH_3)_2CHBr$. Inductive effect of three methyls inhibits bimolecular hydrolysis of $(CH_3)_3CBr$, and hydrolysis is unimolecular or first-order (S_N1); rate-controlling step is formation of $(CH_3)_3C^+$.

Allyl-type halides very reactive. Activation in an α—β=γ system. Alternate description: atom or group No. 1 in a 1—2—3=4 system activated by 3,4-double bond; allylic activation. Theory of reactivity of allyl compounds: replacements are promoted by resonance stabilization of intermediate carbonium ion: CH_2=$CH\overset{+}{C}H_2 \longleftrightarrow \overset{+}{C}H_2CH$=$CH_2$.

Evidence: C_6H_5CH=$CHCH_2Br$ with KOAc gives both products expected from hybrid ion. Grignard coupling: $RMgBr + CH_2$=$CHCH_2Br \longrightarrow RCH_2CH$=$CH_2$. Allylic bromination with N-bromosuccinimide.

Vinyl-type halides very inert. No Grignard reagent from CH_2=$CHBr$ or from chlorobenzene. Inertness of vinyl halides attributed to resonance:

$$CH_2=CH—Br \longleftrightarrow \bar{C}H_2—CH=Br^+$$

The C—Br link has some double-bond character and is hence shortened and stabilized.

Polyhalogen Compounds

Methylene chloride a heavier-than-water extraction solvent.

Haloform reaction. Steps in reaction of acetone with NaOCl: replacement of activated hydrogen atoms in one methyl group through the enol (the second and third chlorine atoms attack the already chlorinated carbon atom); alkaline cleavage of a bond connecting oxidized and chlorinated carbon atoms. Practical preparation of chloroform from either acetone or ethanol. Value of the reaction as a route to acids.

Iodoform test. Properties of CHI_3 favorable for identification: odor, color, sparing solubility in water, solid substance (mixed m.p. determination). Compounds that give positive test: methyl ketones, ethanol, sec-alcohols that yield methyl ketones on oxidation.

Carbon tetrachloride (from CS_2), a fire extinguisher. Ethylene dichloride (CH_2=CH_2 + Cl_2) and s-tetrachloroethane (CH≡CH + 2 Cl_2) powerful solvents. Ethylidene chloride (CH_3CHO + PCl_5 $\longrightarrow CH_3CHCl_2$). Dichlorodifluoromethane (3 CCl_4 + 2 SbF_3), a refrigerant fluid. Teflon (polymerization of CF_2=CF_2), a plastic of superior resistance to solvents and chemicals.

Reactions of Use in Synthesis

Grignard coupling: $RMgX + BrCH_2CH$=CH_2 $\longrightarrow RCH_2CH$=CH_2.

Allylic bromination: —CH=CHCH_2— $\longrightarrow$ —CH=CHCHBr— (with N-bromosuccinimide).

Hypohalite oxidation of methyl ketones to acids: $RCOCH_3 \longrightarrow RCOOH$.

PROBLEMS

1. Suggest methods suitable for the preparation of each of the following halides from the corresponding alcohol:
   (a) n-$C_{18}H_{37}Cl$
   (b) $CH_3CH_2CCl(CH_3)_2$
   (c) $CH_3CH_2CH_2CHBrCH_3$
   (d) n-$C_6H_{13}I$

2. Arrange the following compounds in the expected order of decreasing activity:
   (a) $CH_3CHBrCH_2CH_2CH_3$
   (b) $(CH_3)_2CHCH_2CH_2Br$
   (c) $(CH_3)_2C$=$CBrCH_2CH_3$
   (d) $(CH_3)_2C$=$CHCH_2Br$

3. Write electronic formulas for allyl bromide and its resonance-hybrid ion. Calculate the formal charges. Does each carbon atom have an octet of electrons?

4. (a) Write the electronic formula for vinyl bromide and for the structure contributing to resonance, and test the formulas by calculation of formal charges. (b) How could you deduce, without such calculation, that the terminal carbon atom carries a negative charge? (c) Why does not the structure $\overset{+}{C}H_2$—CH=Br⁻ contribute to the resonance?

5. Which of the following substances would be expected to give a positive iodoform test?

   (a) CH₃CH₂CH₂CH(CH₃)CH₂OH
   (b) CH₃CH₂CH₂CHOHCH₃
   (c) CH₃CH(CH₃)CHOHCH₂CH₃
   (d) CH₂OHCH₂OH
   (e) CH₃COCH₂CH₂CH₂COOH
   (f) CH₃COOH
   (g) C₆H₅CHOHCH₃
   (h) (CH₃)₃COH

6. Starting with allyl bromide and any other components desired, suggest syntheses for:

   (a) 4-Methylpentene-1
   (b) 1,2,3-Tribromopropane
   (c) 1,2-Dibromopropane
   (d) 2,3-Dibromopropene-1

READING REFERENCES

E. H. Huntress, *Organic Chlorine Compounds*, Wiley, New York (1948)

A. E. Remick, *Electronic Interpretations of Organic Chemistry*, Wiley, New York (1949)

E. D. Hughes, "Mechanisms of Reactions of Carbon Compounds," *Chemistry of Carbon Compounds* (E. H. Rodd, Ed.) IA, 157–194, Elsevier (1951); "Reactions of Halides in Solution," *Quart. Reviews*, **5**, 245 (1951)

CARBOXYLIC ACIDS

Acetic acid, a typical carboxylic acid, has a dissociation constant (k_a) of 1.75×10^{-5}, which means that it is a weak or sparingly dissoci-

$$k_a = [H^+][OAc^-]/[HOAc]$$

ated acid. A 0.1 N aqueous solution is dissociated only to the extent of 0.4%. In contrast, 0.1 N solutions of hydrochloric and sulfuric acid are about 62% ionized. Carbonic acid is still more feebly acidic than acetic acid; the apparent dissociation constant for separation of the first proton is 3.4×10^{-7}. The intermediate position of acetic acid is illustrated by the fact that the acid is liberated from sodium acetate by hydrochloric acid but in turn liberates carbonic acid from sodium bicarbonate. The classical dissociation constant of an acid, k_a, does not provide a convenient basis for comparison of different acids, and *Acidity constant,* in this book acidic strength will be expressed as the negative logarithm *pK_a* of the dissociation constant, pK_a. Thus $pK_a = -\log k_a$; for acetic acid ($k_a = 1.75 \times 10^{-5}$), $pK_a = -(-5 + 0.24) = 4.76$. For separation of the first proton of carbonic acid, $pK_a = 6.5$.

The acidity of carboxylic acids is another manifestation of activation by a suitably located double bond. The carbonyl double bond in the 3,4-position activates the hydrogen at position 1 and promotes its separation as a proton because the anion produced is stabilized by resonance in two identical structures. Resonance thus provides the

Resonance
stabilization
of ion

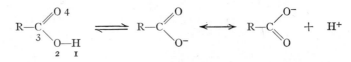

driving force for ionization. Nitrous acid, $HON{=}O$, and nitric acid, $HONO_2$, also have a hydroxyl group attached to an unsaturated atom and dissociate to hybrid ions; the latter is the more unsaturated and it is the stronger acid because the ion is stabilized through resonance in three structures:

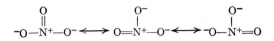

Carbonic acid can afford a resonance-stabilized ion but is a weaker

$$\underset{\text{(unstable)}}{\overset{\displaystyle OH}{\underset{|}{O=C-OH}}} \qquad \underset{\text{(stable)}}{\overset{\displaystyle CH_3}{\underset{|}{O=C-OH}}}$$

acid than acetic because it is unstable and exists in aqueous solution only in slight amount in equilibrium with carbon dioxide and water.*

Nomenclature. — The acids more frequently encountered are known by trivial (common) names based upon some early observed or special source in nature (formic, butyric, etc.) or upon a feature of structure (trimethylacetic). Since there are only two C_4-acids, the name isobutyric acid is an unambiguous designation for the branched-chain isomer, $(CH_3)_2CHCOOH$; but among higher homologs, substances similar to isobutyric acid are also termed *iso* compounds, for example: isovaleric acid, $(CH_3)_2CHCH_2COOH$; isocaproic acid, $(CH_3)_2CHCH_2CH_2COOH$. In the Geneva system the carbon of the carboxyl group is taken as the first atom in the longest carbon chain in the molecule; thus pelargonic acid, the straight-chain C_9-acid, is nonanoic acid. The position adjacent to the carboxyl group is known as the α-position and more distant positions are defined as β, γ, δ, etc. For example, $CH_3CHBrCOOH$ is α-bromopropionic acid; $HOCH_2CH_2CH_2COOH$ is γ-hydroxybutyric acid.

Acidic Strength. — The initial members of the series of normal acids and their acidity constants are as follows:

Acid		pK_a	Acid		pK_a
Formic	HCO_2H	3.77	*n*-Butyric	$CH_3(CH_2)_2CO_2H$	4.82
Acetic	CH_3CO_2H	4.76	*n*-Valeric	$CH_3(CH_2)_3CO_2H$	4.81
Propionic	$C_2H_5CO_2H$	4.88	Caproic	$CH_3(CH_2)_4CO_2H$	4.85

Formic acid is distinctly more acidic than the homologs of the type RCO_2H, all of which have pK_a values in the range 4.8–4.9. An interpretation of the effect of the group A on the ionization of the acid A—COOH advanced by G. N. Lewis in 1923 was the first recognition of what is now known as an inductive effect (8.5). If A is electron-attracting, the inductive displacement of the electron pair between carbon and A in the direction of A will cause secondary displacements

*Calculation indicates that if carbonic acid were stable in water solution it would be a stronger acid than acetic acid.

9.2

9.3

Formic acid exceptional

Explained by inductive effect

of electrons of the C:O and O:H bonds and hence facilitate separation of the hydroxylic hydrogen as a proton:

$$A \leftarrow \overset{\overset{O}{\|}}{C} \!:\! \overset{..}{\underset{..}{O}} \!:\! H \;\rightleftharpoons\; A \!-\! \overset{\overset{O}{\|}}{C} \!:\! \overset{..}{\underset{..}{O}} \!:\!^{-} + H^{+}$$

A group B that repels electrons will produce a displacement in the opposite direction and decrease the extent of ionization. Since acetic

$$B \rightarrow \overset{\overset{O}{\|}}{C} \!:\! \overset{..}{\underset{..}{O}} \!:\! H \;\rightleftharpoons\; B \!-\! \overset{\overset{O}{\|}}{C} \!:\! \overset{..}{\underset{..}{O}} \!:\!^{-} + H^{+}$$

acid is a weaker acid than formic, the methyl group has less attraction for electrons than a hydrogen atom, or is relatively electron-repelling: $CH_3 \rightarrow COOH$. The conclusion agrees with that inferred from the effect of methyl substituents on the rate of bromination of ethylenes (4.17). The higher normal homologs are so close to acetic acid in pK_a that any difference in electron release between methyl, ethyl, and higher groups must be so slight as to be obscured in the transmissal of the inductive effect through two covalent links.

Substitution of one of the α-hydrogen atoms of acetic acid by chlorine greatly increases the acidic strength: $CH_2ClCOOH$, pK_a 2.81. Chlorine, therefore, is strongly electron-attracting and produces displacements of the type $Cl \leftarrow C(=O) \leftarrow O \leftarrow H$. The constants of bromoacetic acid (2.87) and of iodoacetic acid (3.13) show that the order of electron attraction corresponds with the order of decreasing electronegativity. That the inductive effect of a substituent decreases rapidly with increasing distance from the hydroxylic hydrogen is shown by comparison of α- and β-chloropropionic acid. The α-chloro acid is much more acidic than the parent acid, whereas the β-chloro

CH₃CH₂COOH	CH₃CHClCOOH	ClCH₂CH₂COOH
Propionic acid	α-Chloropropionic acid	β-Chloropropionic acid
pKₐ 4.88	pKₐ 2.80	pKₐ 4.08

isomer is only slightly more acidic. Substitution in acetic acid of one, two, and three α-chlorine atoms produces progressive shifts to greater acidic strength, and trichloroacetic acid (pK_a 0.08) almost reaches the acidity of mineral acids. The order of inductive effect of substituent groups, deduced partly from the effect on the strength of acids and bases, is as follows:

Order of inductive effects
9.4

$$Cl > Br > I > OCH_3 > OH > C_6H_5 > CH\!=\!CH_2 > H < CH_3 < CH_2CH_3 < CH(CH_3)_2 < C(CH_3)_3$$

Decreasing electron attraction   Decreasing electron release

Boiling Points. — Boiling points of the carboxylic acids are not far from those of alcohols of comparable molecular weight and are much higher than those of alkanes or alkyl chlorides of similar molecular size. Thus $CH_3(CH_2)_3COOH$ has the molecular weight 102.1 and the boiling point 187°. As in the case of the alcohols, the relatively low volatility is attributed to association of the hydroxylic molecules through hydrogen bonding. Cryoscopic determinations in hydrocarbon solvents and X-ray crystallographic measurements both indicate that carboxylic acids exist largely in a dimeric form, formulated as shown. The boiling point of formic acid (100.5°) is about that characteristic of unassociated substances of molecular weight comparable to that of formic acid dimer (92).

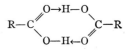

The solubility relationships of carboxylic acids conform to the usual rule for hydroxylic compounds. Formic, acetic, propionic, and *n*-butyric acid are miscible with water in all proportions, the next few members of the series are partially soluble, and the C_9-acids and higher homologs are practically insoluble.

Occurrence and Special Sources. — **Formic acid,** a vesicatory liquid of pungent odor, was so named because it is a constituent of certain ants (L. *formica*, ant). It occurs also in several plants, including the nettle, and the irritating effect resulting from contact with the plant is due in part to injection of the acid under the skin. The method of manufacture involves combination of carbon monoxide with pulverized sodium hydroxide at moderate temperatures and pressures;

$$\text{NaOH} + \text{CO} \xrightarrow[\text{100 lbs./sq. in.}]{120-150°} \text{H}-\text{C}\overset{\displaystyle O}{\underset{\displaystyle \text{ONa}}{}}$$

Sodium formate

the resulting sodium formate when treated with sulfuric acid yields free formic acid.

Acetic acid is the sour principle of vinegar resulting from air oxidation of the alcohol present in wine or hard cider under the influence of specific bacteria (e.g., in mother of vinegar), which provide a biological catalyst or enzyme that promotes oxidation. The fortified wines port and sherry do not turn sour on standing in opened bottles because the delicate enzyme is inactivated by alcohol in any but very dilute solutions. Dilute solutions of pure alcohol in water fail to undergo microbiological oxidation because the microorganism requires for normal growth nitrogenous substances and mineral salts such as are present in beers and wines. Formerly the chief source of acetic acid was pyroligneous acid, the dilute aqueous solution of methanol and acetic acid resulting from destructive distillation of wood. Pure acetic acid, m.p. 16.6°, is called glacial because it freezes at temperatures frequently encountered in the laboratory; the melting point is depressed to such an extent by small amounts of water that samples remaining liquid on cooling are readily recognized as impure. Modern processes of manufacture involve air oxidation of ethanol over a metal catalyst and hydration of acetylene and oxidation of the resulting acetaldehyde (5.9).

Many acids occur in nature as esters, RCOOR′, which on hydrolysis yield an acid, RCOOH, and an alcohol, R′OH. The main constituents of animal and vegetable fats are esters of glycerol, or glycerides, which on hydrolysis yield mixtures of straight-chain C_{12} to C_{18} acids having an even number of carbon atoms. A glyceride containing n-butyric acid is a minor component of butter, and rancidity of butter is due to release of free butyric acid by hydrolysis. The C_3 to C_6 acids all possess characteristically pungent and disagreeable odors.

Glycerides of higher fatty acids

METHODS OF PREPARATION

9.6

Oxidation Reactions. — Acids can be obtained by oxidation of primary alcohols or aldehydes. Thus the n-heptaldehyde obtainable from castor oil provides a source of n-heptylic acid, and β-chloropropionic acid can be prepared by a synthesis utilizing oxidation of a primary alcohol:

Oxidation of —CH=, —CHO, and —COCH₃

1. $n\text{-}C_6H_{13}CHO \xrightarrow[95\text{-}97\%]{KMnO_4,\ H_2SO_4\ (20°)} n\text{-}C_6H_{13}COOH$
     n-Heptaldehyde   n-Heptylic acid

2. $HOCH_2CH_2CH_2OH \xrightarrow[50\text{-}60\%]{dry\ HCl} ClCH_2CH_2CH_2OH \xrightarrow[78\text{-}79\%]{HNO_3\ (25\text{-}30°)} ClCH_2CH_2COOH$
     Trimethylene glycol   Trimethylene   β-Chloropropionic
            chlorohydrin   acid

Oxidation of ethylenic compounds having the grouping RCH= affords carboxylic acids. Acids are also obtainable by hypohalite oxidation of methyl ketones or of alcohols of the type $RCHOHCH_3$, for example:

$$(CH_3)_3CCOCH_3 \xrightarrow[71\text{-}74\%]{NaOBr} (CH_3)_3CCOOH$$
Pinacolone   Trimethylacetic acid

9.7

Grignard and Nitrile Syntheses. — Replacement of the halogen atom of an alkyl halide by a carboxyl group can be accomplished by two alternate synthetic methods. One is addition of a Grignard reagent to the carbonyl group of carbon dioxide and hydrolysis of the magnesiohalide derivative:

RMgX + CO₂

$$(CH_3)_3CCl \xrightarrow{Mg,\ ether} (CH_3)_3CMgCl\ +\ C{\Large\diagup}^{O}_{\diagdown O} \longrightarrow$$

$$(CH_3)_3CC{\Large\diagup}^{O}_{\diagdown OMgCl} \xrightarrow[69\text{-}70\%\ overall]{H_2O} (CH_3)_3CCOOH$$
                 Trimethylacetic acid

Carbonation of an alkylmagnesium halide can be accomplished by bubbling carbon dioxide into a solution of the Grignard reagent or by pouring the solution on dry ice.

The second synthesis consists in preparation and hydrolysis of a substance of the type $RC\equiv N$, known both as an alkyl cyanide and as a nitrile. The preparation involves interaction of an alkyl halide with sodium or potassium cyanide in aqueous-alcoholic solution, and hydrolysis is accomplished under catalysis with either an acid or a base:

$$RX \ + \ KCN \ \longrightarrow \ \underset{\substack{\text{Alkyl cyanide}\\\text{(nitrile)}}}{RC\equiv N} \ + \ KX$$

$$RC\equiv N \ + \ 2H_2O \ \xrightarrow{\text{H}^+ \text{ or OH}^-} \ RCOOH \ + \ NH_3$$

$R\,C\equiv N$
Acid nitrile or alkyl cyanide

If hydrochloric acid is employed for hydrolysis, the ammonia is bound as ammonium chloride, whereas on alkaline hydrolysis ammonia is liberated and the carboxylic acid is obtained by acidification of the reaction mixture containing the alkali salt. Typical applications to synthesis are:

1. $Br(CH_2)_3Br \ \xrightarrow[77-86\%]{2NaCN} \ NC(CH_2)_3CN \ \xrightarrow[83-85\%]{HCl} \ \underset{\text{Glutaric acid}}{HOOC(CH_2)_3COOH}$

2. $\underset{\substack{\text{Ethylene}\\\text{chlorohydrin}}}{HOCH_2CH_2Cl} \ \xrightarrow[79-80\%]{NaCN} \ \underset{\text{Ethylene cyanohydrin}}{HOCH_2CH_2CN} \ \xrightarrow[75-80\%]{NaOH} \ \underset{\beta\text{-Hydroxypropionic acid}}{HOCH_2CH_2COOH}$

The intermediate alkyl cyanides are called nitriles when it is desired to emphasize the structural relation to the acids which they yield on hydrolysis; thus methyl cyanide, CH_3CN, is the nitrile of acetic acid, or acetonitrile; ethyl cyanide, CH_3CH_2CN, is propionitrile.

The triple bond between carbon and nitrogen can enter into various additions. Hydrolysis can be conducted in two steps, the first of which affords an amide. Nucleophilic attack of the triple bond and

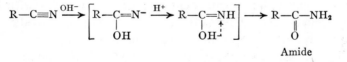

Partial hydrolysis to an amide

rearrangement of an activated hydrogen atom of the intermediate product find analogy in the hydration of acetylene. Amides can be prepared as products of mild hydrolysis and can be hydrolyzed to acids under more drastic conditions:

$$\underset{}{R-\overset{O}{\overset{\|}{C}}-NH_2} \ + \ H{-}OH \ \longrightarrow \ R-\overset{O}{\overset{\|}{C}}-OH \ + \ NH_3$$

133

Of the two methods available for conversion of alkyl halides into acids, the Grignard synthesis is the more generally applicable. The alternate cyanide procedure usually gives good results as applied to primary halides, but the reagent is so strongly basic that with secondary and tertiary halides some alkene formation is inevitable. Thus *t*-butyl bromide is converted by sodium cyanide largely into isobutene.

PROPERTIES AND REACTIONS

9.8

Formic and Acetic Acid. — Formic acid has the structure of both an acid and an aldehyde and is susceptible to ready oxidation, as

Dual nature

$$\text{Acid} \qquad \text{Aldehyde}$$

noted earlier (7.22), whereas other carboxylic acids are not; it reduces ammoniacal silver hydroxide solution to metallic silver (silver-mirror test).

The exceptional acidity of formic acid has been mentioned; the pK_a value is about one unit lower than that of acetic acid. In the concentrated form, the acid is a pungent, highly corrosive liquid capable of raising blisters on the skin. In further contrast with typical members of the series, formic acid undergoes decomposition when heated in a closed system at moderately elevated temperatures somewhat above the boiling point. The standard laboratory process for

Decomposition

$$\text{H}{-}\text{COOH} \xrightarrow{160°} CO_2 + H_2$$

generation of carbon monoxide is dehydration of formic acid with sulfuric acid:

$$\text{H}{-}\text{CO}{-}\text{OH} \xrightarrow{H_2SO_4} CO + H_2O$$

Stable to oxidation

Acetic acid, unlike formic acid and also unlike acids with hydrocarbon groups larger than methyl, is very resistant to oxidation and is frequently used as solvent for chromic acid oxidation of alcohols and alkenes. Furthermore acetic acid is almost invariably produced on drastic oxidative degradation of both saturated and unsaturated compounds containing methyl groups attached to carbon, and the reaction is used in the Kuhn-Roth diagnostic method for determination of the number of C-methyl groups present (1933). Oxidation is accomplished by chromic acid in sulfuric acid solution, excess reagent is reduced with hydrazine, the mixture is neutralized with alkali, phosphoric acid is added, and the acetic acid is distilled and deter-

Kuhn-Roth determination of C-methyl

mined by titration with standard alkali. Natural products containing the grouping —$CH_2C(CH_3)$=$CHCH_2$— give one equivalent of acetic acid for every such unit present. Kuhn-Roth analysis of $CH_3(CH_2)_{16}CO_2H$ indicates one methyl group (terminal), whereas two C-methyl groups are found for $CH_3(CH_2)_7CH(CH_3)(CH_2)_8CO_2H$. A *gem*-dimethyl group, —$C(CH_3)_2$—, gives rise to but one equivalent of acetic acid.

Metal Salts. — The characteristic acidity and ability to form salts with bases is a distinctive property by which carboxylic acids are differentiated from alcohols, aldehydes, ketones, ethers, and esters. Carboxylic acids, whether soluble in water or not, liberate carbon dioxide from a sodium carbonate or bicarbonate solution, and on titration with standard sodium hydroxide solution consume an equivalent amount of base.

9.9

Sodium and potassium salts are very different in physical properties from the free acids, for they are partly inorganic and are ionic. They are all solids even if the parent acid is liquid, and they dissolve in water even though the free acid is insoluble. Because of the ionic character, they are not soluble in ether or in a hydrocarbon solvent. For example, caproic acid ($C_5H_{11}COOH$) is a liquid sparingly soluble in water, soluble in ether, capable of being distilled, and showing a characteristic melting point of $-1.5°$; sodium caproate ($C_5H_{11}COONa$) is a solid, soluble in water but insoluble in ether, and it is nonvolatile and fusible only above $300°$. The differentiation in properties provides a useful basis for separation of acids from mixtures with other organic compounds. Such a mixture can be dissolved in ether and the acidic component quantitatively extracted by shaking the solution with aqueous alkali; the separated alkaline layer can be extracted with fresh ether to remove traces of suspended neutral substances and then acidified, and the uncontaminated acid is then obtained either as a precipitate or by ether extraction.

Use in separations

Decarboxylation and **Kolbe electrolysis** of salts of carboxylic acids have been described in Chapter 3.

Halogenation. — Acetic acid can be chlorinated in the presence of a trace of iodine, and yields in succession chloroacetic acid, di-, and trichloroacetic acid. In contrast with the photochemical chlorination of methane, the halogen substitution can be conducted in discrete

9.10

$$CH_3COOH \xrightarrow{Cl_2(I_2)} CH_2ClCOOH \xrightarrow{\text{Higher temp.}} CHCl_2COOH \xrightarrow{\text{Higher temp.}} CCl_3COOH$$

stages, and either the mono- or the dichloro compound can be prepared in good yield and in satisfactory purity by merely introducing chlorine slowly until the proper increase in weight is observed. Bro-

Catalysts; I_2, PCl_3

mination of acids also can be effected readily, for example with use of phosphorus trichloride as catalyst:

$$CH_3CH_2CH_2CH_2CH_2CO_2H \xrightarrow[\text{83-89\%}]{\text{Br}_2(\text{PCl}_3),\ 65-70°} CH_3CH_2CH_2CH_2CHBrCO_2H$$

α   α-Bromocaproic acid
Caproic acid

Bromine enters exclusively the activated α-position adjacent to the unsaturated carbonyl group, and activation by C=O can be understood as affording opportunity for production of an enol, through which

$$\underset{\underset{\text{H}\ 1}{|\ 2}}{RCH}-\underset{3}{C}=\underset{4}{O} \rightleftharpoons RCH=\overset{\overset{\text{OH}}{|}}{C}-OH \xrightarrow{Br_2} \left[\underset{\underset{\text{Br}\ \text{Br}}{|\ \ |}}{RCHC}-OH\right] \xrightarrow{-HBr} \underset{\underset{\text{Br}}{|}}{RCHC}=O$$

Enol

the α-bromo acid can be formed by a process of addition-elimination. An acid $RCH_2CH_2CO_2H$ yields first the α-bromo acid and then the α,α-dibromo acid, $RCH_2CBr_2CO_2H$; but, as expected, β- or other positions in the chain are not attacked. The acid $(CH_3)_3CCO_2H$ has no hydrogen on the α-carbon atom and it does not yield a halo-substitution product. Information regarding the structure of an unknown mono or polycarboxylic acid can sometimes be gained by determination of the number of α-bromine atoms that can be introduced.

9.11   **Inertness to Additions.** — Although the carboxyl group contains a carbonyl group, acids and their salts generally do not enter into addition reactions characteristic of aldehydes and ketones. A free acid reacts initially with a Grignard reagent to produce a magnesio-halide salt and a hydrocarbon, but the salt fails to respond to a further molecule of Grignard reagent in the manner of carbonyl compounds;

$$R-C\overset{\displaystyle O}{\underset{\displaystyle OH}{\big<}} + CH_3MgI \longrightarrow R-C\overset{\displaystyle O}{\underset{\displaystyle OMgI}{\big<}} + CH_4$$

hydrolysis affords the original acid. A carboxyl group, however, does not necessarily interfere with Grignard addition to a carbonyl group present in the same molecule, except to the extent that the initially formed —COOMgX group may decrease the solubility in ether, and frequently a successful result is obtained by using two equivalents of Grignard reagent. The carbonyl group of acids is resistant to methods of reduction that are applicable to the corresponding esters. The only general method of reducing free acids to alcohols, $RCOOH \longrightarrow RCH_2OH$, is by use of the remarkable reducing agent lithium aluminum hydride (7.8). With this one exception, acids are distinctly less reactive than their esters. The explanation, at least in the case of reactions such as Grignard addition which, if it occurred, would involve a carboxylate ion, is that the ion does not contain a true carbonyl group but a hybrid link that partakes of the character of both a double and a single bond. An ester is incapable of comparable resonance and hence behaves as a true carbonyl compound.

ESTERS

Esters are one of three common types of derivatives of carboxylic acids. They are readily obtainable by acid-catalyzed esterification (7.24) or by one of the alternate methods described below, and they can be reconverted efficiently into the acids by alkaline hydrolysis. Because of the ready interconversion and because esters possess certain advantageous physical characteristics, it is frequently expedient to esterify an acid or acid mixture in order to effect purification, separation, or characterization. Methyl and ethyl esters are unassociated and distil at temperatures lower than the corresponding associated acids, even though the molecular weights are higher. Methyl esters boil an average of 62° below the acids, and ethyl esters boil some 42° below the acids. Both methyl and ethyl formate boil at temperatures lower than the component acid and alcohols. The more volatile esters are also more stable to heat than the free acids and can be distilled satisfactorily in cases where the acid undergoes decomposition. Esters of solid acids melt at lower temperatures than the acids and often more sharply and without decomposition; they are more soluble in organic solvents and crystallize more satisfactorily. A methyl ester invariably has a higher melting point than the corresponding ethyl ester.

Volatile esters have characteristic fruity odors. The disagreeable-smelling acids butyric and valeric are converted by esterification into pleasantly fragrant derivatives. Esters, usually in the form of mixtures, are responsible for the flavor and fragrance of many fruits and flowers, and artificial flavoring essences are mixtures of synthetic esters empirically compounded to reproduce the flavor and aroma of natural fruits and extracts (apple, raspberry, cherry, etc.).

Preparation. (*a*) **Fischer Esterification.** — The method of esterification introduced by E. Fischer consists in refluxing the acid with excess alcohol in the presence of about 3% of hydrogen chloride, sulfuric acid, or boron fluoride etherate. The operation is simple, and when an unbranched acid is esterified with a primary alcohol the yield of pure ester is usually high. However, alkyl groups attached to

$$RCH_2COOH + HOCH_2R' \underset{}{\overset{H^+}{\rightleftharpoons}} RCH_2COOCH_2R' + H_2O$$

either the α-carbon atom of the acid or the carbinol carbon atom of the alcohol exert a blocking effect, or steric hindrance, which may retard the reaction and cause the equilibrium to be less favo:able to the ester. Thus the rate of esterification of acetic acid with isopropyl alcohol is just half that of esterification of the acid with methanol or ethanol. The highly branched trimethylacetic acid when heated with isobutyl alcohol at 155° for one hour gives only 8% of the ester, as compared with 33% for n-butyric acid.

Surprisingly, the rate of esterification of t-butyl alcohol with acetic acid is slightly greater than the rate of reaction of methanol with the same acid. Studies employing isotopic tracer elements have established the fact that esterification of a tertiary alcohol proceeds by a mechanism different from that involved in the case of a primary (or secondary) alcohol. When ordinary benzoic acid containing the O^{16}-isotope is esterified with heavy methanol, $CH_3O^{18}H$, in the presence of hydrogen chloride, the water formed has the ordinary isotopic composition, and hence the reaction proceeds as follows:

$$C_6H_5C{\overset{O}{\diagup}}OH \; + \; HO^{18}CH_3 \;\;\xrightarrow{H^+}\;\; C_6H_5C{\overset{O}{\diagup}}O^{18}CH_3 \; + \; H_2O$$

The hydroxyl group eliminated thus comes from the acid rather than from the primary alcohol. This fact, as well as the role of the acid catalyst, can be interpreted in terms of a mechanism of esterification applicable to primary and secondary alcohols. A proton from the

(a) $R—\overset{\overset{O}{\parallel}}{C}—OH \; + \; H^+ \;\longrightarrow\; R—\overset{\overset{O}{\parallel}}{C}—\overset{+}{\underset{H}{O}H}$

Mechanism of esterification of RCH_2OH and R_2CHOH

(b) $R'OH \; + \; \overset{\overset{O}{\parallel}}{\underset{R}{C}}—\overset{+}{\underset{H}{O}H} \;\longrightarrow\; R'\overset{\delta+}{O}\cdots\overset{\overset{O}{\parallel}}{\underset{R}{C}}\cdots\overset{\delta+}{\underset{H}{O}H} \;\longrightarrow\; R'\overset{+}{\underset{H}{O}}—\overset{\overset{O}{\parallel}}{\underset{R}{C}} \; + \; H_2O$

Transition state

(c) $\overset{+}{\underset{H}{RCOOR'}} \;\longrightarrow\; RCOOR' + H^+$

mineral acid accepts a pair of unshared electrons from the hydroxylic oxygen atom of the organic acid to form an oxonium ion (a), similar to the hydronium ion from water; in a rate-controlling bimolecular reaction, this is attacked from the rear by the alcohol with expulsion of water to form the substituted oxonium ion (b), which loses a proton to give the ester (c). The proton required in the first step is regenerated in the last step. That the proton functions in the sense of a Lewis acid, or electron acceptor, explains why the reaction is also catalyzed effectively by boron fluoride, which is also a powerful electron acceptor (7.34). In the esterification of a tertiary alcohol with a carboxylic acid the hydroxyl group of the alcohol, rather than of the acid, is eliminated. The following mechanism appears applicable:

$$(CH_3)_3COH \xrightarrow{H^+} (CH_3)_3\overset{+}{C}OH \xrightarrow{-H_2O} (CH_3)_3C^+ \xrightarrow{R-\overset{\overset{\displaystyle O}{\|}}{C}-OH}$$

(a)   (b)

Mechanism of esterification of R_3COH

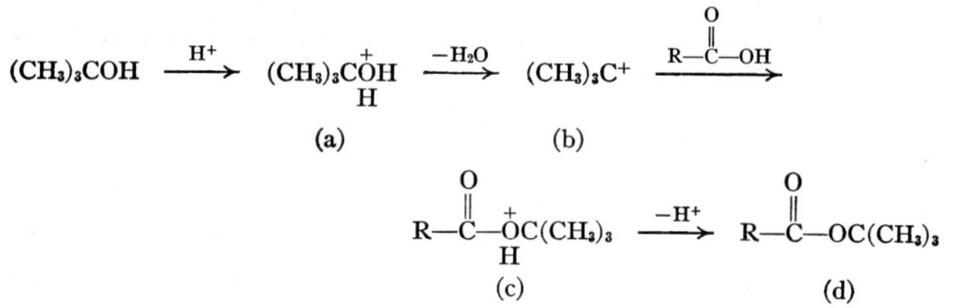

$$R-\overset{\overset{\displaystyle O}{\|}}{C}-\overset{+}{O}C(CH_3)_3 \xrightarrow{-H^+} R-\overset{\overset{\displaystyle O}{\|}}{C}-OC(CH_3)_3$$

(c)   (d)

The product of initial addition of a proton is an oxonium ion (a) that loses water to form a carbonium ion (b) because of the combined electron-releasing power of the three methyl groups. The carbonium ion combines with the acid to form a substituted oxonium ion (c) that expels a proton to form the ester (d). The catalytic role of the proton is accounted for, and the differing behavior of the tertiary alcohol is interpreted as due to the inductive effect of the three alkyl groups in promoting formation of a carbonium ion.

Acid hydrolysis is the reverse of acid esterification. ~~The rates of alkaline hydrolysis of esters of primary and secondary alcohols are the same as the rates of the acid-catalyzed esterifications.~~ However, esters of tertiary alcohols are resistant to alkaline hydrolysis for the reason that a basic medium does not promote formation of the carbonium ion intermediate.

(*b*) **Silver Salt Method.** — In those instances where direct acid-catalyzed esterification is slow or inefficient, satisfactory results can be obtained by treatment of the dry silver salt of the acid with an alkyl halide:

9.14

$$RCOO\underset{\llcorner \text{-----} \lrcorner}{Ag + X}R' \longrightarrow RCOOR' + AgX$$

Not subject to steric hindrance

The reaction, analogous to the Williamson synthesis of ethers, proceeds through metathesis involving fission of the O—Ag bond, for it is not materially impeded by the presence of branching alkyl groups. The silver salt often can be precipitated by dissolving the acid in dilute aqueous ammonia, boiling off the excess, and adding silver nitrate solution. The method has the objection of being lengthy and expensive.

(*c*) **With Diazomethane.** — An elegant route to methyl esters consists in treatment of the acid with an ethereal solution of diazomethane:

9.15

$$RCOOH + CH_2N_2 \longrightarrow RCOOCH_3 + N_2$$

           Diazomethane   Methyl ester

The reagent is a yellow gas, and can be prepared conveniently in the form of a solution in ether. When the yellow ethereal solution is added in portions to a solution or suspension of the acid in ether at room temperature, nitrogen is evolved at once and the yellow color is discharged; when the yellow color persists, an indication of excess diazomethane, the solution is warmed on the steam bath to expel excess reagent and, since the only by-product is a gas, a solution of the desired ester in ether results. The method is generally applicable and is not subject to hindrance effects. Diazomethane is a resonance hybrid of several forms:

A resonance hybrid

$$\overset{-}{CH_2}\!-\!\overset{+}{N}\!\equiv\!N \quad\longleftrightarrow\quad CH_2\!=\!\overset{+}{N}\!=\!\overset{-}{N} \quad\longleftrightarrow\quad \overset{+}{CH_2}\!-\!N\!=\!\overset{-}{N}$$

One convenient method of preparation is as follows (McKay[1], 1948):

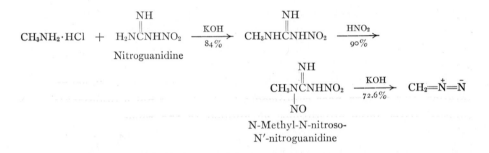

$$\underset{\text{Nitroguanidine}}{CH_3NH_2\cdot HCl \;+\; H_2N\overset{\overset{\displaystyle NH}{\|}}{C}NHNO_2} \xrightarrow[84\%]{KOH} CH_3NH\overset{\overset{\displaystyle NH}{\|}}{C}NHNO_2 \xrightarrow[90\%]{HNO_2}$$

$$\underset{\substack{\displaystyle NO \\ \text{N-Methyl-N-nitroso-} \\ \text{N'-nitroguanidine}}}{CH_3\overset{\overset{\displaystyle NH}{\|}}{N}CNHNO_2} \xrightarrow[72.6\%]{KOH} CH_2\!=\!\overset{+}{N}\!=\!\overset{-}{N}$$

The reagent is toxic and explosive and hence requires special handling.

9.16

$\overset{\overset{\displaystyle +OR'}{\|}}{RC}\!-\!O^{-}$
Resonance:
decreases polarity
of carbon

Reactions. (*a*) **Grignard Synthesis.** — Esters contain a carbonyl group capable of Grignard additions but less reactive than that of aldehydes and ketones. The practicable application of the Grignard synthesis is limited to the reaction: RCOOR′ + 2 R″MgX (and hydrolysis) ⟶ R″₂RCOH; the reaction cannot be stopped readily at the ketone stage because the ketone is more reactive than the ester.

9.17

(*b*) **Reduction to Alcohols.** — Esters are easily reducible to give two alcohols, one having the carbon content of the acid residue and the other of the alcoholic component:

Intermediates:
RCH(OH)OR′, RCHO

$$RCOOR' \;+\; 4\,H \;\longrightarrow\; RCH_2OH \;+\; HOR'$$

Bouveault-Blanc
reduction

One method of reduction is with lithium aluminum hydride (7.8). Another, the Bouveault-Blanc method, consists in refluxing the ester with metallic sodium and an alcohol. Ethyl alcohol is commonly used to furnish hydrogen, but butyl alcohol is sometimes employed in reduc-

[1] Arthur F. McKay, b. 1916 Truro, Nova Scotia; Ph.D. Toronto (Wright); Queen's University, Monsanto Canada, Ltd.

tion of higher esters to provide a higher reflux temperature. Practical examples are as follows:

1. $(CH_2)_8$ $\begin{array}{c}CO_2C_2H_5 \\ CO_2C_2H_5\end{array}$ $\xrightarrow[73-76\%]{C_2H_5OH,\ Na}$ $(CH_2)_8$ $\begin{array}{c}CH_2OH \\ CH_2OH\end{array}$

Diethyl sebacate   Decamethylene glycol (m.p. 72°)

2. $CH_3(CH_2)_7CH{=}CH(CH_2)_7CO_2C_4H_9$ $\xrightarrow[82-84\%]{C_4H_9OH,\ Na}$ $CH_3(CH_2)_7CH{=}CH(CH_2)_7CH_2OH$

Butyl oleate   Oleyl alcohol (liq., b.p. 195°/8 mm.)

(c) **Hydrolysis.** — The hydrogen-ion catalyzed reaction of an acid with an alcohol to give an ester is reversible, and the same equilibrium state can be reached starting with the products of the reaction, the ester and water. The acid catalysts suitable for esterification are just as effective in bringing about hydrolysis, and one method of hydrolyzing an ester consists in refluxing the substance with a large excess of water containing hydrochloric acid. The mechanism and interme-

9.18

$$RCOOR' \ + \ \underset{(excess)}{HOH} \ \xrightleftharpoons{H^+} \ RCOOH \ + \ R'OH$$

diates of the hydrolytic reaction are the same as those for esterification. Esterification is catalyzed by hydroxide ions as well as by protons, and though base-catalyzed esterification is not a practicable process, bases have advantages as applied to the reverse reaction. When an ester is heated with water containing slightly more than one equivalent of sodium hydroxide, hydrolysis to the alcohol and the organic acid is followed by combination of the acid with alkali, and the equilibrium is displaced:

$$RCOOR' \ + \ H_2O \ \xrightleftharpoons{OH^-} \ R'OH \ + \ RCOOH \ \xrightarrow{NaOH} \ RCOONa$$

Saponification efficient

The combination of a reversible reaction followed by an irreversible step insures complete reaction, and hence alkaline hydrolysis (saponification) is the more efficient method of cleaving esters.

(d) **Alcoholysis, or Ester Interchange.** — When the methyl ester of an acid is refluxed with excess ethyl alcohol containing a few percent of hydrogen chloride or sulfuric acid, it is converted to a large extent into the ethyl ester. An equilibrium is set up, and the extent of conversion is dependent upon the relative amounts of methyl and ethyl alcohol present in either the free or combined form:

9.19

$$RCOOCH_3 \ + \ \underset{(excess)}{C_2H_5OH} \ \xrightleftharpoons{H^+} \ RCOOC_2H_5 \ + \ CH_3OH$$

An ethyl ester can be transformed similarly into the methyl derivative by ester interchange. Rapid interchange of alkyl groups also can be brought about with use of a catalytic amount of sodium alkoxide,

Methyl to ethyl ester or the reverse

and this fact is the basis for the statement in the preceding section that esterification is subject to basic catalysis.

(e) **Ammonolysis.** — Esters are converted by interaction with ammonia into amides, neutral derivatives of acids already encountered as products of partial hydrolysis of nitriles. The reagents H—OH, H—OR, and H—NH₂ thus all act upon esters in the same manner, with elimination of the original alkoxyl group, possibly through initial addition to the double bond. The reactions of hydrolysis and alcoholysis require an acidic or a basic catalyst; ammonia itself provides basic conditions favorable for the transformation. Ammonolysis of

Amide formation

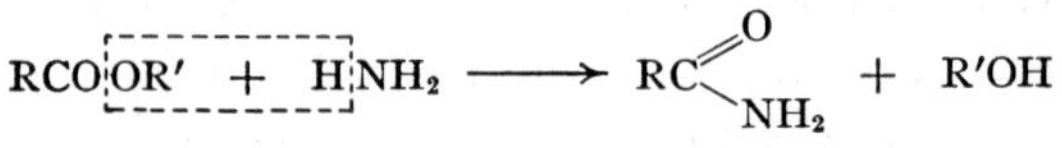

$$RCO\underline{OR'} + H\underline{NH_2} \longrightarrow RC{\overset{\displaystyle O}{\diagdown}}_{NH_2} + R'OH$$
Amide

an ester usually is carried out with either aqueous or alcoholic ammonia at room temperature; sometimes the mixture is cooled in order to avoid attack of another reactive group in the molecule, for example:

$$\underset{\text{Ethyl chloroacetate}}{ClCH_2COOC_2H_5} + aq.\ NH_3 \xrightarrow[62-87\%]{0-5°} \underset{\text{Chloroacetamide (m.p. 120°)}}{ClCH_2CONH_2}$$

With the exception of formamide, amides are crystalline solids at room temperature, and they are frequently prepared from liquid acids or esters for purposes of identification by mixed melting-point determinations.

Other substances related to ammonia react with esters in an analogous manner; hydrazine, for example, reacts as follows:

A hydrazide

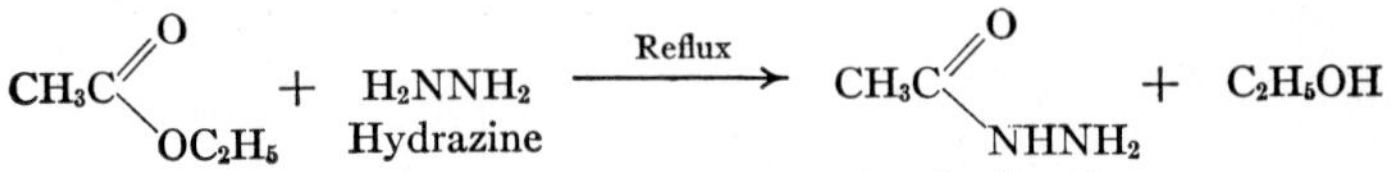

$$CH_3C{\overset{\displaystyle O}{\underset{OC_2H_5}{\diagup}}} + \underset{\text{Hydrazine}}{H_2NNH_2} \xrightarrow{\text{Reflux}} CH_3C{\overset{\displaystyle O}{\underset{NHNH_2}{\diagup}}} + C_2H_5OH$$
Acethydrazide
(m.p. 67°)

ACYL HALIDES

9.21

Acyl halides are reactive, low-boiling derivatives in which the hydroxyl group of an acid is replaced by a halogen atom. They bear the same relationship to acids as alkyl halides do to alcohols, and

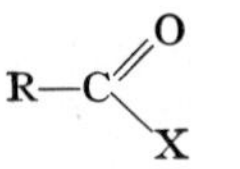

Acyl halide

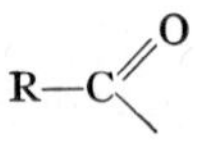

Acyl group

replacement of hydroxyl by halogen has a similar effect on the boiling point in each case:

n-C₃H₇CO$\boxed{\text{OH}}$, b.p. 162.5° n-C₅H₁₁$\boxed{\text{OH}}$, b.p. 138.0°

n-C₃H₇CO$\boxed{\text{Cl}}$, b.p. 102° n-C₅H₁₁$\boxed{\text{Cl}}$, b.p. 105.7°

(mol. wt. 106.55)   (mol. wt. 106.60)

The acyl chloride and alkyl chloride selected for illustration have practically the same molecular weights, and the boiling point in each case is very close to that of n-heptane (unassociated liquids).

Preparation. — Replacement of the hydroxyl group of acids by chlorine is accomplished with the reagents employed for bringing about the corresponding transformation of alcohols, namely phosphorus trichloride, phosphorus pentachloride, thionyl chloride. The type reactions are:

$$3 \text{ RCOOH} + \text{PCl}_3 \longrightarrow 3 \text{ RCOCl} + \text{H}_3\text{PO}_3$$
$$\text{RCOOH} + \text{PCl}_5 \longrightarrow \text{RCOCl} + \text{POCl}_3 + \text{HCl}$$
$$\text{RCOOH} + \text{SOCl}_2 \longrightarrow \text{RCOCl} + \text{SO}_2 + \text{HCl}$$

Some considerations guiding the choice of reagent are indicated by the following combinations found satisfactory for preparative purposes:

1.   CH₃COOH $\xrightarrow[70\%]{\text{PCl}_3}$ CH₃COCl (b.p. 52°) + H₃PO₃ (dec. 200°)
      Acetic acid   Acetyl chloride

2.   C₆H₅COOH $\xrightarrow[90\%]{\text{PCl}_5}$ C₆H₅COCl (b.p. 197.2°) + POCl₃ (b.p. 107.2°)
      Benzoic acid   Benzoyl chloride

3. n-C₃H₇COOH $\xrightarrow[85\%]{\text{SOCl}_2 \text{ (b.p. 77°)}}$ n-C₃H₇COCl (b.p. 102°) + SO₂ + HCl
      n-Butyric acid n-Butyryl chloride

Acid chlorides are so sensitive to hydrolysis, particularly when liquid, that it is impracticable to separate the reaction products from accompanying inorganic materials by extraction of the latter with water, and the only method of purification is distillation. Phosphorus trichloride is a satisfactory reagent in example 1 because the low-boiling acetyl chloride can be distilled from the nonvolatile residue of phosphorous acid. If phosphorus trichloride were used in the case of benzoic acid, however, benzoyl chloride could not be distilled from the reaction mixture because it boils at about the temperature at which phosphorous acid begins to decompose; phosphorus pentachloride is better in this case because the inorganic reactant is phosphorus oxychloride, which is more volatile than the organic product and can be removed by distillation prior to distillation of the benzoyl chloride (2). Phosphorus pentachloride would be a poor choice for preparation of n-butyryl chloride, the boiling point of which is very close to that of phosphorus oxychloride; thionyl chloride gives satisfactory results (3). It may be necessary to employ excess thionyl chloride, and hence the boiling point of the product must be sufficiently above or below that of thionyl chloride to permit separation. For some purposes the crude materials can be used without purification. Thus benzoic acid can be warmed with phosphorus trichloride, the mixture cooled, and the upper layer of the acid chloride decanted from a lower layer of phosphorous acid and employed directly.

9.23 **Replacement Reactions.** — Acetyl chloride fumes in moist air as the result of liberation of hydrogen chloride. The higher acid chlorides are somewhat more resistant to hydrolysis because they are less soluble in water. Alcohols and ammonia act upon acid chlorides in the same way as water acts, and the three reactions are summarized as follows:

Hydrolysis	$RCOCl + HOH \longrightarrow RCOOH + HCl$	
Alcoholysis	$RCOCl + HOR' \longrightarrow RCOOR' + HCl$	
Ammonolysis	$RCOCl + HNH_2 \longrightarrow RCONH_2 + HCl$	

In these reactions resulting in replacement of halogen by a hydroxyl, an alkoxyl, or an amino group, acid chlorides are more reactive than alkyl chlorides or even than alkyl iodides. This reactivity seems surprising when it is considered that the chlorine atom is linked to an unsaturated carbonyl group, for unsaturated halides of the type of vinyl chloride, $CH_2{=}CHCl$, are notably unreactive. An explanation is based on the fact that the carbonyl group is endowed with specific additive power not shared by an ethylenic double bond. Probably all three of the apparent replacements proceed by an addition, with formation of an unstable intermediate from which hydrogen chloride is eliminated with the same ease that water separates from an unstable *gem*-diol, for example:

Addition-elimination mechanism

$$R-\underset{\|}{C}-O + HOCH_3 \rightleftharpoons \left[R-\underset{\underset{OCH_3}{|}}{\overset{\overset{Cl}{|}}{C}}-OH \right] \longrightarrow R-\underset{\underset{OCH_3}{|}}{\overset{\|}{C}}=O + HCl$$

The halogen atom is apparently susceptible to replacement not because it is actually labile but as a consequence of linkage to a functional group capable of entering into additions; even if the addition reaction is an equilibrium proceeding to only a slight extent, the irreversible decomposition of the addition product can displace the equilibrium and lead to complete conversion.

9.24 **Grignard Reaction.** — In the reaction with a Grignard reagent an acid chloride, like an ester, yields first a ketone and then, with more reagent, a tertiary alcohol. The initial step proceeds more rapidly than the corresponding reaction of an ester, and there is more differentiation between the first and second steps. Consequently ketones

$$\text{RCOCl} \xrightarrow{\text{R'MgX}} \text{RCOR'} \xrightarrow{\text{R'MgX, H}_2\text{O}} \begin{array}{c} \text{R}\diagdown \\ \text{R'} \rightarrow \text{COH} \\ \text{R'}\diagup \end{array}$$

can be prepared in reasonable yield by using just one equivalent of Grignard reagent and adding it by portions to a solution of the acid chloride (inverse Grignard reaction), in order to avoid exposure of the ketone formed to the action of the reagent. Investigations of other organometallic compounds have established the cadmium derivatives as preferred reagents for conversion of acid chlorides into ketones (Gilman,[2] 1936). Addition of one equivalent of anhydrous cadmium chloride to an ethereal solution of a Grignard reagent affords the corresponding alkylcadmium halide:

$$\text{RMgX} + \text{CdCl}_2 \longrightarrow \text{RCdCl} + \text{MgXCl}$$

Alkylcadmium halides for ketone synthesis

The cadmium derivative can combine with an acid chloride, but adds to the carbonyl group of the initially formed ketone less readily than a Grignard reagent, and hence the reaction is easily arrested at the ketone stage:

$$\text{RCdX} + \text{R'COCl} \longrightarrow \text{RCOR'} + \text{CdXCl}$$

Formation of a ketone in the reaction of an acyl halide with an organometallic halide can be interpreted as the result of either direct replacement or initial addition to the carbonyl group and subsequent elimination of a metal dihalide, as follows:

$$\begin{array}{c} \text{Cl} \\ | \\ \text{R—C=O} \end{array} + \text{R'MgCl} \longrightarrow \left[\begin{array}{c} \text{Cl} \\ | \\ \text{R—C—O—MgCl} \\ | \\ \text{R'} \end{array} \right] \longrightarrow \begin{array}{c} \text{R—C=O} \\ | \\ \text{R'} \end{array} + \text{MgCl}_2$$

Evidence permitting a decision between the two possibilities is available from a study of the reactivity of a series of acid fluorides, chlorides, and bromides to a given Grignard reagent as evaluated in competitive experiments (J. R. Johnson[3]). The order of reactivity is found to be RCOF > RCOCl > RCOBr, which is just the reverse of the order of lability of the carbon–halogen bonds in alkyl halides as determined in replacement reactions: C—Br > C—Cl > C—F. That the acid fluoride is the most, rather than the least, reactive member of the series indicates that the reaction can hardly involve direct severance of the carbon–halogen linkage, and suggests an initial addition to the carbonyl group. The halogen atom then influences the speed of the reaction merely to the extent that it modifies the additive power of the carbonyl group, and this effect may be partly a function of its size,

Evidence supporting addition mechanism

More reactive

Less reactive

[2] Henry Gilman, b. 1893 Boston; Ph.D. Harvard (Kohler); Iowa State College
[3] John R. Johnson, b. 1900 Chicago; Ph.D. Illinois (Adams); Cornell Univ.

a large atom tending to block free access of the Grignard reagent to the unsaturated center. The relationship between an acid fluoride and an acid bromide is indicated schematically in the margin. A second factor is the relative electronegativity of the halogens, for the addition reaction may require partial polarization of the carbonyl group in the sense $> \overset{+}{C}\!\!-\!\!\overset{-}{O}$. Since fluorine is the most electronegative, or electron-accepting, of the halogens, the fluorine atom would cause a drift of electrons away from the carbon atom and hence increase the fractional positive charge to an extent greater than is realized in an acid chloride or bromide.

9.25

$RCO_2H \longrightarrow RCH_2CO_2H$

Arndt [4]-Eistert [5] Reaction. — This method for conversion of an acid to the next higher homolog involves reaction of an acid chloride with diazomethane to form a diazo ketone, which loses nitrogen to form the acid:

$$RCOCl + CH_2N_2 \xrightarrow{-HCl} \underset{\text{Diazo ketone}}{RCOCHN_2} \xrightarrow{H_2O} RCH_2CO_2H + N_2$$

In an improved procedure (Wilds,[6] 1948) the reaction is conducted in a high-boiling solvent at 160–180°. Evidence that the reaction involves migration of the R group is that the labeled diazo ketone $C_6H_5C^{13}OCHN_2$ gives $C_6H_5CH_2C^{13}O_2H$. A plausible mechanism, similar to that of a Wagner-Meerwein rearrangement (7.21), is illustrated for one of the resonance structures of the diazo ketone (a).

Mechanism

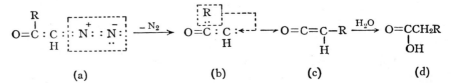

(a)   (b)   (c)   (d)

Loss of nitrogen produces the bivalent-carbon product (b), and the alkyl group migrates with its pair of electrons to fill the open sextet and produce the ketene (c), which in the absence of water is isolable. This intermediate, by addition of water and ketonization, affords the acid (d).

ANHYDRIDES

9.26

With the exception of formic acid, which on dehydration yields carbon monoxide, carboxylic acids form anhydrides by elimination of water between two molecules of the acid. Anhydrides of normal acids up to C_{12} are liquids; acetic anhydride is a mobile liquid with a pungent,

[4] Fritz Arndt, b. 1885 Hamburg, Germany; Ph.D. Freiburg (Howitz); Breslau, Istanbul
[5] Bernd Eistert, b. 1902 Ohlau, Schleswig; Darmstadt, BASF Ludwigshaven
[6] Alfred L. Wilds, b. 1915 Kansas City; Ph.D. Michigan (Bachmann); Univ. Wisconsin

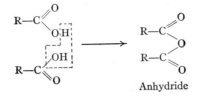

Anhydride

irritating odor. Anhydrides have nearly twice the molecular weights of the acids from which they are derived, and they boil at somewhat higher temperatures. Acetic anhydride (b.p. 139.6°, mol. wt. 102.09) boils at a higher temperature than esters, halogen compounds, and hydrocarbons of comparable molecular weight.

A laboratory method of preparing acetic anhydride is the reaction of acetyl chloride with anhydrous sodium acetate (compare the Williamson synthesis of an ether). An industrial process utilizes the

Preparation
9.27

From ketene

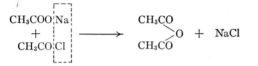

highly unsaturated and reactive ketene, prepared by cracking acetone:

$$H CH_2-\overset{\displaystyle CH_3}{C}=O \xrightarrow{700-750°} CH_2=C=O + CH_4$$

Ketene (b.p. − 56°)

Methane results from the pyrolysis by elimination of the methyl group along with an activated hydrogen in the α-position. Ketene can be prepared in the laboratory in the generator illustrated in Fig. 9.1. Vapor of refluxing acetone comes in contact with a glowing grid of resistance wire and undergoes cracking; unchanged acetone is condensed and returned to the boiling flask, and the ketene evolved in the gas stream along with methane is absorbed directly by a liquid reagent or in a solution.

Ketene combines with most reagents containing either hydroxyl or amino (—NH₂) groups; it reacts readily with acetic acid to give acetic anhydride, probably by addition to the carbonyl group and migration of the enolic hydrogen atom (cf. 9.25):

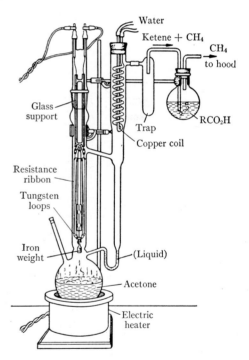

Water
Ketene + CH₄
CH₄ to hood
Glass support
Trap
Copper coil
RCO₂H
Resistance ribbon
Tungsten loops
Iron weight
(Liquid)
Acetone
Electric heater

FIG. 9.1. — Ketene Generator

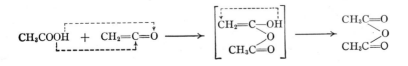

Higher anhydrides that are crystalline solids are prepared by heating the acid with acetyl chloride; the acetic acid formed serves as solvent from which the anhydride crystallizes on cooling:

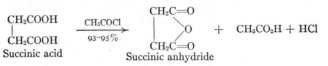

Hydrolysis and Ammonolysis. — Anhydrides are not so sensitive to water as acyl halides, but are more easily hydrolyzed than esters. Thus acetic anhydride can be hydrolyzed in a few minutes by boiling water without a catalyst. The anhydride dissolves in cold water to the extent of 12 g. per 100 g., and if the solution is kept at room temperature the substance undergoes complete hydrolysis only after an hour or two, whereas acetyl chloride is hydrolyzed at once. The reac-

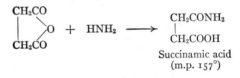

tion with ammonia parallels that with water and is used for preparation of monoamides of dibasic acids.

9.28   **Alcoholysis; Acetylation of Alcohols.** — Anhydrides react with alcohol as with water and ammonia; succinic anhydride, for example, affords the monoester of the corresponding dibasic acid. The most

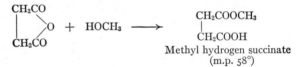

important application of the general reaction is acetylation of primary and secondary alcohols, that is, conversion of these substances into their acetyl derivatives:

$$RCH_2OH \xrightarrow{(CH_3CO)_2O} RCH_2OCOCH_3$$
$$R_2CHOH \xrightarrow{(CH_3CO)_2O} R_2CHOCOCH_3$$

Acetylation can be conducted by warming the alcohol with acetic anhydride alone, but usually advantage is taken of the accelerating action of a small amount of concentrated sulfuric acid, boron fluoride, or a basic catalyst such as sodium acetate or pyridine (C_5H_5N). Catalysis by a base, for example pyridine (Py), can be pictured as involving formation of the powerfully nucleophilic alkoxide ion, $ROH + Py \longrightarrow RO^- + Py^+H$, attack by this of the anhydride (1) to give (2), and reaction of this with the catalyst cation (Py^+H) with formation of the ester (3) and regeneration of the catalyst. The function of

Pyridine
(b.p. 115°)

an acid catalyst is attributable to formation of the intermediates
(4) and (5). Tertiary alcohols ordinarily are not acylable, and a

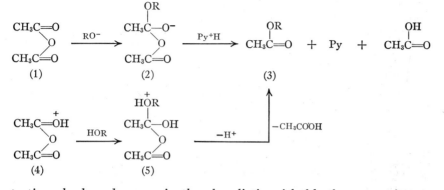

tertiary hydroxyl group is thereby distinguishable from a primary
or secondary group. Acetylation is useful for investigation of polyhydroxy compounds, since the number of entering acetyl groups
can be established both by elementary analysis of the purified reaction product and by an acetyl determination, consisting in alkaline hydrolysis of a weighed sample and acidification, distillation,
and titration of the acetic acid in the distillate. Two acetyl groups
can be introduced into ethylene glycol and three into glycerol, whereas a glycol of the type $R_2C(OH)CH_2CH_2OH$ gives only a monoacetyl
derivative.

SUMMARY

Carboxylic Acids

Acidic character. Activation of H in —COOH by 3,4-double bond. Other acids with OH on an unsaturated atom (e.g. HONO, HONO_2, HOSO_2OH). Carbonic acid unstable; weaker than acetic acid (CH_3CO_2H liberates CO_2 from carbonates and bicarbonates).

Dissociation of acetic acid: classical constant, $k_a = 1.75 \times 10^{-5}$; acidity constant, $pK_a = -\log k_a = 4.76$. Carbonic acid, $pK_a = 6.5$ (first proton). Formic acid, $pK_a = 3.77$ (stronger than acetic). Higher homologs of acetic acid close to acetic acid in pK_a.

Effect of substituents on acidic strength (G. N. Lewis). Displacement of an electron pair in an unsymmetrical molecule. An electron-attracting group A in A—COOH induces displacement of electrons away from the hydroxylic H and facilitates its separation as a proton. An electron-releasing group B (B—COOH) decreases ionization. Since CH_3COOH is weaker acid than HCOOH, methyl is electron-repelling as compared with hydrogen

(compare evidence from bromination of alkenes). α-Chloro substitution greatly increases acidic strength; Cl is strongly electron-attracting. Inductive effect of Cl decreased in β-position. Order of relative inductive effect of various groups (see 9.3).

Hydrogen-bonded cyclic dimer accounts for abnormally high boiling point.

Occurrence, sources. Formic acid in ants and nettles; manufacture of sodium formate from NaOH + CO. Acetic acid in vinegar as result of microbiological oxidation of ethanol. Production by distillation of wood, by air oxidation of ethanol, from acetylene through acetaldehyde.

Synthesis. (a) Oxidation of primary alcohols and of aldehydes (heptaldehyde from castor oil). (b) Carbonation of a Grignard reagent. (c) Nitrile (cyanide) synthesis. Hydrolysis of a nitrile to an amide and of the latter to an acid. Limitation: KCN (strong base) may eliminate HX from secondary or tertiary halide.

Formic acid — unique properties. Partly aldehydic and susceptible to oxidation. Pyrolysis $\longrightarrow$ $CO_2 + H_2$. $H_2SO_4 \longrightarrow CO + H_2O$. Acetic acid very stable to oxidation. Kuhn-Roth determination of C-methyl groups.

Metal salts (partly inorganic). Soluble in water; insoluble in ether, nonvolatile, difficultly fusible. Use in diagnosis, separation, purification.

Halogenation with I_2-catalyst. Practical route to CH_2ClCO_2H, $CHCl_2CO_2H$, CCl_3CO_2H. Limitation to halogenation in α-position. Interpretation of replacement of α-hydrogen activated by 3,4-double bond: addition of Br_2 to double bond of enol and loss of HBr.

Inertness of carboxylic acids to additions. Resistant to addition of Grignard reagents, hydrogenation, reduction with $Na + C_2H_5OH$. Exception:

$$RCOOH + LiAlH_4 \longrightarrow RCH_2OH$$

Esters

Properties. Fruity odors. Boiling points normal and much lower than those of the acids.

Preparation. (a) Fischer esterification: $RCOOH + ROH + HCl(H_2SO_4, BF_3)$. Equilibrium favorably displaced by use of excess ROH. Catalyst speeds attainment of equilibrium (from either direction). Esterification retarded by steric hindrance associated with branching in the alkyl group of the acid or of the alcohol (except in tertiary alcohols). Esterification of C_6H_5COOH with $CH_3O^{18}H$ proves that hydroxyl group eliminated comes from the acid and not from the alcohol. Mechanism: combination of the acid with a proton to form an oxonium ion; reaction with $R'OH$ with expulsion of water ($R'OH$ approaches on the side opposite that occupied by $-\overset{+}{O}H_2$); expulsion of proton. Catalytic function of proton served equally well by other electron acceptors (Lewis acids), e.g. BF_3. Esterification of tertiary alcohol involves formation of carbonium ion, R_3C^+ (inductive effect of three alkyl groups), and hence elimination of the hydroxyl group from the alcohol rather than the acid. Esters of tertiary alcohols resistant to alkaline hydrolysis.

Silver salt method. Not subject to steric hindrance because reaction involves fission of O—Ag bond.

Diazomethane: $RCOOH + CH_2N_2 \longrightarrow RCOOCH_3 + N_2$. Resonance structures:

$$\overset{-}{CH_2}-\overset{+}{N}\equiv N \longleftrightarrow CH_2=\overset{+}{N}=\overset{-}{N} \longleftrightarrow \overset{+}{CH_2}-N=\overset{-}{N}$$

Yellow gas, explosive, toxic. Preparation from nitroguanidine.

Reactions. (a) Grignard; ester carbonyl group less reactive than ketone carbonyl group. (b) Reduction to alcohols: lithium aluminum hydride; Bouveault-Blanc method ($Na + C_2H_5OH$); preparation of $HO(CH_2)_6OH$ from ester of a dibasic acid. (c) Hydrolysis. Catalysis by base the most efficient because of displacement of equilibrium. (d) Alcoholysis or ester interchange. Acid or base catalyst (e.g. $NaOCH_3$) promotes equilibration; position of equilibrium depends on relative concentration of the two alcohols. (e) Ammonolysis $\longrightarrow$ amides (solids for identification). Hydrazine $\longrightarrow$ hydrazides.

Acyl Halides

Boiling points normal; well below those of parent acids.

Preparation with PCl_3, PCl_5, or $SOCl_2$ (choice depends on ease of separation of products by distillation).

Replacement of Cl by OH (hydrolysis), OR (alcoholysis), NH_2 (ammonolysis). Probable mechanism: addition to carbonyl group and loss of HCl.

Grignard reaction. Inverse reaction (slow addition of RMgX to $R'COCl$ gives $RCOR'$ in fair yield). Improvement (Gilman): $RCdCl$ less reactive and less prone to add to the $RCOR'$ produced. Evidence of addition mechanism (J. R. Johnson): reactivity to $R'MgX$ is $RCOF > RCOCl > RCOBr$ (reverse of that expected for replacement). Superior reactivity of RCOF attributable in part to small size of fluorine atom and to the fact that F is the most electronegative (electron-accepting) of the halogens (increases polarization of carbonyl group).

Arndt-Eistert reaction: $RCOCl \longrightarrow RCOCHN_2 \longrightarrow RCH_2CO_2H$. Mechanism: loss of N_2 gives product with bivalent carbon; alkyl migration gives a ketene, which adds water.

Anhydrides

Preparation. (a) $CH_3COONa + CH_3COCl$. (b) Addition of CH_3COOH to ketene ($CH_2=C=O$; from pyrolysis of acetone). (c) Dehydration of higher acid with $(CH_3CO)_2O$. Succinic acid $\longrightarrow$ succinic anhydride. (d) Acetylation of primary and secondary alcohols (under ordinary conditions tertiary alcohols do not react and are thus distinguishable from primary and secondary types). Mechanism of base- and acid-catalyzed acetylation.

PROBLEMS

1. Compare the acidity constants (pK_a) of acids of the type A—CH_2CO_2H, where $A = CH_3$, OH ($pK_a = 3.83$), I ($pK_a = 3.13$), and Cl. What are the relative positions in the periodic table of the key elements in the group A?
2. Which of the following substances would you expect to be the more acidic?
   (a) Malonic acid, $HOOCCH_2COOH$
   (b) Succinic acid, $HOOCCH_2CH_2COOH$
3. Write formulas for:
   (a) Isovaleric acid
   (b) α,β-Dibromobutyric acid
   (c) Triethylacetic acid
   (d) Octanoic acid
4. Which synthesis, Grignard or nitrile, would you pick for effecting the following transformations:
   (a) $CH_3CH_2CHBrCH(CH_3)_2 \longrightarrow$
   Ethylisopropylacetic acid
   (b) $CH_3CHOHCH_2CH_2Cl \longrightarrow$
   γ-Hydroxyvaleric acid
5. Devise a synthesis of succinic acid,

   $$HO_2CCH_2CH_2CO_2H,$$

   from ethanol.
6. How could $(CH_3)_2CHCH_2COCH_3$ be converted into isovaleric acid?
7. Outline a procedure for the isolation of n-butyric acid from a mixture of the substance with n-amyl alcohol, n-amyl chloride, and ethyl n-valerate.
8. What method of experimentation would distinguish between the following isomeric acids?
   (a) $CH_3CH_2CH(CH_3)CO_2H$
   (b) $(CH_3)_2CHCH_2CO_2H$
   (c) $(CH_3)_3CCO_2H$
9. Write electronic formulas showing how a redistribution of electrons in one of the structures

representing the resonant nitrate ion gives a second structure.
10. Would you expect the hydrogen-bonded dimer of acetic acid to be subject to resonance stabilization? (See formula for alcohol dimer, 7.3; note that the bonding hydrogen is closer to one oxygen atom than to the other.)
11. Write an electronic representation of diazomethane.
12. Suggest methods for the preparation of the methyl esters of each of the following acids. If a catalyst is to be used, suggest a specific one.
   (a) $(CH_3)_3CCH_2CO_2H$
   (b) $CH_3CH_2C(CH_3)_2CO_2H$
   (c) $CH_3CH{=}CHCO_2H$
   (d) n-$C_{11}H_{23}COOH$, starting with
   n-$C_{11}H_{23}COOCH_2CH_2CH_3$
13. Write an electronic formulation showing the mechanism of the esterification of acetic acid with methanol, with boron fluoride as catalyst.
14. Indicate a synthesis of $(CH_3)_2CHCOCH_3$ from isobutyric acid.
15. How could bromoacetyl chloride be prepared from acetic acid?
16. What products would you expect to result from the interaction of ketene with water and with ethanol?
17. By what sequence of reactions could succinic acid be transformed into

   $$CH_3OCOCH_2CH_2COCl?$$

18. A substance of the formula $C_4H_{10}O_4$ yields on acetylation with acetic anhydride a derivative of the formula $C_{12}H_{18}O_8$. How many hydroxyl groups are present in the substance? What is the probable structure?
19. Devise a synthesis of 2,5-dimethylhexadiene-2,4 starting with succinic acid.
20. Compare the reactivities of acid chlorides, anhydrides, esters, and ethers.

READING REFERENCES

C. E. Entemann, Jr., and J. R. Johnson, "The Relative Reactivity of Various Functional Groups toward a Grignard Reagent," *J. Am. Chem. Soc.*, **55**, 2900 (1933)

J. F. G. Dippy, "Dissociation Constants of Monocarboxylic Acids," *Chem. Rev.*, **25**, 151 (1939)

H. D. Springall, "Modern Physico-chemical Views on Acids and Bases," *Chemistry of Carbon Compounds* (E. H. Rodd, Ed.), Elsevier (1951)

R. P. Bell, "The Use of the Terms Acid and Base," *Quart. Reviews*, **1**, 113 (1947)

chapter 10

ALDEHYDES AND KETONES

10.1

Typical aldehydes and ketones are carbonyl compounds having, respectively, one and two alkyl groups joined to the carbonyl function.

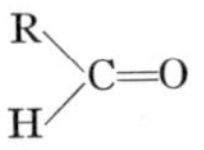

Aldehyde 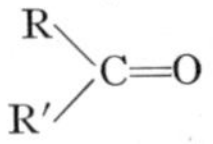   Ketone

Formaldehyde is exceptional in that the carbonyl group carries two hydrogen atoms and no alkyl groups, and it exhibits unique properties. Differences in the behavior of aldehydes and ketones in additions to the carbonyl group are determined by the number, size, and character of the alkyl substituents.

Nomenclature

Aldehydes are so named because they are obtainable by dehydrogenation of alcohols (<u>al</u>cohol <u>dehyd</u>rogenated), and the generic name ketone is derived from that of the simplest member of the series, acetone. The group —CHO is called a formyl group. The common names of aldehydes are taken from those of the acids into which the substances are convertible by oxidation. Ketones can be designated according to the substituent groups, for example, diethyl ketone, methyl ethyl ketone. In the Geneva system, the aldehydic and ketonic groups are indicated by the endings -al and -<u>one</u>, respectively. Thus propionaldehyde is propanal and acetone is propanone; positions of functional groups are indicated by numbers where there is ambiguity, for example, 2,5-dimethylhexanone-3 for $(CH_3)_2CHCH_2$-$COCH(CH_3)_2$. Other examples are:

$CH_3COCH_2COCH_3$
Pentanedione-2,4
(acetylacetone)

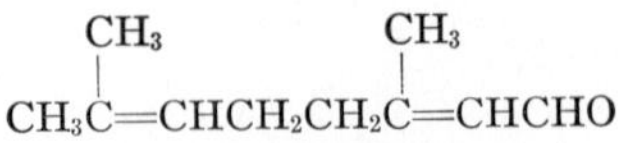

$$CH_3\overset{\overset{\displaystyle CH_3}{|}}{C}=CHCH_2CH_2\overset{\overset{\displaystyle CH_3}{|}}{C}=CHCHO$$
3,7-Dimethyloctadiene-2,6-al-1
(citral)

The boiling points are slightly above those of paraffins and other unassociated liquids of comparable molecular weight:

COMPOUND	MOL. WT.	B.P., °C.
$CH_3CH_2CH_2CH_2CH_2CHO$	100.16	129
$CH_3COCH_2CH_2CH_2CH_3$	100.16	127.2
$CH_3CH_2COCH_2CH_2CH_3$	100.16	124
$CH_3CH_2CH_2CH_2CH_2CH_2CH_3$	100.20	98.4

The slight elevation in boiling point may be attributable to some association due to electrostatic attraction between contributing resonance forms polarized in the sense: $R_2\overset{+}{C}{-}\overset{-}{O}$, equivalent to $R_2\overset{\delta_+}{C}={\overset{\delta_-}{O}}$.

METHODS OF PREPARATION

Oxidation of Alcohols. — A primary alcohol on oxidation yields an aldehyde as the initial product, and this is convertible on further oxidation into an acid. The aldehyde initially formed is more sus-

$$RCH_2OH \xrightarrow{\text{[O]}} RCHO \xrightarrow{\text{[O]}} RCOOH$$

ceptible to oxidation than the starting material, and if the outcome of an oxidation were dependent solely upon the relative reactivities, the oxidative process would not be practicable. Advantage can be taken however of the greater volatility of the aldehyde. Thus ethanol yields an aldehyde of boiling point some 55° lower. Because of the marked temperature differential, acetaldehyde can be distilled from

$$CH_3CH_2OH \xrightarrow{\text{K}_2\text{Cr}_2\text{O}_7,\text{ dil. H}_2\text{SO}_4,\ 50°} CH_3CHO$$
(b.p. 78.3°) (b.p. 20.8°)

the reaction mixture as it is formed: ethanol is added dropwise to a solution of potassium dichromate in dilute sulfuric acid maintained at a temperature (50°) below the boiling point of ethanol and above that of acetaldehyde. The alcohol is retained in the mixture until it undergoes oxidation, and acetaldehyde is removed by distillation and is thereby protected from further oxidation.

Ketones are more stable to oxidation than aldehydes and are obtained readily from secondary alcohols. Thus cyclohexanone is obtained in high yield by oxidation of cyclohexanol with a solution of sodium dichromate in acetic acid solution.

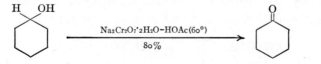

Oppenauer Oxidation. — This method consists in refluxing a secondary alcohol with aluminum *t*-butoxide and excess acetone; the net result is dehydrogenation of the alcohol with transference of the hydrogen atoms to acetone as acceptor. The equilibrium actually

$$\underset{R'}{\overset{R}{>}}CHOH \; + \; (CH_3)_2C=O \; \underset{\longleftarrow}{\overset{Al[OC(CH_3)_3]_3}{\rightleftharpoons}} \; \underset{R'}{\overset{R}{>}}C=O \; + \; (CH_3)_2CHOH$$

(excess)

involves the aluminum derivative of the secondary alcohol, formed by interchange with the aluminum derivative of *t*-butyl alcohol, which itself is stable to oxidation. The equilibrium is displaced in the desired direction by use of a large excess of acetone. The reaction has the advantage of being specific to the alcoholic group and hence applicable to alcohols having unsaturated centers that would be attacked by ordinary oxidizing agents.

10.4   **Aldehydes from Glycols and Alkenes.** — Preparative use can be made of the cleavage of *vic*-glycols by lead tetraacetate or periodic acid (7.23) and of the formation of aldehydes by ozonolysis of alkenes (4.25):

$$\underset{\overset{|}{OH} \; \overset{|}{OH}}{RCH-CHR} \; \xrightarrow{Pb(OCOCH_3)_4 \text{ or } HIO_4} \; 2\,RCHO$$

$$RCH=CHR \; \xrightarrow{O_3} \; Ozonide \; \xrightarrow{H_2, \, Pt} \; 2\,RCHO$$

10.5   **From Acids.**   (*a*) **Pyrolysis of Metal Salts.** — When calcium acetate is heated strongly it undergoes decomposition to acetone and calcium carbonate. The reaction is like the thermal decomposition

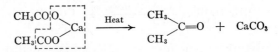

of sodium acetate in the presence of sodium hydroxide to give the more stable carbonate and methane. The reaction illustrated once constituted the chief method of manufacturing acetone; the required calcium acetate was obtained from pyroligneous acid. The reaction has general application for synthesis of symmetrical ketones. Instead

$$(RCOO)_2Ca \; \xrightarrow{Heat} \; R_2CO \; + \; CaCO_3$$

of preparing the salt as a dry solid prior to pyrolysis, the acid can be distilled through a heated tube packed with metal oxide. Thus manganous oxide impregnated on pumice is employed in a catalytic process for conversion of acetic acid into acetone; the vaporized acid passing

$$2\,CH_3COOH \; \xrightarrow{MnO, \, 300°} \; (CH_3)_2CO \; + \; H_2O \; + \; CO_2$$

through the catalyst tube forms manganous carbonate, which breaks down to the oxide and carbon dioxide.

An application of the pyrolytic method is used in the preparation of cyclic ketones from dibasic acids; for example, a mixture of adipic acid with about 5% of barium hydroxide is heated until distillation

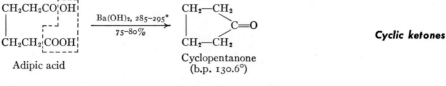

Adipic acid

Cyclopentanone
(b.p. 130.6°)

of the reaction product is complete. The reaction proceeds best in the production of five- and six-membered ring compounds.

Rosenmund[1] Reaction. — A useful method of transforming an acid into an aldehyde having the same carbon chain is catalytic hydrogenation of the acid chloride. The success of the method depends upon

$$R-C\underset{Cl}{\overset{O}{<}} + H_2 \xrightarrow{Catalyst} R-C\underset{H}{\overset{O}{<}} + HCl$$

differentiation between the speed of replacement of halogen by hydrogen and that of hydrogenation of the resulting aldehyde. The technique introduced by Rosenmund consists in adding a small amount of a poison containing sulfur, which does not seriously inhibit the desired reduction of the highly reactive acid chloride but effectively stops hydrogenation of the aldehyde. A stream of hydrogen is passed

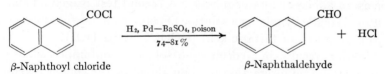

β-Naphthoyl chloride

β-Naphthaldehyde

through a boiling solution of the acid chloride in a hydrocarbon solvent, and the exit gas is passed into standard alkali; the course of the reaction is followed from the amount of hydrogen chloride absorbed.

Special Methods. — Production of **acetaldehyde** by the catalyzed hydration of acetylene (5.9) and the preparation of **acetone** as a product of bacterial fermentation of sugars (7.14) have been mentioned. **Chloral** is made by the action of chlorine on ethanol; the alcoholic group is oxidized by the halogen during the reaction.

$$CH_3CH_2OH + 4 Cl_2 \longrightarrow CCl_3CHO + 5 HCl$$
Chloral

The α,β-unsaturated aldehyde **acrolein** is obtained by dehydration of glycerol with acidic reagents. The reaction involves preferential

[1] Karl W. Rosenmund, b. 1884 Berlin; Ph.D. Berlin (Diels); Kiel

elimination of the secondary, rather than a primary, alcoholic hydroxyl group, a hydrogen shift in the resulting enol, and elimination of water between an activated α-hydrogen atom and a hydroxyl group in the

Acrolein from glycerol

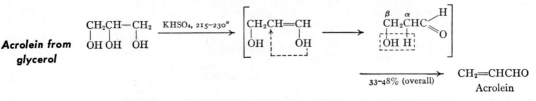

$$\xrightarrow{} \underset{\text{Acrolein}}{CH_2{=}CHCHO}$$
33–48% (overall)

β-position. Acrolein is a highly reactive, volatile liquid with a sharp, irritating odor; it has a marked tendency to polymerize.

REACTIONS

10.8

Oxidation. — Aldehydes, having a hydrogen atom on the oxidized carbon of the carbonyl group, are subject to ready oxidation, whereas ketones are not, and the two types of compounds can be distinguished by qualitative tests with oxidizing agents specific for aldehydes. One reagent is a solution of silver nitrate in excess ammonium hydroxide, containing the complex ion $Ag(NH_3)_2{}^+$. The aldehyde is oxidized to

Tests for aldehydes

$$RCHO \ + \ 2\,Ag(NH_3)_2OH \ \longrightarrow \ RCOONH_4 \ + \ 2\,Ag \ + \ 3\,NH_3 \ + \ H_2O$$

the acid, which forms the ammonium salt, and the complex metal ion is reduced to metallic silver, which is deposited on the walls of a test tube as an adherent film or mirror. A second test reagent, Fehling's solution, is made by mixing a solution of copper sulfate with an alkaline solution of a salt of tartaric acid (HOOCCHOHCHOHCOOH); this combination results in a deep blue solution containing a complex cupric ion, and on interaction with an aldehyde the copper is reduced to the univalent stage, and a red precipitate of cuprous oxide is

$$RCHO \ + \ 2\,Cu^{++} \ + \ NaOH \ + \ H_2O \ \longrightarrow \ RCOONa \ + \ Cu_2O \ + \ 4\,H^+$$
(Fehling's solution)

indicative of a reaction. Thus aldehydes give a positive silver-mirror test and reduce Fehling's solution, whereas ketones do not. These reagents are specific to aldehydes and do not attack alcohols or ethylenic compounds.

Oxidative cleavage of ketones

Although ketones, in contrast with aldehydes, are resistant to usual oxidizing agents, they are subject to oxidative fission by a powerful reagent such as hot nitric acid. The molecule can be ruptured on both sides of the carbonyl group, and several acid fragments may be formed:

$$RCH_2{\mid}CO{\mid}CH_2R' \ \xrightarrow{HNO_3} \ RCO_2H \ + \ RCH_2CO_2H \ + \ R'CO_2H \ + \ R'CH_2CO_2H$$

Such reactions are seldom of value. In a cyclic ketone fission of a carbon–carbon linkage does not give two fragments but opens the ring to give a dibasic acid, for example:

Cyclopentanone — Glutaric acid

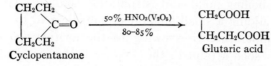

The substance is symmetrical and the same acid results from fission of either connecting linkage. The next higher homolog, adipic acid, can be prepared by nitric acid oxidation of either cyclohexanone or its precursor, cyclohexanol:

Cyclohexanol — Adipic acid

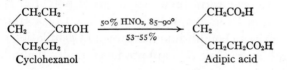

A ketone *per se* presents no point of vulnerability to oxidative attack, and the reaction probably proceeds by oxidation of the enolic form

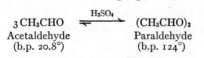

Proceeds through the enol

Ketone — Enol

present in equilibrium. The enol is removed continuously from the equilibrium by irreversible oxidation, and eventually the entire lot of ketone is transformed through the enolic intermediate into the oxidation product or products. α-Bromination of ketones, as of acids (9.10), similarly proceeds through the enol form.

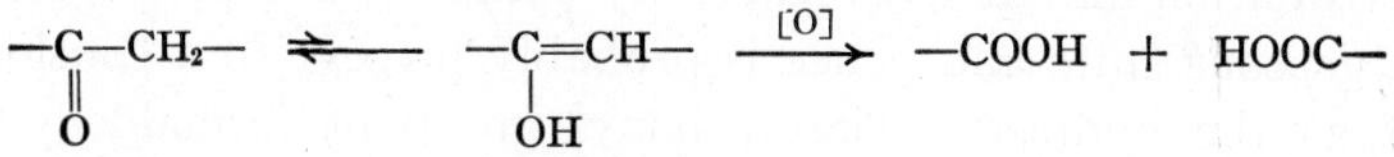

Polymerization of Aldehydes. — Acetaldehyde, a volatile liquid of pungent smell and marked reactivity, undergoes rapid polymerization under the influence of a trace of sulfuric acid to a less volatile and unreactive trimer, **paraldehyde.** The reaction is reversible but reaches equilibrium when the conversion is about 95% complete. Since paraldehyde is inert to oxidizing agents and shows no addition 10.9

$$3\,CH_3CHO \xrightleftharpoons{H_2SO_4} (CH_3CHO)_3$$

Acetaldehyde (b.p. 20.8°) — Paraldehyde (b.p. 124°)

reactions characteristic of carbonyl compounds, the carbonyl group of acetaldehyde must be utilized in linking the three molecules together. Paraldehyde is therefore formulated as having a six-membered

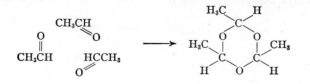

Cyclic trimer

oxide ring. Conversion of acetaldehyde into paraldehyde, as well as regeneration of acetaldehyde, is easily accomplished because the monomer is volatile and is miscible with water, whereas the trimer has a higher boiling point and is sparingly soluble. The polymer is prepared by adding a small amount of sulfuric acid to acetaldehyde, when the temperature rises owing to the exothermic reaction and equilibrium is soon attained; the mixture is then washed with water to remove the small amount of acetaldehyde and the acid catalyst, and the undissolved paraldehyde is dried and distilled. In the absence of acid the trimer suffers no depolymerization on distillation or on storage, and since it is inert, nonvolatile, and not subject to oxidation, this is a convenient form in which to store potential acetaldehyde. Depolymerization is accomplished by addition of a trace of sulfuric acid, which gives an equilibrium mixture, and distillation of the acetaldehyde; progressive amounts are produced under the influence of the catalyst till regeneration is complete.

Formaldehyde in aqueous solution does not display the sensitivity to air oxidation and general reactivity characteristic of the aldehyde in the gaseous state and hence is probably present to a considerable extent as the hydrate. The carbonyl group of formaldehyde has

$$CH_2{=}O \ + \ HOH \ \rightleftharpoons \ HO{-}CH_2{-}OH$$
$$\text{Formaldehyde hydrate}$$

greater additive power than that of higher aldehydes and the equilibrium is particularly favorable to the *gem*-diol. This hydrate has not been isolated, for evaporation of the aqueous solution gives a mixture of chain polymers of varying chain length, evidently arising from elimination of water between successive molecules of formaldehyde

Chain polymer

$$HOCH_2OH \ + \ nHOCH_2OH \ + \ HOCH_2OH \longrightarrow HOCH_2(OCH_2)_nOCH_2OH$$
$$\text{Paraformaldehyde}$$

hydrate. The polymer mixture known as paraformaldehyde is an amorphous solid of high molecular weight that is insoluble in water. Depolymerization occurs at a temperature of 180–200°, and hence paraformaldehyde is a convenient source of anhydrous, gaseous formaldehyde for synthetic use.

10.10   **Addition of Sodium Bisulfite.** — A reaction characteristic of aldehydes and of some ketones is addition of sodium bisulfite, employed in a saturated (40%) aqueous solution. Equilibrium is reached, but the carbonyl component can be converted almost entirely into the

$$RC\!\!\begin{array}{c} H \\ \diagdown \\ O \end{array} + \ \underset{\text{(large excess)}}{NaHSO_3} \ \rightleftharpoons \ RC\!\!\begin{array}{c} H \\ \diagup OH \\ \diagdown SO_3Na \end{array}$$
$$\text{Bisulfite-addition}$$
$$\text{compound}$$

addition product by use of excess bisulfite. The addition product is a crystalline salt and has the usual characteristics of an ionic compound; it is very soluble in water but subject to salting out by the common-ion effect, and it is insoluble in ether, infusible, and nonvolatile. Since the reaction is reversible, the aldehyde can be regenerated by adding to an aqueous solution of the product an amount of sodium carbonate or hydrochloric acid sufficient either to neutralize or to destroy the free sodium bisulfite present in equilibrium. Because of their specific physical properties and ease of formation and decom-

$$RC\underset{SO_3Na}{\overset{H}{\diagdown}}OH \rightleftharpoons RCHO + NaHSO_3$$

$$\xrightarrow{\frac{1}{2}Na_2CO_3} Na_2SO_3 + \frac{1}{2}CO_2 + \frac{1}{2}H_2O$$

$$\xrightarrow{HCl} NaCl + SO_2 + H_2O$$

position, bisulfite-addition products are useful for separation and purification of carbonyl compounds. To separate an aldehyde from an alcohol, for example, the mixture is shaken with excess saturated sodium bisulfite solution to form and to salt out the addition product; this is collected as a white solid and washed with bisulfite solution, ethanol, and then ether, to eliminate all traces of the original alcohol; the dried solid is dissolved in water and treated with sodium carbonate or hydrochloric acid; the liberated aldehyde is precipitated or obtained by distillation or by extraction with ether. Similar separations can be made from hydrocarbons, ethers, alkyl halides, carboxylic acids, and esters, since the carbonyl group of an ester is not sufficiently reactive to combine with sodium bisulfite. An aldehydic component that is completely insoluble in water often can be converted into an addition product by being dissolved in alcohol prior to treatment with aqueous bisulfite solution.

Although the reaction is general for aldehydes, only a limited number of ketones form bisulfite-addition products in practical amounts. Data are given in Table I for the extent of reaction of various carbonyl compounds with an equivalent amount of bisulfite (at 0–25°). With acetaldehyde equilibrium is reached rapidly, and nearly complete conversion is obtained even in the absence of excess bisulfite. Higher aldehydes behave in much the same manner, regardless of the size of the lone alkyl group, presumably because the substances all have in common the formyl group, —CHO. Acetone reacts less rapidly and to a less extent, but still the conversion surpasses that observed with higher homologs. In the series of ketones having one methyl group the extent of reaction decreases as the second alkyl group increases either in size or in extent of branching:

$$\underset{RCH_2CH}{\overset{O}{\overset{\|}{}}} > \underset{CH_3CCH_3}{\overset{O}{\overset{\|}{}}} > \underset{RCH_2CCH_3}{\overset{O}{\overset{\|}{}}} > \underset{R_2CHCCH_3}{\overset{O}{\overset{\|}{}}} > \underset{R_3CCCH_3}{\overset{O}{\overset{\|}{}}}$$

TABLE I

REACTION WITH ONE EQUIVALENT OF ALKALI BISULFITE

COMPOUND	PERCENTAGE OF BISULFITE COMPOUND	
	IN $\frac{1}{2}$ HR.	IN 1 HR.
$CH_3CO \cdot H$	88.0	88.7
$RCO \cdot H$		70–90
CH_3COCH_3	47.0	56.2
$CH_3CH_2COCH_3$	25.1	36.4
$CH_3CH_2CH_2COCH_3$	14.8	23.4
$(CH_3)_2CHCOCH_3$	7.5	12.3
$(CH_3)_3CCOCH_3$	5.6	5.6
$CH_3CH_2COCH_2CH_3$		2
$C_6H_5COCH_3$		1
$\begin{matrix} CH_2CH_2 \\ CH_2 \quad\quad C=O \\ CH_2CH_2 \end{matrix}$		35

Relative reactivity of carbonyl compounds

Evidently a hydrogen atom imposes little obstacle to the addition of sodium bisulfite to the carbonyl group, a methyl group exerts some blocking action, and larger and more bulky groups further impede formation of the addition product. Diethyl ketone reacts to only a negligible extent, and unless a ketone of the type RCOR′ contains at least one methyl group it is incapable of yielding a bisulfite-addition product. The behavior of the ketone $C_6H_5COCH_3$ (acetophenone) shows that a phenyl group inhibits bisulfite addition. Bisulfite-addition products can be prepared satisfactorily only from aldehydes and from methyl ketones other than those containing an aromatic group. The blocking, or hindering, effect is markedly reduced by ring formation, for cyclohexanone reacts about as readily as methyl ethyl ketone and to a greater extent than diethyl ketone.

Limits of reaction

10.11   Addition of Hydrogen Cyanide. — Hydrogen cyanide adds to carbonyl compounds by nucleophilic attack of the positively polarized carbon atom; the reaction product is a cyanohydrin. The reagent

Mechanism

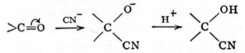

is volatile and highly toxic and is advantageously generated in the course of the reaction. One procedure is to mix the carbonyl compound with an aqueous solution of sodium or potassium cyanide and add a mineral acid. Another is to convert the carbonyl compound

$(CH_3)_2CO \xrightarrow[\text{77–78\%}]{NaCN + H_2SO_4 \text{ (10–20°)}} \begin{matrix} CH_3 \quad\quad OH \\ C \\ CH_3 \quad\quad CN \end{matrix}$

Acetone cyanohydrin
(b.p. 82° at 23 mm.)

into its bisulfite-addition product, which is then treated with an
equivalent amount of sodium cyanide, as in one synthesis of mandelic

$$C_6H_5CHO \xrightarrow{NaHSO_3} C_6H_5CH(OH)SO_2Na \xrightarrow{NaCN}$$
Benzaldehyde

$$C_6H_5CH(OH)CN \xrightarrow[50-52\% \text{ (overall)}]{\text{Hydrolysis (HCl)}} C_6H_5CH(OH)COOH$$
Mandelonitrile
(m.p. −10°)
Mandelic acid
(m.p. 118°)

acid. Sodium cyanide acts as a base and neutralizes the sodium bisulfite in equilibrium with the bisulfite compound with formation of
sodium sulfite; the simultaneously liberated aldehyde and hydrogen
cyanide then combine to give the cyanohydrin. The example cited,
in which the intermediate cyanohydrin is converted into mandelic
acid by acid hydrolysis, illustrates use of hydrogen cyanide addition
for synthesis of α-hydroxy acids.

The reaction with hydrogen cyanide is an equilibrium, and the
addition can be reversed by treatment of the cyanohydrin with moist
silver oxide. The scope of the reaction is nearly the same as that for
the addition of bisulfite, that is, cyanohydrin formation is applicable
to aldehydes, to most methyl ketones other than those having a phenyl
group, and to cyclic ketones. The carbonyl group of an ester is indifferent to hydrogen cyanide.

Grignard Reaction. — The useful synthetic reaction involving
addition of an alkyl- or arylmagnesium halide to a carbonyl group is
applicable with few exceptions to both aldehydes and ketones. Those
limitations encountered are instances where the hydrocarbon groups
in either the carbonyl component or the Grignard reagent are of such
a highly branched or bulky nature as to restrict the free space available
for formation of the addition complex and thus to impose hindrance.
Diisopropyl ketone adds methylmagnesium iodide in the normal
fashion, but with isopropylmagnesium bromide the addition reaction
is repressed, and the ketone instead suffers reduction at the expense
of the organometallic reagent with formation of the magnesiohalide
derivative of diisopropylcarbinol and propylene:

$$\underset{CH_3}{\overset{CH_3}{>}}CHCCH\underset{CH_3}{\overset{CH_3}{<}} + \underset{CH_3}{\overset{CH_3}{>}}CHMgBr \longrightarrow \underset{CH_3}{\overset{CH_3}{>}}CHCHCH\underset{CH_3}{\overset{CH_3}{<}} + CH_3CH=CH_2$$

Even if the carbonyl component contains hydroxyl or carboxyl
groups that rapidly destroy the Grignard reagent, just as water does,
a satisfactory addition frequently can be accomplished by using sufficient excess reagent to allow for destruction of an amount equivalent
to the hydroxyl groups present. For example, such substances as
$RCO(CH_2)_nCH_2OH$ and $HOOC(CH_2)_nCHO$ react with a first mole of

methylmagnesium iodide with liberation of methane, and then add a second mole to form the derivatives:

$$\underset{\underset{CH_3}{|}}{\overset{\overset{OMgI}{|}}{R}C}(CH_2)_nCH_2OMgI \qquad\qquad IMgOOC(CH_2)_n\underset{\underset{CH_3}{|}}{CHOMgI}$$

Liberation of methane by compounds with hydroxyl or other active-hydrogen groups is the basis of a useful analytical method introduced by Zerewitinoff (1912) and elaborated by others, particularly Kohler [2] (1930). In the original method a weighed sample is treated with excess methyl Grignard reagent and the volume of evolved methane measured; the number of equivalents of gas liberated indicates the number of hydroxyl groups. The procedure can be modified to include determination of the amount of reagent that adds to the molecule by using a measured amount of Grignard solution of known content, measuring the methane evolved on reaction with the test sample, and then adding water and measuring the methane evolved from the remaining reagent not utilized for addition. A microapparatus (Kohler: Grignard machine) including technical improvements intro-

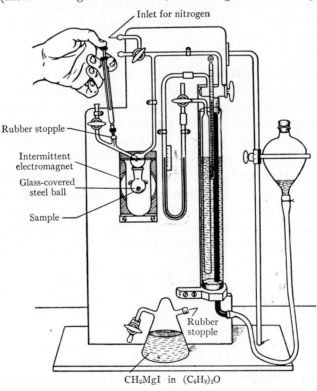

Inlet for nitrogen

Rubber stopple

Intermittent electromagnet

Glass-covered steel ball

Sample

Rubber stopple

CH₃MgI in (C₄H₉)₂O

Fig. 10.1.— Grignard Machine for the Determination of Active-Hydrogen Atoms and Carbonyl Groups

[2] Elmer Peter Kohler, 1865–1938; b. Egypt, Penna.; Ph.D. Johns Hopkins (Remsen); Bryn Mawr Coll., Harvard Univ.

duced by Lauer[3] is illustrated in Fig. 10.1. A measured volume of Grignard solution, withdrawn from a reservoir with a hypodermic syringe and introduced into the apparatus without exposure to moist air, is mixed with a weighed sample of the substance to be analyzed, and the mixture is agitated by the oscillation of a glass-covered steel ball.

Reduction. — Most aldehydes and ketones can be reduced to the corresponding primary and secondary alcohols by **catalytic hydrogenation** or with **lithium aluminum hydride.** Chemical methods of reduction are usually applicable to aldehydes and in some instances to ketones. The reduction of a ketone by the combination of a metal with either an acid or a base often does not follow the normal course exclusively, but proceeds also by a process described as **bimolecular reduction** because the reduction product is derived from two molecules of the starting material. Thus acetone is reduced by metal combinations only in part to isopropyl alcohol and affords in addition a considerable amount of the product of bimolecular reduction, pinacol: $(CH_3)_2C(OH)C(OH)(CH_3)_2$. Pinacol is a useful synthetic intermediate and is prepared by the action of amalgamated magnesium on dry acetone in benzene solution, followed by hydrolysis of the magnesium derivative. The reaction probably involves attachment of magnesium to the oxygen atoms of two molecules of acetone, to form a transient diradical and then magnesium pinacolate, which is subsequently

$$2(CH_3)_2CO \xrightarrow{Mg} \begin{matrix}(CH_3)_2\overset{.}{C}-O\\(CH_3)_2\overset{.}{C}-O\end{matrix}\!\!\!\!>\!Mg \longrightarrow \begin{matrix}(CH_3)_2C-O\\|\\(CH_3)_2C-O\end{matrix}\!\!\!\!>\!Mg \xrightarrow[43-50\%]{H_2O} \begin{matrix}(CH_3)_2COH\\|\\(CH_3)_2COH\end{matrix}$$

Pinacol

Diradical mechanism of pinacol formation

hydrolyzed to pinacol. Anhydrous pinacol is a liquid, b.p. 174.4°; it forms a crystalline hydrate containing six molecules of water of crystallization. Pinacol hydrate, $C_6H_{12}(OH)_2 \cdot 6\,H_2O$ (named from *pinako-*, Gr., tabletlike, referring to the crystalline form of the hydrate), melts at 45°. Ketones generally undergo bimolecular reduction to a considerable extent with metal combinations such as zinc and acid, sodium, magnesium, or aluminum amalgam. With the same reagents aliphatic aldehydes are reduced unimolecularly to the corresponding alcohols, as they are on catalytic hydrogenation. The difference between aldehydes and ketones appears attributable to the greater availability of the carbonyl group of the former substances for the simultaneous addition to both carbon and oxygen.

A process for reduction of both aldehydes and ketones is the **Meerwein-Ponndorf method** (1925–26), which consists in heating a

[3] Walter M. Lauer, b. 1895 Thomasville, Penna.; Ph.D. Minnesota (Hunter); Minnesota

carbonyl compound in benzene or toluene solution with aluminum isopropoxide and distilling the acetone from the resulting equilibrium

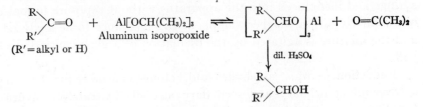

mixture. The reaction is the counterpart of the subsequently discovered Oppenauer oxidation of an alcohol with excess acetone (10.3). The reaction is specific to the carbonyl group, and can be employed for reduction of unsaturated aldehydes and ketones.

$$CH_3CH=CHCHO \xrightarrow[85-90\%]{Al(OC_3H_7)_3} CH_3CH=CHCH_2OH$$
Crotonaldehyde · · · · · · · · · · · · · · · Crotyl alcohol

10.14　　　**Aldol Condensation.** — When a solution of acetaldehyde is treated with a small quantity of sodium hydroxide, two molecules of the substance combine in an equilibrium process and afford aldol, or β-hy-

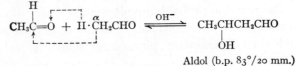

Aldol (b.p. 83°/20 mm.)

droxy-*n*-butyraldehyde. The reaction, which is promoted best by bases, involves addition of one molecule of acetaldehyde to the carbonyl group of another molecule, and is dependent upon the activated character of the hydrogen in the α-position to the carbonyl group of the adding molecule. Thus aldol condensation is shown only by aldehydes having at least one hydrogen in the α-position, and not by such substances as trimethylacetaldehyde, $(CH_3)_3CCHO$, or benzaldehyde, C_6H_5CHO. Propionaldehyde gives an aldol condensation product by utilization of one of the activated α-hydrogens, and not one of the β-hydrogens:

$$CH_3CH_2CHO + \underset{\beta CH_3}{\overset{\alpha}{CH_2CHO}} \rightleftharpoons CH_3CH_2CH-\underset{OH\ CH_3}{CHCHO}$$

Base-catalyzed aldolization, like cyanohydrin formation, involves nucleophilic addition. In an initial, slow step (a) the basic catalyst abstracts a proton from the aldehyde to give the anion required for the more rapid step of addition (b); the terminal step (c) regenerates the catalytic anion.

(a) $OH^- + HCH_2CHO \rightleftharpoons H_2O + \bar{C}H_2CHO$

(b) $CH_3CH{=}O + \bar{C}H_2CHO \rightleftharpoons CH_3CHCH_2CHO$
$\qquad\qquad\qquad\qquad\qquad\qquad\quad | $
$\qquad\qquad\qquad\qquad\qquad\qquad\quad O^-$

(c) $CH_3CHCH_2CHO + H_2O \rightleftharpoons CH_3CHCH_2CHO + OH^-$
$\qquad\;\; | \qquad\qquad\qquad\qquad\qquad\qquad\;\; | $
$\qquad\;\; O^- \qquad\qquad\qquad\qquad\qquad\qquad OH$

Aldol is subject to ready dehydration because of the presence of a β-hydroxyl group adjacent to an activated α-hydrogen atom. Conditions are thus particularly favorable for elimination of water, and aldol is converted into crotonaldehyde either by heating the isolated product alone or with a trace of mineral acid or by merely warming the aqueous solution of the equilibrium mixture resulting from aldol-

$$\underset{\text{Aldol}}{\overset{\beta\qquad\alpha}{CH_3CH{-}CHCHO}} \xrightarrow{\;-H_2O\;} \underset{\qquad\beta\quad\;\alpha}{CH_3CH{=}CHCHO}$$

Crotonaldehyde

ization. Crotonaldehyde is a representative α,β-unsaturated aldehyde available by aldol condensation and dehydration.

The carbonyl group of acetone has less additive power than that of acetaldehyde, although comparably activated α-hydrogen atoms are present. Aldol condensation occurs under the influence of basic catalysts, but the position of equilibrium is unfavorable to formation of the condensation product, diacetone alcohol. Even so, a special

$$\underset{\text{Acetone (b.p. 56.1°)}}{\overset{CH_3}{\underset{CH_3}{>}}C{=}O} + H{\cdot}CH_2COCH_3 \xrightleftharpoons{Ba(OH)_2} \underset{\text{Diacetone alcohol (b.p. 166°)}}{\overset{CH_3}{\underset{CH_3}{>}}\underset{\underset{OH}{|}}{C}{-}CH_2COCH_3}$$

technique makes possible efficient preparation of the condensation product. Solid barium hydroxide is used as catalyst and promotes reaction on contact with acetone. It is placed in a filter-paper thimble in an extraction apparatus (Soxhlet) in which acetone is distilled into a vertical condenser, the condensate trickles over the solid catalyst, and the liquid then filters by gravity through the thimble and is returned to the boiling flask. The acetone flowing over the barium hydroxide is converted into diacetone alcohol in small amounts approaching the equilibrium concentration, but once the resulting solution has passed through the filter and is out of contact with catalyst, the dimeric condensation product does not revert to acetone but accumulates in the boiling flask as the more volatile acetone is continually removed by distillation and recycled. By operation of such a unit for about four days, 1.5 liters of acetone can be converted into diacetone alcohol in 71% yield.

Cannizzaro Reaction of Aldehydes. — Another reaction, characteristic of aldehydes having no α-hydrogen atoms and applicable chiefly in the aromatic series, is oxidation of one molecule of the aldehyde at the expense of another, which suffers reduction. The reaction, which bears the name of the Italian discoverer Cannizzaro[4] (1853), is brought about by the action of a concentrated solution of sodium or potassium hydroxide on an aldehyde, for example benzaldehyde.

$$2 \ C_6H_5CHO \ + \ KOH \ \xrightarrow{60\% \ KOH} \ C_6H_5CO_2K \ + \ C_6H_5CH_2OH$$

Benzaldehyde   Potassium   Benzyl alcohol
                                    benzoate

The oxidation product, benzoic acid, can be isolated in 85–95% yield, and the reduction product in 80% yield. This type of compensated oxidation-reduction process is called disproportionation. The reaction is interpreted as involving (a) interaction of the aldehyde with hydrox-

Mechanism

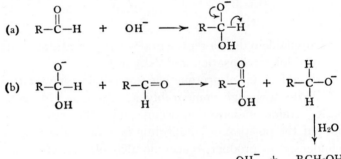

ide ion to produce an anion which, by virtue of the electron displacements indicated, has reducing properties and can donate a hydride ion (H⁻) as in (b) to a second molecule of aldehyde.

In the aliphatic series the reaction is encountered only with substances such as formaldehyde and trimethylacetaldehyde, which possess no activated hydrogen atom in the α-position and therefore

Pentaerythritol

$$
\begin{array}{c}
CH_2{=}O \\
\uparrow \\
H{----}\rfloor \\
O{=}H_2C \quad H{-}\overset{|}{C}{-}CHO \quad \xrightarrow{Ca(OH)_2} \quad
\left[HOCH_2{-}\overset{\displaystyle CH_2OH}{\underset{\displaystyle CH_2OH}{C}}{-}CHO \right] \quad \xrightarrow[73.5\% \ overall]{CH_2{=}O, \ H_2O}
\\
H{----}\rceil \\
\downarrow \\
CH_2{=}O
\end{array}
$$

$$
HOCH_2{-}\overset{\displaystyle CH_2OH}{\underset{\displaystyle CH_2OH}{C}}{-}CH_2OH \quad + \quad HCOOH \ (as \ Ca \ salt)
$$

Pentaerythritol (m.p. 260°)

[4] Stanislao Cannizzaro, 1826–1910; b. Palermo, Italy; stud. Pisa (Piria); Genoa, Palermo, Rome

are incapable of undergoing the more rapid aldol condensation. The
Cannizzaro reaction is involved in the preparation of pentaerythritol,
a polyhydric alcohol employed in the manufacture of the explosive
tetranitrate ester (PETN, 7.27). This method consists in treating
acetaldehyde with about five equivalents of formaldehyde in an
aqueous solution of calcium hydroxide at 15–45°. The initial step is
an aldol condensation, and since formaldehyde possesses the more
reactive carbonyl group of the two components and acetaldehyde alone
contains activated α-hydrogen atoms, the reaction consists in addition
of acetaldehyde to three formaldehyde molecules. The next step is a
crossed Cannizzaro disproportionation between the initially formed
trihydroxyaldehyde and formaldehyde, which results in reduction of
the former to pentaerythritol and oxidation of the latter to formic
acid.

Condensation with Amines. — Among reagents for the carbonyl
group are various derivatives of ammonia containing the amino
group, —NH₂. One reagent, hydroxylamine, represents a combination of the structures of water and of ammonia; and another, hydrazine, is structurally comparable to hydrogen peroxide, to which it
bears the same relation as ammonia does to water. These amine

$$\left.\begin{array}{c} H \cdot OH \\ H \cdot NH_2 \end{array}\right\} HO \cdot NH_2, \text{Hydroxylamine} \qquad HO \cdot OH\} H_2N \cdot NH_2, \text{Hydrazine}$$

reagents condense with aldehydes and ketones with elimination of
water between the two molecules and formation of an unsaturated
nitrogen-containing derivative. The products of condensation with

$$\text{>C=O + H_2N— } \longrightarrow \text{ >C=N—}$$

hydroxylamine are oximes, and can be designated as aldoximes or
ketoximes, according to the nature of the carbonyl component. The

$$CH_3CH=O + H_2NOH \longrightarrow CH_3CH=NOH$$
$$\text{Acetaldoxime (m.p. 47°)}$$
$$(CH_3)_2C=O + H_2NOH \longrightarrow (CH_3)_2C=NOH$$
$$\text{Acetoxime (m.p. 60°)}$$

condensations proceed readily on warming the components in aqueous
or alcoholic solution, and the examples indicate that oximes are
crystalline solids even though the carbonyl compounds from which they
are derived are volatile liquids. The oximes are thus solid derivatives
of service for identification.

Hydrazine reacts in a similar manner to form a hydrazone, but
this derivative possesses a free amino group and can condense with
another molecule of the carbonyl component. Derivatives of hydra-

$$\underset{\text{Aldehyde}}{RCH=O} + \underset{\text{Hydrazine}}{H_2NNH_2} \longrightarrow \underset{\text{Hydrazone}}{RCH=NNH_2} \xrightarrow{RCHO} \underset{\text{Azine}}{RCH=NN=CHR}$$

Crossed Cannizzaro reaction

10.16

Oximes

Hydrazones

167

zine in which this double condensation is obviated by the presence of a substituent group have more practical value than hydrazine itself. One is phenylhydrazine, which yields phenylhydrazone

Phenylhydrazones

$$C_6H_5CHO \xrightarrow{H_2NNHC_6H_5} C_6H_5CH=NNHC_6H_5$$

Benzaldehyde   Benzaldehyde phenylhydrazone
(liquid)   (m.p. 156°)

derivatives. The phenylhydrazone of acetaldehyde is also a crystalline solid, m.p. 99°. Replacement of the oxygen atom of a carbonyl group by the residue $=NNHC_6H_5$ is attended with decided increase in molecular weight and consequent decrease in solubility, and hence an aldehyde or a ketone often can be precipitated from a dilute solution in the form of the phenylhydrazone and identified by the melting point of this derivative. 2,4-Dinitrophenylhydrazine, $(NO_2)_2C_6H_3NHNH_2$, is a still more favorable reagent, since the molecular weight increase

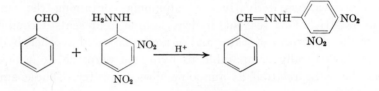

amounts to 180; the derivative formulated melts at 237°. The 2,4-dinitrophenylhydrazones of saturated aldehydes and ketones are yellow and those of α,β-unsaturated carbonyl compounds are orange or red. Another reagent is semicarbazide, $H_2NNHCONH_2$; this generally gives derivatives that melt at higher temperatures than oximes or phenylhydrazones.

Semicarbazones

$$CH_3CHO + H_2NNHCONH_2 \longrightarrow CH_3CH=NNHCONH_2$$

Semicarbazide   Acetaldehyde semicarbazone
(m.p. 162°)

All the condensations cited are reversible, and oximes, phenylhydrazones, and semicarbazones can be hydrolyzed by boiling with dilute hydrochloric acid with regeneration of the free carbonyl compound. Aldehydes and ketones are isolated frequently from reaction mixtures in the form of one of these crystalline, sparingly soluble derivatives, and then recovered by acid hydrolysis.

$$OH^- + H_2NOH \longrightarrow H_2O + H\bar{N}OH \xrightarrow{R_2C=O}$$

(a)

Mechanism

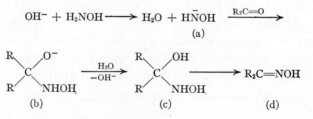

These condensations appear to proceed by an addition-elimination mechanism initiated by abstraction of a proton from the reagent (e.g., hydroxylamine) by hydroxide ion, and addition of the anion (a) to the carbonyl group, with eventual formation of (c) and dehydration to (d).

Wolff-Kishner Reduction. — This method of reduction of a carbonyl group to a methylene group, discovered independently in Germany (Wolff,[5] 1912) and in Russia (Kishner,[6] 1911), involves formation and pyrolytic decomposition of a hydrazone under basic

$$\ce{>C=O} \xrightarrow{\ce{H2NNH2}} \ce{>C=NNH2} \xrightarrow{\ce{OH^-}, 200°} \ce{>CH2} + \ce{N2}$$

$$\ce{>C=O} \longrightarrow \ce{>CH2}$$

catalysis. In an improved procedure (Huang-Minlon, 1946) the carbonyl compound is refluxed briefly in triethylene glycol, a high-boiling, water-miscible solvent, with aqueous hydrazine and sodium hydroxide to form the hydrazone; water is then allowed to distil till the temperature rises to a point favorable for decomposition of the hydrazone (200°); and the mixture is refluxed for several hours to complete the reduction.

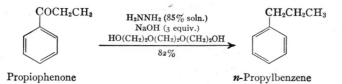

Propiophenone → n-Propylbenzene

$$\text{H}_2\text{NNH}_2 \text{ (85\% soln.)}$$
$$\text{NaOH (3 equiv.)}$$
$$\text{HO(CH}_2)_2\text{O(CH}_2)_2\text{O(CH}_2)_2\text{OH}$$
$$82\%$$

Acetals and Ketals. — Under catalysis by dry hydrogen chloride a typical aldehyde adds a molecule of ethyl alcohol to form a moderately stable addition product (hemiacetal), which combines with a second molecule of the alcohol and yields a stable derivative known as an acetal. Acetals are *gem*-diethers but, unlike the corresponding

$$\ce{CH3CH=O} + \ce{HOC2H5} \xrightarrow{\ce{HCl}} \ce{CH3CH<^{OH}_{OC2H5}} \xrightarrow{\ce{HOC2H5} (\ce{H+})} \ce{CH3CH<^{OC2H5}_{OC2H5}}$$

Hemiacetal   Acetal (b.p. 104°)

unstable *gem*-diols, can be obtained as pure, distillable liquids. Acetal formation is reversible, and acetals are hydrolyzed easily with water and a mineral acid catalyst (compare the acid-catalyzed depolymerization of paraldehyde). Acetals are stable to basic reagents and oxidizing agents and are used to protect the aldehydic function during synthetic operations involving other parts of the molecule.

[5] Ludwig Wolff, 1857–1919; b. Neustadt/Hardt; Ph.D. Strasbourg (Fittig); Jena; *Ber.*, **62**A, 145 (1929)
[6] N. M. Kishner, 1867–1935; b. Moscow; Ph.D. Moscow (Markownikoff); Tomsk, Moscow

A protective derivative of ketones that has proved useful in synthesis is the ethyleneketal, made by refluxing a ketone in ethylene

Useful protective derivative

$$\begin{array}{c} R \\ R \end{array}\!\!C=O \ + \ \begin{array}{c} HOCH_2 \\ HOCH_2 \end{array} \xrightarrow{\ H^+\ } \begin{array}{c} R \\ R \end{array}\!\!C\!\!\begin{array}{c} O-CH_2 \\ O-CH_2 \end{array} \ + \ H_2O$$

Ethyleneketal

glycol in the presence of an acid catalyst under a take-off condenser for removal of the water formed. The protective group is easily removed by acid hydrolysis. Sulfur analogs of alcohols of the formula RSH, known both as mercaptans and as thiols, have greater additive power than alcohols, and the reagent ethanedithiol, $HSCH_2CH_2SH$, reacts readily with ketones at room temperature. The resulting

$$\begin{array}{c} R \\ R \end{array}\!\!C=O \xrightarrow[BF_3 \cdot HOAc]{HSCH_2CH_2SH} \begin{array}{c} R \\ R \end{array}\!\!C\!\!\begin{array}{c} S-CH_2 \\ S-CH_2 \end{array} \xrightarrow{Ni, H_2} \begin{array}{c} R \\ R \end{array}\!\!CH_2$$

Ethylenethioketal

$$\begin{array}{c} \\ \end{array}\!\!C=O \ \longrightarrow \ \begin{array}{c} \\ \end{array}\!\!CH_2$$

ethylenethioketal is hydrolyzed with too great difficulty to be useful as a protective derivative but can be desulfurized with Raney nickel (with adsorbed hydrogen), with the result that the original carbonyl oxygen is replaced by two atoms of hydrogen.

ENOLS AND ENOLATES

10.19

Tautomerism. — The behavior of ketones on oxidation and on bromination was interpreted above as proceeding through a minute amount of an enolic form present in equilibrium with the ketone in consequence of activation of a hydrogen in the α-position to the unsaturated carbonyl group. When a second carbonyl group is present in such a position as to accentuate the activation by the first, the equilibrium may be sufficiently favorable to permit isolation of the enol. The classical example of a compound known in both ketonic and enolic forms is the β-keto ester ethyl acetoacetate, CH_3COCH_2-$CO_2C_2H_5$, commonly known as acetoacetic ester, in which the hydrogens of the methylene group are activated by a carbonyl group on one side and an ester-carbonyl group on the other. Analytical chemical reactions (K. H. Meyer,[7] 1911) and physical measurements (molecular refraction, von Auwers,[8] 1918) established that ordinary, liquid acetoacetic ester consists of an equilibrium mixture containing approximately 7% of the enol form. The phenomenon of reversible interconversion of isomers is known as tautomerism. A hydrogen atom of the

Keto and enol forms of acetoacetic ester

[7] Kurt Hans Meyer, 1883–1952; b. Dorpat, Germany; Ph.D. Leipzig; BASF Ludwigshaven; Univ. Geneva
[8] Karl von Auwers, 1863–1939; b. Gotha, Germany; Ph.D. Berlin (Hofmann); Marburg; *Ber.*, **72A**, 111 (1939)

methylene group, activated by the carbonyl group on the one side and the carbethoxy group on the other, migrates from carbon to oxygen to

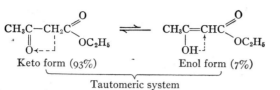

Keto form (93%)   Enol form (7%)

Tautomeric system

give the enol, and since in this substance the hydrogen is also activated, it can migrate back again. The tautomeric migration of hydrogen in either direction is an α,γ-shift. The keto form has been isolated

$$-\overset{\beta}{\underset{\gamma O}{C}}-\overset{\alpha}{\underset{H}{C}}H- \rightleftarrows -\overset{\beta}{C}=\overset{\gamma}{\underset{\alpha OH}{C}}H-$$

by cooling a solution of the equilibrium mixture, when the ketonic form eventually separates as a crystalline solid, m.p. $-39°$. The enolic tautomer alone is acidic, and treatment of the mixture with one equivalent of sodium converts all the material into the sodium enolate, sodioacetoacetic ester, $CH_3C(O^+Na^-)=CHCO_2C_2H_5$. The liquid enol has been isolated by passing hydrogen chloride gas into a suspension of the sodio derivative in petroleum ether at $-78°$. At ordinary temperatures each form slowly reverts in part to the other to give the same equilibrium mixture. Equilibrium is established rapidly when either form is treated with a trace of alkali. The position of equilibrium is different in different solvents and varies with temperature. Other β-keto esters form tautomeric systems of varying enol content; the similarly constituted 1,3-diketones are even more prone to enolize, whereas diesters of the malonic ester type are less enolic, as shown in the following comparison:

$C_2H_5OOCCH_2COOC_2H_5$	$CH_3COCH_2COOC_2H_5$	$CH_3COCH_2COCH_3$
Diethyl malonate	Ethyl acetoacetate	Acetylacetone
Trace	7%	72%

Enol content of the equilibrium mixture

Although the methylene group of all three compounds is sufficiently acidic to permit formation of a sodio derivative, the two moderately unsaturated carbethoxy groups of malonic ester do not provide sufficient activation to stabilize the enol form, whereas acetylacetone, with two powerfully unsaturated carbonyl groups, exists largely in the enolic form. Acetoacetic ester has a combination of the two unsaturated groups and occupies an intermediate position.

An interesting observation is that when ordinary acetoacetic ester is distilled very slowly in a quartz apparatus, the distillate consists

CHAPTER 10

almost exclusively of the enolic form (K. H. Meyer, 1920). Quartz is required because glass has a sufficiently alkaline reaction to catalyze interconversion of the tautomers. The preferential distillation of one tautomer indicates that the hydroxylic enol form is more volatile than the keto form. The relationship is just the opposite of that noted with ordinary alcohols and ketones, for alcohols are highly associated in the liquid state and boil at temperatures about 30° higher than ketones of comparable molecular weight. The unusual volatility of the enolic form of acetoacetic ester is attributed to hydrogen bonding between the hydroxyl group and the carbonyl group of the ester function. The coordinate link closes a labile but significant six-membered ring of the type described as a **chelate ring** (Gr. *chēlē*, claw). The hydroxylic hydrogen atom is thus rendered unavailable for bonding with a second molecule, and the substance is not associated.

$$CH_3C \overset{CH-C-OC_2H_5}{\underset{O-H}{\diagup}} O$$

Enol-acetoacetic ester

10.20 **Acetoacetic Ester in Synthesis.** — The enolic β-keto ester is prepared by condensation of two molecules of ethyl acetate in the presence of sodium ethoxide; the reaction is reversible, but a high yield can be obtained by distillation of the alcohol formed with displacement of the equilibrium (McElvain,[9] 1937). The reaction is an application of a general reaction known as *ester condensation*. The anion

$$CH_3C \overset{O}{\underset{}{\|}} \!\!-OC_2H_5\ +\ HCH_2COOC_2H_5\ +\ NaOC_2H_5 \xrightarrow[75-76\%]{}$$

Ester condensation

$$Na^+[CH_3COCHCOOC_2H_5]^-\ +\ 2\,C_2H_5OH$$
Sodioacetoacetic ester

$$\Big\downarrow HCl$$

$$CH_3COCH_2COOC_2H_5$$
Ethyl acetoacetate
(acetoacetic ester, b.p. 180°)

of the sodio derivative has the properties of a resonance hybrid, and the carbon atom of the original methylene group carries sufficient negative charge to be susceptible to alkylation on reaction with an

Alkylation of aceto-acetic ester

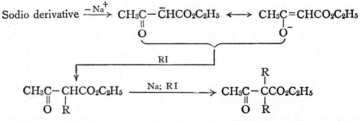

alkyl halide. The product still has an activated hydrogen and forms a sodio derivative, through which another alkyl group can be intro-

[9] Samuel M. McElvain, b. 1897 Duquoin, Ill.; Ph.D. Illinois (Adams); Wisconsin

duced. The significance of these reactions is that β-keto esters on hydrolysis with dilute alkali yield β-keto acids which, because the β-carbon atom carries both a carbonyl and a carboxyl group, undergo smooth decarboxylation at moderate temperature (e.g., 100°) to give

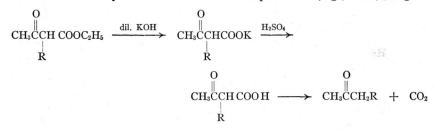

ketones. **Ketonic** hydrolysis, as the process is called, coupled with mono- or dialkylation, thus affords a useful synthetic sequence.

Acetoacetic ester synthesis
10.21

The **Dieckmann** [10] **reaction** involves ester condensation of dibasic esters into cyclic β-keto esters; for example, diethyl adipate (1) affords 2-carbethoxycyclopentanone (2). This can be alkylated by

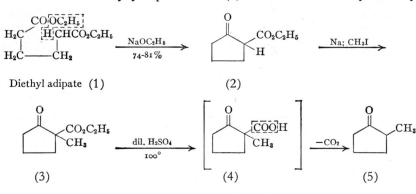

Synthesis of cyclic ketones

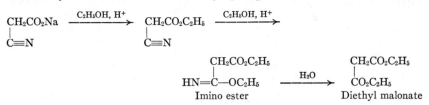

reaction of its sodio enolate with methyl iodide, and the ester (3) on acid hydrolysis affords 2-methylcyclopentanone (5).

Malonic Ester Synthesis. — Diethyl malonate, commonly called malonic ester, is made by the action of ethanol and a mineral acid on sodium cyanoacetate. The carboxyl group is liberated and esterified,

10.22
Preparation of $CH_2(CO_2C_2H_5)_2$

$$CH_2CO_2Na \quad \xrightarrow{C_2H_5OH,\ H^+} \quad CH_2CO_2C_2H_5 \quad \xrightarrow{C_2H_5OH,\ H^+}$$
$$\overset{|}{C}{\equiv}N \qquad\qquad\qquad\qquad \overset{|}{C}{\equiv}N$$

$$\underset{\text{Imino ester}}{HN{=}C{-}OC_2H_5} \quad \overset{\begin{array}{c}CH_2CO_2C_2H_5\\|\end{array}}{} \quad \xrightarrow{H_2O} \quad \underset{\text{Diethyl malonate}}{\overset{\begin{array}{c}CH_2CO_2C_2H_5\\|\\CO_2C_2H_5\end{array}}{}}$$

and addition of ethanol to the nitrile group gives the imino ester, which is hydrolyzed on addition of water.

[10] Walter Dieckmann, 1869–1925; b. Hamburg, Germany; Ph.D. Munich (Bamberger); Munich

Although the enol form of malonic ester is present in only trace amounts and is not isolable, the ester reacts with sodium to form an enolate, which is stabilized by resonance. The enolate, represented

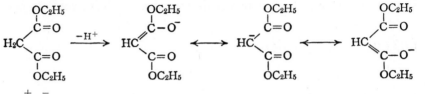

as $\overset{+}{Na}\overset{-}{CH}(CO_2C_2H_5)_2$, can be alkylated to $RCH(CO_2C_2H_5)_2$, and when this is hydrolyzed the substituted malonic acid readily loses carbon dioxide and affords a substituted monocarboxylic acid; the β-carboxy acid, $HOOCCH_2COOH$, thus behaves like a β-keto acid,

$$RCH\underset{COOC_2H_5}{\overset{COOC_2H_5}{\diagup}} \xrightarrow{\text{Hydrol.}} RCH\underset{COOH}{\overset{COOH}{\diagup}} \xrightarrow{\text{Heat}} RCH_2COOH + CO_2$$

$RCOCH_2COOH$. Combination of the alkylation reaction with that of decarboxylation provides an effective synthesis of acids; the overall process accomplishes replacement of the halogen atom of the alkyl halide by the acetic acid residue. An example is the synthesis of

$$RX \xrightarrow{\text{Malonic ester synthesis}} RCH_2COOH$$

caproic acid starting with *n*-butyl bromide. Metallic sodium is dissolved in ethanol to give a solution of sodium ethoxide, and malonic ester is slowly introduced, followed by an equivalent amount of *n*-butyl bromide. The substituted malonic ester is separated by re-

$$CH_3(CH_2)_2CH_2Br + CH_2(COOC_2H_5)_2 + NaOC_2H_5 \xrightarrow[80-90\%]{}$$

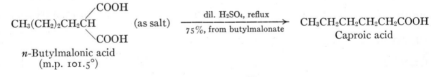

Diethyl *n*-butylmalonate (b.p. 235–240°)

$$CH_3(CH_2)_2CH_2CH\underset{COOH}{\overset{COOH}{\diagup}} \quad \text{(as salt)} \quad \xrightarrow[75\%,\text{ from butylmalonate}]{\text{dil. } H_2SO_4,\text{ reflux}} CH_3CH_2CH_2CH_2CH_2COOH$$
Caproic acid

n-Butylmalonic acid
(m.p. 101.5°)

moving the bulk of the alcohol and adding water, and it is hydrolyzed with boiling potassium hydroxide solution. The resulting *n*-butyl-malonic acid can be isolated as a solid and the decarboxylation conducted by heating the molten material at 150°. A simpler method is to render the aqueous solution strongly acidic with sulfuric acid and reflux the mixture; the mineral acid catalyzes loss of carbon dioxide at a temperature not much above 100°.

A monosubstituted malonic ester still has a hydrogen atom replaceable by sodium and therefore available for a second alkylation. The general method thus can be extended to the synthesis of dialkylacetic acids:

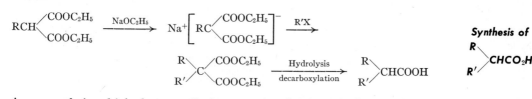

An example in which the two alkyl groups are the same is the synthesis of diethylacetic acid. Malonic ester is either converted into the mono- and then the diethyl derivative or treated with two equivalents each of sodium ethoxide and ethyl iodide and so diethylated directly. The disubstituted malonic ester is hindered and hence more resistant to alkaline hydrolysis than a monosubstituted ester.

$$CH_2(CO_2C_2H_5)_2 \longrightarrow C_2H_5CH(CO_2C_2H_5)_2 \longrightarrow (C_2H_5)_2C(CO_2C_2H_5)_2 \longrightarrow$$

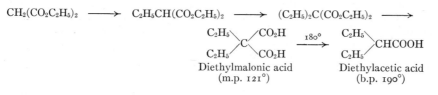

Diethylmalonic acid   Diethylacetic acid
(m.p. 121°)   (b.p. 190°)

SUMMARY

Aldehydes and ketones (Geneva: -als, -ones) slightly associated in liquid phase. Rate and equilibrium of additions to carbonyl group influenced by bulk of attached groups (steric hindrance) and degree of polarization of double bond.

Preparation

From alcohols by oxidation or dehydrogenation. Lower aldehydes (more volatile than the alcohols) protected from oxidation by distillation from reaction mixture. Ketones less sensitive.

Oppenauer oxidation: aluminum t-butoxide and excess acetone (hydrogen acceptor). Applicable to unsaturated alcohols.

Aldehydes by cleavage of glycols with $Pb(OAc)_4$ or HIO_4; ozonization of alkenes.

Ketones by pyrolysis of acid salts: $(RCOO)_2Ca$ $\longrightarrow R_2CO$. Cyclic ketones from dibasic acids, e.g. adipic acid $\longrightarrow$ cyclopentanone.

Rosenmund reaction:

$$RCOCl + H_2 \text{ (special catalyst)} \longrightarrow RCHO.$$

Special methods: CH_3CHO from $HC\equiv CH$; acetone by bacterial fermentation; chloral by chlorination of ethanol; acrolein by H_2SO_4-dehydration of glycerol.

Reactions

Aldehydes recognizable by reducing properties: silver mirror test; reduction of Fehling's solution (ketones negative).

Oxidative fission of ketones (dil. HNO_3). Probable involvement of enol form. Preparation of dibasic acids from cyclic ketones: cyclopentanone $\longrightarrow$ glutaric acid; cyclohexanone $\longrightarrow$ adipic acid.

Polymerization. Acetaldehyde with acid catalyst $\longrightarrow$ paraldehyde (cyclic trimer). Depolymerization of paraldehyde by addition of catalyst and slow distillation. Formaldehyde in water (probably as hydrate) $\longrightarrow$ paraformaldehyde (chain polymer).

Bisulfite-addition products. Equilibrium displaced by use of excess $NaHSO_3$. Products are water-soluble, ether-insoluble solids. Aldehyde or ketone regenerated by treatment with HCl or Na_2CO_3. Influence of size of alkyl groups on extent of addition. Reaction practically limited to aldehydes and methyl ketones.

HCN-addition: cyanohydrins, synthesis of α-hydroxy acids (e.g. mandelic acid). Use of HCN generated *in situ* ($NaCN + H_2SO_4$; bisulfite addition compound + NaCN). A little more general than bisulfite addition. Reversed by AgOH.

Grignard reaction. Very general, but with highly branched ketone addition may fail and a secondary or tertiary alkylmagnesium halide may effect reduction, with conversion of RMgX to an alkene. An OH or COOH group in the carbonyl compound consumes one mole of reagent but may not interfere with addition of second mole. Zerewitinoff-Kohler method of determining active-hydrogen and carbonyl groups (reaction with excess CH_3MgI, measurement of CH_4 evolved before and after addition of water).

Reduction of aldehydes and ketones by catalytic hydrogenation or with $LiAlH_4$ gives normal products. Reduction of ketones with metal combinations proceeds in part bimolecularly, e.g. acetone ($Mg-Hg + H_2O$) $\longrightarrow$ pinacol (diradical intermediate).

Meerwein-Ponndorf reduction: aluminum isopropoxide + isopropyl alcohol; displacement of equilibrium by distillation of acetone formed. Applicable to unsaturated carbonyl compounds (e.g. crotonaldehyde).

Aldol condensation. Requires activated α-H. Usually base-catalyzed. Aldol easily dehydrated to crotonaldehyde (activated α-H adjacent to β-OH). Mechanism: addition of $\bar{C}H_2CHO$ to carbonyl group. Acetone (less reactive carbonyl group) gives only a little diacetone alcohol in equilibrium, but product can be prepared with use of solid $Ba(OH)_2$ as catalyst in Soxhlet extractor; the more volatile monomer is separated and recycled by distillation.

Cannizzaro reaction: disproportionation induced by strong alkali in an aldehyde with no α-H. Mechanism: donation of H^-. Pentaerythritol from acetaldehyde and formaldehyde.

Condensation with amine derivatives. Hydrazine $\longrightarrow$ hydrazones. Phenylhydrazine $\longrightarrow$ phenylhydrazones. Hydroxylamine $\longrightarrow$ oximes. Semicarbazide $\longrightarrow$ semicarbazones. Use in diagnosis and identification. Mechanism of addition and elimination.

Wolff-Kishner reduction:

$$R_2C = NNH_2 \longrightarrow R_2CH_2.$$

Acetals and ketals: $RCHO + HOC_2H_5$ (dry HCl). Stable to bases, decomposed by aqueous acid. Ethylene glycol gives cyclic ketals (protection of carbonyl). Formation and desulfurization of ethylenethioketals.

Enols and Enolates

Tautomerism of acetoacetic ester:

$CH_3COCH_2CO_2C_2H_5$ (93%) $\rightleftharpoons$
$\quad\quad CH_3C(OH) = CHCO_2C_2H_5$ (7%).

Interconversion by α,γ-shift. Isolation of keto and enol forms. Equilibration with acid or base. Diethyl malonate less enolic, acetylacetone more enolic.

Acetoacetic ester synthesis. Preparation by ester condensation:

$$2\ CH_3CO_2C_2H_5 \xrightarrow{NaOC_2H_5} CH_3COCH_2CO_2C_2H_5.$$

Mono- and dialkylation of the enolate. Ketonic hydrolysis of the β-keto ester: $RCOCHR'CO_2C_2H_5$ $\longrightarrow RCOCH_2R'$. Dieckmann reaction (ester condensation of diester to cyclic ketone).

Malonic ester synthesis. Preparation from CH_2CNCO_2Na. Alkylation of sodio derivative, hydrolysis, and decarboxylation. Thus: RX $\longrightarrow$ RCH_2CO_2H or R_2CHCO_2H.

PROBLEMS

1. Give Geneva names for:
   (a) $CH_3CH(OH)COCH_2CH_3$
   (b) $(CH_3)_2CHCH_2CH_2CH_2C(CH_3) = CHCH_2OH$
   (c) $OHCC(CH_3) = CHCH = CHC(CH_3) = CHCHO$
2. Suggest an appropriate method for the preparation of each of the following compounds from the starting materials indicated:
   (a) Methyl ethyl ketone from *sec*-butyl alcohol
   (b) Methyl *n*-hexyl ketone from capryl alcohol, $CH_3(CH_2)_5CH(OH)CH_3$

176

(c) Methyl allyl ketone, starting with acetaldehyde and allyl bromide

(d) Sebacic acid-half aldehyde,

$$O=CH(CH_2)_8COOH,$$

from undecylenic acid,

$$CH_2=CH(CH_2)_8COOH$$

(e) *n*-Valeraldehyde from *n*-valeric acid

3. Indicate the steps required for transformation of cyclohexanone into cyclopentanone. How could the reverse transformation be accomplished?

4. Summarize quantitative and qualitative differences in reactions of aldehydes and ketones.

5. Cite specific comparisons that establish the order of reactivity of the carbonyl groups in the following compounds: acetone, diethyl ketone, acetaldehyde, chloral, diisopropyl ketone.

6. How could cinnamaldehyde,

$$C_6H_5CH=CHCHO,$$

be converted into cinnamyl alcohol,

$$C_6H_5CH=CHCH_2OH?$$

7. Predict the result of treatment of isobutyraldehyde with cold, dilute aqueous sodium hydroxide solution.

8. Predict the result of the action of a concentrated solution of alkali on trimethylacetaldehyde.

9. Suggest a synthesis of β-hydroxyisovaleric acid, $(CH_3)_2C(OH)CH_2COOH$, from acetone.

10. Suggest a procedure by which the aldehydic group of the compound $CH_3COCH_2CH_2CHO$ could be protected and the substance converted into the aldehyde-acid $HOOCCH_2CH_2CHO$.

11. One commercial process for making *n*-butyl alcohol starts with an aldol condensation of acetaldehyde. Formulate the process.

12. Cite specific examples establishing the relative reactivity of the carbonyl group of ketones and esters.

13. A substance $C_5H_{12}O$ yields an oxidation product $C_5H_{10}O$ that reacts with phenylhydrazine and gives a positive iodoform test. The original substance also can be dehydrated with sulfuric acid to a hydrocarbon C_5H_{10}, and this on oxidation yields acetone. What is the structure of the substance?

14. A substance $C_5H_8O_2$ forms a dioxime, gives a positive iodoform test and a positive silver mirror test, and can be converted into *n*-pentane. What is its structure?

15. Predict the result of the following reactions:
(a) Ethylene oxide + HCN
(b) $CH_3COCH_3 + (CH_3)_3CCHO$ (with a trace of alkali)

16. Starting with three-carbon components, devise syntheses for:
(a) Diethyl ketone   (c) Isovaleric acid
(b) Hexanone-3

17. A hydrocarbon C_7H_{12} yields cyclopentanecarboxylic acid on chromic acid oxidation. On reaction with concentrated sulfuric acid followed by hydrolysis it yields an alcohol, $C_7H_{14}O$, that gives a positive iodoform test. What is the structure of the hydrocarbon?

18. A compound $C_7H_{14}O_2$ (I) reacts with acetic anhydride to give $C_7H_{13}O(OCOCH_3)$ (II); it does not react with phenylhydrazine. When treated with $Pb(OAc)_4$, I gives $C_7H_{12}O_2$ (III), which with H_2NOH gives $C_7H_{12}(=NOH)_2$, reduces Fehling's solution, and on treatment with NaOI consumes 4 moles of the reagent to give iodoform and $HOOC(CH_2)_4COOH$. Give a brief interpretation of the significance of each of the observations recorded and deduce the structure of I.

19. Suggest an ionic mechanism for the ester condensation of ethyl acetate to acetoacetic ester.

20. Formulate syntheses for the following compounds from malonic ester and any halogen compounds desired:
(a) $(CH_3)_2CHCH_2CO_2H$
(b) $CH_3CH_2CH(CH_3)CO_2H$
(c) $HOOCCH_2CH_2CH_2CH_2CH_2CO_2H$

21. Predict the relative enol content of the C-methyl and C-acetyl derivatives of acetoacetic ester:

$$\begin{array}{cc} CH_3 & COCH_3 \\ | & | \\ CH_3COCHCOOC_2H_5 & CH_3COCHCOOC_2H_5 \end{array}$$

and

22. Account for the existence of two forms of oxalacetic acid (13.12).

READING REFERENCES

L. C. Cooley, "Acetone," *Ind. Eng. Chem.*, **29**, 1399 (1937)

C. F. H. Allen and A. H. Blatt, "The Carbon-Oxygen Double Bond," in H. Gilman, *Organic Chemistry*, 2nd Ed., I, 643–657, Wiley, New York (1943)

H. Adkins, "Equilibria and Rates in the Formation of Acetals and Semicarbazones," in H. Gilman, *Organic Chemistry*, 2nd Ed., I, 1046–1052, Wiley, New York (1943)

G. W. Wheland, *Resonance in Organic Chemistry*, Chapt. 7.9, "Tautomerism," Wiley (1955)

AMINES

Amines are derivatives of ammonia in which one or more hydrogen atoms are replaced by an alkyl group, and they are called primary, secondary, and tertiary amines according to the number of such substituents:

RNH_2
Primary
amine

Secondary
amine

Tertiary
amine

If but one group is introduced, the substance has a primary amino group (NH_2) and is a primary amine even though the alkyl substituent may be secondary or tertiary, for example *t*-butylamine, $(CH_3)_3CNH_2$. Methyl- and ethylamine were discovered in 1849 by Wurtz, and a general method of preparing secondary and tertiary as well as primary amines was discovered shortly by Hofmann [1] (1849). Methylamine is a gas and has a boiling point (-6.5) somewhat higher than that of ammonia (b.p. $-33.3°$). The odor of the also volatile ethylamine is so similar to that of ammonia that when Wurtz first had the material in hand he did not recognize it as a new substance until the alkaline gas by chance came near a flame and took fire. In general, amines that are either gases or fairly volatile liquids of moderate molecular weight have a pronounced odor similar to that of ammonia but less pungent and more fishlike. Dimethylamine and trimethylamine are constituents of herring brine. The lower amines are very soluble in water. The straight-chain amine $CH_3CH_2CH_2NHCH_2CH_2CH_3$, of molecular weight 101.2, has the boiling point 111°, which is slightly above that characteristic of unassociated liquids (100°). The slight

[1] August Wilhelm von Hofmann, 1818–1892; b. Giessen, Germany; professor at Bonn, Royal College of Chemistry, London (1845–64), Berlin; see reading ref., also *Ber.*, **25**, 3369 (1892); **35**, 4502 (1902)

association indicated is attributed to hydrogen bonding; since nitrogen is less electronegative than oxygen, the bonding is less pronounced than in alcohols. The branched-chain isomer $(CH_3)_2CHNHCH(CH_3)_2$ is more volatile (b.p. 84°).

Basic Properties. — Amines, like ammonia, give an alkaline reaction in aqueous solution and form salts with acids. The essential process is combination of the amine, functioning as an electron donor

$$(CH_3)_3N: \ + \ \begin{cases} \text{(a) } H^+ & \longrightarrow \quad (CH_3)_3\overset{+}{N}:H \\ \text{(b) } B(CH_3)_3 & \longrightarrow \quad (CH_3)_3N^+:B^-(CH_3)_3 \end{cases}$$
(Lewis acids)   Trimethylamine—Tri-
methylboron, m.p. 128°

or Lewis base, with the electron-accepting proton (a), and analogous combination occurs with other Lewis acids, for example trimethylboron (b). The new bond formed in case (b) is a coordinate covalent bond. The alkaline reaction noted when an amine is dissolved in water is due to excess hydroxide ion concentration following withdrawal of hydrogen ions by the combination (a), and the overall result can be represented thus:

$$R_3N: \ + \ \overset{+}{H}O\overset{-}{H} \ \rightleftharpoons \ R_3\overset{+}{N}:H \ + \ OH^-$$

The amine may be present in part as the unstable hydrate, R_3NHOH. The basic dissociation constant of an amine (k_b) is expressed as the product of the concentrations of the ammonium and hydroxide ions divided by the total concentration of unionized material, $[CH_3NH_2]$, for example:

$$k_b = \frac{[CH_3NH_3^+][OH^-]}{[CH_3NH_2]}$$

*pK_b measures
basic strength*

Basic strength is conveniently expressed as the negative logarithm of the basic dissociation constant; thus $pK_b = -\log k_b$. A strong base has a low pK_b value (NaOH, pK_b about 0), a weak one has a value approaching the limit $pK_b = 14$. Typical aliphatic amines listed in the margin with their pK_b values are all more strongly basic than ammonia; aromatic amines, typified by aniline, are much weaker bases. That methylamine and ethylamine are stronger bases than ammonia by 1.4–1.5 pK_b units is attributable to the electron release of the methyl or ethyl group, which increases the electron density on nitrogen and hence increases its affinity for a proton; the relationship of the higher members is still obscure.

NH_3, 4.75
CH_3NH_2, 3.37
$(CH_3)_2NH$, 3.22
$(CH_3)_3N$, 4.20
$CH_3CH_2NH_2$, 3.27
$(CH_3CH_2)_2NH$, 2.89
$(CH_3CH_2)_3N$, 3.36
$C_6H_5NH_2$ (Aniline), 9.30

Salts with mineral acids are analogous to ammonium salts, and are formed both in aqueous solution and under anhydrous conditions, for example by passing hydrogen chloride gas into an ethereal solution of the amine, in which case the amine salt separates quantitatively as a white solid. Alternate conventional methods of formulating and naming amine salts are illustrated for the salt of methylamine and hydrochloric acid:

CH_3NH_3Cl
Methylammonium
chloride

$CH_3NH_2 \cdot HCl$
Methylamine
hydrochloride

Salt formation involves an increase in the valence of nitrogen from three to five, and the fifth linkage is polar; the reaction is represented as follows:

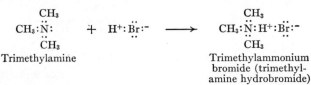

Trimethylamine

Trimethylammonium
bromide (trimethyl-
amine hydrobromide)

Tests for amines and salts

The hydrogen ion accepts the unshared pair of electrons of the nitrogen atom with formation of a covalent bond, and the nitrogen-containing group thereby acquires a positive charge. Amine salts, owing to their ionic character, contrast with amines in physical properties. They are all odorless, nonvolatile solids, even though the amines from which they are derived are odoriferous gases or liquids, and they are insoluble in ether or in hydrocarbon solvents, which dissolve the typically organic amines. With the exception of substances of very high molecular weight, the salts are readily soluble in water and exist in the solution in ionized condition. The solubility in water is decreased by addition of excess of the appropriate mineral acid, and use is made of the common-ion effect in crystallization of amine salts. Ability to form salts is a property distinctive of amines and can be recognized easily by simple qualitative tests. An amine of low molecular weight may be substantially as soluble in water as it is in dilute hydrochloric acid, but if so it will be in the range of the odoriferous amines, and the fact of salt formation will be evident from obliteration of the odor on addition of excess acid. Odorless amines invariably are at most only partially soluble in water, and salt formation is apparent from the fact that they can be brought into solution by addition of a mineral acid. Similarly, an amine salt can be recognized by addition of sodium hydroxide to the aqueous solution. The alkali is a much stronger base than the amine, and liberation of the amine is evident either from the odor or from separation of an oil or solid. For recovery of an amine from a salt, the material set free by addition of alkali is collected by filtration of a solid, extraction with ether, or steam distillation of a volatile amine.

11.3

Quaternary Ammonium Compounds. — Tertiary amines when heated with alkyl halides combine to form compounds similar to ammonium salts but having four alkyl groups attached to nitrogen and hence called quaternary ammonium salts. These salts are solid

$$(CH_3)_3N \xrightarrow{CH_3I} (CH_3)_4N^+I^-$$
Tetramethylammonium
iodide

ionic substances readily soluble in water and insoluble in ether and comparable to hydrochlorides and hydrobromides of the same tertiary amines. They are also difficultly fusible and when strongly heated decompose into a tertiary amine and an alkyl halide. The tetra-alkylammonium salts contrast with amine hydrohalides and simple ammonium salts in behavior toward alkalis, for no free amine is liberated and instead there results an equilibrium mixture containing a stable quaternary ammonium hydroxide, for example:

$$(CH_3)_4\overset{+}{N}I^- + KOH \rightleftharpoons (CH_3)_4NOH^- + KI$$
Tetramethylammonium
hydroxide

The tetraalkyl derivative cannot decompose by loss of water in the manner characteristic of ammonium hydroxide and amine hydrates and therefore affords a high concentration of hydroxide ion. The substance is a strong base comparable to sodium or potassium hydroxide, which explains why the equilibrium constant in the above reaction is close to unity. The preparation of a quaternary ammonium base is accomplished by treatment of the halide in aqueous solution with silver hydroxide, for silver halide precipitates and the equilibrium is displaced. The filtered aqueous solution can be evap-

$$(CH_3)_4\overset{+}{N}I^- + AgOH \longrightarrow (CH_3)_4\overset{+}{N}OH^- + AgI$$

orated without decomposition of the organic base, which can be obtained as a crystalline solid, usually as a deliquescent hydrate. Concentrated solutions of quaternary ammonium hydroxides have a caustic, corrosive action similar to alkalis and cannot be stored in glass vessels without contamination due to attack of the container.

PREPARATION OF AMINES

Alkylation of Ammonia. — One of several fundamental discoveries made by Hofmann in pioneering investigations of amines is that alkyl groups can be introduced directly into ammonia by interaction with an alkyl halide and subsequent treatment with alkali (1849). The reaction is general but is subject to the disadvantage that higher

11.4

$$RX \xrightarrow{HNH_2} RNH_2 \cdot HX \xrightarrow{NaOH} RNH_2$$

substitution inevitably occurs. When ethyl bromide reacts with ammonia, the halide initially adds to the trivalent nitrogen to give an ammonium salt, but this enters into equilibrium with ammonia still present with liberation of a certain amount of ethylamine. The primary amine then competes with ammonia for the alkyl halide and yields some of the secondary amine salt; repetition of the process affords the tertiary amine salt, and in the presence of excess alkyl halide the reaction may even continue to production of the quaternary ammonium salt. A primary amine thus is not the exclusive product

$$C_2H_5Br \ + \ NH_3 \ \longrightarrow \ C_2H_5N^+H_3Br^-$$

$$C_2H_5N^+H_3Br^- \ + \ NH_3 \ \rightleftharpoons \ C_2H_5NH_2 \ + \ NH_4Br$$

$$C_2H_5NH_2 \ + \ C_2H_5Br \ \longrightarrow \ (C_2H_5)_2N^+H_2Br^-$$

$$(C_2H_5)_2N^+H_2Br^- \ + \ NH_3 \ \rightleftharpoons \ (C_2H_5)_2NH \ + \ NH_4Br$$

Mixtures

of a reaction conducted with equivalent amounts of reagents, but is contaminated with secondary and tertiary amines, and in the preparation of a secondary amine by the reaction $RNH_2 + R'Br$, some of the corresponding tertiary amine invariably is formed. Thus the method of alkylation is practicable for preparation of pure products only where an adequate method of separation or purification is available. When the halogen atom of an expensive intermediate is to be replaced by a primary amino group, it is expedient to use a large excess of ammonia in order to suppress formation of disubstituted ammonia, as in the following preparation:

$$CH_3\underset{\underset{Br}{|}}{C}HCO_2H \ \xrightarrow[65-70\%]{NH_3 \text{ (70 equivalents)}} \ CH_3\underset{\underset{NH_2}{|}}{C}HCO_2H$$
Alanine

11.5

Reduction of Unsaturated Nitrogen Compounds. — Oximes, nitriles (cyanides), and amides are all reduced by lithium aluminum hydride to amines; those of the following types yield identical products:

Reduction with LiAlH₄

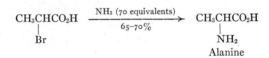

Oximes and nitriles are reducible also by other methods, but amides resist reduction by reagents other than the metal hydride. **Amides**

Examples:

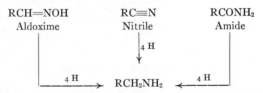

of the types RCONHR′ and RCONR′R″ are reduced by lithium aluminum hydride to secondary and tertiary amines, respectively.

Example:

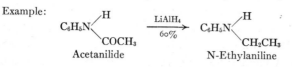

$$\underset{\text{Acetanilide}}{C_6H_5N\begin{matrix}H\\COCH_3\end{matrix}} \xrightarrow[60\%]{LiAlH_4} \underset{\text{N-Ethylaniline}}{C_6H_5N\begin{matrix}H\\CH_2CH_3\end{matrix}}$$

Nitro compounds

Reduction of nitro compounds is a particularly useful route to aromatic amines, since nitro compounds are available by nitration of benzenoid hydrocarbons; nitrobenzene (4.33), for example, affords aniline in high yield by a variety of methods of reduction. Nitro-

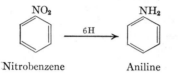

Nitrobenzene Aniline

alkanes are less readily available and less common but can be obtained industrially by vapor-phase nitration of alkanes and in the laboratory by the reaction $RX + AgNO_2 \longrightarrow RNO_2 + AgX$ [Victor Meyer, 1872; improved method, N. Kornblum, 1955: $RX + NaNO_2$ in a mixture of urea and dimethylformamide, $HCON(CH_3)_2$]. Nitromethane is prepared from sodium chloroacetate by the reactions formulated in 37% overall yield. Nitroalkanes are seldom used for

$$ClCH_2CO_2Na \xrightarrow{NaNO_2} O_2NCH_2CO_2Na \xrightarrow[85°]{H_2O} CH_3NO_2 + NaHCO_3$$

preparation of the corresponding amines but are of value for the synthesis of amino alcohols. The unsaturated nitro group of nitromethane activates the methyl group for base-catalyzed aldol condensation, for example, with benzaldehyde to give a nitro alcohol reducible to the amino alcohol, β-phenyl-β-hydroxyethylamine.

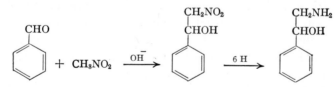

11.6 **Hofmann Reaction.** — A reaction discovered by Hofmann in 1881 affords primary amines in excellent yields uncontaminated with secondary amines. The method consists in treatment of an amide with sodium hypochlorite or hypobromite and results in elimination of the carbonyl group of the amide as carbon dioxide. The mechanism

$$R{-}C\begin{matrix}{/\!\!/}O\\ \backslash NH_2\end{matrix} + NaOBr \xrightarrow{NaOH} RNH_2 + NaBr + CO_2$$

Overall reaction

of this remarkable transformation is well established. The reaction proceeds in two stages, of which the first consists in formation of a bromoamide by substitution of bromine for one of the hydrogen atoms attached to nitrogen and activated by the adjacent carbonyl group. Bromoamides are stable in the absence of excess alkali and can be prepared in good yield by adding sufficient dilute alkali to a mixture

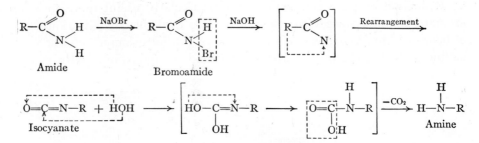

Mechanism

of equivalent amounts of the amide and of bromine to produce a corresponding amount of sodium hypobromite. The bromoamide when warmed with excess alkali decomposes to the primary amine and carbon dioxide as the result of elimination of hydrogen bromide and formation of a transient intermediate and rearrangement to an isocyanate by migration of the alkyl group from carbon to nitrogen. The electronic formulation shows that the nitrogen atom of the intermediate has only a sextet of electrons; this condition of instability

Electron sextet

$$O \qquad\qquad O \qquad\qquad O$$
$$R:C:N:Br: \xrightarrow{-HBr} R:C:N \longrightarrow C::N:R$$
$$H$$

induces migration of the alkyl group with the pair of shared electrons from carbon to nitrogen, which completes the nitrogen octet. Actually elimination of hydrogen bromide and alkyl migration are synchronous steps in a concerted reaction and the intermediate probably has no appreciable life period. Isocyanates have been isolated in some instances and are well characterized compounds, usually prepared by condensation of amines with phosgene:

$$RNH_2 + ClCOCl \longrightarrow RNHCOCl \longrightarrow RN{=}C{=}O + HCl$$

Isocyanates are subject to hydrolysis by alkalis; indeed this reaction was employed by Wurtz in the first preparation of an alkylamine. The hydrolysis step is formulated as involving addition of water to the carbonyl group, migration of hydrogen, and decarboxylation of a carboxyamine (carbamic acid), for which ample analogy exists.

These many changes proceed efficiently, and in an actual prepara-

tion no intermediate need be isolated. Hofmann obtained excellent
yields of pure primary amines from a number of amides, for example:

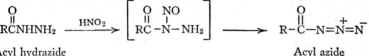

$$\underset{\text{Caproamide}}{CH_3CH_2CH_2CH_2CH_2CONH_2} \xrightarrow[88\%]{NaOBr} \underset{n\text{-Amylamine}}{CH_3CH_2CH_2CH_2CH_2NH_2}$$

The **Curtius**[2] **reaction** (1894), also available for preparation of
primary amines, utilizes an acyl azide prepared either from an acid
chloride and sodium azide ($RCOCl + NaN_3$) or by the action of
nitrous acid on an acyl hydrazide (from an ester and hydrazine, 9.20).

11.7

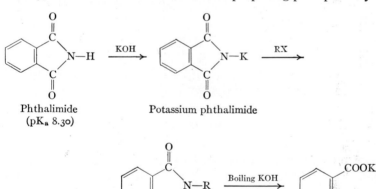

Acyl hydrazide   Acyl azide

*Rearrangement to
an isocyanate*

Isocyanate

When heated in a solvent, the acyl azide loses nitrogen with rearrangement to an isocyanate, as in the Hofmann reaction.

Gabriel Synthesis. — Gabriel,[3] working in Hofmann's laboratory
in 1887, introduced a useful method of preparing pure primary amines

11.8

Phthalimide   Potassium phthalimide
(pK_a 8.30)

*Affords pure
primary amines*

$+$ RNH_2

consisting in alkylation of a derivative of ammonia in which two of
the positions are temporarily occupied by blocking groups to
prevent introduction of more than a single alkyl substituent. The
cyclic substance phthalimide, employed as the ammonia derivative,
possesses a hydrogen atom doubly activated by carbonyl groups;

[2] Theodor Curtius, 1857–1928; Ph.D. Leipzig (Kolbe); successor (1902) to Victor Meyer
at Heidelberg
[3] Siegmund Gabriel, 1851–1924; b. Berlin; Ph.D. Heidelberg; Berlin; *Ber.*, **59A**, 1 (1926)

this activation renders the compound acidic and capable of forming metal salts, which react with alkyl halides. The alkylated phthalimide is then hydrolyzed with alkali and the liberated amine is removed from the alkaline mixture by steam distillation.

REACTIONS

11.9

Acylation. — Primary and secondary amines react with acetic anhydride or acetyl chloride to give acetyl derivatives in which a hydrogen atom of the amino group is replaced by an acetyl group. Although

$$(CH_3)_2CHCH_2NH_2 \xrightarrow{(CH_3CO)_2O} (CH_3)_2CHCH_2NHCOCH_3 + CH_3CO_2H$$

Primary amine   Acetylisobutylamine (m.p. 107°)

$$\begin{array}{c} (CH_3)_2CH \\ (CH_3)_2CH \end{array}\!\!\!>\!\!NH \xrightarrow{CH_3COCl} \begin{array}{c} (CH_3)_2CH \\ (CH_3)_2CH \end{array}\!\!\!>\!\!NCOCH_3 + HCl$$

Secondary amine   Acetyldiisopropylamine (liq., b.p. 222–225°)

Neutral derivatives:
$RNHCOCH_3$ and
R_2NCOCH_3

a primary amine has two replaceable hydrogen atoms, diacetyl compounds are rarely encountered. The monoacetyl derivatives of primary and secondary amines are useful for characterization and identification, particularly since acetylation often converts a liquid amine into a solid product. Furthermore, basic amines are converted by acetylation into neutral substances, for the acid-forming acetyl residue counterbalances the basic quality of the trivalent nitrogen. Thus acetyl amines do not form salts with mineral acids and are not extracted from an ethereal solution by hydrochloric acid.

A tertiary amine has no replaceable hydrogen and is indifferent to acetic anhydride. The differentiation between amines that are easily acetylated and those that fail to react is useful both in classifying unknown compounds with respect to type and in effecting separations and purifications. For example, a tertiary amine contaminated with primary and secondary amines can be freed from these materials by adding enough acetic anhydride to react with all acylable material and extracting a solution of the mixture in ether with dilute hydrochloric acid; the neutral acetyl derivatives of primary and secondary amines remain in the ether layer, and the tertiary amine is selectively extracted and can be recovered from the aqueous acid layer by neutralization with alkali.

11.10

A much used acylating agent of the aromatic series is benzoyl chloride, C_6H_5COCl, which reacts to give benzoyl derivatives of the types $RNHCOC_6H_5$ and $R_2NCOC_6H_5$. Another aromatic acid chloride, benzenesulfonyl chloride ($C_6H_5SO_2Cl$), is employed in the

Hinsberg test for distinguishing between primary and secondary amines. A reaction of the usual type occurs in each case, but the products are distinguished by the fact that those from primary amines form water-soluble alkali salts whereas those from secondary amines do not; both types are insoluble in acid. Tertiary amines do not react with the reagent. The salt-forming property of the benzene-

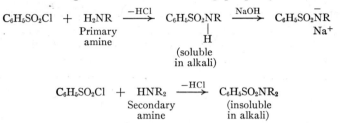

$$C_6H_5SO_2Cl + H_2NR \xrightarrow{-HCl} C_6H_5SO_2NR \xrightarrow{NaOH} C_6H_5SO_2\overset{-}{N}R$$

Primary amine

$\underset{H}{|}$

(soluble in alkali)

Na^+

$$C_6H_5SO_2Cl + HNR_2 \xrightarrow{-HCl} C_6H_5SO_2NR_2$$

Secondary amine

(insoluble in alkali)

sulfonamide derivative of a primary amine is attributable to the presence of a remaining amino hydrogen atom activated by the unsaturated sulfonyl group. The derivative of a secondary amine has no corresponding hydrogen atom, and hence is not acidic. Like other acyl derivatives, benzenesulfonamides of both types can be hydrolyzed, with regeneration of the amines. The benzenesulfonamide from a primary amine can be alkylated and the product hydrolyzed, and in this way the original amine can be converted into a pure N-alkyl derivative:

Sulfonyl group

$$RNH_2 \xrightarrow{C_6H_5SO_2Cl, NaOH} R\overset{-}{N}SO_2C_6H_5 \xrightarrow{(CH_3)_2SO_4} RNSO_2C_6H_5 \xrightarrow{Hydrol.} RNH$$

Na^+

$\underset{CH_3}{|}$ $\underset{CH_3}{|}$

Reaction with Nitrous Acid. — The three types of amines all respond differently to nitrous acid. A primary amine reacts with liberation of nitrogen and formation of an alcohol. A possible interpretation of the transformation is indicated in the formulation. The

$$R-N{\overset{H}{\underset{H}{\big<}}} + HO-N=O \longrightarrow \left[R-\underset{}{N}-N=\overset{H}{\overset{|}{O}} \longrightarrow R-\overline{|N=N|}-OH \right] \longrightarrow ROH + N_2$$

nitrogen liberated is quantitatively equivalent to the primary amine employed, and since the gas can be collected and its volume measured accurately, the reaction provides a useful method of determining the amount of primary amino nitrogen present in a weighed sample of a given substance. If the reaction mixture is kept strongly acidic (pH 3) during treatment with nitrous acid, the amine may be convertible into the corresponding alcohol, though the high acidity may result in dehydration of a secondary or a tertiary alcohol. In a less acidic medium the alkyl group frequently rearranges; for example, *n*-propylamine gives isopropyl alcohol, propylene, and a trace of *n*-propyl alcohol.

Secondary amines combine with nitrous acid by elimination of water between two molecules and consequent replacement of the lone amino hydrogen atom by a nitroso group (—NO); the products (yellow) are nitrosoamines. The reaction corresponds to the first

$$\begin{array}{c} R \\ \diagdown \\ \diagup \\ R' \end{array} N\!-\!H \ + \ HON\!=\!O \ \longrightarrow \ \begin{array}{c} R \\ \diagdown \\ \diagup \\ R' \end{array} N\!-\!N\!=\!O \ + \ H_2O$$

Secondary amine   Nitrosoamine

step postulated in the reaction of a primary amine and the difference in the final outcome is that the initial product has no hydrogen available for migration and is stable. Tertiary amines, having no replaceable hydrogen, neither liberate nitrogen nor form nitroso derivatives, and at most form with nitrous acid unstable salts that are destroyed on neutralization.

11.12   **Thermal Decomposition of Quaternary Ammonium Hydroxides** (Hofmann, 1851). — The mono-, di-, and trimethyl derivatives of ammonium hydroxide, like the parent substance, exist only in aqueous solution, and on evaporation of the solution lose the elements of water and revert to the free amines. The quaternary compound, tetramethylammonium hydroxide, has no hydrogen atom available for elimination of water and in aqueous solution is stable and strongly basic. When heated somewhat above the boiling point of water, however, the substance decomposes and yields trimethylamine and methanol. Other quaternary bases likewise undergo thermal decom-

Elimination of methanol

$$[(CH_3)_4N]^+OH^- \xrightarrow{\ 130-135°\ } (CH_3)_3N \ + \ CH_3OH$$

Tetramethylammonium
hydroxide (pentahydrate, m.p. 63°)

position, but if the alkyl group eliminated in the process contains two or more carbon atoms the nitrogen-free reaction product is not the alcohol but the corresponding alkene. Thus tetraethylammonium hydroxide when heated breaks down into triethylamine, ethylene,

Alkene formation

$$[(CH_3CH_2)_4N]^+OH^- \xrightarrow{\ 100°\ } (CH_3CH_2)_3N \ + \ CH_2\!=\!CH_2 \ + \ H_2O$$

(tetrahydrate, m.p. 50°)

and water. This behavior is typical of the bases as a class, and formation of an alcohol in the one instance where production of an alkene is impossible represents a special case. Furthermore, elimination of a methyl group as methanol occurs less readily than the splitting off of any higher alkyl group as the alkene. If the hydroxide contains both methyl and ethyl groups, as in $[(CH_3)_3NCH_2CH_3]^+OH^-$ or $[(CH_3CH_2)_3NCH_3]^+OH^-$, decomposition invariably affords ethylene and not methanol. When a still higher group competes with methyl, the latter holds fast to nitrogen and the higher group is

severed with loss of a β-hydrogen and formation of an alkene. The
decomposition proceeds readily and in good yield at moderate tem-

$$\underset{\underset{OH^-}{}}{(CH_3)_3\overset{+}{N}}-\overset{|}{\underset{\beta}{\underset{|}{C}}}-\overset{|}{\underset{|}{CH}}- \longrightarrow (CH_3)_3N + \overset{|}{\underset{|}{C}}=\overset{|}{\underset{|}{C}} + H_2O$$

peratures; it often can be effected by merely boiling an aqueous
solution of the base.

Hofmann Degradation. — Hofmann saw in this smoothly occurring
reaction and in the greater firmness of attachment of methyl than of
other groups a general scheme applicable both to determination of
structures of amines and to preparation of ethylenic compounds. The
first step consists in treating an amine with excess methyl iodide to
replace all available amino hydrogens by methyl groups and then to
produce the quaternary salt or methiodide from the tertiary amine
(exhaustive methylation). Analysis reveals whether the starting
material is a primary, secondary, or tertiary amine, for these types
allow the introduction of three, two, or one methyl group, respectively.
The iodide is then converted with moist silver oxide into the quaternary ammonium hydroxide and this is pyrolyzed. In special cases

11.13

*Exhaustive methyl-
ation and decomposi-
tion of $R_4N^+OH^-$*

$$RCH_2CH_2NH_2 \xrightarrow{CH_3I} \underset{I^-}{RCH_2CH_2\overset{+}{N}(CH_3)_3} \xrightarrow{AgOH} \underset{OH^-}{RCH_2CH_2\overset{+}{N}(CH_3)_3}$$
$$\xrightarrow{Heat} RCH=CH_2$$

such a process is preferred for preparation of alkenes. If an amine of
unknown structure is under investigation, it can be degraded by the
Hofmann procedure into a simpler, nitrogen-free substance having
an unsaturated center of assistance in further characterization. Many
naturally occurring nitrogen bases of elaborate structure have been
profitably investigated by this method. Several tertiary amines have
been encountered in which the nitrogen atom is substituted by one
methyl group and two higher groups that differ from each other and
are both complex. In this case exhaustive methylation and pyrolysis
of the quaternary ammonium hydroxide (1) releases one of the large
groups in a form suitable for characterization, and repetition of the
process (2) releases the other:

$$\underset{R'CH_2CH_2}{\overset{RCH_2CH_2}{\diagdown}}N \cdot CH_3 \longrightarrow \underset{R'CH_2CH_2}{\overset{RCH_2CH_2}{\diagdown}}\underset{OH^-}{\overset{+}{N}(CH_3)_2} \xrightarrow{(1)}$$

$$R'CH_2CH_2N(CH_3)_2 + RCH=CH_2$$
$$\downarrow$$
$$\underset{OH^-}{R'CH_2CH_2\overset{+}{N}(CH_3)_3} \xrightarrow{(2)} R'CH=CH_2 + (CH_3)_3N$$

189

11.14

Amides of the type $RCONH_2$ are related to acids in the same way that amines are related to alcohols, and they are also acyl derivatives of ammonia. They are neutral, owing to the combination of an acid-forming and a base-forming group. Acetamide, CH_3CONH_2, is comparable in this respect to acetylmethylamine, $CH_3NHCOCH_3$, which is also defined as N-methylacetamide (the prefixed letter denotes that the substituent is attached to the nitrogen atom).

Typical amides are crystalline solids, and since they are easily prepared from acids they are often employed for characterization of liquid acids. Amides have abnormally high boiling points; *n*-valer-

CH_3CONH_2	$CH_3CH_2CONH_2$	$CH_3(CH_2)_{16}CONH_2$	$C_6H_5CONH_2$
Acetamide	Propionamide	Stearamide	Benzamide
(m.p. 82.0°, b.p. 222°)	(m.p. 80°, b.p. 213°)	(m.p. 109°)	(m.p. 130°)

amide, of molecular weight 101.15, boils in the range 100–130° at 6 mm. pressure.

11.15

Preparation. — Acids can be converted into amides by the action of ammonia on their ester, acid chloride, or anhydride derivatives, as already noted; the route through the halide is usually the most convenient. A method useful in technical operations consists in pyrolysis of the ammonium salt of the acid, for example:

$$CH_3COONH_4 \xrightarrow[\text{87–90\%}]{\text{Slow distillation}} CH_3CONH_2 + H_2O$$
[from $CH_3COOH + (NH_4)_2CO_3$]

Amides also result from partial hydrolysis of nitriles (9.7). One procedure for conversion of nitriles into amides consists in use as catalyst

Ion-exchange resin as catalyst

of an ion-exchange basic resin, for example, the commercial product IRO–400, a water-insoluble polymer containing quaternary ammonium chloride groups. The resin is stirred with dilute alkali and the resulting resin base is washed free of sodium chloride and of excess alkali and added to a solution of the nitrile. Brief boiling (1 hr.) of

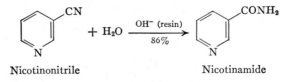

Nicotinonitrile   Nicotinamide

the suspension effects hydrolysis to the amide stage and no further, and the filtered solution of the amide is free from inorganic salts.

11.16

Hydrolysis

Reactions. — Hydrolysis of amides to acids proceeds smoothly but requires somewhat drastic conditions, for these substances are much less reactive than esters. Prolonged refluxing with a mixture of acetic and hydrochloric acid or with alcoholic alkali (in a copper flask) may

be required, but the material is not damaged in the process, and the
acid is usually obtainable in good yield. The primary amino group
present is attacked by nitrous acid in the manner characteristic of
primary amines, and this reaction affords a satisfactory method of
hydrolysis.

$$R-C\!\!\begin{array}{c}{}^O\\ {}_{NH_2}\end{array} + HNO_2 \longrightarrow R-C\!\!\begin{array}{c}{}^O\\ {}_{OH}\end{array} + N_2 + H_2O$$

Amides are convertible into nitriles by dehydration, usually accomplished by the action of phosphorus pentoxide or of boiling acetic
anhydride. The reaction represents reversal of the partial hydrolysis
of a nitrile and may proceed through the enolic form, present in small
amounts in equilibrium with the amide. The N-bromination of amides

$$R-\overset{O}{\overset{\|}{C}}-NH_2 \rightleftharpoons \left[R-\overset{\overset{OH}{|}}{C}=N{H} \right] \overset{-H_2O}{\longrightarrow} R-C\equiv N$$

with neutral sodium hypobromite to the derivatives RCONHBr and
the alkaline cleavage of these substances to amines have been described (11.6).

Imides. — The dibasic succinic acid can be converted by usual
methods into a neutral diamido derivative, succinamide. This substance when strongly heated could conceivably suffer dehydration to
a nitrile, but instead it loses ammonia and yields a cyclic diacyl-sub-
stituted ammonia derivative, succinimide. Succinimide is a weak
acid (pK$_a$ 10.52) capable of forming salts with alkalis. Phthalimide
(11.8), a substance of similar structure, is even more strongly acidic.
Two acyl substituents more than compensate for the basic character

$$\begin{array}{c}CH_2CONH_2\\ |\\ CH_2CONH_2\\ \text{Succinamide}\\ \text{(m.p. 260° dec.)}\end{array} \overset{\text{Heat}}{\longrightarrow} \begin{array}{c}CH_2C\!\!\begin{array}{c}{}^O\\ \\ \end{array}\\ | \qquad NH\\ CH_2C\!\!\begin{array}{c}\\ {}_O\end{array}\\ \text{Succinimide}\\ \text{(m.p. 126°)}\end{array}$$

inherent in trivalent nitrogen; the imido hydrogen atom is activated
by both carbonyl groups, and separates as a proton. Imides are hydrolyzed more readily than the usual amides. Thus succinimide is
convertible in good yield to the monoamido compound succinamic
acid, HOOCCH$_2$CH$_2$CONH$_2$, m.p. 157°. This half-amide probably
is an intermediate in the reaction of succinimide with sodium or
potassium hypobromite, a useful application of the Hofmann reaction
to the preparation of an amino acid.

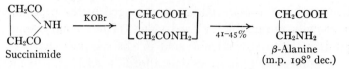

Succinimide

$$\text{CH}_2\text{CO} \diagdown \text{NH} \xrightarrow{\text{KOBr}} \left[\begin{array}{c} \text{CH}_2\text{COOH} \\ | \\ \text{CH}_2\text{CONH}_2 \end{array} \right] \xrightarrow[41-45\%]{} \begin{array}{c} \text{CH}_2\text{COOH} \\ | \\ \text{CH}_2\text{NH}_2 \end{array}$$

β-Alanine
(m.p. 198° dec.)

N-Bromosuccinimide

N-Bromosuccinimide is prepared by adding bromine to an ice-cold solution of succinimide in alkali and quickly collecting the material that precipitates. The bromine atom in this bromoimide is described

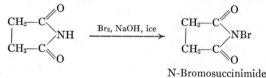

N-Bromosuccinimide

as a positive halogen, since on hydrolysis it combines with the negative hydroxide ion to form hypobromous acid; an alkyl bromide on hydrolysis affords hydrobromic acid. N-Bromosuccinimide is useful for allylic bromination of alkenes (8.10) and unsaturated esters, as

$$\text{CH}_3\text{CH}=\text{CHCOOCH}_3 + \text{N-Bromosuccinimide} \xrightarrow[86\%]{\text{Boiling CCl}_4}$$

Methyl crotonate

$$\text{BrCH}_2\text{CH}=\text{CHCOOCH}_3 + \text{Succinimide}$$

Methyl γ-bromocrotonate

formulated for methyl crotonate. In the presence of water N-bromosuccinimide functions as a mild oxidizing agent capable of oxidizing certain secondary alcoholic groups.

Urea: $(\text{NH}_2)_2\text{C}=\text{O}$, m.p. 132.7°. — Urea is important as a normal product of metabolism in the animal organism and as starting material for manufacture of plastics. It is the diamide of carbonic acid and can be prepared by the action of ammonia on the corresponding acid chloride, phosgene (ClCOCl). One industrial method of preparation consists in heating carbon dioxide with ammonia under pressure (1), and a second in partial hydrolysis of cyanamide (2).

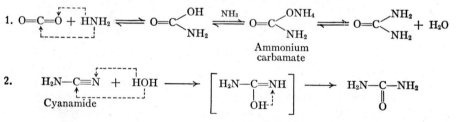

Preparation

1.
Ammonium carbamate

2.
Cyanamide

Secretion in urine

The normal individual excretes in the urine some 28–30 g. of urea per day, formed as a product of metabolism of proteins. The substance can be isolated as the nitric acid salt, urea mononitrate, $\text{H}_2\text{NCONH}_2 \cdot \text{HNO}_3$. Because of the presence of two amino groups and only one acid-forming group, urea is more basic than an ordinary amide and forms mono salts.

SUMMARY

Types. Primary, RNH_2; secondary, R_2NH; tertiary, R_3N; quaternary, $R_4N^+X^-$ and $R_4N^+OH^-$; nitrogen-substituted derivatives, $RNHCOCH_3$ (N-acetylamine).

Boiling points. Straight-chain amines only slightly associated (N, less electronegative than O, has less capacity for H-bonding). Branching increases volatility.

Basic properties. R_3N as a Lewis base (donates electrons to proton). Analogous combination with $B(CH_3)_3$ (coordinate covalent bond). Classical basic dissociation constant (k_b). Basic strength expressed as $pK_b = -\log k_b$. Examples of strong, intermediate, and weak bases: KOH

and $(CH_3)_4N^+OH^-$, pK_b approaching zero; CH_3NH_2, pK_b 3.4; NH_3, pK_b 4.7; $C_6H_5NH_2$ (aniline), pK_b 9.3.

Salts, e.g. $RNH_3^+Cl^-$ (salted out by H^+Cl^-). Odorless solids soluble in water and insoluble in ether. Note contrasting properties of free amines: lower members gases or liquids of NH_3-like odor, higher members if odorless are water-insoluble, ether-soluble. Amines and salts thus easily recognized by tests with acids or bases.

Quaternary compounds. $R_3N + RI \longrightarrow R_4N^+I^-$. Quaternary ammonium hydroxide ($R_4N^+I^-$ + AgOH) stable in water solution and strongly basic (cf. KOH).

Preparation

$RX + NH_3 \longrightarrow RNH_2$. Disadvantage: gives some R_2NH and R_3N. For replacement of X by NH_2, e.g. preparation of alanine, $CH_3CH(NH_2)CO_2H$, use large excess of NH_3.

Lithium aluminum hydride reduction of oximes, nitriles, amides. Reduction of nitro compounds: (a) nitrobenzene $\longrightarrow$ aniline, (b) aldol condensation of benzaldehyde with nitromethane and reduction to an amino alcohol.

Hofmann hypobromite method. Mechanism:

amide $\longrightarrow$ bromoamide $\longrightarrow$ intermediate containing nitrogen atom with an electron-sextet that promotes migration of alkyl group $\longrightarrow$ isocyanate $\longrightarrow$ carbamic acid $\longrightarrow$ primary amine. High yields of pure products.

Curtius reaction. Ester $\longrightarrow$ hydrazide ($RCONHNH_2$) $\longrightarrow$ azide ($RCON_3$) $\longrightarrow$ isocyanate $\longrightarrow$ carbamic acid $\longrightarrow$ primary amine.

Gabriel synthesis. Alkylation of potassium phthalimide and hydrolysis.

Reactions

Acetylation. Acetic anhydride converts primary and secondary amines into N-acetyl derivatives (neutral, not extracted from ether by HCl); no reaction with tertiary amines.

Hinsberg test. Benzenesulfonyl chloride ($C_6H_5SO_2Cl$) with RNH_2 (+ NaOH) gives an alkali-soluble derivative ($C_6H_5SO_2NHR$); with R_2NH gives an alkali-insoluble derivative; does not react with R_3N. Preparative use:

$RNH_2 \longrightarrow RNHSO_2C_6H_5 \longrightarrow$
$\qquad RN(CH_3)SO_2C_6H_5 \longrightarrow RNHCH_3$

Nitrous acid. $RNH_2 \longrightarrow ROH + N_2$ (rear-

rangement in R group above pH 3). $R_2NH \longrightarrow R_2NNO$ (yellow nitrosoamine). R_3N does not react.

Thermal decomposition of quaternary ammonium hydroxides.

$$(CH_3)_4N^+OH^- \longrightarrow R_3N + CH_3OH$$
$$(CH_3CH_2)_4N^+OH^- \longrightarrow R_3N + CH_2{=}CH_2$$

In mixed types methyl always stays fixed to N and a higher group is eliminated as an alkene. Hofmann degradation of an amine: exhaustive methylation and conversion into quaternary ammonium hydroxide, e.g. $RCH_2CH_2N^+(CH_3)_3OH^-$; pyrolysis to $RCH{=}CH_2 + (CH_3)_3N$.

Amides ($RCONH_2$, $RNHCOCH_3$)

Neutral (acyl group balances basic nitrogen). High boiling points indicate association. $RCONH_2$ prepared conveniently from $RCOCl$ (also from esters and anhydrides) or by partial hydrolysis of RCN (efficient procedure with ion-exchange resin).

Conversion to acids by hydrolysis or by action of HNO_2. Dehydration to nitriles. Conversion to haloamides (e.g. N-bromoacetamide, $CH_3CONHBr$) by avoidance of excess alkali.

Imides

Example: succinimide by loss of NH_3 from the diamide of succinic acid. Acidic character due to activation of the imide hydrogen by two carbonyl groups. Conversion of succinimide to β-alanine

($H_2NCH_2CH_2CO_2H$). Conversion with Br_2 + NaOH into N-bromosuccinimide, useful for allylic bromination and as mild oxidizing agent.

Diamide of carbonic acid, a product of metabolism of proteins excreted in urine (30 g./day). Isolable as mononitrate (basic, one extra NH₂ group). Starting material for plastics. Preparation: phosgene + NH₃; CO₂ + NH₃ under pressure; cyanamide + H₂O.

PROBLEMS

1. Name the following compounds and indicate the class to which each belongs:
   (a) CH₃CH₂CH(CH₃)NH₂
   (b) (CH₃CH₂)₂NCH(CH₃)₂
   (c) (CH₃)₂C(NH₂)CH₂CH₃
   (d) CH₃NHCH₂CH(CH₃)₂
   (e) (CH₃CH₂CH₂)₂N(CH₃) · HCl
   (f) [(CH₃)₂CH]₄NBr
   (g) CH₃CH₂CH₂N(NO)CH₂CH₃
   (h) CH₃CONHCH₂CH₃
   (i) (CH₃)₃CCONH₂

2. Arrange the following compounds in order with respect to acidic or basic properties: methylamine, acetamide, phthalimide, tetramethylammonium hydroxide, urea, acetylmethylamine, succinimide, β-alanine (H₂NCH₂CH₂COOH).

3. Suggest convenient chemical methods for isolating in a pure form the chief component of each of the following mixtures:
   (a) Triethylamine, containing traces of ethylamine and diethylamine
   (b) Diethylamine, contaminated with ethylamine and triethylamine
   (c) Ethylamine, containing di- and triethylamine

4. How could n-propylamine and n-amylamine be prepared from n-butyl alcohol?

5. Suggest a method other than one proceeding through the halogen derivative for the preparation of sec-butylamine from sec-butyl alcohol.

6. If n-butyl bromide is to be converted into n-butylamine, what would be the advantage of using the Gabriel synthesis rather than direct ammonolysis? Comment on the practicability of converting the alcohol into the aldehyde, preparing the oxime, and reduction.

7. Indicate the steps involved in transformation of a nitrile into an acid and of an acid into a nitrile. Would you expect an aldoxime to be convertible directly to a nitrile?

8. Formulate the Hofmann degradation as applied to cyclohexylamine.

9. How could the Hofmann degradation be applied to the determination of the structure of the following cyclic base:

10. Is there any similarity in electronic state between trimethylboron and the trimethylcarbonium ion?

11. Write an electronic formulation for elimination of nitrogen from an acid azide (RCON₃) in the Curtius reaction.

12. What structures contribute to the resonant hybrid anion from succinimide?

13. With the aid of electronic formulas, explain more fully the statement (11.17) that the bromine atom in N-bromosuccinimide is relatively positive since the substance on hydrolysis affords HOBr, whereas RBr yields HBr.

14. Thermal decomposition of quaternary ammonium hydroxides with formation of alkenes is an example of the rather general phenomenon that high or moderately high temperatures favor formation of unsaturated compounds. A number of other examples have been cited in earlier chapters; how many can you cite?

15. A physiologically active alkaloid A, isolated in 1885 by a Japanese investigator from the Chinese herb mahuang, became well known in the western world only in 1925, but has since been used widely in medicine, chiefly for treatment of bronchial asthma. The substance has the formula C₁₀H₁₅ON; it forms a hydrochloride from which the base is regenerated; it does not react with carbonyl reagents, and the iodoform test is also negative. Compound A reacts with acetic anhydride to give a neutral substance B, C₁₄H₁₉O₃N, and with nitrous acid to give a neutral yellow oil C, C₁₀H₁₄O₂N₂. Permanganate oxidation of A gives benzoic acid, and oxidation of A with periodic acid affords benzaldehyde, acetaldehyde, and methylamine. Deduce the structure of A and devise a method for its synthesis.

REVIEW PROBLEMS

Since this chapter concludes the survey of general aliphatic chemistry, questions pertaining to this subject as a whole are appended here for review. An answer, if not apparent, may be deducible from suggestions given in the back of the book; otherwise the cross reference can be consulted.

A. Transformations

The following transformations are to be effected either in one step or in a sequence of reactions.

1. Acetylene $\longrightarrow$ n-butane

2. Acetone and allyl bromide $\longrightarrow$
$$(CH_3)_2C{=}CHCH{=}CH_2$$

3. $CH_3CH_2CH{=}CHCH{=}CH_2 \longrightarrow$
$$CH_2{=}CHCH{=}CHCH{=}CH_2$$

4. $CH_3COCH_2CH_2CO_2CH_3 \longrightarrow$
$$CH_3COCH_2CH_2CH_2OH$$

5. $CH_3COCH_2CH_2COOCH(CH_3)_2 \longrightarrow$
$$CH_3CH_2CH_2CH_2COOCH(CH_3)_2$$

6. Acetone + acetylene $\longrightarrow$
$$CH_2{=}C(CH_3)CH{=}CH_2 \text{ (isoprene)}$$

7. $CH_3CH_2CH_2CH_2CO_2H \longrightarrow$
$$CH_3CH_2CH_2CH(NH_2)CO_2H$$

8. $CH_3CH_2CH_2CH_2CO_2H \longrightarrow$
$$CH_3CH_2CH{=}CHCO_2H$$

9. $CH_3CH_2CHO \longrightarrow$
$$CH_3CH_2CH{=}CH(CH_3)CH_2OH$$

10. Cyclohexanone $\longrightarrow$ cyclohexylamine

11. $CH_3CH_2COCH_2CH_3 \longrightarrow$

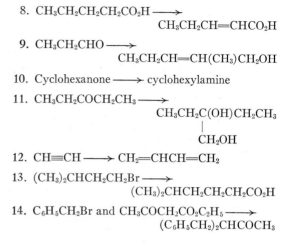

12. $CH{\equiv}CH \longrightarrow CH_2{=}CHCH{=}CH_2$

13. $(CH_3)_2CHCH_2CH_2Br \longrightarrow$
$$(CH_3)_2CHCH_2CH_2CH_2CO_2H$$

14. $C_6H_5CH_2Br$ and $CH_3COCH_2CO_2C_2H_5 \longrightarrow$
$$(C_6H_5CH_2)_2CHCOCH_3$$

B. Reagents

Since a problem in synthesis may require one of the following reagents, methods by which they can be obtained from simple starting materials should be reviewed.

15. Acetylene

16. Ethylene oxide

17. Allyl bromide

18. Acrolein

19. Ketene

20. Acetic anhydride

21. Acrylonitrile

22. Malonic ester

23. Acetoacetic ester

C. Syntheses

Starting materials: methanol, ethanol, n- and i-propyl alcohol, n-, i-, sec-, and t-butyl alcohol, cyclohexanol. These nine alcohols make available a number of derivatives: RX, RMgX, RCO$_2$H, RCOOR′, RCOR′, alkenes. Conversion to such intermediates is not included in the answers. Accessory reagents assumed to be available are: inorganic reagents, solvents, CH_2N_2, H_2NOH, H_2NNH_2.

24. $(CH_3)_2CHCH_2CH{=}CH_2$

25. $CH_3CH_2CH_2CH{=}C(CHO)(CH_2CH_3)$

26. n-Octane

27. Methyldi-n-butylcarbinol

28. $(CH_3)_3CCH_2CH(CH_3)_2$

29. $CH_3CH{=}CHCO_2H$

30. $CH_3CH(CH_3)CH_2COCH(CH_3)CH_3$

31. $CH_3CH(CH_3)COCH(CH_3)CH_3$

32. $(CH_3)_3CCOOH$

33. $(CH_3)_3CCOOCH_3$

34. $(CH_3)_3CCH_2CO_2H$

35. $(CH_3)_3CCH_2NH_2$

36. $HOCH_2CH_2CH_2CH_2CH_2CH_2OH$

37. $CH_3CH_2CH_2CH(OH)CH_2OH$

READING REFERENCE

Lord Playfair, Sir F. A. Abel, W. H. Perkin, and H. E. Armstrong, "Hofmann Memorial Lecture," *J. Chem. Soc.*, **69**, 575–732 (1896)

STEREOCHEMISTRY

OPTICAL ISOMERISM

An important phase of organic chemistry is associated with the phenomenon of the polarization of light, discovered by Étienne Louis Malus in 1808. Ordinary white light consists of rays of different wave length vibrating in many planes, and if light of a single wave length is selected, either with a special light source (sodium lamp) or with filters, the resulting monochromatic light likewise consists of waves vibrating in many planes at right angles to the direction of propagation. Malus discovered that light transmitted by a crystal of Iceland spar, a transparent variety of the doubly refractive mineral calcite ($CaCO_3$) found in Iceland, differs from normal light in being polarized in a single plane determined by the orientation of the crystal, or polarizer. The character of the crystal permits passage of only those light waves vibrating in a specific plane and transmits two rays, ordinary and extraordinary, which are polarized in planes at right angles to each other. Experimentation with plane polarized light is

simplified by use of the Nicol prism (William Nicol, Edinburgh), a device made by bisecting a rhombohedron of Iceland spar obliquely through the obtuse corners and uniting the parts with a cement (Canada balsam) of an index that allows complete reflection of the ordinary ray at the interface; this is thereby rejected from the field of vision, and the extraordinary ray of plane polarized light alone is transmitted. A rough analogy to the operation of a Nicol prism is that a closed book will permit easy insertion of a table knife between the pages only when the knife is held in a specific plane.

Although Malus' experiments were terminated by his premature death in 1812 at the age of 37, investigation of the interesting phenomenon was actively pursued by the French physicists D. F. Arago and J. B. Biot.[1] It was soon observed that a quartz crystal cut parallel to the axis and traversed by plane polarized light normal to the surface rotates the plane of polarization, and Biot ascertained that some quartz crystals turn the beam of light to the right whereas others turn it to the left. A few years later the mineralogist Haüy noticed that some specimens of quartz crystals exist in two hemihedral forms, each characterized by a set of faces arranged in either a right-handed or left-handed sense and constituting just half of the faces required to give a symmetrical crystal. Such crystals, illustrated in Fig. 12.1, are enantiomorphous, that is, related to each other as the right hand is to the left hand. The examples illustrated represent rare specimens; ordinarily hemihedry is discernible in but a small portion of the quartz crystals examined, and then only on careful scrutiny. Sir John Herschel in 1820 suggested a possible relationship between the crystallographic and optical properties of quartz, and experiment established that crystals with the faces inclined to the right and to the left rotate the plane of polarized light in opposite directions.

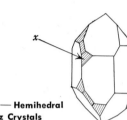

FIG. 12.1. — Hemihedral
Quartz Crystals

Biot in 1815 discovered that certain naturally occurring organic compounds rotate plane polarized light in either the liquid or the dissolved state. Oil of turpentine, solutions of sugar, of camphor, and of tartaric acid were found to exhibit this property and are described as optically active. The importance of the discovery was apparent to Biot, who pointed out that, whereas in the previously observed phenomena the optical activity was associated with a specific crystalline structure and disappeared with destruction of the crystalline form, the ability of the organic substances to rotate the plane of polarization in the noncrystalline state must be inherent in the molecules.

Polarimeter. — Subsequent experimentation showed that a number of organic compounds possess optical activity; those that rotate plane polarized light to the right, or in a clockwise direction, are defined as dextrorotatory (positive), whereas those rotating in the opposite sense are called levorotatory (negative). The extent of rotation for a given amount of material can be determined with a polarimeter (Fig. 12.2). This instrument contains two Nicol prisms traversed by a beam of monochromatic light. One, the polarizer, is mounted in a fixed position and transmits plane polarized light to a tube of known length with glass windows at the two ends, in which the solution to be examined is placed. The second Nicol prism, the analyzer,

---

[1] Jean Baptiste Biot, 1774–1862; b. Paris; physicist, Collège de France

CHAPTER 12

is mounted on a movable axis and can be rotated as desired; the angle of rotation is measured on a circular scale. The zero point on the scale is that which, with the polarimeter tube either empty or containing a solvent devoid of optical activity, permits maximum transmission of light, an indication that the analyzer has been oriented in the same optical plane as the polarizer; if the analyzer is now turned through an angle of 90°, a point of minimum light transmission is reached, and the Nicols are said to be crossed. When a solution of an optically active substance is placed in the polarimeter tube, light transmitted by the polarizer is rotated to a certain extent either to

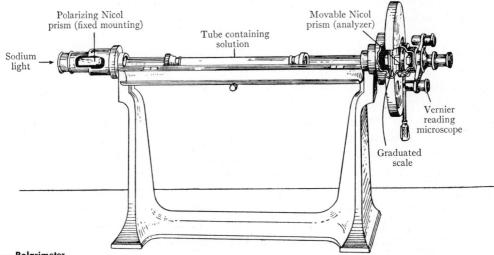

FIG. 12.2. — Polarimeter

the right or to the left; light reaching the eyepiece is thus diminished in intensity, but by rotating the analyzer a point can be found where the original intensity is restored and at which the analyzer is aligned with the plane of light emerging from the polarimeter tube; the angle of rotation in either the dextro or levo sense is read from the scale.

Rotatory power of a given substance in the dissolved state is dependent on the concentration of the solution, the length of the polarimeter tube, the temperature of measurement, the wave length of light used, and the nature of the solvent. Results are reported in terms of the specific rotation, $[\alpha]$, defined as the rotation in degrees due to a solution containing 1 g. of substance in 1 ml. of solution examined in a 1-decimeter polarimeter tube. The rotation value, which

Specific rotation

$$[\alpha] = \frac{\text{Observed rotation}}{\text{Length of tube in dm.} \times \text{concentration (g. per ml.)}}$$

may be to the right (positive) or to the left (negative), is reported with a notation of the temperature and either the nature or wave length of the light source. Sodium light is usually employed and is indicated by the letter D (D line of the spectrum), for example, $[\alpha]_D^{25°}$; if the green line of mercury of wave length 5461 Å is used, the symbol is $[\alpha]_{5461}^T$. The specific rotation of cane sugar in aqueous solution is $[\alpha]_D^{20°} = +66.5°$.

Work of Pasteur. — Louis Pasteur,[2] on completion of the curriculum at the École Normale in Paris, sought to strengthen his knowledge of crystallography by repeating a series of careful measurements published a few years earlier (1841) by de la Provostaye on the crystalline forms of various salts of tartaric acid. Tartaric acid, now known to have the structure HOOCCH(OH)CH(OH)COOH, is present in grapes and is obtained from tartar, a by-product of the wine industry; tartar consists largely of potassium acid tartrate, which is insoluble in alcohol and separates as a sludgy precipitate as the alcohol concentration increases during fermentation. Pasteur's determinations agreed substantially with those reported previously, but as the work proceeded he noticed a very interesting fact that had escaped his predecessor, namely, that all tartrates show undoubted evidence of hemihedral faces. The phenomenon is frequently obscured by irregular development of the crystals, by chance deformations, or by arrestment of the development of faces, but nevertheless Pasteur, by repeating crystallizations where necessary under modified conditions, established that every one of nineteen tartrates investigated exhibits hemihedral faces. A further observation that seemed significant was that the tartrates are all hemihedral in the same sense or direction. Since Biot had found the tartrates to be optically active in the same sense, and Herschel had suggested a correlation between the hemihedral and optical characteristics of quartz crystals, Pasteur was led to think that a relation might exist between the hemihedry of the tartrates and the property of deviating the plane of polarized light in the dissolved state.

Hemihedral tartrate crystals

This hypothesis, however, appeared to be invalidated by an observation reported in 1844 by the chemist and crystallographer Mitscherlich[3] concerning the sodium ammonium salt of racemic acid, a by-product of the crystallization of tartaric acid, the main acidic product of alcoholic fermentation, and which was first studied by Berzelius in 1831 (L. *racemus*, grape). The substance was found to have the same composition as tartaric acid but different physical properties; this early instance of isomerism led Berzelius to coin the name descriptive of the phenomenon. Biot examined racemic acid and its salts and found that they are optically inactive, in contrast with dextrorotatory tartaric acid. Mitscherlich then made a crystal-

Sodium ammonium racemate

[2] Louis Pasteur, 1822–95; b. Dôle, Dep. Jura; Dijon, Strasbourg, Lille, Paris (Sorbonne)
[3] Eilhard A. Mitscherlich, 1794–1863; b. Neuerde, Ostfriedland; Berlin

lographic comparison of the sodium ammonium salts of tartaric and racemic acid and reported that these two salts of the same chemical composition have the same crystalline form, the same double refraction, and consequently the same inclination of their optical axes, and in short differ only in that one is dextrorotatory and the other optically inactive. Since the existence of optically active and inactive isomers of identical crystalline form would be contradictory to the relationship tentatively postulated, Pasteur had the audacity to think that Mitscherlich might have overlooked the existence of hemihedry in the tartrate, and he reinvestigated the two salts in the hope of finding the tartrate hemihedral and the inactive racemate symmetrical. He found that sodium ammonium tartrate affords hemihedral crystals, like all other tartrates previously studied, but discovered to his great surprise and in apparent contradiction to his hypothesis, that sodium ammonium racemate is hemihedral also. He then observed that "the hemihedral faces which in the tartrate were all turned the same way were in the racemate inclined sometimes to the right and sometimes to the left." Pasteur carefully picked out a quantity of the crystals that were hemihedral to the right and a further quantity of those hemihedral to the left and examined their solutions separately in the polarimeter; he thereupon made the exciting observation that the former material rotated the plane of polarized light to the right and the latter to the left. When equal weights of the two kinds of crystals were dissolved in water, the solution of the mixture, like the starting material, was indifferent to polarized light. In this experiment, conducted in 1848, Pasteur had for the first time achieved the resolution of an optically inactive compound into the component, optically active parts. By precipitation of the lead or barium salts of each substance and digestion of these with sulfuric acid, the free acids were obtained. One proved identical with the natural, dextrorotatory tartaric acid, or *d*-tartaric acid, whereas the other was a heretofore unknown substance exhibiting rotation to the same extent in the opposite direction and hence called the *levo* acid, or *l*-tartaric acid.

The first resolution

Pasteur's striking discovery was referred to Biot for review before presentation to the Academy of Sciences, and this veteran worker required the young investigator to repeat the experiment before his eyes with a sample of racemic acid that he himself had studied and found optically inactive. Pasteur prepared a solution of the sodium ammonium salt with reagents that Biot likewise provided, and the solution was set aside for slow evaporation in one of the rooms at the Collège de France. In due course Pasteur was called in to collect and separate the crystals. Biot prepared the solutions and examined first the more interesting solution, that which Pasteur declared should show levorotation, and the elderly discoverer of the phenomenon of optical activity in organic compounds was immensely impressed on observing that it was indeed levorotatory.

It was recognized only some time later that the resolution achieved by Pasteur is dependent upon a critical temperature factor. If sodium ammonium racemate is crystallized from a hot concentrated solution, the crystals separating have the same form and are symmetrical; they show no sign of hemihedrism. In this case each crystal contains equal parts of the *dextro* and the *levo* form and is optically inactive; the racemate salt is a molecular compound having the analysis of a monohydrate, $Na(NH_4)C_4H_4O_6 \cdot H_2O$. It is only when the separation of crystals occurs at a temperature below a critical transition point of 28° that hemihedral crystals composed respectively of molecules of the *dextro* and the *levo* salt separate side by side to give a crystal mixture known as a conglomerate; this consists of crystals of sodium ammonium *d*-tartrate and sodium ammonium *l*-tartrate, both of which are tetrahydrates: $Na(NH_4)C_4H_4O_6 \cdot 4\,H_2O$. Transition temperatures are often observed in inorganic chemistry between different hydrates of a given salt or between double and single salts. For example, a solution of sodium and magnesium sulfate deposits crystals of $Na_2SO_4 \cdot 10\,H_2O$ and $MgSO_4 \cdot 7\,H_2O$ at temperatures below 22°, but yields the double salt $Na_2SO_4 \cdot MgSO_4 \cdot 4\,H_2O$ at higher temperatures. Pasteur adopted a technique of slow crystallization from a very dilute solution and thereby had the good fortune to have operated at a temperature below the transition point, whereas previous investigators evidently had conducted crystallization at higher temperatures and had obtained only the inactive racemate. The initial resolution accomplished in 1848 is particularly remarkable because of the rarity of such instances; in a century of subsequent research, only nine other examples have been encountered in which crystallization at any temperature affords a conglomerate of sufficiently large crystals displaying hemihedry to permit their segregation by hand picking under a lens. Fortunately, two other methods are now known for resolution of inactive molecular compounds composed of dextro- and levorotatory components, described as *dl*-compounds, or racemates, or racemic forms; both were discovered by Pasteur in the period 1848–54, before he turned his attention to fermentation. He also discovered a fourth form of tartaric acid called mesotartaric acid. These developments are discussed later.

Critical transition temperature

A rare phenomenon

Dextro- and *levo*-tartaric acid have the same melting point, solubility in a given solvent, dissociation constant, and density, and they exhibit the same chemical behavior. In fact the two substances are

CHAPTER 12

d- and l-Tartaric acid

identical in every respect except that they rotate the plane of polarized light in opposite directions (but to the same extent) and that they form crystals that are hemihedral in the opposite sense. Pasteur, in view of the hypothesis that he had entertained on first examining the racemate, thought there must be a connection between the optical activity of the substances in solution and the hemihedral forms of the crystals. The relationship between the crystals of *d-* and *l-*tartaric acid is the same as that illustrated in Fig. 12.1 for right- and left-handed quartz crystals. The two are similar but not superposable, and the one is to the other as an object is to its mirror image; the crystals are thus asymmetric, for they possess no plane of symmetry. In an interpretation of the new phenomenon, now described as optical isomerism, Pasteur concluded that the tartaric acids must possess asymmetry within the molecule itself. Although the concept of structural formulas was developed only many years later, Pasteur had the vision to foresee the need of something beyond structural formulas for full understanding of organic compounds. He recognized that two substances identical in composition may differ in the arrangement of the atoms in space and envisioned arrangements showing asymmetry in opposite senses. "Are the atoms of the *dextro* acid grouped on the spirals of a right-handed helix," questioned Pasteur in 1860, "or situated at the corners of an irregular tetrahedron, or have they some other asymmetric grouping? We cannot answer these questions. But it cannot be a subject of doubt that there exists an asymmetric arrangement having a nonsuperposable image. It is not less certain that the atoms of the *levo* acid possess precisely the inverse asymmetric arrangement."

12.6

Isomerism of the Lactic Acids. — Pasteur's brilliant deductions were so far ahead of the thought of the time that many years elapsed before any substantial advance was made in the understanding of optical isomerism. Although other optically active compounds were examined from time to time, the only investigations other than those of Pasteur that proved fruitful were those on the lactic acids. Scheele (1780) had discovered in sour milk a substance which he called lactic acid and which was subsequently found to arise by bacterial fermentation of milk sugar (lactose) and other naturally occurring sugars. The structure is now known to be that of α-hydroxypropionic acid. Berzelius (1807) discovered a similar acidic substance as a constituent of muscle tissue extractable with water, and the substance was characterized by Liebig (1832) as having the same composition as the fermentation lactic acid. The acids have properties unfavorable for purposes of identification and comparison, for they are very soluble both in water and in organic solvents and are obtained only with

Two acids of the same structure

CH₃—C—COOH
Lactic acid

202

considerable difficulty as low-melting, highly hygroscopic, and generally ill-defined solids (m.p. 26°). Thus a reliable conclusion regarding the relationship of the two acids was first reached by Engelhard (1848) from a comparison of a series of salts with respect to solubility, crystalline form, amount of water of crystallization, and course of dehydration. The comparison established that the lactic acids constitute two distinct chemical entities but have the same composition. It was also established that the acid present in lean flesh in amounts that increase with increasing muscular exertion is a dextrorotatory substance, which hereafter can be referred to as *d*-lactic acid. On the other hand fermentation lactic acid, at least as originally obtained, is optically inactive.

After the advent of the structural theory of Kekulé (1859), the problem of the structures of the interesting lactic acids received considerable attention, particularly in the hands of Wislicenus.[4] In a series of researches initiated at Zurich in 1863, Wislicenus applied the methods both of synthesis and of degradation, and though he encountered early difficulties and uncertainties in identification of materials of different origin, he eventually secured unequivocal evidence that the two natural acids have the same structure (1873). Thus they are both decomposed by hot sulfuric acid to acetaldehyde and formic acid, and they both yield acetic acid on oxidation. The alternate

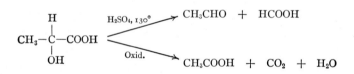

structure $HOCH_2CH_2COOH$ was thereby excluded, for this could not yield products with an intact methyl group. Indeed Wislicenus synthesized this structural isomer from ethylene chlorohydrin through the nitrile, and proved that it differs from each of the lactic acids. Synthesis of α-hydroxypropionic acid from acetaldehyde gave a product identical with the optically inactive fermentation lactic acid:

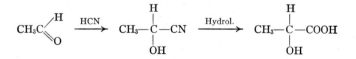

At the conclusion of his experiments of 1873, Wislicenus wrote: "If molecules can be structurally identical and yet possess dissimilar properties, this difference can be explained only on the ground that it is due to a different arrangement of the atoms in space."

[4] Johannes Wislicenus, 1835–1902; b. Germany; Zurich, Würzburg, Leipzig; *Ber.*, **37**, 4861 (1904)

Theory of van't Hoff and Le Bel. — A theory which met the requirements envisioned by Pasteur and set forth clearly by Wislicenus twenty-five years later, was announced independently in 1874 by van't Hoff in the Netherlands (September) and by Le Bel in France (November). The theory, already outlined (1.4), states that the four valences of carbon are directed to the corners of a tetrahedron, at the center of which the carbon atom is situated. If four different atoms or groups are attached at the four corners, then the molecule *Cabcd* is asymmetric and can exist in two forms. The three-dimensional models cannot be superposed upon each other and hence are different, even though they represent the same structural arrangement of atoms. They bear a relationship to each other corresponding to that which exists between right- and left-handed quartz crystals, or between an object and its mirror image. A tetrahedral carbon atom carrying four different groups therefore must invariably constitute a center of asymmetry and permit two arrangements in space. This asymmetry allows for existence of two isomers identical in all respects except optical properties. Asymmetry is possible only if all four valences of carbon are utilized by different groups; for example, if the substituent *c* in the above space formulas is replaced by a second *a* group, the formulas become identical.

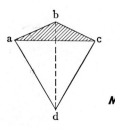

Mirror-image isomers

The young scientists (van't Hoff was 22, Le Bel, 27), who had met as students of Wurtz in Paris but who had not discussed the problem of isomerism, arrived at essentially the same theoretical concept by different reasoning. Le Bel was impressed by the correlation suggested by Pasteur between the rotatory power of the tartrates and the hemihedral character of the crystalline forms and saw that molecular asymmetry can exist if four different groups are united to a single carbon atom, whatever the geometrical form of the molecule may be. van't Hoff, inspired to reflect on the problem by the publications of Wislicenus on lactic acid, reasoned that the four valences of the carbon atom cannot lie in a single plane at right angles to one another, or isomerism would be encountered in substances such as CH_2RR and $CH_2R_1R_2$, and proposed the tetrahedral arrangement as an explanation for both the nonexistence of such isomerism and the existence of optical isomers of the formula $CR_1R_2R_3R_4$. A regular tetrahedral arrangement has been proved by X-ray measurements for tetramethylmethane and for pentaerythritol, $C(CH_2OH)_4$. The van't Hoff-Le Bel theory derived initial substantiation from the fact that at the time thirteen optically active compounds of established struc-

The theory is substantiated

ture were known and they all contained at least one asymmetric carbon atom, designated C* in the following examples:

Lactic acid,	CH₃C*H(OH)COOH
Aspartic acid,	HOOCC*H(NH₂)CH₂COOH
Asparagine,	HOOCC*H(NH₂)CH₂CONH₂
Malic acid,	HOOCC*H(OH)CH₂COOH
Active amyl alcohol,	CH₃CH₂C*H(CH₃)CH₂OH

Wislicenus welcomed the theory as an answer to the problem that his own experiments had raised, and he sponsored van't Hoff's work to the extent of writing a supporting introduction to a German translation of the original Dutch pamphlet. Kolbe, who was reaching the end of his career, took an opposite view and wrote a scathing criticism of the "fanciful nonsense" and "supernatural explanations" of the two "unknown" chemists. Within a decade, however, those few observations that had appeared contradictory to the theory were shown to be in error (e.g., supposed activity of propyl alcohol, due to contamination with amyl alcohol) and abundant new evidence was accumulated in substantiation of the concept. Kolbe had died, and Wislicenus had been appointed to his post at Leipzig.

In the face of opposition

Compounds with One Asymmetric Carbon Atom. — As predicted by the theory, the inactive lactic acid resulting from fermentation of carbohydrates was found to contain equal parts of *d*-lactic acid, identical with that found in muscle, and of the optical isomer *l*-lactic acid; indeed fermentation can yield an excess of either the *d*- or the *l*-acid, depending on the microorganism. Spatial arrangement or configuration of the molecules of the optical isomers is conveniently represented by affixing to a regular tetrahedron the four groups H, CH₃, OH, COOH; this formulation can be done in two ways, as follows:

12.8

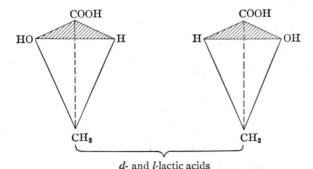

d- and l-lactic acids

Space formulas

A representation of the lactic acids with three-dimensional models of convenience in interpretations of stereochemical phenomena is shown in Fig. 12.3. In such models the atoms and groups joined to the asymmetric carbon are represented by differently shaded balls. These

Mechanical models

groups differ actually in the space that they occupy; a hydrogen atom, for example, is small in comparison to a carboxyl group (ratio of

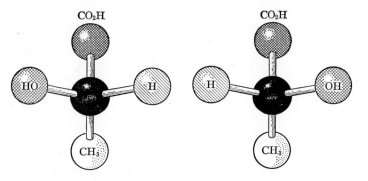

FIG. 12.3.— Models of the Mirror-Image Forms of Lactic Acid

atomic weight units, 1:45), and a more accurate representation of the molecular characteristics is afforded by Stuart models (1934), illustrated in Fig. 12.4. The atoms are represented by spheres of appropriate relative diameters and appropriate facings to indicate effective spheres of bound atoms on a scale of actual interatomic distances.

Models to scale

O   ■ C   □ H

FIG. 12.4.— Stuart Models of *d*- and *l*-Lactic Acid

Enantiomers

Whatever models or space formulas are used, each form of lactic acid is seen to be asymmetric, since it possesses no plane of symmetry, or since the two forms are like right- and left-handed screws. Because such mirror-image isomers bear the relationship to each other of enantiomorphous crystals of quartz or of sodium ammonium racemate, they are described as a pair of enantiomers (Gr. *enantio-*, opposite). In all instances where the *d*- and *l*-forms have been isolated in satisfactory purity, the physical constants of the enantiomers are the same within experimental error. This concordance is illustrated by data given in Table I for the optically active mandelic acids. Although the enantiomers melt at the same temperature, a mixture of a small

TABLE I

MANDELIC ACIDS, $C_6H_5CH(OH)COOH$

Example of properties

	M.P., ° C.	SOLUBILITY, G./100 G. $H_2O^{20°}$	ACIDIC DISSOCIATION, $pK_a^{25°}$	SPECIFIC ROTATION, $[\alpha]_D^{20°}$ 2% IN H_2O
d-Acid	132.8	8.54 g.		+ 155.5°
l-Acid	132.8	8.64 g.	3.37	− 154.4°
dl-Acid	118.5	15.97 g.	3.38	inactive

amount of the *d*-acid depresses the melting point of the *l*-form, and vice versa; hence the method of mixed melting-point determination detects even a subtle difference. That the melting point of the *dl*-acid, or racemic form, is below the melting points of the component acids is purely fortuitous, for such molecular compounds can have properties not predictable from those of the component parts. Relative solubilities are likewise unforetellable. The acidic dissociation constant is a property of the dissolved molecules and is independent of the characteristics of the solid materials, and the fact that the *dl*-acid has the same value as that found for the *l*-acid is evidence that the enantiomers correspond in acidity. Chemical properties are also independent of the physical forms, and the *d*-, *l*-, and *dl*-acids exhibit the same chemical characteristics; they react in the same way with the same reagents, and the reactions proceed at the identical rate in the three cases. Correspondence in physical properties is accounted for by any of the models illustrated, for in each enantiomer the same groups are present and have the same spatial relationship to one another and to the asymmetric carbon atom. If any attractions or repulsions between groups are manifested in one form, they are equally operative in the other. That one acid rotates the plane of polarized light to the right is a phenomenon associated with asymmetry of the molecule in a manner not as yet fully interpretable, but it is understandable that the mirror-image counterpart shows equal rotatory power in the opposite sense.

Synthesis. — The lactic acid obtained from acetaldehyde by the cyanohydrin synthesis is optically inactive and consists of a *dl*-modification. Indeed any synthesis of a compound having a single asymmetric carbon atom yields a *dl*-form or racemate; that is, it affords the same number of *d*- and of *l*-molecules. A simple explanation is found in the van't Hoff-Le Bel theory. If acetaldehyde is represented by a space formula in which the carbon atom of the carbonyl group

12.9

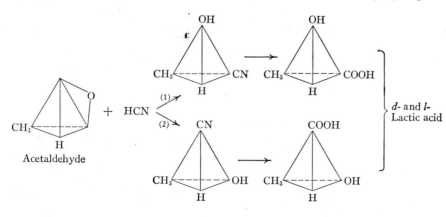

d- and *l*-Lactic acid

Asymmetry resulting from addition

207

is indicated by a tetrahedron with methyl at one corner and hydrogen at another and with the other two corners united to oxygen by a double link, the molecule has a plane of symmetry bisecting the oxygen atom and the hydrogen and methyl substituents. This symmetry means that there is no difference in the two linkages of the carbonyl group, and hence that in the reaction with hydrogen cyanide the same opportunity exists for opening of one linkage as of the other, (1) and (2). Since an experiment on even a microscale involves many millions of molecules, the law of the probability of occurrence of two equally likely events is applicable with accuracy, and the carbonyl group must open, on the average, to an equal extent in the two possible directions. Asymmetry is established in the initial addition; the two enantiomeric cyanohydrins are formed in equal amounts, and equal amounts of the *d*- and *l*-acids result on hydrolysis.

Another reaction producing an asymmetric center is the synthesis of *α*-hydroxybutyric acid starting with the *α*-bromination of butyric

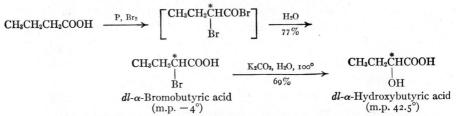

acid by the action of bromine and red phosphorus (Hell-Volhard-Zelinsky method); the initial reaction product is the acid bromide, which undergoes halogenation in the *α*-position more readily than the free acid. The crude *α*-bromo acid bromide is not isolated, but is

Asymmetry resulting from substitution

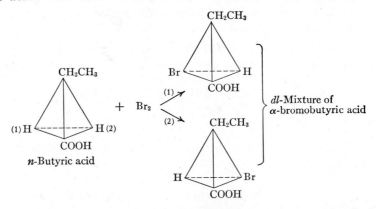

poured slowly into hot water to hydrolyze the more reactive halogen atom. The resulting *α*-bromo acid is then hydrolyzed to the hydroxy acid by prolonged boiling with water containing one molecular equivalent of potassium carbonate, and under these conditions there is little elimination of hydrogen bromide from the α,β-position to produce crotonic acid. Asymmetry is established with replacement of one of the two α-hydrogen atoms by bromine, and a space model shows that there is exactly the same opportunity for replacement of one as of the other. Again the law of chance dictates formation of equal amounts of the two possible products, and hence a *dl*-mixture results at this stage. These two examples typify the general situation in the synthesis of compounds that can exist in mirror-image forms, for the production of an asymmetric carbon atom is invariably accomplished by either an addition reaction, in which either of two linkages of a double bond is utilized, or the replacement of one of two identical atoms or groups.

Correlations and Conventions. — The dextrorotatory lactic acid from muscle tissue forms metallic salts that are all levorotatory. Actually both the acid and its salts are so weakly rotatory that the absolute difference in rotation between them is slight and the reversal in the sign of rotation therefore of little significance (see formulas). The salts, as well as the likewise weakly levorotatory methyl ester,

CH_3CHCO_2H	$(CH_3CHCO_2)_2Zn$	$CH_3CHCO_2CH_3$	CH_3CHCO_2H	CH_3CHCO_2H	
$\mid$	$\mid$	$\mid$	$\mid$	$\mid$	*Variable rotation*
OH	OH	OH	OCH_3	OC_2H_5	*in a single series*
$+3.3°$	$-6.0°$	$-8.2°$	$-75.5°$	$-66.4°$	

$[\alpha]_D$ of *d*-lactic acid and derivatives

are reconvertible into the weakly dextrorotatory free acid; these substances all have the same configuration, or orientation of groups in space. The methyl and ethyl ethers of dextrorotatory lactic acid also belong to the same configurational series, even though they are relatively strongly levorotatory. Thus the magnitude and even the direction of rotation in a given stereochemical series is subject to variation according to the nature of groups attached to the asymmetric center. Therefore the sign of rotation of one member of the series, for example free *d*-lactic acid, is not a satisfactory characterization of the configurational feature common to all members of the series.

A method for designation of configurational relationships that has gained general acceptance was introduced by Emil Fischer (1891), modified by M. A. Rosanoff (1906), and fully interpreted by C. S. Hudson [5] (1949). Dextrorotatory glyceraldehyde, $HOCH_2CH(OH)CHO$, is taken as the reference standard and is arbitrarily assigned a configuration that is defined in terms of the perspective tetrahedral model (a) or the equivalent, symmetrically oriented model (b). In both

[5] Claude S. Hudson, 1881–1952; b. Atlanta; Ph.D. Princeton; U.S. Public Health Service; E. L. Hirst, "The Hudson Memorial Lecture," *J. Chem. Soc.*, 4732 (1954)

(a) and (b) the solid line connecting H and OH represents an edge of the tetrahedron that projects in front of or above the plane of the paper, and the dotted line connecting CHO and CH₂OH is an edge of

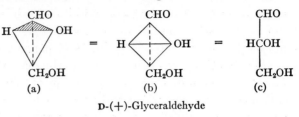

D-(+)-Glyceraldehyde

the tetrahedron that would be unseen in an opaque mechanical model. For convenience in writing and printing, Fischer defined the following convention for planar projection of the three-dimensional model: the model is oriented as in (b) with the carbon chain vertical and to the rear and the hydrogen and hydroxyl standing out in front; the model is then imagined to be flattened and the groups are laid on the plane of the paper in the order that they appear in the model, as in (c). The planar projection (c) must be thought of in terms of the actual model that it represents (H and OH extending toward the front); it can be turned around in the plane of the paper, but must not be imagined to be lifted and inverted. If the carbon chain contains two or more adjacent asymmetric carbon atoms (see tartaric acid, below), the projection is made in the same way from a model oriented with CHO or equivalent group at the top, CH₂OH or equivalent at the bottom, the carbon chain vertical and to the rear, and H and OH groups extending to the front.

The second convention is that the configuration of dextrorotatory glyceraldehyde is designated by the small capital roman D; the opposite configuration is designated L. The reference substance is thus D-glyceraldehyde; a fuller description is given by the name D-(*d*)-glyceraldehyde; in which D indicates the configuration and *d* records the incidental fact that the substance is dextrorotatory. The same information is given by the name D-(+)-glyceraldehyde, which is less confusing and therefore preferable.

Any compound that has been shown to contain an asymmetric carbon atom of the same configuration as that of D-glyceraldehyde belongs to the D-series. This is true of the acid resulting from oxidation of the aldehydic function; the substance is levorotatory and is therefore named D-(−)-glyceric acid. If the CHO group of glyceral-

COOH	COOH	CH₂COOH
HCOH	HCOH	HCOH
CH₂OH	CH₃	COOH
D-(−)-Glyceric acid	D-(−)-Lactic acid	D-(−)-Malic acid

dehyde is oxidized and the CH_2OH group is reduced, the resulting substance is lactic acid. Experimental correlation has established that levorotatory lactic acid, or *l*-lactic acid or (−)-lactic acid, corresponds in configuration to the reference standard and therefore is D-(−)-lactic acid. In the projection formula, hydroxyl is thus to the right and hydrogen to the left; this formula corresponds to the models shown at the right-hand side in Figs. 12.3 and 12.4 and in the corresponding tetrahedral diagrams. The designation of configuration eliminates confusion associated with the opposite sign of rotation of the lactic acids and their simple derivatives. Thus the statement that esterification of L-(+)-lactic acid gives the L-(−)-ester indicates that the direction of rotation changes but the configuration remains the same. Natural malic acid belongs to the D-series; it is weakly levorotatory in dilute aqueous solution and becomes weakly dextrorotatory as the concentration is increased.

Natural *d*-tartaric acid has two similar asymmetric carbon atoms. When the asymmetric carbon atom written at the bottom in the for-

l-Tartaric acid corresponds to D-glyceraldehyde

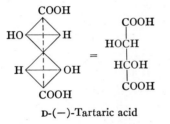

D-(−)-Tartaric acid

mula is compared with that of D-glyceraldehyde and CHOHCOOH is taken as equivalent to CHO and COOH is taken as equivalent to CH_2OH each equivalent center in *d*-tartaric acid is found to have the configuration opposite to that of the standard. The enantiomeric *l*-tartaric acid is thus the one that belongs to the D-series; it is D-(−)-tartaric acid and is formulated as shown.

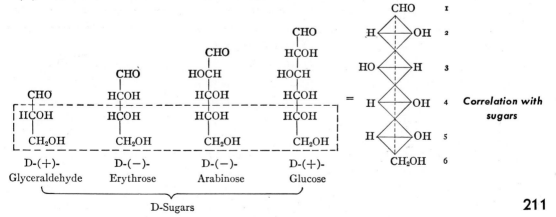

Correlation with sugars

| D-(+)- Glyceraldehyde | D-(−)- Erythrose | D-(−)- Arabinose | D-(+)- Glucose |

D-Sugars

211

D-Glyceraldehyde was chosen as reference standard because it is the simplest member of the sugar series and corresponds in configuration to one of four asymmetric carbon atoms in the key sugar glucose. The complete series of related sugars includes the further members arabinose and erythrose, of projection formulas shown. The lowermost asymmetric center of each of the higher sugars (C_5 in glucose) has the configuration of D-glyceraldehyde, and hence the substances all belong to the D-series; it is incidental that D-glucose is dextrorotatory and the others levorotatory.

12.11

Compounds with Two Dissimilar Asymmetric Carbon Atoms. — Addition reactions of olefins frequently give rise to substances having two asymmetric carbon atoms, for example:

$$CH_3CH_2CH=CHCH_3 \xrightarrow{\text{[O], H}_2\text{O}} CH_3CH_2\overset{*}{C}H-\overset{*}{C}HCH_3$$
$$\underset{OH}{|} \quad \underset{OH}{|}$$

$$HOOCCH=CHCOOH \xrightarrow{\text{HOCl}} HOOC\overset{*}{C}H-\overset{*}{C}HCOOH$$
$$\underset{OH}{|} \quad \underset{Cl}{|}$$

$$C_6H_5CH=CHCH_3 \xrightarrow{\text{Cl}_2} C_6H_5\overset{*}{C}H-\overset{*}{C}HCH_3$$
$$\underset{Cl}{|} \quad \underset{Cl}{|}$$

In each example the two asymmetric centers are dissimilar, and each therefore can contribute to a certain different extent to the rotatory power of the molecule as a whole in either a *dextro* or *levo* sense. If the contribution of one center of asymmetry is designated as $\pm a$ and the other as $\pm b$, then the possible combinations are:

Four optically active isomers

$$
\begin{array}{cccc}
+a & -a & +a & -a \\
+b & -b & -b & +b \\
\hline
\multicolumn{2}{c}{dl\text{-Form}} & \multicolumn{2}{c}{d'l'\text{-Form}}
\end{array}
$$

The theory therefore predicts four possible isomers, grouped in two pairs of enantiomeric modifications, or *dl*-mixtures, and this prediction has been verified. For example, two substances corresponding to the formula $C_6H_5\overset{*}{C}HBr\overset{*}{C}HBrCOOH$ are known; both are optically inactive but distinguished from each other by a difference in melting point, and both have been shown to constitute racemic mixtures. One, cinnamic acid dibromide, m.p. 201°, has been resolved into the active components of specific rotations +67.5° and −68.3°, and the other, allocinnamic acid dibromide, m.p. 90°, is also resolvable. Space formulas can be written for the four isomers, but since the configurations relative to glyceraldehyde are not known, a given formula cannot be assigned to a particular isomer. A first formula is constructed by joining two tetrahedrons together and affixing appropriate groups to the free corners in an arbitrary manner, for example, as in I. This arbitrary formula can be taken as representing a *d*-acid, in which the

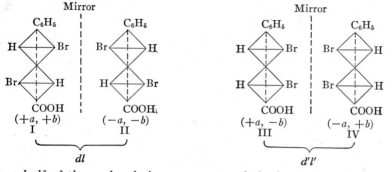

upper half of the molecule is a $+a$ part and the lower half a $+b$ part. Formula II, representing the enantiomer of I, is constructed by visualizing the image of I in a mirror, and the upper and lower halves are, by definition, $-a$ and $-b$ parts. Formula III is made up of the upper half of I $(+a)$ and the lower half of II $(-b)$, and IV is its mirror image. Projection formulas utilizing the simplification that the asymmetric carbons are represented merely as the intersections of the lines connecting substituents are as follows:

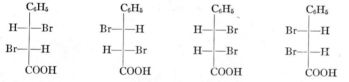

The two racemates are appropriately designated as *dl-* and *d′l′-* forms, and it is understandable that they should differ in melting point and other physical properties and indeed even in the rates at which they undergo reactions. The *d*-acid I is composed of two different asymmetric molecular halves $(+a, +b)$, and the combination is neither duplicated nor mirrored in either the *d′*-acid III $(+a, -b)$ or the *l′*-acid IV $(-a, +b)$. Stereoisomers that, like the *d*-, *d′*-, and *l′*-acids, are not identical and yet are not mirror images, are defined as **diastereoisomers** (Gr. *dia*, apart). The *l*-acid II is the enantiomer of I, but is a diastereoisomer of III and IV.

Compounds with Several Dissimilar Asymmetric Carbon Atoms.
— If three centers of asymmetry present in a given molecule can contribute in either a positive or negative sense to the extent of *a*, *b*, and *c* to the rotatory power of the molecule as a whole, then the possible combinations are:

$+a$	$-a$	$-a$	$+a$	$+a$	$-a$	$+a$	$-a$
$+b$	$-b$	$+b$	$-b$	$-b$	$+b$	$+b$	$-b$
$+c$	$-c$	$+c$	$-c$	$+c$	$-c$	$-c$	$+c$
dl		*d′l′*		*d″l″*		*d‴l‴*	

Eight different optically active forms are possible, falling into four pairs of mirror-image isomers. A general relationship by which the number of isomers can be calculated is: number of optically active forms = 2^n (where n is the number of dissimilar asymmetric carbon atoms). When n = 4 the number of optically active forms possible is sixteen, and indeed an instance is known in the sugar series in which all sixteen isomers predicted by the van't Hoff-Le Bel theory are known.

Tartaric Acids. — The tartaric acid series is the classical example of compounds possessing two similar asymmetric carbon atoms. Pasteur had established that the inactive racemic acid can be resolved into *d*- and *l*-forms and is in fact *dl*-tartaric acid, and he had discovered another inactive

*CH(OH)COOH
|
*CH(OH)COOH

isomer, mesotartaric acid. This isomer, typical of other substances which are therefore described generally as *meso* modifications, is produced along with the *dl*-acid by heating *d*-tartaric acid with water at 165° and can be isolated from the mixture in the form of the sparingly soluble acid potassium salt. The existence of two active and two inactive tartaric acids is readily explained. Since the rotatory contribution of each of two similar centers of asymmetry can be represented as ±*a*, the following forms are predicted:

$$
\begin{array}{cc}
+a \quad -a & +a \\
+a \quad -a & -a \\
\hline
\textit{dl-Form} & \textit{meso Form}
\end{array}
$$

The combination of equal parts of the *d*- and the *l*-acid constitutes one inactive form, and the second or *meso* form is inactive because the molecule has a plane of symmetry. Mesotartaric acid is sometimes called an internally compensated inactive form, since there exists within each molecule a balancing of the right- and left-handed tendencies; *dl*-tartaric acid is inactive by virtue of compensation of an external nature: the presence of like numbers of two kinds of molecules.

The space formula and relative configuration of *l*-tartaric acid, or D-(−)-tartaric acid, have been discussed (12.10). The complete series is represented in both tetrahedral formulas and projections. The two asymmetric carbon atoms of *d*-tartaric acid make equal dextrorotatory contributions, and, as the formulas are written, the arrangement of the groups COOH, OH, and H is clockwise, or right-handed, in both the upper and lower centers. In the case of *l*-tartaric acid the arrangement is counterclockwise throughout, and in the *meso* acid the upper and lower centers are right- and left-handed, respectively.

Some properties of the two active and two inactive forms of tar-

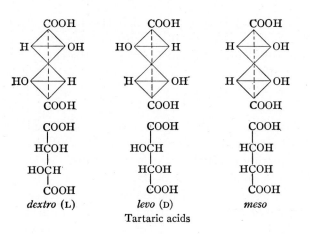

Tetrahedral and projection formulas

dextro (L)   levo (D)   meso

Tartaric acids

taric acid are given in Table II. A noteworthy point is that the *dl*-form, racemic acid, melts at a higher temperature than the optically

TABLE II

PROPERTIES OF THE TARTARIC ACIDS

Acid	M.P., ° C.	$[\alpha]_D^{25°}$, 20% AQ. SOLUTION	SOLUBILITY, G. PER 100 G. H_2O	ACIDIC DISSOCIATION	
				pK_{a_1}	pK_{a_2}
dextro	170	$+12°$	139	2.93	4.23
levo	170	$-12°$	139	2.93	4.23
dl (racemic)	206	inactive	20.6	2.96	4.24
meso	140	inactive	125	3.11	4.80

active components. This property is not inconsistent with the observation, already noted, that the melting point of the *d*-acid is depressed by admixture with a *small* amount of the *l*-acid, and vice versa, for racemic acid is not a mixture of the active forms but a molecular compound having its own characteristics. The situation can be appreciated by consideration of diagrams giving the melting points (or freezing points) of mixtures of the *d*- and *l*-acids of compositions varying from 100% of the one to 100% of the other. Figure 12.5, case A,

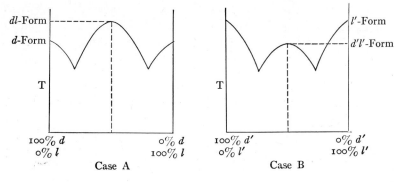

Case A   Case B

FIG. 12.5. — Melting Point-Composition Diagrams

gives the typical relationship to which the tartaric acids conform. The melting point of the *d*-acid is depressed by successive additions of the *l*-form till a eutectic point is reached; the curve then rises to a maximum at the 50:50 point, corresponding to the melting point of the molecular (*dl*-) compound, which in this instance is higher than that of either component. An equally characteristic relationship is shown in case B; here the diagram again consists of two complementary halves, each having a eutectic point, but the *dl*-compound has a lower melting point than the active forms. In either case A or B, addition of a small amount of one of the active forms to the *dl*-compound depresses the melting point. In those instances where equal parts of two enantiomers fail to combine to a molecular compound but afford a racemic mixture or conglomerate, this 50:50 mixture melts lower than mixtures of any other composition melt, and addition of an active isomer to the inactive form raises the melting point. This difference provides a method of distinguishing racemic compounds from racemic mixtures.

12.15

Resolution of Racemic Modifications. — Resolution of an inactive substance into its optically active components can be accomplished only rarely by crystallization and mechanical separation, as in the classical experiment of Pasteur, or by subsequently introduced modifications. Pasteur's contributions, however, included the discovery of a method of resolution that is both practicable and capable of wide application. Either through scientific curiosity or because of an instinct for thorough investigation, the gifted experimentalist prepared and characterized all conceivable salts derived from the combination of tartaric acids with both inorganic and organic bases, including naturally occurring, optically active amine bases. The salts of *d*- and *l*-tartaric acid with metals, ammonia, and aniline were identical in solubility and other physical properties; but Pasteur observed

Pasteur's second method

that with salts derived from asymmetric, optically active natural bases such as quinine or strychnine "all is changed in an instant. The solubility is no longer the same and the properties all differ as much as in the case of the most distantly related isomers." The reason is apparent from consideration of an example. If a *dl*-acid is neutralized with a dextrorotatory (*d'*) base, one of the two salts produced is composed of two right-handed parts (*dd'*), and the other is made up of

$$\text{Enantiomers} \begin{cases} d\text{-Acid} \\ l\text{-Acid} \end{cases} + \; d'\text{-Base} \; \longrightarrow \; \begin{cases} dd'\text{-Salt} \\ ld'\text{-Salt} \end{cases} \text{Diastereoisomers}$$

right- and left-handed components (*ld'*). The two salts obviously differ in rotatory power and are in fact diastereoisomers. If the

acidic and basic components are strongly rotatory, the *dd'*-salt probably will be dextrorotatory; the *ld'*-salt is composed of oppositely
acting but unbalanced parts and may show either positive or negative
rotation.   In any case, the two salts have different rotatory values,
different solubilities, and different melting points; they therefore are
separable by fractional crystallization, and the course of separation
can be followed by determination of appropriate physical constants.
Once one salt has been secured pure, it can be treated with sodium
hydroxide, the resolving *d'*-base recovered, and the optically active
acid liberated by acidification of the alkaline solution.

The method is equally applicable to resolution of a synthetic
dl-amine with an optically active acid.   Sometimes resolution of a
neutral compound is accomplished most advantageously by conversion into a derivative capable of salt formation.   An often efficient
modification in the procedure of resolution consists in treating a
dl-base with half the amount of a resolving organic acid required for
neutralization, together with a further half equivalent of hydrochloric
acid.   Equilibrium is set up among the two pairs of salts, but those
derived from the organic acid are distinctly less soluble than the hydrochlorides.   Thus the less soluble of the two diastereoisomeric organic
salts tends to crystallize, and the solution contains chiefly the hydrochloric acid salt of the enantiomeric amine.

Microbiological Separation of Racemic Modifications. — Pasteur
discovered in 1858–60 that when the microorganism *Penicillium
glaucum*, the green mold found on aging cheese and rotted fruits, is
grown in a dilute aqueous solution of nutrient salts (phosphates, ammonium salts) containing racemic acid, the originally optically inactive solution slowly becomes levorotatory.   The microorganism
preferentially assimilates the *d*-form of tartaric acid, and if the process
is interrupted at an appropriate point the unnatural *l*-tartaric acid
can be isolated.   If the process is allowed to continue, the *l*-form
eventually is consumed, but natural *d*-tartaric acid is attacked by the
microorganism much more rapidly.

12.16

*Preferential attack
by molds of the
natural form*

Many instances are known of preferential utilization of one of
two enantiomers by microorganisms or even by higher organisms.
The action is attributable to the enzyme systems of the organisms.
Thus *dl*-mandelonitrile becomes levorotatory when acted on by the
enzyme emulsin.   Since the enzyme is optically active, the selective
action may be associated with formation of an intermediate complex
that plays a role analogous to that of the diastereoisomeric salts involved in the method of resolution described in the preceding
section.

The microbiological method of separation is seldom of preparative value, particularly since one of the two forms, usually the more interesting natural one, is sacrificed. Its chief value is in determining whether or not a given substance is resolvable. Whereas racemic acid is acted upon by *Penicillium glaucum* and gives a levorotatory solution, mesotartaric acid under the same conditions develops no optical activity.

12.17 **Racemization.** — Conversion of half a given quantity of an optically active compound into the enantiomer is defined as racemization. The experiment by Pasteur in which *d*-tartaric acid was converted by the action of water at 165° into a mixture of the *meso* and *dl*-acids involved racemization of a part of the material. The racemic (*dl*) acid occurring as a by-product of the production of *d*-tartaric acid in the wine industry probably arises by partial racemization of the *d*-acid during processing.

Racemization occurs especially readily with compounds having a carbonyl group adjacent to an asymmetric carbon carrying a hydrogen atom, for example tartaric acid, lactic acid, and glyceraldehyde. Where the specific grouping indicated is lacking, racemization usually proceeds with difficulty, if at all. Thus, in contrast with mandelic acid, $C_6H_5CHOHCOOH$, atrolactic acid, $C_6H_5C(CH_3)OHCOOH$, does not undergo racemization. These facts suggest that the α-hydrogen atom plays a part and that enolization is involved. If the activated

*Ready racemization
through an enol*

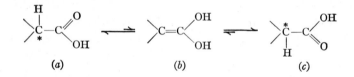

(*a*) (*b*) (*c*)

α-hydrogen atom in (*a*) migrates to oxygen in an equilibrium process to give an enol (*b*), the center of asymmetry is destroyed temporarily by production of a double bond, and when the hydrogen migrates back to the carbon atom, the process can involve opening of either of the two linkages of the symmetrical double bond, and hence can afford either the original configuration (*a*) or the opposite configuration (*c*); the chances being equal, a mixture of equal parts of (*a*) and (*c*) results. Since all the transformations are reversible, formation of only a minute amount of the enol would result in eventual racemization of the entire material. The interpretation is strengthened by the fact that racemization is promoted by acids and bases, reagents which catalyze enolization.

In a compound having more than one asymmetric carbon atom, selective racemization of an asymmetric center adjacent to a carbonyl

group and possessing a hydrogen atom available for enolization is
possible, for example:

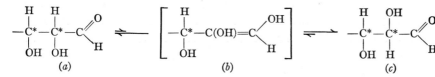

The result is transformation of the original substance (a) partially into the isomer (c), which has been selectively inverted at a single asymmetric center and is described as an epimer of the first substance. Epimerization is not complete, for equilibrium between the isomers is reached; the point of equilibrium by no means corresponds to 50% conversion, but varies from compound to compound. The reason for this difference from an ordinary racemization is that the other center or centers of asymmetry exert control over the course of ketonization of the enolic intermediate (b); opening of the double bond is not fortuitous, but occurs under the directive influence of the stable asymmetric part of the molecule with preference for one or the other of the possible configurations of the labile center. The term epimer is used to designate a pair of diastereoisomers that correspond in configuration of all but one of several centers of asymmetry and that have the opposite configuration at this one center. Epimers may or may not be interconvertible.

Asymmetric Synthesis. — The phenomenon of an asymmetric directive influence on the course of reactions is also applicable to processes of synthesis. One application is demonstrated by experiments on the reduction of esters of pyruvic acid, $CH_3COCOOH$ (McKenzie,[6] 1904–09). Reduction of the carbonyl group of the methyl

12.18

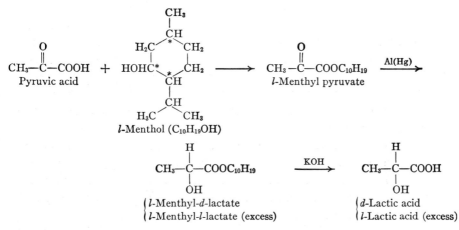

---

[6] Alexander McKenzie, 1869–1951; b. Dundee, Scotland; Ph.D. St. Andrews (Purdie); London, Dundee; *J. Chem. Soc.*, 270 (1952)

or ethyl ester of this α-keto acid can proceed equally well in opposite steric directions and affords the methyl or ethyl ester of *dl*-lactic acid, CH₃CHOHCOOH. When, however, the acid is esterified with the optically active natural alcohol *l*-menthol, reduction gives a mixture containing an excess of the ester of *l*-lactic acid; the product resulting on hydrolysis and removal of the *l*-menthol is optically active and consists of a mixture of *dl*- and *l*-lactic acid.

The key step in asymmetric synthesis is production of a new center of asymmetry, and this affords two diastereoisomers, such as *l*-menthyl *d*-lactate and *l*-menthyl *l*-lactate. In the two molecules the corresponding groups are located at different distances from each other, and not in a mirror-image relationship, and the two substances differ not only in the rate with which they react with given reagents but also in the rate of their formation from a common starting material. Thus the control exercised by a center of asymmetry already present over the production of a new asymmetric center amounts to a preferential rate of formation of one of the two possible diastereoisomers. Neither the direction nor the extent of the preference is ordinarily predictable.

Explanation

Asymmetric synthesis is important in transformations of compounds containing asymmetric carbon atoms. An aldehydic substance having the grouping I affords two products of the cyanohydrin synthesis in *unequal* amounts (II and III). The same is true of hydrogenation of an ethylenic compound having the partial structure IV; both saturated substances usually are formed, but often one product predominates.

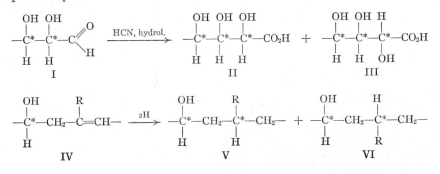

12.19

Walden Inversion. — An interesting phenomenon discovered by Walden [7] (1896) is that when one substituent directly attached to an asymmetric carbon atom is replaced by another, the original center of asymmetry sometimes, but not always, becomes inverted in the process, with the result that its configuration in the product is the

___

[7] Paul Walden, b. 1863 Livland, Russia; stud. Riga, Leipzig, Munich, Odessa; St. Petersburg, Rostock, Tübingen

opposite of that in the starting material. The phenomenon is distinct from that of racemization, for one optically active compound is converted into another, rather than into a *dl*-mixture, and it is not a matter of change in the direction of rotation, which may or may not follow and is coincidental, but rather a question of change in the absolute configuration. Examples are the interconversions of optically active chlorosuccinic and malic acids shown in the chart with projection formulas giving configurations relative to the configuration of glyceraldehyde (*l*-malic acid = D-series). *l*-Chlorosuccinic acid on hydrolysis with potassium hydroxide affords a hydroxy acid of opposite

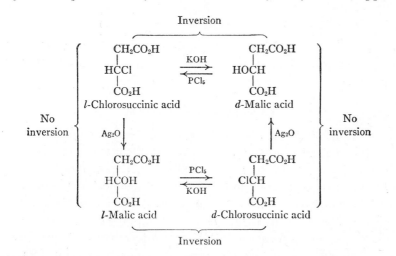

configuration. That the dextrorotatory character of the product is fortuitous can be appreciated from the fact that the malic acids show but feeble rotatory power, with considerable dependence on the concentration of the solutions. The evidence indicates, however, that a Walden inversion occurs in this reaction and in the reverse change brought about by phosphorus pentachloride. On the other hand, the chlorosuccinic acids are hydrolyzed by silver oxide without inversion.

Whether or not a given displacement proceeds with inversion, with retention of configuration, or with partial or total racemization depends upon the reagent, the conditions of the experiment, and the specific characteristics of the substance undergoing reaction. The combination of these factors determines the particular mechanism by which the reaction proceeds. If the hydrolysis of an alkyl bromide (I) is bimolecular, the anion attacks the molecule from the rear (S_N2 mechanism; see 8.4). This backside attack affords a transition state in which the hydroxide ion has given up part of its charge to bromine and in which neither group is fully joined to carbon or fully separated. In the transition state the fractionally charged (δ^-) OH and Br lie in a line and the groups a, b, and c lie in a plane perpendicular to this line. Bromine is then expelled as the anion from one side, with synchronous attachment of hydroxyl to the other side by a covalent link.

S_N2 Reaction with inversion

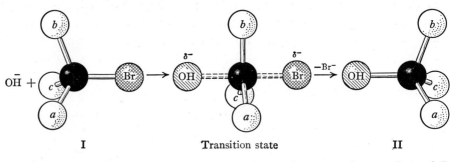

I	Transition state	II

The result is the alcohol II, of configuration opposite to that of I. The process of inversion is thus like the turning of an umbrella inside out in the wind.

GEOMETRICAL ISOMERISM

12.20   The concept of geometrical isomerism introduced in Chapter 4 (4.12) is that the double bond consists of one σ and one π bond and that restriction of rotation as the result of overlap of p orbitals in the formation of the π bond permits existence of *cis* and *trans* forms of any alkene in which each carbon atom is unsymmetrically substituted. In his classical paper of 1874, van't Hoff employed the crude concept of a double bond as formed by joining two tetrahedra at two corners, but he correctly predicted all types of geometrical isomerism that have subsequently been discovered. The first experimental demonstration of the existence of a pair of geometrical isomers as postulated by van't Hoff was in a research by Wislicenus in 1887 on two acids that result from pyrolysis of malic acid: maleic acid (m.p. 130°) and fumaric acid (m.p. 287°). That the difference between them is asso-

HOCHCOOH
| $\xrightarrow{160°}$ CHCOOH $\xrightarrow{Na(Hg)}$ CH₂CO₂H
CH₂COOH   CHCOOH |
l-Malic acid   { Maleic acid (4%)   CH₂CO₂H
                             { Fumaric acid (90%)   Succinic acid

ciated with the double bond is established by its disappearance on hydrogenation; both isomers yield succinic acid. The formulas show that the *cis*, but not the *trans*, isomer should form a cyclic anhydride

comparable to succinic anhydride. Maleic acid indeed forms an anhydride (m.p. 57°), but, since fumaric acid yields the identical anhydride under more drastic conditions, a molecular rearrangement must occur in one of the two reactions and the evidence is inconclusive. However, the anhydride can be hydrolyzed with cold water, that is, under conditions where rearrangement is excluded, and maleic acid is the sole product. Therefore maleic acid has the *cis* configuration, and the product of dehydration is maleic anhydride. Fumaric acid is the *trans* isomer, and when heated strongly or treated with chemical dehydrating agents under forcing conditions, rearranges into maleic acid, which then yields the anhydride:

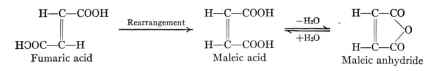

H—C—COOH	H—C—COOH	H—C—CO
‖	‖	‖ >O
HOOC—C—H	H—C—COOH	H—C—CO
Fumaric acid	Maleic acid	Maleic anhydride

Fumaric acid → (Rearrangement) → Maleic acid ⇌ (−H₂O / +H₂O) → Maleic anhydride

That the more symmetrical *trans* configuration is more stable than the *cis* is shown by the higher melting point of fumaric acid (Table III), the greater density (closer packing), the lesser solubility, and by the fact that when maleic acid is heated in a sealed tube to prevent escape of water it yields fumaric acid as the chief product (trace of *dl*-malic acid). The heats of combustion show that maleic acid has an energy

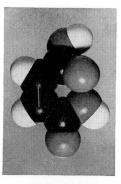

Maleic acid

TABLE III

PHYSICAL PROPERTIES OF MALEIC AND FUMARIC ACID

	MALEIC ACID cis	FUMARIC ACID trans
Melting point	130°	287°
Solubility in water, g. per 100 ml. at 25°	78.8	0.7
Density	1.590	1.635
Heat of combustion, kg.-cal. per mole	327	320
pK_{a_1}	1.9	3.0
pK_{a_2}	6.5	4.5

content 7 kg.-cal. higher than fumaric acid and therefore has greater tendency to undergo change. That the *cis* isomer is the more strongly acidic, as judged by comparison of the constants for the first dissociation, pK_{a_1}, means that the ionizing tendency of one carboxyl group is enhanced by the second unsaturated group in a near-by position. The greater spread between the first and second dissociation constants observed with maleic acid is also understandable. Once a proton has separated from the *cis* dibasic acid, the negatively charged group exerts an attractive force on the second hydrogen atom in the neighboring position and opposes its liberation as a proton.

The energy-richer *cis* isomer is convertible into fumaric acid at room temperature under the catalytic influence of hydrochloric or

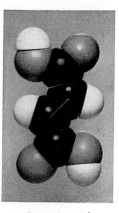

Fumaric acid

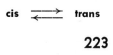

cis ⇌ trans

hydrobromic acid. The halogens as well as the halogen acids are effective catalysts for the rearrangement; for example, diethyl maleate is transformed rapidly into the ester of fumaric acid by a trace of iodine. The transformations represent the reversion of a labile isomer to a more stable form under the driving force derived from the higher energy content. The reverse change is brought about by irradiation of an aqueous solution of fumaric acid with ultraviolet light at 45–50°; within a few hours, equilibrium is reached corresponding to isomerization of 75% of the material. Here the *trans* isomer acquires radiant energy by absorption, and the energy level is built up to that of the *cis* isomer. Although this uphill transformation has theoretical interest, a more practicable preparation of maleic acid consists in warming malic acid with acetyl chloride, distilling the mixture, and hydrolyzing the resulting maleic anhydride. An industrial preparation of maleic anhydride consists in catalytic vapor-phase oxidation of benzene with atmospheric oxygen:

Preparation of maleic anhydride

$$\text{benzene} \xrightarrow{[O]} \text{maleic anhydride} + CO_2, H_2O$$

12.21

Other *cis-trans* Isomers. — Crotonic and isocrotonic acid, geometrical isomers of the structure $CH_3CH=CHCOOH$, represent a typical case where the method of determining configuration by correlation with a ring compound is not applicable. The problem, however, was solved by von Auwers (1923) by relating one isomer to fumaric acid by the preparation of each substance from a common intermediate under conditions shown not to permit rearrangements. The product

Correlation of crotonic and fumaric acid

$$
\begin{array}{c}
CCl_3-C-H \\
\parallel \\
H-C-COOH
\end{array}
\xrightarrow[60\%]{Zn, HOAc}
\begin{array}{c}
CHCl_2-C-H \\
\parallel \\
H-C-COOH
\end{array}
\xrightarrow[74\%]{Na(Hg)}
\begin{array}{c}
CH_3-C-H \\
\parallel \\
H-C-COOH
\end{array}
$$

γ,γ,γ-Trichlorocrotonic acid

Crotonic acid

$$\xrightarrow[66\%]{\text{concd. } H_2SO_4 \text{ at } 30°}
\begin{array}{c}
HOOC-C-H \\
\parallel \\
H-C-COOH
\end{array}$$

Fumaric acid

of stepwise reduction of the trichloro compound proved to be the higher-melting ("solid") crotonic acid, and therefore this, like fumaric acid, has the *trans* configuration. From the properties of the two unsaturated acids, listed under the formulas, it is seen that the rela-

$$
\begin{array}{c}
H-C-CH_3 \\
\parallel \\
H-C-COOH
\end{array}
$$

Isocrotonic acid (*cis*)
(m.p. 15.5°, pKa 4.44, kg.-cal./mole 486,
g./100 ml. H2O25° 40.0)

$$
\begin{array}{c}
CH_3-C-H \\
\parallel \\
H-C-COOH
\end{array}
$$

Crotonic acid (*trans*)
(m.p. 72°, pKa 4.70, kg.-cal./mole 478,
g./100 ml. H2O25° 8.3)

tionships are the same as those of the dibasic acids. The *trans* isomer, with the relatively large methyl and carboxyl groups balanced on the two sides of the molecule, has the more symmetrical structure, and it has the higher melting point, is less soluble, and has a lower energy content; this form also is produced readily by catalyzed rearrangement of the liquid *cis* isomer.

Those instances in which it has been possible to correlate physical properties with chemically established configurations provide a rational, but not infallible, basis on which to deduce the probable configurations of other pairs of isomers. Thus the unsaturated fatty acids oleic and elaidic are regarded as the *cis* and *trans* isomers, respectively, because the former has the lower melting point and the higher heat of combustion and is convertible into the more stable isomer under the catalytic influence of nitric or nitrous acid.

$$H—C—(CH_2)_7CH_3$$
$$\|$$
$$H—C—(CH_2)_7COOH$$
Oleic acid
(m.p. 13°, 16°; kg.-cal./mole 2682)

$$CH_3(CH_2)_7C—H$$
$$\|$$
$$H—C—(CH_2)_7COOH$$
Elaidic acid
(m.p. 44°, kg.-cal./mole 2664)

Steric Course of Additions. — Kekulé and Anschütz [8] (1880–81) established that, on controlled oxidation with alkaline permanganate at a low temperature, maleic acid yields mesotartaric acid and fumaric acid yields *dl*-tartaric acid. Both reactions are analogous to the hy-

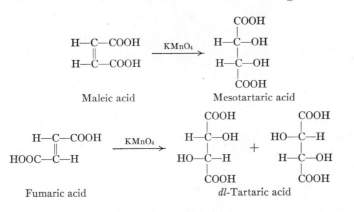

droxylation of cyclohexene with osmium tetroxide to the *cis* diol (4.22) and are described as *cis* additions because both hydroxyl groups attack the unsaturated carbon atoms from the same side. Mesotartaric acid is neither a *cis* nor a *trans* glycol, since free rotation is possible about the single bond, and it is purely fortuitous that in the conventional formula carboxyl groups are put at top and bottom and hence the

[8] Richard Anschütz, 1852–1937; b. Darmstadt, Germany; Ph.D. Heidelberg; Bonn; *Ber.*, **74A**, 29 (1941)

hydroxyls appear on the same side. The double bonds of maleic acid (I) are perpendicular to the plane in which the atoms lie and one (1) extends to the front (solid line) and the other (2) to the rear (dotted

cis Addition

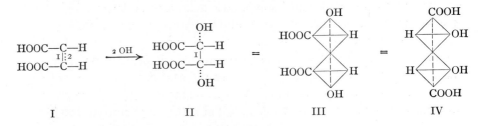

line). If the hydroxyls approach from the rear and open the rear bond (2), the product is II, in which the hydroxyls are to the rear and which is therefore equivalent to the tetrahedral model III, arranged as in the Fischer convention. According to the convention that the order COOH ⟶ OH ⟶ H is right-handed (12.13), the upper carbon in III is right-handed and the lower one left-handed; the clockwise and counterclockwise nature can be inferred equally well from II. If each carbon of III is turned in the direction COOH⟶ OH ⟶ H until carboxyls are at top and bottom, the conventional formula IV of mesotartaric acid is obtained. *cis* Hydroxylation of fumaric acid gives different products, according to the bond opened. Rear-attack of V by opening of bond 2 gives VI, in which both car-

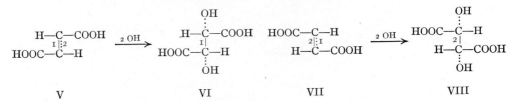

bon atoms are seen to be left-handed. Since frontal attack is not easily represented, alternate opening of bond 1 can be considered by turning V upside down as in VII, in which bond 1 is to the rear and can be opened as before by rear attack. The product VIII contains two right-handed carbons. Thus VI and VIII represent *l*- and *d*-tartaric acid; the probability of opening being the same for each bond, the *dl*-product results.

To the early chemists *cis* addition appeared to be the normal, expected mode of reaction. Hence reactions that seemed to proceed in the opposite sense were viewed with suspicion and regarded as abnormal. Thus on addition of bromine maleic acid gives the *dl*-product and fumaric acid gives the *meso*-dibromide. van't Hoff noted that halogens and halogen acids are effective catalysts for interconversion of *cis-trans* isomers and postulated that the unexpected additions are

cis Addition at first regarded as normal

attended with catalyzed rearrangement of the olefinic starting materials. Michael,[9] however, in a series of investigations of the addition of bromine and hydrogen halides to maleic and fumaric acid and to acetylenedicarboxylic acid (1892–95) demonstrated beyond question that *trans* addition can be accomplished under conditions such *Fact of trans addition established* that interconversions do not occur, and his work led to eventual acceptance of *trans* addition. Indeed *trans* addition is now recognized as the normal mode of reaction of reagents except a few that form cyclic intermediates, and it is adequately interpreted (f) as a two-step process involving electrophilic attack followed by backside attack

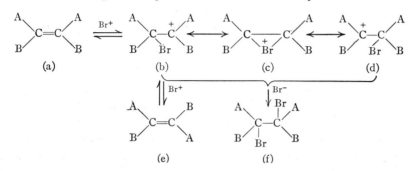

(a) (b) (c) (d)

Mechanistic interpretation

(e) (f)

of a carbonium ion (b, d) or a bromonium ion (c). An electrophilic reagent used in only catalytic amounts may cause *cis-trans* isomerization (e) through a singly bonded carbonium ion such as (b), in which free rotation is possible.

cis Additions known to proceed through cyclic intermediates are hydroxylation with permanganate or with osmium tetroxide (4.22). *cis Additions* *cis* Additions of hydrogen to the double and triple bond (4.27, 5.10) *involving ring* are believed to involve cyclic intermediates. The formation of an *intermediates* oxide by reaction of an alkene with perbenzoic acid (4.26) can proceed only by *cis* addition. An oxide can be hydrolyzed to a glycol (water at 160°) or cleaved with hydrobromic acid to a bromohydrin, and the reactions are analogous to the reaction of the cyclic bromonium ion (c) above with bromide ion to give a *trans* dibromide. Thus fission

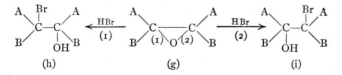

(h) (g) (i)

Oxide cleavage (trans)

of an oxide ring (g) is always attended by Walden inversion of the carbon atom to which the severed bond was initially joined and the product is a *trans* glycol or bromohydrin. Thus if bond (1) suffers

[9] Arthur Michael, 1853–1942; b. Buffalo, N. Y.; stud. Heidelberg, Berlin, École de Médecine, Paris; Tufts, Harvard

fission inversion occurs at this point and the carbon to the left in (h) has the configuration opposite to that in the oxide; cleavage at (2) gives the alternate *trans* bromohydrin (i). Hydroxylation of an alkene with hydrogen peroxide in acetic acid solution (4.22) involves formation of an oxide and its cleavage by the acidic solvent to give a mono or diacetate, which on saponification affords the *trans* glycol.

12.23

Cis and *trans* **Elimination.** — The main facts regarding formation of an alkene by elimination of HX from an alkyl halide or of HOH from an alcohol are summarized as follows. If the reaction is conducted in solution under ionic conditions *trans* elimination occurs

Ionic

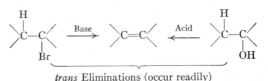

trans Eliminations (occur readily)

more easily than *cis* elimination; if only *cis* elimination is possible the substance may be resistant to dehydrohalogenation or dehydration under practicable conditions. The difference is understandable from a consideration of the intermediate transition state (8.6), which has ideal stability when the attacking and departing groups are as far removed as possible and in a plane with the two carbon atoms. In a nonionic, high-temperature dehydration of an alcohol, for example by pyrolysis of the benzoate, *cis* elimination occurs more readily than *trans* elimination.

Behavior on pyrolysis:

Nonionic

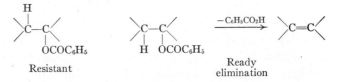

Resistant   Ready elimination

12.24

Stereoisomerism of Cyclic Compounds. — The opportunity for a *cis* and a *trans* arrangement of groups characteristic of the structure HOOCCH=CHCOOH is encountered in the ring structure of cyclopropane-1,2-dicarboxylic acid:

$$HOOCCH\!-\!CHCOOH$$
$$\diagdown \diagup$$
$$CH_2$$

The carbon atoms of the cyclopropane ring lie in a plane, and the two carboxyl groups can either project on the same side or on opposite sides of this plane. The three-membered ring, however, lacks the symmetry of a double bond, and models of all possible forms of the cyclopropanedicarboxylic acids, as shown in Fig. 12.6, show that three configurations are possible. One configuration is that of the *cis* form I, and as long as the two carboxyl groups are represented as being on the same side of the molecule it makes no difference whether these are represented as being above or below the plane of the ring or whether they are affixed to carbon atoms 1 and 2 or 1 and 3. The molecule as written has a plane of symmetry passing through carbon atom 3 and the two attached hydrogen atoms. When the carboxyl

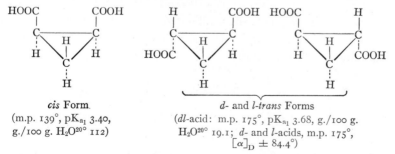

FIG. 12.6.— Cyclopropanedicarboxylic Acids

I   II   III

cis   *trans*

groups are placed on opposite sides of the plane of the ring, two arrangements are possible, II and III. These possess no plane of symmetry and are asymmetric; they are not superposable and are mirror images of each other. The theory thus predicts existence of one *cis* and two *trans* forms, and the prediction has been verified by experiment. One isomeric cyclopropanedicarboxylic acid, m.p. 139°, is nonresolvable and readily forms an anhydride from which it can be regenerated on hydrolysis; it is therefore assigned the *cis* configuration. Another isomeric form, m.p. 175°, yields no anhydride and is identified as the *dl-trans* form by the observation that it is resolvable.

The relationships can be summarized by a conventional representation in which the ring system is imagined to be in a plane at right angles to the paper with the attached groups either above (full lines) or below (dotted lines) this plane. Paralleling the relationship between maleic and fumaric acid, the *cis* form is the more labile and

cis Form.
(m.p. 139°, pK$_{a_1}$ 3.40, g./100 g. H$_2$O$^{20°}$ 112)

d- and *l-trans* Forms
(*dl*-acid: m.p. 175°, pK$_{a_1}$ 3.68, g./100 g. H$_2$O$^{20°}$ 19.1; *d-* and *l-*acids, m.p. 175°, [α]$_D$ ± 84.4°)

is converted into the *dl-trans* form when heated with 50% sulfuric acid at 150°. The higher melting point, lower solubility, and weaker

229

acidic strength of the *trans* form are further marks of this configuration.

The example cited is typical only of those cyclic compounds in which the two parts of the ring extending between the unsymmetrically substituted carbon atoms are different, for, if they are the same, the situation is exactly like that of the maleic-fumaric type of isomers. Thus cyclohexane-1,4-dicarboxylic acid presents merely the same opportunity for geometrical isomerism found in ethylenic compounds:

Symmetrical ring

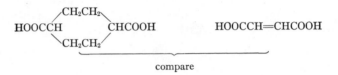

compare

Of the two modifications of the acid that have been isolated, neither forms an anhydride and neither is resolvable. The configurations indicated are assigned on the basis of physical properties and relative stability to isomerization.

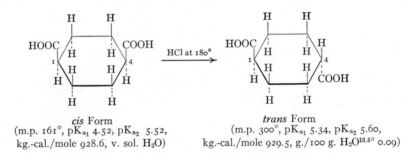

cis Form
(m.p. 161°, pK$_{a_1}$ 4.52, pK$_{a_2}$ 5.52,
kg.-cal./mole 928.6, v. sol. H$_2$O)

trans Form
(m.p. 300°, pK$_{a_1}$ 5.34, pK$_{a_2}$ 5.60,
kg.-cal./mole 929.5, g./100 g. H$_2$O$^{16.5°}$ 0.09)

If the two carboxyl groups are located at the 1,2- or 1,3-positions in the cyclohexane ring, the ring system becomes unsymmetrical, and the same opportunity exists for both geometrical and optical isomerism as in the cyclopropane series. The isomeric cyclohexane-1,2-dicarboxylic acids (hexahydrophthalic acids), for example, are represented in the following formulations:

*Unsymmetrical
ring*

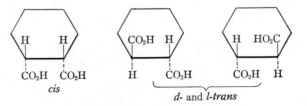

cis

d- and *l-trans*

SUMMARY

History

Polarization of light (Malus, 1808). Nicol prism (transmits a single ray of polarized light). Rotation of plane polarized light by quartz crystals that are hemihedral (having half the faces required for symmetry). Discovery that certain organic compounds exhibit optical activity in solution (Biot, 1815). Principle of the polarimeter. Specific rotation, $[\alpha]$. Dextrorotation $(+)$, levorotation $(-)$.

Discoveries of Pasteur. Resolution of racemic acid into d- and l-tartaric acids (1848) by slow crystallization of the sodium ammonium salt at a temperature fortuitously below a critical transition point. Recognition that the tartaric acids must possess molecular asymmetry. Discovery of a fourth, optically inactive, isomer (mesotartaric acid). Discovery of the only other methods yet known for resolving a dl-compound or a racemate.

The lactic acids: d-acid of muscle tissue, dl-acid from bacterial fermentation of milk sugar. Wislicenus' proof (1863–73) of identity of structure; synthesis of dl-acid; conclusion that the acids differ in the arrangement of atoms in space.

Theory of van't Hoff and Le Bel (1874). Concept of the tetrahedral nature of the carbon atom. Asymmetry attending attachment to carbon of four different atoms or groups. Correlation of optical activity with the presence of an asymmetric carbon atom.

Optical Isomerism

Compounds with one asymmetric carbon atom. Models of d- and l-lactic acid. Inference that d- and l-forms must be identical in all chemical and physical properties except effect on plane polarized light. Mirror-image isomers called enantiomers. Syntheses of compounds having an asymmetric carbon atom involve a process of either addition or substitution that offers equal probability of producing the d- or l-form; hence a dl-mixture invariably results.

Correlations and conventions. Salts and derivatives of d-lactic acid differ in magnitude and even sign of rotation, but they correspond in configuration and belong to the same stereochemical series. Conventional reference standard: dextrorotatory glyceraldehyde defined as D-$(+)$-glyceraldehyde. E. Fischer's projection formulas; method of orienting model. Other members of the D-series of particular importance: D-$(-)$-lactic acid, D-$(-)$-tartaric acid (unnatural isomer), D-$(+)$-glucose (natural, carbon atom 5).

Compounds with dissimilar asymmetric carbon atoms. Possible variations when two asymmetric carbon atoms are present: $+a +b$, $-a -b$, $+a -b$, $-a + b$. Tetrahedral formulas and planar projections for four isomeric acids $C_6H_5CHBrCHBrCO_2H$. Definition of diastereoisomers: nonidentical isomers of the same structure that are not mirror-image isomers (enantiomers). Number of isomers $= 2^n$ (n = number of dissimilar asymmetric carbon atoms).

Tartaric acids: d-, l-, dl- (racemic), and meso-. Variations for two similar asymmetric carbon atoms: $+a +a$, $-a -a$, $+a -a$ (meso). Tetrahedral and projection formulas. Melting-point diagrams of d-, l-, and dl-forms.

Resolution of a dl-acid by formation of salts with a d'-base: dd'-salt and ld'-salt are diastereoisomers of different rotation and different solubility, separable by fractional crystallization. Resolution of a dl-amine with an optically active acid.

Microbiological separation of racemates. The microorganism *Penicillium glaucum* assimilates d-tartaric faster than l-tartaric acid. Dependence upon optically active enzymes. Use in distinguishing between dl- and *meso*-forms.

Racemization: conversion of d- or l-form to dl-form. Occurs readily where asymmetric carbon carries a hydrogen atom and is adjacent to a carbonyl group. Mechanism through enol. Epimerization: partial transformation to an isomer that is inverted at one of two or more centers of asymmetry (epimer); realizable whenever enolization involving a single center is possible, i.e. in

$$\overset{*}{-}CHOH\overset{*}{C}HOHCOOH.$$ Position of equilibrium varies from compound to compound.

Asymmetric synthesis. Production of a new center of asymmetry in an optically active compound can give two diastereoisomers, one of which is favored by a preferential rate of formation. Example: hydrogenation of pyruvic acid (CH_3COCO_2H) esterified with an optically active alcohol (menthol).

Walden inversion. Replacement of a group attached to an asymmetric carbon atom often gives a product of the opposite stereochemical series. Example: D-$R_1R_2R_3CCl \longrightarrow$ L-$R_1R_2R_3COH$. Explanation: bimolecular reaction involving backside attack, transition state, expulsion of group as ion (umbrella turned inside out).

van't Hoff's prediction of *cis-trans* forms of unsymmetrically substituted alkenes confirmed.

Maleic and fumaric acid by dehydration of malic acid (fumaric acid the chief product). Reduction of both isomers to succinic acid, which forms a cyclic anhydride. Maleic acid forms an anhydride easily; fumaric gives the same anhydride with greater difficulty, but rearrangements obscure relationships. Reversion of the anhydride to maleic acid on low-temperature hydrolysis proves maleic acid to have *cis* configuration. Fumaric acid (*trans*) is the more symmetrical and has the higher melting point, lower solubility, greater density. Higher heat of combustion of maleic acid (*cis*) indicates greater energy content, greater lability. Energy-rich *cis* form rearranges to stable *trans* form on catalysis by X_2 or HX. Reverse transformation, *trans* $\longrightarrow$ *cis* accomplished by irradiation (absorption of energy).

Other *cis-trans* isomers. Crotonic acid (*trans*) and isocrotonic acid (*cis*): $CH_3CH = CHCOOH$ Oleic acid (*cis*) and elaidic acid (*trans*):

$$CH_3(CH_2)_7CH = CH(CH_2)_7COOH$$

Steric course of additions. *Cis* addition in reactions of alkenes with alkaline permanganate (*cis* glycols), perbenzoic acid (ethylene oxides), and osmium tetroxide (osmic esters convertible to *cis* glycols). *Trans* addition of halogens, halogen acids, hypohalites. Mechanism involving carbonium ion intermediate.

Elimination of HX from an alkyl halide or of HOH from an alcohol. In usual ionic dehydrohalogenations and dehydrations *trans* elimination occurs more readily than *cis* elimination. Situation reversed for nonionic, pyrolytic dehydrations.

Stereoisomerism of Cyclic Compounds

Three isomeric cyclopropane-1,2-dicarboxylic acids: *cis* (optically inactive), *d-trans* and *l-trans*. Resolvability of *trans* isomer confirms assignment of configurations based upon anhydride formation and physical properties. Diagrammatic formulation.

Both *cis* and *trans* forms of cyclohexane-1,4-dicarboxylic acid optically inactive. Cyclohexane-1,2-dicarboxylic acids: *cis* (inactive), *d-* and *l-trans*.

PROBLEMS

1. Would you expect the reaction of methyl ethyl ketone with phenylmagnesium bromide to proceed in a single steric direction?

2. Write projection formulas for all the stereoisomeric forms of $HOOCCH(CH_3)CHBrCOOH$. Which are enantiomers and which diastereoisomers?

3. How many optically active forms corresponding to the following formulas are possible?

(a) $CH_3CH_2CH(OH)CHClCH_3$
(b) $(CH_3)_2CHCH_2CH(CH_3)COOH$
(c) $C_6H_5CHBrCH_2CH(OH)CH_2CH(NH_2)COOH$
(d)
$CH_2(OH)CH(OH)CH(OH)CH(OH)CH(OH)CHO$

4. An acid of the formula $C_5H_{10}O_2$ is optically active. What is its structure?

5. A derivative of one of the tartaric acids is optically active but gives optically inactive products when esterified with diazomethane or when hydrolyzed. What is it?

6. Give the number and nature of the possible stereoisomers, if any, corresponding to each of the following formulas:

(a) $(CH_3)_2CHCH(NH_2)CH_2CH(CH_3)_2$
(b) $CH_3CH_2C(CH_3) = C(CH_3)_2$
(c) $C_6H_5CH = CHCOC_6H_5$
(d) $CH_2 = CHCH_2CH(NH_2)COOH$
(e) $C_6H_5CHBrCHBrCOC_6H_5$
(f) $(C_6H_5)_2C = CHCH_2CH_2CH = C(C_6H_5)_2$
(g) $CH_3CH(OH)CH(OH)CH_3$
(h) $HOCH_2CH(OH)CH(OH)CH(OH)CHO$

7. When a dextrorotatory isomer of the formula $HOCH_2CH(OH)CH(OH)CHO$ is boiled with dilute hydrochloric acid the rotatory power increases for a time and then becomes constant. What is the nature of the change?

8. How could you establish a rigid proof that crotonic and isocrotonic acid both have the structure $CH_3CH = CHCOOH$?

9. Formulate all possible stereoisomeric forms of cyclobutane-1,2-dicarboxylic acid and cyclobutane-1,3-dicarboxylic acid.

10. What are the possibilities for stereoisomerism in butene-2, ricinoleic acid (7.7), and menthol (12.18)?

11. Certain substances of the type $R_1R_2R_3R_4N^+X^-$

have been resolved into optically active components. What inference can be drawn regarding the spatial character of the nitrogen atom?

12. van't Hoff made a prediction, verified some sixty years later, concerning the stereochemistry of allenes of the following type:

What phenomenon would you anticipate in such a structure?

13. The compound formulated below, which exhibits brilliant blue fluorescence in dilute aqueous solution and which has affinity for cotton fabric, is employed, in its most stable steric form, as a brightening agent, or colorless dye added to soap to increase whiteness of washed goods. What change would you expect to occur when the washed material is exposed to sunlight?

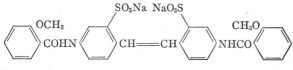

14. Which of the following pairs of diastereoisomers are epimers, and which epimer pairs offer prospect for easy interconversion?

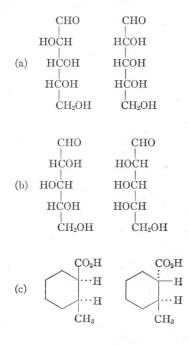

(d)
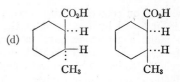

15. Identify the following isomer pairs. (1) Are they enantiomers, epimers, diastereoisomers, geometrical isomers, structural isomers, or identical? (2) Is either or both members of the pair optically active?

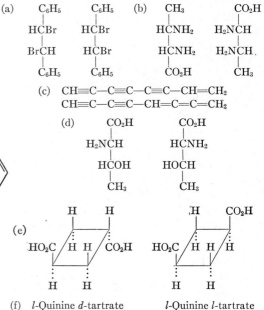

(f) *l*-Quinine *d*-tartrate   *l*-Quinine *l*-tartrate

16. Mescal, a preparation from the tops of the small cactus *Lophophora williamsii*, is used as a stimulant and antispasmodic, especially among Mexican Indians, who also employ it as a mild intoxicant in various ceremonials. The active principle, mescaline, was isolated in 1896 by A. Heffter (Leipzig) from material supplied by Parke, Davis and Co. Mescaline (A), $C_{11}H_{17}O_3N$, melts at $36°$, is optically inactive, sparingly soluble in water or in sodium hydroxide solution, but soluble in dilute hydrochloric acid. Zerewitinoff determination shows the presence of one active hydrogen, and reaction with acetic anhydride in pyridine gives a neutral derivative (B), $C_{13}H_{19}O_4N$. When A is shaken with benzenesulfonyl chloride and aqueous alkali the substance gradually dissolves, and acidification of the solution gives a crystalline precipitate (C), $C_{17}H_{21}O_5NS$.

Mescaline on reaction with excess methyl iodide, followed by treatment of the product with moist silver oxide, gives a product D, $C_{14}H_{25}O_4N$, which when heated decomposes to trimethylamine and a neutral compound E, $C_{11}H_{14}O_3$. Ozonization of E gives formaldehyde and an aromatic aldehyde, F, $C_{10}H_{12}O_4$, characterized by Zeisel determination as having three methoxyl groups. The trihydroxy compound resulting on demethylation has an infrared absorption band characteristic of an unchelated aldehydic group. Deduce the structure of mescaline and suggest a synthesis from the aldehyde F.

READING REFERENCES

Louis Pasteur, *Researches on Molecular Asymmetry*, Alembic Club Reprints, No. 14 (1905)

P. F. Frankland, "Pasteur Memorial Lecture," *J. Chem. Soc.*, **71**, 683–711 (1897)

R. Vallery-Radot, *The Life of Pasteur*, translation by R. L. Devonshire, Doubleday Page, Garden City (1926)

J. H. van't Hoff, *Chemistry in Space*, translation by J. E. Marsh of *Dix Années dans l'Histoire d'une Théorie*, Oxford (1891)

P. F. Frankland, "The Walden Inversion" (Presidential Address), *J. Chem. Soc.*, **103**, 713 (1913)

R. L. Shriner, R. Adams, and C. S. Marvel, "Stereoisomerism," in H. Gilman, *Organic Chemistry*, 2nd Ed., I, 214–488, Wiley, New York (1943)

C. S. Hudson, "Emil Fischer's Stereo-Formulas," *Advances in Carbohydrate Chemistry*, Vol. 3, Chapt. 1, Academic Press (1948)

RING FORMATION AND STABILITY

ALICYCLIC COMPOUNDS

Stereochemical factors play an important part in determining the reactivity, stability, and ease of formation of nonbenzenoid compounds containing rings of carbon atoms and described as alicyclic (aliphatic cyclic). In the series of cycloalkanes, only the 3- and 4-ring hydrocarbons have appreciable chemical reactivity. Cyclopropane approaches ethylene in susceptibility to addition reactions. It undergoes catalytic hydrogenation fairly readily, with opening of the ring and formation of *n*-propane. Cyclopropane reacts also with bromine,

$$CH_2\text{—}CH_2 \quad \xrightarrow{\text{H}_2,\ \text{Ni} (120°)} \quad CH_3CH_2CH_3$$
$$\underset{CH_2}{\diagdown \diagup}$$

hydrogen bromide, and sulfuric acid, with cleavage of the three-membered ring. The reaction of hydrogen bromide with substituted cyclopropanes follows the Markownikoff rule of addition to alkenes; the ring is opened between the carbon atoms carrying the largest and the smallest number of hydrogen atoms, and the halogen becomes affixed to the latter position. Cyclopropane derivatives also form

$$CH_3CH_2CH\text{—}CH_2 \xrightarrow{\text{HBr}} CH_3CH_2CHCH_2CH_3$$
$$\underset{CH_2}{\diagdown \diagup} \qquad\qquad\qquad \underset{Br}{|}$$

$$\underset{CH_3}{\overset{CH_3}{\diagdown}}C\text{—}CHCH_3 \xrightarrow{\text{HBr}} \underset{CH_3}{\overset{CH_3}{\diagdown}}C\text{—}CH\underset{CH_3}{\overset{CH_3}{\diagup}}$$
$$\underset{CH_2}{\diagdown \diagup} \qquad\qquad\qquad \underset{Br}{|}$$

colored complexes with tetranitromethane, a property characteristic of alkenes. In contrast with ethylene, however, cyclopropane is not attacked by permanganate or by ozone. The difference is illustrated by the permanganate oxidation of the unsaturated cyclopropane derivative shown in the formulation. Compounds containing the cyclopropane ring can be distinguished from alkenes by a qualitative test

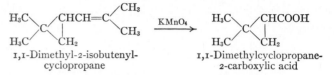

1,1-Dimethyl-2-isobutenyl-
cyclopropane

1,1-Dimethylcyclopropane-
2-carboxylic acid

with permanganate, a reagent also used to remove traces of propylene from cyclopropane.

Cyclobutane is not so reactive as cyclopropane, for it is inert at ordinary temperatures to bromine and to hydrogen iodide. The ring can be opened by hydrogenation, but under conditions more drastic than those required for opening the cyclopropane ring. Cyclopentane

Cyclobutane less reactive

$$\begin{matrix} CH_2-CH_2 \\ | \qquad | \\ CH_2-CH_2 \end{matrix} \xrightarrow{\text{H}_2,\ \text{Ni (200°)}} CH_3CH_2CH_2CH_3$$

and cyclohexane are similar in chemical characteristics and are comparable to the corresponding open-chain alkanes. Five- and six-membered rings are not opened by permanganate, ozone, bromine, hydrogen bromide, or even by hydrogenation. Cyclopentane and cyclohexane are thus less reactive than cyclobutane.

13.2

Baeyer Strain Theory. — Baeyer[1] in 1885 advanced an interpretation of the varying reactivity of cycloalkanes with ring size based on the fact that in a tetrahedral carbon atom the normal angle between a pair of valence bonds is 109° 28'. He postulated that deviation from the normal angle would result in internal strain and consequent high energy content and reactivity. The double bond was regarded as a highly strained two-membered ring and the reactivity of alkenes in additions was attributed to demand for relief from the strain of distorted linkages. The strain expected from the calculated distortion is less with cyclopropane, slight in cyclobutane, and negligible in cyclopentane, which accords with the observed order of chemical reactivity. The relative energy content is indicated quantitatively by the heats of combustion, and the data of Table I show that in the

TABLE I

HEATS OF COMBUSTION AND VALENCE ANGLES

	Cycloalkanes					
	$CH_2=CH_2$	C_3	C_4	C_5	C_6	C_7
Kg.-cal./CH_2 group	170.0	168.5	165.5	158.7	157.4	158.3
Bond angle deviation	+54° 44'	+24° 44'	9° 44'	0° 44'	(−5° 16')	(−9° 33')

[1] Adolf von Baeyer, 1835–1917; b. Berlin; Ph.D. Berlin; Strasbourg, Univ. Munich; Nobel Prize 1905; W. H. Perkin, "Baeyer Memorial Lecture," *J. Chem. Soc.* **123**, 1520 (1923)

series from ethylene to cyclopentane energy content decreases with decreasing deviation from the normal valence angle. The reactivity of ethylene is now attributed to the availability of π electrons, but the Baeyer concept of strained rings still provides the most satisfactory interpretation of the decreasing reactivity of cyclopropane and cyclobutane and the lack of reactivity of cyclopentane.

The carbon atoms of cyclopentane form a practically strain-free planar ring, and Baeyer assumed that hydrocarbons with larger rings would also be planar. Consequently, the calculation for cyclohexane indicated a small negative bond angle deviation in the sense of an expansion of the normal valence angle. This part of the theory implied that compounds containing very large rings would be too unstable to exist. At the time the theory was advanced even cyclopentane and cyclohexane derivatives were rare, and compounds with larger rings were unknown. Thermochemical data now available (Table I) show that

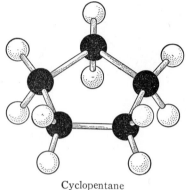

Cyclopentane

cyclopentane, cyclohexane, and cycloheptane have very nearly the same energy content and indeed that six- and seven-membered rings are not under strain due to expansion of bond angles.

Sachse-Mohr Concept of Strainless Rings. — In 1890 Sachse suggested that in rings of six or more members the carbon atoms do not lie in a plane as supposed by Baeyer but assume a strain-free, puckered configuration. In the case of a six-carbon ring two strain-free forms are possible, a chair form and a boat form, which are shown in the photographs of models. Sachse's proposal

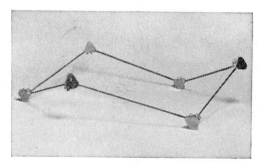

Chair form

13.3

was initially discounted because cyclohexane exists in one form and not two, but nearly thirty years later Mohr [2] (1918) revived the idea and pointed out that interconversion of the chair and boat forms can be accomplished in models by rotations about single bonds without distortion of the normal valence angles; he reasoned that the two forms may be of so closely equivalent energy content as to be indistinguishable. Mohr saw further that resistance to interconversion should be greater in the structure of decalin (decahydronaphthalene), in which two six-carbon rings share two carbon atoms in

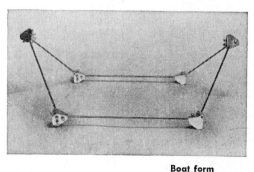

Boat form

[2] Ernst Mohr, 1873–1926; b. Dresden, Germany; Ph.D. Kiel; Heidelberg; *Ber.*, **59A**, 39 (1926)

CHAPTER 13

Decalin

Decalins

common, and predicted the existence of two stable stereoisomeric forms, *cis* and *trans*, for which conventional representations are as follows:

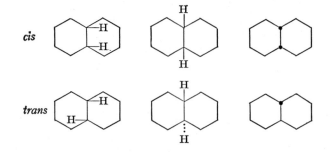

Mohr's paper was favorably received, and the concept of nonplanar, strainless rings was unequivocally proved by W. Hückel[3] (1925), who isolated the two postulated steric forms of decalin, of the properties

	cis-Decalin	*trans*-Decalin
Melting point	$-43.3°$	$-31.5°$
Boiling point	$194°$	$185°$
Specific gravity, D_4^{20}	0.895	0.870
Molar heat of combustion, kg.-cal.	1502.4	1500.3

noted, and who prepared all the theoretically possible isomers of the α- and β-monohydroxy derivatives of each hydrocarbon. The hydrocarbons are both stable, and transformation of the *cis* into the *trans* form is accomplished only under drastic conditions (treatment with aluminum bromide).

13.4

Muscone and civetone

Baeyer's inference that multimembered ring compounds would be too unstable to exist was disproved finally in a striking manner in the work of Ruzicka[4] at Zurich (1926) on the active principles of the rare perfume bases musk and civet. Dried musk is a dark-colored powdery substance of powerful odor obtained from an egg-sized gland situated near the abdomen of the male musk deer, a small wild animal found in mountainous regions of central Asia, particularly the Himalayas; the apparent function of musk is to attract the female animal. Civet occurs similarly in the African civet cat (male and female), and the active fragrant principle is civetone. Muscone, the principle of musk, is an optically active saturated ketone and civetone is an inactive, unsaturated ketone. Civetone on hydrogenation absorbed an amount of gas indicative of the presence of one double bond and gave a saturated ketone (2) which on oxidation yielded a dibasic acid (3) of the

[3] Walter Hückel, b. 1895 Charlottenburg, Germany; Ph.D. Göttingen (Windaus); Freiburg, Greiswald, Tübingen
[4] Leopold Ruzicka, b. 1887, Vukova, Yugoslavia; Ph.D. Karlsruhe (Staudinger); Utrecht, Zurich ETH; Nobel Prize 1939

same carbon content, which shows that the carbonyl group is present
in a ring. Reduction of the carbonyl group of civetone to a methylene

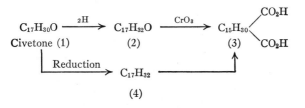

group (4) and oxidation gave an identical acid (3), and hence the
carbonyl group and the double bond of the natural product must be
in the same ring. Oxidation of civetone itself gave the acids HO_2C-
$(CH_2)_3CO_2H$, $HO_2C(CH_2)_6CO_2H$, and $HO_2C(CH_2)_7CO_2H$, the last of
which shows that the ring must include at least seven methylene
groups. Formula I meets this requirement and also accounts for the

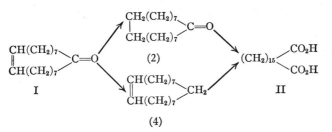

production from (2) and (4) of a common oxidation product, shown by
synthesis to have the structure II. That civetone has the structure I
was finally proved by controlled permanganate oxidation to a keto
dibasic acid, the structure of which was established by synthesis:

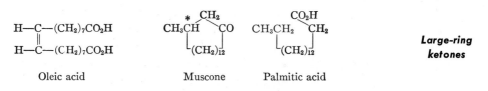

Civetone and muscone occur in secretions rich in fat, and it may
be significant that civetone is structurally related to one common
fat component, oleic acid, and that muscone has at least the carbon

$$H-C-(CH_2)_7CO_2H$$
$$H-C-(CH_2)_7CO_2H$$

Oleic acid

$$\overset{*}{CH_2}$$
$$CH_3CH \quad CO$$
$$\lfloor(CH_2)_{\overline{12}}\rfloor$$

Muscone

$$CO_2H$$
$$CH_3CH_2 \quad CH_2$$
$$\lfloor(CH_2)_{\overline{12}}\rfloor$$

Palmitic acid

skeleton of another, palmitic acid. M. Stoll[5] (1948) found that the
relationship of civetone to oleic acid extends to the stereochemistry.

[5] Max Stoll, b. 1899 Zurich; Ph.D. and D.Sc. Zurich ETH (Ruzicka); Firmenich and
Co., Geneva

The carbonyl group of muscone was protected by ketal formation (10.18), bromine was added to the double bond, and the dibromide

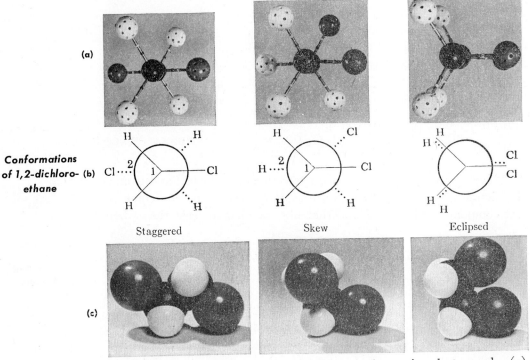

was dehydrohalogenated (KOH, amyl alcohol) to the acetylene. Selective hydrogenation under conditions suitable for production of a *cis* ethylene and hydrolytic elimination of the ketal group, gave material identical with natural civetone. Stoll effected synthesis of both the *cis* and *trans* isomers; the large-ring compounds have no unusual chemical properties and are evidently free from strain.

CONFORMATION

13.5   The term conformation is used to designate a particular shape or arrangement in space of a molecule in which more than one arrangement is possible by rotations about single bonds. In 1,2-dichloroethane, CH_2ClCH_2Cl, complete freedom of rotation about the σ bond could lead to an infinite number of conformations, three of which,

Conformations of 1,2-dichloroethane

Staggered   Skew   Eclipsed

called staggered, skew, and eclipsed, are shown in photographs (a). Each molecule is viewed along a line close to the axis of the carbon–

carbon bond, so that C_1 (front) nearly obscures C_2 (rear). The first and third forms represent two extremes; in the staggered form the two chlorines (black) are maximally separated and in the eclipsed form they are as close as possible. The skew form represents a condition intermediate between the other two. In the projection formulas (b) the view is along the C—C axis. The carbon atom nearest the eye is numbered 1 and its other three bonds are represented by full lines; that to the rear (C_2) is represented by a circle and its bonds by dotted lines. The relative stability is determined by the proximity of the dominant chlorine atoms, which tend to repel each other, and hence the staggered form is the most stable and the eclipsed form the least stable. The relationship is appreciated best from Stuart models (c), viewed from the side. In the staggered form the large chlorine atoms are too remote for any but feeble repulsion, whereas in the eclipsed form they are so close that the repulsive force produces maximal instability. In conventional terminology the instability of an eclipsed conformation is ascribed to an eclipsed **interaction**; practically, an interaction, which makes for instability, can be understood as due to mutual repulsion of atoms or groups. The magnitude of the effect depends somewhat upon the nature of the substituents, but is generally greater the larger the groups. A skew interaction is always stronger than a staggered interaction and weaker than an eclipsed interaction.

The staggered and skew rotational isomers of 1,2-dichloroethane are not isolable but are nevertheless recognizable from characteristic infrared and Raman spectra, one of which fades out ahead of the other as the temperature is lowered. Evidence from both spectrographic analysis and dipole moment measurements over a wide range of temperature shows that the staggered form is more stable than the skew form by 1.2 kg.-cal. and that the eclipsed form has no reality.

Appreciable differences in conformational stability are encountered in ethanes substituted with large atoms or groups, for example the two stilbene dibromides, *meso* and *dl*. The large bromine atoms tend

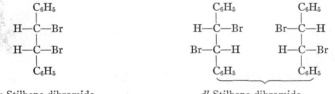

meso-Stilbene dibromide
M.p. 237°; sol. in 1025 parts ether[18°]

dl-Stilbene dibromide
M.p. 114°; sol. in 3.7 parts ether[18°]

to repel each other but the phenyl groups exercise still greater mutual repulsion and hence in both isomers the conformation of maximal stability is that in which the two phenyl groups are as far from each

Eclipsed, skew, and staggered interactions

Interaction = repulsion

13.6

other as possible. It will be seen from the projection formulas that, with the two phenyl groups in a transoid arrangement, the two large

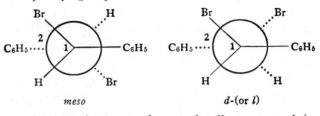

meso   *d-*(or *l*)

bromines of the *meso*-form are also maximally separated (staggered) but those of the *dl*-form are bunched on one side of the molecule in a skew arrangement. The *meso*-form is thus symmetrical and the *dl*-form

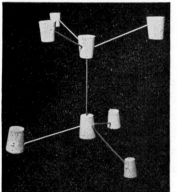

unsymmetrical, and the difference is reflected in a marked contrast in melting point and solubility. X-ray diffraction measurements confirm the predominant conformations indicated, since the Br—Br distances found are: *meso*, 4.50 Å; *dl*, 3.85 Å. That conformation influences chemical reactivity is shown by the fact that on debromination of the two dibromides with potassium iodide in acetone the *meso*-dibromide reacts about one hundred times faster than the *dl*-isomer. In the first case the bromines undergoing elimination are maximally separated and in a plane with the two carbon atoms, and hence the conditions are ideal for *trans* elimination. Debromination of the skew *dl*-dibromide requires

excitation of the molecule sufficient to overcome the energy barrier to rotation to a conformation in which the bromine atoms are *trans*.

Cyclohexane. — The orientation of bonds in the chair conformation of cyclohexane is best appreciated from the model (d), of which

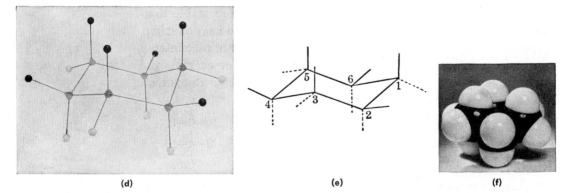

(d)   (e)   (f)

(e) is the conventional projection. Bonds that extend or are inclined upwards are designated β and are represented in (d) by attached black balls and in (e) by full lines; bonds that are downward are

designated α (white balls, dotted lines). A useful concept introduced by Hassel[6] (1943) differentiates between bonds of two types, whether they are α or β. The β bonds extending up from C_1, C_3, and C_5, as

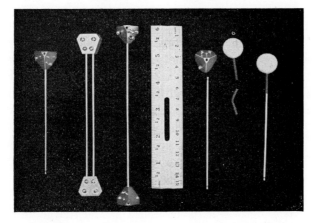

well as the α bonds extending down from C_2, C_4, and C_6, are parallel to the axis of symmetry of the ring, and these six bonds are called axial (a). The other six bonds radiate more or less in the plane of the

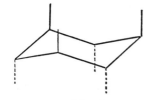

Axial bonds (a)

Equatorial bonds (e)

The Hassel concept

Cyclohexane bonds (chair)

ring and are called equatorial (e): 1α, 2β, 3α, 4β, 5α, 6β. The Stuart model of cyclohexane (f) shows clearly the contrast of the three axial β-hydrogens and the nearly coplanar α and β equatorial hydrogens. The bunched axial hydrogens exert repulsive interactions, and they are less accessible than equatorial hydrogens to external reagents.

The stability of the chair conformation can be estimated from inspection of the six ethane units in the model (d). If this is viewed along the axis of one of the carbon–carbon bonds, as in (g), the ethane unit is seen to be in the skew arrangement. Since the molecule is symmetrical, the chair conformation lacks maximal stability by a fac-

[6] Odd Hassel, b. 1897 Oslo, Norway; Ph.D. Berlin; Univ. Oslo
* Dimensions of Barton models [D. H. R. Barton, *Chem. Ind.* (1956)]: C—H (left, center-to-center), 10.9 cm.; C=C, 13.3 cm.; C—C, 15.4 cm. The setscrew fitting into the groove near the end of the rod (to right of ruler) insures permanent union with accurate spacing and still permits free rotation about the single bond. Balls (*not* to scale) from the O. H. Johns Glass Co. model set can be attached with the spiral springs that come with the set; a slight kink in the spring holds it on securely. Barton models are supplied by Wilkens-Anderson Co., Chicago.

tor of six skew interactions. Thermochemical data show that the strain energy of a single skew interaction is at most slight. Thus the heat of combustion per methylene group of cyclohexane is 157.4 kg.-cal., and this is precisely the currently accepted average value for the heat of combustion for each presumably strain-free methylene group in the series of homologous *n*-alkanes, in which each ethane unit is free to assume the stable, staggered conformation. The comparison would suggest that cyclohexane is free from strain derived from hydrogen repulsions, as well as from strain associated with bond distortion. However, the individual figures upon which the average is based vary from 157.2 to 157.9 kg.-cal., and each is subject to the uncertainty that it is a small difference between large numbers (e.g., for *n*-pentane and *n*-butane, $845.16 - 687.98 = 157.18$ kg.-cal./CH_2). A skew repulsion in an alicyclic ring does appear to make a significant, if slight, contribution to instability, or strain energy, and the magnitude of the effect, based on thermochemical data for the decalins (13.9), is assumed to be 0.7 kg.-cal. per skew interaction. The strain energy of the chair form of cyclohexane is thus estimated as 4.2 kg.-cal./mole.

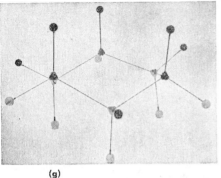

(g)

Strain energy, skew = 0.7

The boat conformation is shown in perspective formula (h) and model (i). Four of the carbon atoms lie in a plane (2,3,5,6), above

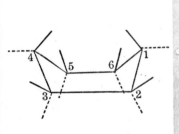

(h)

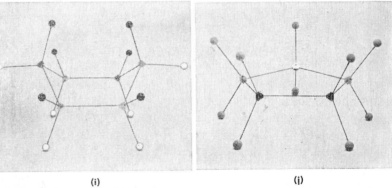

(i)   (i)

Strain energy, eclipsed = 1.3 + 0.7 = 2.0

which C_1 and C_4 rise to form bow and stern. The following ethane units have the reasonably stable skew arrangement: 1,2-, 3,4-, 4,6-, and 6,1-. However, the 2,3- and 5,6-units, which form the sides of the boat, have the unstable eclipsed conformation. The same is true of all five ethane units of cyclopentane (j), which has an energy content of 158.7 kg.-cal./methylene group, which is 1.3 kg.-cal. higher than that of a cyclohexane methylene group. Hence the strain energy asso-

ciated with each eclipsed interaction of boat-cyclohexane can be estimated as 2.0 kg.-cal. Furthermore, the two bonds at bow (C_1) and
stern (C_4) pointing upward in a near axial orientation bring the hydrogen atoms into close enough proximity to establish a bow-stern interaction estimated as equivalent to an ethane skew repulsion. Hence
the total strain energy of the boat form is estimated to be 7.5 kg.-cal.
The chair form is thus more stable than the boat form by some 3.3
kg.-cal., which means that the boat form has no reality, except as
part of a cage structure, for example, one formed by a methylene
bridge linking C_1 and C_4 (see camphor, 14.22).

Hassel, in an electron diffraction study of substituted cyclohexanes,
established that the favored conformation is that in which a maximum
number of substituents occupy the relatively distant equatorial positions. A specific interpretation can be illustrated for the case of
methylcyclohexane. The stability is greater when the methyl group

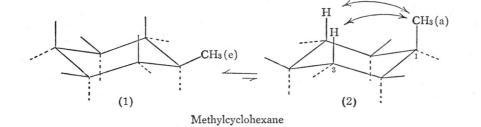

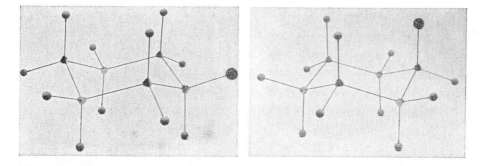

Methylcyclohexane

is equatorial (1) rather than axial (2) because of interactions between
this axial group and the axial hydrogens in the 1,3- and 1,3'-positions
(curved arrows). Such a 1,3-interaction can be assumed to have an
energy parameter comparable to that of a skew interaction, that is,
of 0.7 kg.-cal. The energy difference between (1) and (2) of 1.4
kg.-cal. means that in equilibrated methylcyclohexane the conformation corresponds predominantly to the equatorially substituted
form (1). Actually the conversion of (2) into (1) requires a mere flip

245

of the ring, to which there is little energy barrier; axial methyl at an uptilted bow (2) becomes equatorial methyl at a downtilted bow (1) without losing its identity as β-oriented.

Whereas compounds containing a single cyclohexane ring are often easily convertible from one conformation to another by the ring-flip mechanism, fusion of several alicyclic rings results in structures with centrally located cyclohexane rings which are locked into permanent conformations by attached rings. An extensively studied example is cholesterol, represented in the partial formula I, which shows a chair-form cyclohexene ring (B) locked in invariant position between two other chair-form rings, A (represented as the ring residues A and A'), and C (for full structural formula, see 15.3).* Cholesterol contains a double bond at the 5,6-position capable of adding bromine, and the product of addition has been shown to be the diaxial *trans* dibromide,

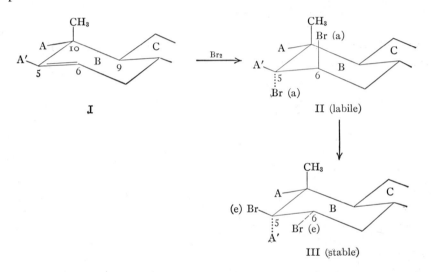

or the 5α,6β-dibromide, II. This initial reaction product is labile, partly because of the unfavorable interaction between axial bromine at C_6 and axial methyl at C_{10}, and it is easily isomerized to the more stable diequatorial product, the alternate *trans* 5β,6α-dibromide III (in the course of this isomerization, terminal ring A undergoes a flip). Both dibromides when treated with zinc dust or sodium iodide undergo *trans* elimination of bromine with regeneration of cholesterol (I), but the labile isomer II reacts faster because the bromine and carbon atoms concerned all lie in a plane with the bromines maximally separated and hence ideally oriented for a four-center transition state requiring minimum activation energy. The formation of the diaxial

* Although the cyclohexane ring is written here in the chair conformation for convenience, the unsaturated ring is believed to have the half-chair conformation (Part II, section 10).

$5\alpha,6\beta$-dibromide in the bromination may be either because a comparable transition state is involved or because the reaction proceeds through a cyclic bromonium ion. Thus hydrolysis of the $5\alpha,6\alpha$-oxide of cholesterol gives the diaxial $5\alpha,6\beta$-diol, analogous to the labile dibromide II.

Since an axial substituent is always close to two other axial substituents or hydrogen atoms, axial hydroxyl groups would be expected to be acylated with greater difficulty than equatorial ones, and corresponding esters should be more resistant to hydrolysis. Such differences in hindrance have been demonstrated in many instances. The reverse relationship holds for oxidation of secondary alcohols with chromic acid: an alcohol with an axially oriented hydroxyl group is the more sensitive to attack. The apparent anomaly is resolved by evidence that the rate-determining step is attack of the carbon–hydrogen bond rather than of the oxygen–hydrogen bond.

Decalins. — Calculations of steric energy of bi- and tricyclic systems (Barton,[7] Turner,[8] Johnson[9]) indicate that the most stable conformations of the decalins are the two-chair forms shown. That the

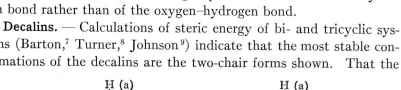

trans-Decalin   *cis*-Decalin

heat of combustion of *trans*-decalin is 2.1 kg.-cal. lower than that of *cis*-decalin indicates greater stability of the *trans* form. In *trans*-

[7] Derek H. R. Barton, b. 1918 Gravesend, Kent, England; Ph.D. and D.Sc. London (Heilbron, E. R. H. Jones); Birkbeck Coll., London, Glasgow

[8] Richard B. Turner, b. 1916 Minneapolis; Ph.D. Harvard (Fieser); Rice Institute

[9] William S. Johnson, b. 1913 New Rochelle, N. Y.; Ph.D. Harvard (Fieser); Univ. Wisconsin

decalin there are six staggered and twelve skew interactions and in *cis*-decalin three staggered and fifteen skew interactions. Since a staggered interaction can be assumed to have an energy parameter of zero, the difference in energy of 2.1 kg.-cal. can be attributed to the presence in *cis*-decalin of an excess of three skew interactions. This is the basis for the estimate of 0.7 kg.-cal. as the strain energy per skew interaction.

RING CLOSURE

13.10   **Alicyclic Rings.** — A direct synthesis of cycloalkanes consists in the action of zinc or sodium on an appropriate open-chain dihalide. With higher homologs, the reaction is akin to the Wurtz coupling of

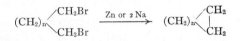

two alkyl residues, and the closure of the cyclopropane ring resembles debromination of a *vic*-dibromide to an olefin. Cyclopropane is obtained in 70% yield by use of zinc dust and alcohol. Although comparable data are not available, it appears that a cyclopropane ring is produced by the general method almost as readily as an ethylenic linkage but that larger rings are closed considerably less readily. Thus hexamethylene bromide affords cyclohexane in only 44% yield. The evident lack of direct correlation between ease of ring closure and relative stability of the ring systems can be attributed to two factors, one of which is the opportunity for ring closure. Two halogen atoms located on adjacent carbon atoms offer a target more vulnerable to attack by zinc than those in trimethylene bromide, where, because of opportunity for free rotation about the two single carbon–carbon bonds, the molecule can assume various conformations, some of which are less favorable to ring formation than others. As the carbon chain is lengthened there is increasing opportunity for an unfavorable orientation of the halogen atoms at distant sites and less chance of an orientation favorable to cyclization. A second factor governing the outcome of cyclizations is the opportunity for competing reactions; this aspect is discussed in a later section concerning cyclization of dibasic acids.

13.11   **Diels-Alder Reaction.** — The synthetic reaction discovered by Diels[10] and Alder[11] (1927) consists in 1,4-addition of a diene to a second

[10] Otto Diels, b. 1876 Hamburg, Germany; Ph.D. Berlin (E. Fischer); Kiel; Nobel Prize 1950
[11] Kurt Alder, b. 1902 Königshütte, Germany; Ph.D. Kiel (Diels); Cologne; Nobel Prize 1950

component having an ethylenic linkage flanked by carbonyl or carboxyl groups, such as maleic anhydride:

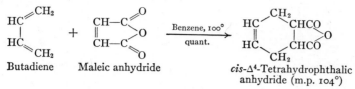

Butadiene   Maleic anhydride   *cis*-Δ⁴-Tetrahydrophthalic
anhydride (m.p. 104°)

The diene system undergoes 1,4-addition and the terminal carbons become affixed at the double bond of the anhydride to produce a six-membered ring. The reaction is generally applicable, and dienes and dienic compounds of a wide variety of types usually enter into the Diels-Alder reaction, though with differences in reactivity. Thus 2,3-dimethylbutadiene, $CH_2=C(CH_3)C(CH_3)=CH_2$, and piperylene, $CH_3CH=CHCH=CH_2$, react more readily than butadiene reacts, and sorbic acid, $CH_3CH=CHCH=CHCOOH$, reacts less readily. Maleic anhydride is a favored dienophile because the two carbonyl groups enhance the additive power of the double bond. The same feature renders quinones capable of adding dienes readily, as in the

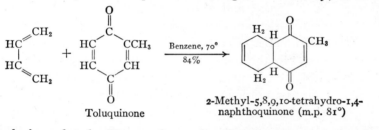

Toluquinone   2-Methyl-5,8,9,10-tetrahydro-1,4-
naphthoquinone (m.p. 81°)

example formulated. Esters of acetylenedicarboxylic acid also function as dienophiles. Olefinic compounds with but one carbonyl group adjacent to the double bond enter into the diene synthesis but may require a higher temperature or a longer time of heating.

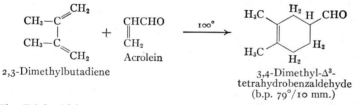

2,3-Dimethylbutadiene   Acrolein   3,4-Dimethyl-Δ³-
tetrahydrobenzaldehyde
(b.p. 79°/10 mm.)

The Diels-Alder reaction is an example of stereospecific *cis* addition and substituents in the dienophile retain their original orientation. Thus adducts from maleic acid or anhydride are always *cis*-dicarboxylic acids or derivatives, and those from fumaric are *trans*. Cyclic dienes can be employed and afford interesting bridge-ring compounds. Thus cyclopentadiene reacts with maleic anhydride to give one of two possible *cis* products, namely that with the anhydride ring inclined toward the newly formed six-membered ring (endo) rather than away from it (exo).

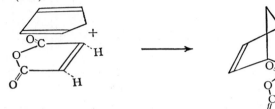

3,6-Endomethylene-Δ⁴-
tetrahydrophthalic anhydride
(m.p. 165°)

DICARBOXYLIC ACIDS AND CYCLIC DERIVATIVES

13.12   The straight-chain dibasic acids (Table II) are all crystalline solids of much higher melting point than monocarboxylic acids of comparable molecular weight. The melting points fall off somewhat as the paraffinic part of the molecule becomes larger, and an alternation is apparent in both melting points and solubilities. Acids

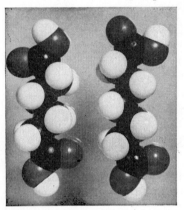

having an even number of carbon atoms are more symmetrical and thus higher melting and less soluble than their immediate higher or lower homologs having an odd number of carbon atoms. From the dissociation constants for the first stage of ionization, it is seen that in oxalic acid the one unsaturated group exerts a strong inductive effect that promotes ionization of the second, which renders the substance one of the strongest organic acids and hence often useful as a condensing agent less destructive and more moderate than mineral acids. The influence of one carboxyl group on the other is evident to a lesser extent when the two

TABLE II

DIBASIC ACIDS

Acid	Formula	M.P., °C.	Solubility, g./100 g. H₂O	Acidic dissociation	
				pK_{a_1}	pK_{a_2}
Oxalic	$HOOC \cdot COOH$	187 [1]	$10.2^{20°}$	1.46	4.40
Malonic	$HOOCCH_2COOH$	135	$138^{16°}$	2.80	5.85
Succinic	$HOOCCH_2CH_2COOH$	185	$6.8^{20°}$	4.17	5.64
Glutaric	$HOOCCH_2CH_2CH_2COOH$	97.5	$63.9^{20°}$	4.33	5.57
Adipic	$HOOC(CH_2)_4COOH$	151	$1.4^{15°}$	4.43	5.52
Pimelic	$HOOC(CH_2)_5COOH$	105	$2.5^{14°}$	4.47	5.52
Suberic	$HOOC(CH_2)_6COOH$	142	$0.14^{16°}$	4.52	5.52
Azelaic	$HOOC(CH_2)_7COOH$	106	$.2^{15°}$	4.54	5.52
Sebacic	$HOOC(CH_2)_8COOH$	134	$.1^{17°}$	4.55	5.52

[1] The dihydrate melts with loss of water at 100°.

are separated by a methylene group (malonic acid) and is still apparent in the next higher homolog (succinic acid), but when the functional groups are separated by three or more carbon atoms, the inductive effect disappears; probably the two groups repel each other and swing the flexible zigzag chain into such a position that they are as remote as possible.

Oxalic acid occurs in the form of its potassium and calcium salts in the cell sap of many plants. **Malonic acid** was discovered as an oxidation product of malic acid (L. *malum*, apple) and was named accordingly:

$$\text{HOOCCH}_2\text{CHOHCOOH} \xrightarrow{[O]} \underset{\substack{\text{Oxalacetic acid}\\ \text{(two forms, m.p. 152°}\\ \text{and 184°)}}}{\text{HOOCCH}_2\text{COCOOH}} \xrightarrow{[O]} \underset{\text{Malonic acid}}{\text{HOOCCH}_2\text{COOH}} + \text{CO}_2$$

Malic acid

Succinic acid was first mentioned by Agricola in 1550 as a product of distillation of the fossil resin amber (L. *succinum*, amber), in which it is present in combined form. **Glutaric acid,** so named because of relationships to glutamic and tartaric acid, can be prepared by nitric acid oxidation of cyclopentanone (10.8). **Adipic acid,** originally obtained by oxidation of various fats (L. *adipis*, fat), is produced in large quantities for the manufacture of nylon by oxidation of cyclohexanol (10.8). **Pimelic acid** is also isolated as a product of the oxidation of fats (Gr. *pimelē*, fat). **Suberic acid** (L. *suber*, cork) is one oxidation product of cork. **Azelaic acid** is so named because it is one product of oxidation of oleic acid with nitric acid (az, from *azote*, nitrogen, + Gr. *elaion*, olive oil):

$$\underset{\text{Oleic acid}}{\text{CH}_3(\text{CH}_2)_7\text{CH}\dot{=}\text{CH}(\text{CH}_2)_7\text{COOH}} \xrightarrow{\text{HNO}_3} \underset{\text{Azelaic acid}}{\text{HOOC}(\text{CH}_2)_7\text{COOH}}$$

Cyclic Anhydrides. — Succinic acid and glutaric acid when warmed with acetic anhydride readily afford cyclic anhydrides. Five-

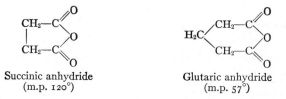

Succinic anhydride
(m.p. 120°)

Glutaric anhydride
(m.p. 57°)

and six-membered ring compounds in which an oxygen atom is incorporated into a heterocyclic ring system represent stable and easily formed structures analogous to related carbocyclic compounds. Physicochemical studies have established that the dimethyl ether molecule is not linear but has a triangular configuration in which the two valences of the oxygen atom extend at an angle of 111°. This is

$$\text{H}_3\text{C} \overset{O}{\underset{111°}{\diagup \diagdown}} \text{CH}_3$$

so close to the normal angle of valences of the tetrahedral carbon atom that an oxygen atom can be regarded as interchangeable with carbon in a ring structure. Thus the five-membered heterocyclic ring in succinic anhydride is probably planar and strain-free, and that in glutaric anhydride probably has a nonplanar, puckered, and strain-free configuration.

No 3- or 4-ring anhydrides

Oxalic and malonic acid show no tendency to form cyclic anhydrides, which would contain three- and four-membered rings. Both acids undergo decarboxylation when heated, particularly readily under catalysis by a mineral acid. Malonic acid is dehydrated by phosphorus pentoxide not to a cyclic anhydride but to the highly unsaturated carbon suboxide (Diels, 1908). This reactive substance

$$
\underset{\text{OH}}{\text{O}=\text{C}}-\text{CH}_2-\underset{\text{OH}}{\text{C}}=\text{O} \xrightarrow{\text{P}_2\text{O}_5} \text{O}=\text{C}=\text{C}=\text{C}=\text{O}
$$

Carbon suboxide, b.p. 7°

adds water to regenerate malonic acid and reacts with ethanol to yield diethyl malonate.

Higher acids give polymeric anhydrides

Adipic acid when refluxed with acetic anhydride is converted into a mixture of chain polymers of varying chain length:

$$
\text{HOOCCH}_2\text{CH}_2\text{CH}_2\text{CH}_2\text{CO}\,\lceil\text{OH}\rceil + n\lceil\text{H}\rceil\text{OOCCH}_2\text{CH}_2\text{CH}_2\text{CH}_2\text{COOH} \xrightarrow{-\,n\text{H}_2\text{O}}
$$

$$
\text{HOOCCH}_2\text{CH}_2\text{CH}_2\text{CH}_2\overset{\text{O}}{\overset{\|}{\text{C}}}-\text{O}-\left[\overset{\text{O}}{\overset{\|}{\text{C}}}\text{CH}_2\text{CH}_2\text{CH}_2\text{CH}_2\overset{\text{O}}{\overset{\|}{\text{C}}}-\text{O}\right]_n\text{H}
$$

Instead of cyclization within the individual molecules to a 7-ring structure (intramolecular condensation), the predominating reaction is condensation between different molecules (intermolecular), and the contrast in behavior to that of succinic and glutaric acid is attributable to a difference in relative opportunities for the two reactions. One carboxyl group separated from the other by a chain of four methylene groups has many opportunities to combine with functional groups of other molecules and relatively few chances of colliding and interacting with the group attached to the same chain, for the chain can assume many positions by rotations about the various single bonds, and only a few of these bring the functional groups into proximity. Thus the longer the chain the less chance there is for intramolecular cyclization and the greater the tendency to form polymers. Pimelic acid and suberic acid similarly yield chain polymers on treatment with dehydrating agents.

13.14   **Cyclic Ketones.** — Five- and six-membered cyclic ketones are produced so readily that acids of the adipic and pimelic types often can be converted into ketones by simply heating the dibasic acid with acetic anhydride and distilling the excess reagent and the product, if volatile, at atmospheric pressure (Blanc, 1907):

$$CH_2CH_2CO|OH| \atop CH_2CH_2|COOH|$$

Adipic acid

$$\xrightarrow{(CH_3CO)_2O, \; distil}$$

$$\begin{matrix} CH_2-CH_2 \\ | \qquad \quad >CO \\ CH_2-CH_2 \end{matrix} \quad + \quad CO_2 \quad + \quad H_2O$$

Cyclopentanone

Blanc observed that acids of the glutaric type, when submitted to the same process of distillation with acetic anhydride, are converted into anhydrides and not into cyclobutanone derivatives, and proposed this reaction as a diagnostic test for distinguishing between dibasic

$$H_2C \begin{matrix} \diagup CH_2COOH \\ \diagdown CH_2COOH \end{matrix}$$

Glutaric acid

$$\xrightarrow{(CH_3CO)_2O \atop Distil}$$

$$H_2C \begin{matrix} \diagup CH_2CO \\ \diagdown CH_2CO \end{matrix} >O$$

Anhydride

acids having a chain of five carbon atoms ($HOOC \cdot C \cdot C \cdot C \cdot COOH$) and those having six or more carbon atoms in the chains (Blanc rule).

Blanc rule

Pyrolysis of the barium salt of adipic acid (10.5) affords cyclo-pentanone in 80% yield, and cyclohexanone is produced in high yield from pimelic acid by the same method. Results obtained in the synthesis of large-ring ketones by pyrolysis of a mixture of the dibasic acid with calcium, thorium, or cerium oxide have revealed an interesting relationship between yield and ring size. The 5- and 6-ring ketones are obtainable in high yield (80%), the yield of the C_7-ketone is moderate and that of the C_8-ketone fair (20%), but the ketones in the range C_9–C_{12} are obtained under optimum conditions in yields of not more than 0.5%. From C_{13} on, however, the yields improve and reach a secondary maximum of about 5% for the C_{18}-ketone, and then fall off to a level of about 2%. Cyclopentadecanone is valued as a synthetic perfume base of musk odor, and the observation that the pyrolytic synthesis afforded the substance in less than 5% yield from a costly dibasic acid stimulated efforts to develop a better synthesis. Ziegler in 1933 applied to the problem a principle that had appeared in the literature (Ruggli, 1912) but had received little attention. The chief obstacle to formation of large-ring compounds is interference from the competing reaction of polymerization. Under ordinary conditions a functional group B collides many more times with the group A of surrounding molecules than with that present in the same molecule, and hence polymerization predominates. Any variation

Yield minimum

$A \wedge\wedge\wedge\wedge\wedge\wedge\wedge\wedge B \qquad A \wedge\wedge\wedge\wedge\wedge\wedge\wedge\wedge B$

Cyclic monomer   Polymer

in the conditions that will suppress polymerization must increase opportunity for intramolecular cyclization, and a means of achieving this objective consists merely in conducting the reaction at high dilution. If each molecule is surrounded largely by solvent molecules and is relatively remote from others of its kind, opportunity for intermolecular collisions is diminished and cyclization given a chance to proceed, even if slowly. As with any unimolecular reaction, the rate of cyclization is independent of the concentration, whereas the velocity of polymerization, which is bimolecular in the initial phase, is decreased enormously at high dilution. For utilization of the dilution principle in the preparation of large-ring ketones it was necessary to employ a cyclization reaction capable of being conducted in a homogeneous liquid phase with all reactants in solution, and Ziegler worked out a suitable adaptation of the Dieckmann reaction.

HYDROXY ACIDS AND LACTONES

13.15   Carboxylic acids containing alcoholic hydroxyl groups respond differently to heat or to dehydrating agents depending upon the relative positions of the two functional groups. The α-hydroxy acid $HOCH_2COOH$, glycolic acid, contains both types of groups required for esterification, and opportunity therefore exists either for formation of an internal ester (lactone) or for production of a polyester under the influence of an acidic esterification catalyst or of heat. Actually the substance is convertible into either a polyester formed by condensation polymerization or a cyclic ester formed by esterification occurring between two molecules of the acid. The cyclic anhydro

α-OH

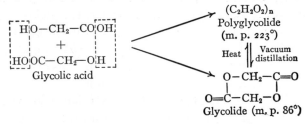

compound glycolide has a heterocyclic ring of six atoms, which is evidently more easily formed or more stable than the three-membered ring that would result from monomeric cyclization.

β-OH β-Hydroxy acids on similar treatment undergo dehydration to α,β-unsaturated acids. The combination of an activated hydrogen

$$\overset{\beta}{R}\overset{\alpha}{CH}CH_2COOH \xrightarrow{-H_2O} RCH=CHCOOH$$
$$|$$
$$OH$$

atom in the α-position and a hydroxyl group at the adjacent β-position affords so favorable an opportunity for elimination of water with establishment of a double bond that this reaction takes precedence over either polymerization or formation of a four-ring structure by monomeric cyclization or of an eight-ring structure by dimeric cyclization.

γ-Hydroxy acids present the possibility for formation of lactones having a favored five-membered ring, and this reaction proceeds with great readiness and predominates over other processes. Cyclic esters

$$CH_2CH_2CH_2COOH \xrightarrow{-H_2O} CH_2CH_2CH_2CO$$

$$\overset{|}{OH}$$

γ-Hydroxybutyric acid

$$CH_2CH_2CH_2CO$$
$$\underset{O}{\lfloor \quad \rfloor}$$

γ-Butyrolactone
(b.p. 206°)

derived from γ-hydroxy acids are γ-lactones. The five-membered ring system is formed with such ease that γ-hydroxy acids are often difficult to isolate as such and tend to revert to the γ-lactones on acidification of an alkaline solution of the hydroxy acid unless the temperature is kept low and excess mineral acid is avoided. γ-Lactones are stable, neutral substances, but the lactone ring usually can be opened by the action of warm alkali. Substances of this type are often formed by isomerization of unsaturated acids by heat or by treatment with hydrobromic or sulfuric acid, for example:

$$\overset{\delta}{CH_2}=\overset{\gamma}{CH}\overset{\beta}{CH_2}\overset{\alpha}{CH_2}COOH \xrightarrow{dil.\ H_2SO_4} CH_3CHCH_2CH_2CO$$

Allylacetic acid
(b.p. 188°)

γ-Valerolactone
(b.p. 207°)

In this instance a δ-lactone would also be possible but is not formed. The marked preference for formation of the five-membered γ-lactone ring is further illustrated by the behavior of acids of the sugar series that have hydroxyl groups in the α-, β-, γ-, δ-, and ε-positions; these regularly form γ-lactones:

$$\overset{\epsilon}{CH_2}-\overset{\delta}{CH}-\overset{\gamma}{CH}-\overset{\beta}{CH}-\overset{\alpha}{CH}-CO\vdots OH \xrightarrow{-H_2O} CH_2-CH-\overset{\gamma}{CH}-CH-CH-CO$$

SUMMARY

Alicyclic Compounds

Reactivity of cycloalkanes. Cyclopropane: hydrogenated readily; ring opened by Br_2, H_2SO_4, HBr (as predicted from Markownikoff rule); inert to permanganate (in contrast with ethylene). Cyclobutane: ring opened by hydrogenation at higher temperature; stable to Br_2, HBr. Cyclopentane and cyclohexane: not hydrogenable; as inert chemically as alkanes.

Baeyer strain theory. Strain due to distortion of normal carbon valence angles decreases from ethylene to cyclopropane to cyclobutane and is negligible in cyclopentane. Correlation with heats of combustion as well as with reactivity. Baeyer misled in assuming strain in larger rings.

Theory of strainless rings. Strain-free, puckered chair and boat forms postulated for cyclohexane (Sachse, 1890). Mohr's postulate (1918) of non-interconvertible *cis* and *trans* forms of decalin. Hückel's isolation (1925) of *cis*- and *trans*-decalin. Evidence that large-ring compounds are not strained: Ruzicka's discovery (1926) that the perfume principles muscone and civetone are ketones with 15- and 17-carbon rings, respectively.

Conformation

Conformation is a specific spatial arrangement where more than one is possible. Conformations of 1,2-dichloroethane: staggered (most stable), skew (less stable), eclipsed (very unstable). Instability due to mutual repulsion described as an interaction.

Stilbene dibromides. Repulsion of phenyl groups to transoid positions determines conformations: *meso*, bromines staggered, symmetrical, higher melting, lower solubility; *dl*, bromines skew, unsymmetrical, less stable. Debromination much faster with *meso*-dibromide because of favorable transoid arrangement of bromines.

Cyclohexane. Hassel concept of axial and equatorial bonds (1943). Calculation of strain energy from ethane interactions: staggered = 0, skew = 0.7 kg.-cal., eclipsed = 2.0 kg.-cal. Boat form less stable than chair form by 3.3 kg.-cal. and hence nonexistent.

Substituted cyclohexanes most stable when substituents are equatorial; 1,3-interactions with axial groups or hydrogens. Interconversion by ring flip. Permanent conformation in fused polycyclic systems. Cholesterol ⟶ diaxial *trans*-dibromide (labile) ⟶ diequatorial *trans*-dibromide (stable). Diaxial dibromide better oriented for *trans* elimination and reacts faster. The 5α,6α-oxide hydrolyzed to the diaxial diol. Equatorial hydroxyl less hindered than axial and more easily acylable. Order reversed in oxidation of secondary alcoholic groups because attack is on H attached to carbon not that on oxygen.

Decalins. Both *cis* and *trans* have chair-chair conformations. Thermochemical data show *trans* to be 2.1 kg.-cal. lower in energy content than *cis;* attributable to an excess in *cis* of three skew interactions.

Ring Closure

Alicyclic rings. In reaction of Zn with $Br(CH_2)_nBr$ small rings are closed easily because of proximity of the two functional groups; with increased chain length probability of favorable orientation of halogen atoms decreases.

Diels-Alder reaction (1928). 1,4-Addition to butadiene of maleic anhydride. Methyl substituents increase reactivity of the diene; carboxyl group decreases reactivity. Dienophiles: quinones, acrolein. Cyclopentadiene and maleic anhydride.

Dicarboxylic Acids

Series: oxalic (HOOCCOOH), malonic (HOOCCH₂COOH), succinic, glutaric, adipic, pimelic, suberic, azelaic, sebacic (mnemonic = memory aid: Oh My, Such Good Apple Pie; Sweet And Sensible). High-melting solids. Alternation in m.p. Occurrence and names.

Cyclic anhydrides. Succinic anhydride (5-ring) and glutaric anhydride (6-ring) formed easily; rings containing oxygen as hetero atom comparable to carbon rings (valences of oxygen extend at an angle of 111°). Adipic and higher acids dehydrated chiefly to polymeric anhydrides (greater opportunity for inter- than for intramolecular condensation). No cyclic anhydrides from oxalic and malonic acid; they are decarboxylated by heat. Malonic acid with P_2O_5 gives carbon suboxide.

Cyclic ketones. Adipic and pimelic acid give cyclopentanone and cyclohexanone in high yield on pyrolysis of barium salts or on distillation with acetic anhydride (Blanc method). Glutaric acid by the Blanc procedure yields the anhydride (5-ring). Pyrolysis of salts of higher dibasic acids affords C_9-C_{13} ketones in only 0.5% yield, C_{14}-C_{18} ketones in up to 5% yield.

Competition between cyclization (monomolecular reaction, rate independent of concentration) and polymerization (initially bimolecular, rate increases with increasing concentration). Dilution principle: high dilution retards polymerization without influencing rate of cyclization.

Behavior on dehydration: α-hydroxy acid ⟶ glycolide (6-ring) + polyglycolide; β-hydroxy acid ⟶ α,β-unsaturated acid; γ-hydroxy acid ⟶ γ-lactone (5-ring). γ-Lactones very stable and formed preferentially from acids having hydroxyl groups at the α-, β-, γ-, and δ-positions; γ-lactones also formed by action of HX on β,γ and γ,δ-unsaturated acids.

PROBLEMS

1. Cite experimental tests that would distinguish between the following isomers of the formula C_5H_{10}: pentene-2; 1,2-dimethylcyclopropane; and cyclopentane.

2. Explain why optically active muscone yields an optically inactive hydrocarbon on reduction of the carbonyl group to a methylene group.

3. One of the 2-methylcyclohexanols, *cis* or *trans*, is converted into the other when heated with a trace of sodium. Which is the more stable isomer, and what is its conformation?

4. Which isomeric form of 1,3-dimethylcyclohexane would you expect to be the more stable, *cis* or *trans?*

5. With the aid of a model, first verify the calculation of the difference in strain energy in *cis* and *trans* decalin. Then determine whether replacement of one bridgehead hydrogen at C_9 in both structures by a β-methyl group increases or decreases the energy difference.

6. Formulate a synthesis of *cis*-cyclohexane-1,2-dicarboxylic acid.

7. Addition products are formed in good yield from each of the following pairs of reactants. Write equations for the reactions.

   (a) Piperylene ($CH_3CH{=}CHCH{=}CH_2$) and maleic anhydride.

   (b) 2,3-Dimethylbutadiene-1,3 and crotonic acid, $CH_3CH{=}CHCO_2H$.

   (c) Butadiene and diethyl acetylenedicarboxylate.

8. Glutaric acid can be prepared in 48% overall yield by a series of reactions starting with the condensation of formaldehyde with diethyl malonate in the presence of diethylamine to $CH_2[CH(COOC_2H_5)_2]_2$. Formulate the process.

9. (a) Explain the formation of malonic acid by the action of water on carbon suboxide.

   (b) What product would you expect to result from treatment of carbon suboxide with ammonia?

READING REFERENCES

W. H. Perkin, "The Early History of the Synthesis of Closed Carbon Chains," *J. Chem. Soc.*, 1347 (1929)

R. C. Fuson, "Alicyclic Compounds and the Theory of Strain," in H. Gilman, *Organic Chemistry*, 2nd Ed., I, 65–116, Wiley, New York (1943)

M. C. Kloetzel, "The Diels-Alder Reaction with Maleic Anhydride," *Organic Reactions*, IV, 1 (1948)

L. Ruzicka, "The Many-Membered Carbon Rings," *Chemistry and Industry*, **54**, 2 (1935)

E. H. Rodd, *Chemistry of Carbon Compounds*, IIA, Chapters I–VIII, by R. A. Raphael, Elsevier (1953)

W. Klyne, *Progress in Stereochemistry*, I, 36–81, Academic Press (1954)

M. S. Newman, *Steric Effects in Organic Chemistry*, Wiley (1956)

CARBOHYDRATES

Classification

Carbohydrates, including the sugars, are among the most abundant constituents of plants and animals, in which they serve many useful functions. They are a source of energy; they form supporting tissues of plants and some animals in the same way that proteins are used by most animals. The name is derived from the fact that many sugars have the empirical formula $C_nH_{2n}O_n$, or $C_n(H_2O)_n$, and hence the French applied the name "hydrate de carbone" or carbohydrate, and the name has been retained even though it is not descriptive. They are classified systematically as monosaccharides, di-, tri-, and tetra-saccharides, and polysaccharides. Practically all natural monosaccharides contain five or six carbon atoms, and are known as pentoses and hexoses, respectively. They are colorless, crystalline substances, usually with a sweet taste. Disaccharides, which are condensation products of two hexose or pentose units, resemble monosaccharides in taste, color, and solubility. Polysaccharides are tasteless, amorphous, insoluble substances of the type formula $(C_6H_{10}O_5)_n \cdot H_2O$ or $(C_5H_8O_4)_n \cdot H_2O$, in which n is known to be large. They are converted on hydrolysis into C_6- or C_5-sugars, as the simple disaccharides are. Cane sugar (sucrose) yields two C_6-sugars or hex-

Inversion of sucrose

$$C_{12}H_{22}O_{11} \;+\; H_2O \;\longrightarrow\; C_6H_{12}O_6 \;+\; C_6H_{12}O_6$$

Sucrose	Glucose	Fructose
$[\alpha]_D + 66.5°$	$[\alpha]_D + 52°$	$[\alpha]_D - 92°$

oses, glucose and fructose. The disaccharide sucrose is dextrorotatory, but the mixture of hexoses resulting on hydrolysis is levorotatory and is known as invert sugar. Honey is largely invert sugar, since bees contain an enzyme (invertase) capable of hydrolyzing sucrose.

The suffix -ose is a generic designation of a sugar. Glucose is an aldehydic sugar with six carbon atoms, or an aldohexose. Fructose is a ketonic hexose or ketohexose.

Structures of Glucose and Fructose. — Both glucose and fructose were recognized as carbonyl compounds by their ability to reduce Fehling's solution (complex cupric ion), a property characteristic of both aldehydes and α-hydroxy ketones:

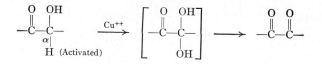

The reaction distinguishes between carbonyl-containing sugars that reduce Fehling's solution (reducing sugars) and those that contain no free or potential carbonyl group and are nonreducing (sucrose). A method for quantitative determination of the reducing sugar in an aqueous solution involves measuring the weight or volume of the cuprous oxide formed on reaction with excess Fehling's solution; several equivalents are consumed.

Both glucose and fructose react with acetic anhydride to give crystalline pentaacetates and therefore the six oxygen atoms in both substances are accounted for as five hydroxyl groups and one carbonyl group, and the formulas may be written $C_5(OH)_5H_7C{=}O$. The nature of the carbon skeleton of glucose and the position of the carbonyl group were established by Kiliani[1] (1886) on discovery that hexoses add hydrogen cyanide. The cyanohydrin (2) from glucose (1) can be represented as in (3) and the acid produced on hydrolysis as (4).

$$C_5(OH)_5H_7C{=}O \xrightarrow{\text{HCN}} C_5(OH)_5H_7C(OH)CN = C_6(OH)_6H_7CN \longrightarrow$$
$$\quad (1) \qquad\qquad\qquad (2) \qquad\qquad\qquad (3)$$

$$C_6(OH)_6H_7CO_2H \xrightarrow{\text{HI, P}} C_6H_{13}CO_2H = CH_3(CH_2)_5CO_2H$$
$$\quad (4) \qquad\qquad\qquad (5) \qquad\qquad (6)$$

Kiliani reduced the hydroxy acid (4) with hydriodic acid and red phosphorus to replace the hydroxyl groups by hydrogen, and identified the reduction product (5) as n-heptylic acid (6). The extra carbon atom introduced on addition of HCN is thus found at the end of a six-carbon straight chain and the carbonyl group is at the end of this chain and is therefore aldehydic. Since a six-carbon aldehyde having five hydroxyl groups can have a stable structure only if just one of these groups is distributed on each of the available five carbon atoms, glucose is inferred to have the formula shown. Kiliani carried out a similar series of reactions with fructose; the final acid is methyl-n-butylacetic acid, from which Kiliani deduced that fructose is a penta-

CHO
|
*CHOH
|
*CHOH
|
*CHOH
|
*CHOH
|
CH₂OH
Glucose

[1] Heinrich Kiliani, 1855–1945; b. Würzburg, Germany; Ph.D. Munich (Erlenmeyer); Freiburg; *Ber.*, **82A**, 1 (1949)

hydroxy ketone with the carbonyl oxygen atom at the 2-position of the chain; it is a 2-ketohexose.

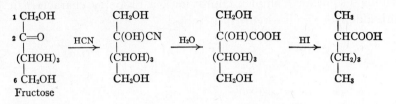

$$
\begin{array}{ccccccc}
\text{1 CH}_2\text{OH} & & \text{CH}_2\text{OH} & & \text{CH}_2\text{OH} & & \text{CH}_3 \\
| & & | & & | & & | \\
\text{2 C}{=}\text{O} & \xrightarrow{\text{HCN}} & \text{C(OH)CN} & \xrightarrow{\text{H}_2\text{O}} & \text{C(OH)COOH} & \xrightarrow{\text{HI}} & \text{CHCOOH} \\
| & & | & & | & & | \\
\text{(CHOH)}_3 & & \text{(CHOH)}_3 & & \text{(CHOH)}_3 & & \text{(CH}_2)_3 \\
| & & | & & | & & | \\
\text{6 CH}_2\text{OH} & & \text{CH}_2\text{OH} & & \text{CH}_2\text{OH} & & \text{CH}_3 \\
\text{Fructose} & & & & &
\end{array}
$$

14.3

Configurations. — Glucose has four dissimilar asymmetric carbon atoms and is therefore one of sixteen possible optical isomers; fructose is one of eight possible 2-ketohexoses. Only two other aldohexoses, mannose and galactose, occur widely in nature, and fructose is the only common natural ketohexose. The synthesis of most of the remaining thirteen aldohexoses and seven 2-ketohexoses was accomplished by Emil Fischer[2] in a brilliant series of investigations of 1891–96 that completely elucidated the configurations of all the known isomers, natural and synthetic. Fischer's representation of natural, dextrorotatory glucose is shown in the accompanying projection formula (convention for projection formulation, 12.10). Mannose is

The natural hexoses

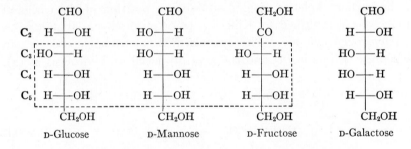

$$
\begin{array}{cccc}
\text{CHO} & \text{CHO} & \text{CH}_2\text{OH} & \text{CHO} \\
\text{C}_2\ \text{H}{-}\text{OH} & \text{HO}{-}\text{H} & \text{CO} & \text{H}{-}\text{OH} \\
\text{C}_3\ \text{HO}{-}\text{H} & \text{HO}{-}\text{H} & \text{HO}{-}\text{H} & \text{HO}{-}\text{H} \\
\text{C}_4\ \text{H}{-}\text{OH} & \text{H}{-}\text{OH} & \text{H}{-}\text{OH} & \text{HO}{-}\text{H} \\
\text{C}_5\ \text{H}{-}\text{OH} & \text{H}{-}\text{OH} & \text{H}{-}\text{OH} & \text{H}{-}\text{OH} \\
\text{CH}_2\text{OH} & \text{CH}_2\text{OH} & \text{CH}_2\text{OH} & \text{CH}_2\text{OH} \\
\text{D-Glucose} & \text{D-Mannose} & \text{D-Fructose} & \text{D-Galactose}
\end{array}
$$

the C_2-epimer of glucose, since it differs only in the configuration at C_2; in the projection formula the hydrogen at C_2 is to the right and hydroxyl to the left. Fructose corresponds in configuration at all three of its asymmetric centers to carbon atoms 3, 4, and 5 of glucose and of mannose. Galactose is the C_4-epimer of glucose. All four natural hexoses correspond in the configuration of the terminal asymmetric center C_5, and Fischer elected the configuration at C_5 as the distinguishing characteristic of a stereochemical series defined as that of natural glucose. He succeeded in relating glucose to D-tartaric acid, which had already been shown to belong to the same steric series as the still simpler compounds D-malic acid and D-glyceraldehyde, which are represented in the conventional projection formu-

[2] Emil Fischer, 1852–1919; b. Euskirchen, Germany; Ph.D. Strasbourg (Baeyer); Erlangen, Würzburg, Berlin; Nobel Prize 1902; *Ber.*, **52A**, 128 (1919)

las with hydroxyl written to the right and hydrogen to the left. The configuration of glucose at C_5 thus defines the D-series, and any sugar,

$$
\begin{array}{cccc}
\text{CHO} & \text{CHO} & & \\
| & | & & \\
\text{(CHOH)}_3 & \text{(CHOH)}_2 & \text{CHO} & \text{CH}_2\text{COOH} \\
| & | & | & | \\
\text{HCOH} & \text{HCOH} & \text{HCOH} & \text{HCOH} \\
| & | & | & | \\
\text{CH}_2\text{OH} & \text{CH}_2\text{OH} & \text{CH}_2\text{OH} & \text{COOH} \\
\text{D-Aldohexose} & \text{D-Aldopentose} & \text{D-(+)-Glyceraldehyde} & \text{D-(−)-Malic acid}
\end{array}
$$

whether it is aldehydic or ketonic and regardless of the number of carbon atoms and the sign of rotation, belongs to the D-series if it corresponds to D-glucose at the penultimate carbon atom. Natural fructose is a D-sugar even though it is levorotatory; for full description it can be called D-(−)-fructose. The formulas selected for conventional representation of D-glyceraldehyde and of D-glucose were arbitrary but were later (1951) proved correct by x-ray crystallography.

A projection formula of an aldose is conveniently abbreviated by writing just the terminal groups and indicating a hydroxyl group to the right or left by a bar. D-Glucose is thus (1), and the enantiomer,

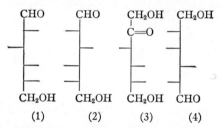

$$
\begin{array}{cccc}
(1) & (2) & (3) & (4)
\end{array}
$$

L-glucose, is (2). D-Fructose can be represented as in (3). A formula can be turned in the plane of the paper until inverted without loss of identity; for example, (4) is as valid a representation of D-glucose as (1).

All sixteen aldohexoses are known, and of these only the three that occur naturally are fermented to ethanol and carbon dioxide by yeast enzymes: D-glucose, D-mannose, and (less rapidly) D-galactose. Natural D-fructose is fermentable. Yeasts are unable to ferment the corresponding enantiomers of the L-series.

Osazones. — Early progress in elucidation of sugar chemistry was handicapped by the difficulty in obtaining crystalline compounds, since sugars, especially when impure, tend to form sirups. One of the outstanding contributions of Fischer was introduction in 1884 of the use of phenylhydrazine, which was found to react with many carbonyl compounds to give sparingly soluble and beautifully crystalline derivatives. Fischer's dissertation for the doctorate under Baeyer ten years earlier had described the discovery, preparation, and uses of phenylhydrazine.* The reaction with sugars proceeded in an un-expected manner, since Fischer found that the products, which he called osazones (-ose + hydrazone), contained two phenylhydrazine residues rather than one. Moreover, glucose and fructose yielded the same product, glucosazone ($C_{18}H_{22}O_4N_4$).

The reaction requires three moles of phenylhydrazine per mole

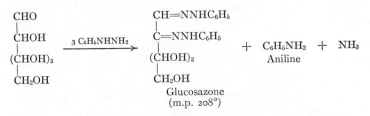

Glucosazone
(m.p. 208°)

of hexose. Fischer was able to isolate mannose phenylhydrazone as an intermediate to the osazone, and F. Weygand[3] (1940) established that osazone formation involves disproportionation of the phenyl-hydrazone (a) to the ketone (b), condensation with a second molecule

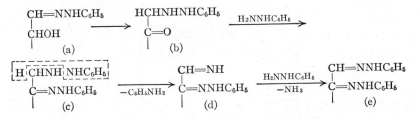

of reagent (c), elimination of aniline (d), and condensation with a third molecule of phenylhydrazine with elimination of ammonia (e). The initial disproportionation occurs because the alcoholic group at C_2 is activated by the carbon–nitrogen double bond. That a further disproportionation involving C_3 does not occur appears attributable to stabilization of the osazone by chelation. In the reaction of glucose with Fehling's solution oxidation progresses down the chain through successively activated positions with consumption of several equiva-lents of reagent.

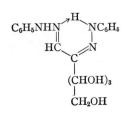

Osazones are bright yellow, crystalline compounds identifiable both from their temperatures of decomposition and from the crystal-line forms. That the solubility in water is markedly less than that of the sugar is understandable, for introduction of two phenylhydra-zine residues into a hexose increases the molecular weight by 64%,

---

* For twelve years following 1891, Fischer suffered from the insidious poisonous effects of phenylhydrazine, which, even so, he later described as his "first and most lasting chemical love."

[3] Friedrich Weygand, b. 1911 Eichelsdorf, Germany; Ph.D. Frankfurt, Heidelberg (Kuhn), Oxford (Robinson); Heidelberg, Strasbourg, Tübingen, Techn. Univ. Berlin-Charlottenburg

and the derivative contains one less hydroxyl group. Thus an osazone, which is produced easily by brief warming of a solution containing the reagent, usually will separate from a dilute solution of an impure sugar.

Formation of osazones is a property of α-hydroxy ketones, for example benzoin, $C_6H_5CHOHCOC_6H_5$, and acetoin, $CH_3CHOHCOCH_3$. Fructose is attacked by the second molecule of phenylhydrazine at the primary alcoholic group at position 1 in preference to the secondary group at the alternate adjacent position 3, and gives the osazone of

$$
\begin{array}{c}
CH_2OH \\
| \\
C=O \\
| \\
(CHOH)_3 \\
| \\
CH_2OH \\
\text{Fructose}
\end{array}
\quad \xrightarrow{\text{3 H}_2\text{NNHC}_6\text{H}_5} \quad
\begin{array}{c}
CH=NNHC_6H_5 \\
| \\
C=NNHC_6H_5 \\
| \\
(CHOH)_3 \\
| \\
CH_2OH \\
\text{Glucosazone}
\end{array}
\quad + \quad C_6H_5NH_2 \; + \; NH_3 \; + \; 2H_2O
$$

glucose. Since osazone formation eliminates asymmetry at C_2 in an aldose, mannose, the C_2-epimer of glucose, also yields glucosazone. The C_4-epimer galactose affords a different osazone.

Actually mannose was discovered by Fischer as a result of experimentation with the phenylhydrazine reagent. Fischer investigated the reduction of glucose with sodium amalgam in alcohol without being aware that in an alkaline medium glucose suffers partial epimerization at C_2 through the enediol with formation of mannose (and some fructose), and hence that reduction under the conditions chosen can afford an alcohol derived from mannose (mannitol) rather than from

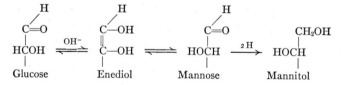

glucose. Reoxidation gave an aldose different from glucose, which Fischer isolated as the phenylhydrazone. Hydrolysis of this derivative afforded the new substance mannose. Fischer found that whereas

$$
\begin{array}{c}
CHO \\
| \\
(CHOH)_4 \\
| \\
CH_2OH \\
\text{Glucose}
\end{array}
\quad \xrightarrow{\text{Na—Hg}} \quad
\begin{array}{c}
CH_2OH \\
| \\
(CHOH)_4 \\
| \\
CH_2OH \\
\text{Mannitol}
\end{array}
\quad \xrightarrow[\text{10\%}]{\substack{\text{1. dil. HNO}_3 \\ \text{2. H}_2\text{NNHC}_6\text{H}_5}} \quad
\begin{array}{c}
CH=NNHC_6H_5 \\
| \\
(CHOH)_4 \\
| \\
CH_2OH \\
\text{Mannose phenylhydrazone}
\end{array}
\quad \xrightarrow[\text{80\%}]{\text{HCl}} \quad
\begin{array}{c}
CHO \\
| \\
(CHOH)_4 \\
| \\
CH_2OH \\
\text{Mannose}
\end{array}
$$

the phenylhydrazones of glucose and mannose are different, the osazones are identical, and he inferred that glucose and mannose differ in configuration at C_2.

Cyanohydrin Synthesis. — The reaction of an aldose with hydrogen cyanide (Kiliani) affords a method of synthesis of higher sugars from lower ones. For example, the cyanohydrin from an aldotetrose is hydrolyzed to an acid and this is lactonized; a γ-lactone (5-ring)

Aldotetrose →
aldopentose

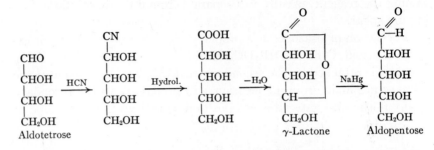

is invariably formed in preference to alternate structures. The γ-lactone is then reduced with sodium amalgam, a reaction which involves fission of the oxide link with restoration of the original γ-hydroxyl group and formation of an aldopentose. The initial reaction of cyanohydrin formation can afford two products, since a new center of asymmetry is produced, but usually one is formed in larger amounts than the other (asymmetric synthesis). Mannose (1), for example, gives mannoheptulose (2) as the predominant product of cyanohydrin synthesis, but the 2-epimer (3) can be isolated in small amounts.

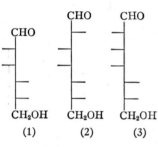

14.6

Oxidation and Reduction. — When glucose is reduced by catalytic hydrogenation or electrolytically under conditions such that isomerization to mannose does not occur, the reduction product is sorbitol. Oxidation with hypobromite attacks the aldehydic group and gives a monobasic acid, gluconic acid; nitric acid attacks both the aldehydic group and the primary alcoholic group to give the dibasic gluco-

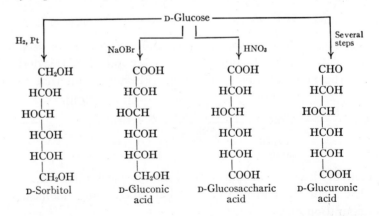

saccharic acid. The aldehyde-acid glucuronic acid has been synthesized from glucose in a series of several steps. Hydroxy compounds foreign to the animal organism are often detoxified by conjugation with glucuronic acid and excreted as glucuronides.

Wohl Degradation. — The correlation of aldohexoses with aldo-pentoses is facilitated by degradation of the former to the latter by a method introduced by Wohl[4] (1893). This involves formation of the

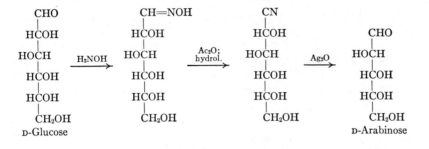

D-Glucose   D-Arabinose

*Reversal of cyano-
hydrin synthesis*

oxime, dehydration to a cyanohydrin, and reversal of the usual cyano-hydrin synthesis. The Wohl degradation eliminates the aldehydic C_1 atom and converts C_2 into a new aldehydic group. Glucose is thus transformed into the pentose arabinose. A second degradation applied

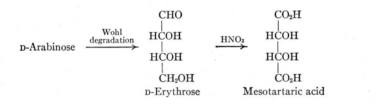

D-Erythrose   Mesotartaric acid

*Correlation with
tartaric acid*

to arabinose affords the tetrose erythrose, and oxidation of the ter-minal groups of this substance with nitric acid gives mesotartaric acid. The overall process thus proves that carbon atoms 4 and 5 in glucose correspond in configuration to the two asymmetric centers of meso-tartaric acid.

Configurations of Tetroses and Pentoses. — The configurations of the two D-tetroses, erythrose and threose, can be distinguished ex-perimentally in a simple manner: nitric acid oxidation and examina-tion of the resulting C_4-diacids for optical activity. The product from erythrose has a plane of symmetry and hence is optically in-active (mesotartaric acid); that from threose is not symmetrical and is optically active (D-tartaric acid). The prefixes erythro- and threo-are used to describe other compounds of these two configurational types.

Two of the four D-pentoses, ribose and arabinose, are C_2-epimers related to erythrose in that they both yield this substance on Wohl

[4] Alfred Wohl, b. 1863 Graudentz; Ph.D. Berlin (Hofmann); Danzig

14.8

degradation; they probably would both be formed from erythrose, if in unequal amount, on Kiliani cyanohydrin synthesis. Xylose and

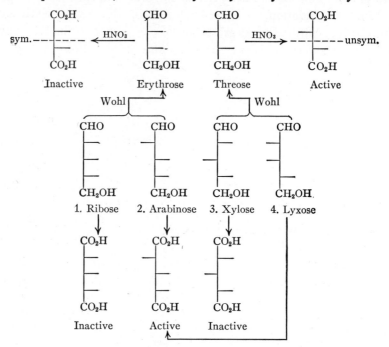

D-Pentoses,
RAXL

C₅-Diacids

lyxose are related in the same way to threose. The C_5-diacids (saccharic acids) resulting on oxidation of the pentoses with nitric acid are characterized as follows: ribose gives an inactive acid and arabinose an active one; xylose gives a different inactive acid, while that from lyxose is active and if the formula is inverted this is seen to be identical with the acid from arabinose. If the configurations were unknown, they could be deduced as follows. Ribose can be assigned formula (1) because it is the only pentose which affords an inactive C_5-diacid and which on Wohl degradation and oxidation gives a likewise inactive C_4-diacid. Arabinose could be shown by osazone formation to be the 2-epimer of ribose, and the configuration thus deduced. The 2-epimers xylose and lyxose are distinguished by the inactivity and activity of the respective C_5-diacids. The fact that arabinose and lyxose yield the same C_5-diacid provides confirmatory evidence.

14.9
Derivation
of formulas

    Aldohexose Configurations. — An aid for remembering the names of the eight D-aldohexoses is: All Altruists Gladly Make Gum In Gallon Tanks. Construct eight outline formulas, and under each write the name of the sugar in the order suggested: Allose, Altrose, Glucose, Mannose, Gulose, Idose, Galactose, Talose. In the line corresponding to C_5, write a bar (or OH) to the right to signify that in each sugar (D-series) C_5-OH is to the right (and hydrogen to the left). In the line representing C_4, write four bars to the right and four to the left. At C_3 write OH twice to the right and twice to the left, and repeat the process; at C_2 write OH alternately to the right and to the left. The result is as shown.

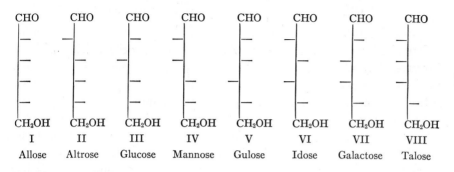

CHO	CHO	CHO	CHO	CHO	CHO	CHO	CHO
CH_2OH	CH_2OH	CH_2OH	CH_2OH	CH_2OH	CH_2OH	CH_2OH	CH_2OH
I	II	III	IV	V	VI	VII	VIII
Allose	Altrose	Glucose	Mannose	Gulose	Idose	Galactose	Talose

The D-aldohexoses in epimer-pairs

The derivation automatically arranges the sugars in four pairs of 2-epimers, and it will be noted that on Wohl degradation the pair I–II yield ribose, III–IV arabinose, V–VI xylose, and VII–VIII lyxose. Steps by which the formula of glucose can be inferred are as follows. (a) Nitric acid oxidation of glucose gives an optically active C_6-diacid; therefore glucose cannot have formula I or VII. (b) The active C_6-diacid from D-glucose is the same as the C_6-diacid from L-gulose. Formulas IV and VI are thereby eliminated, for in these cases the diacids are different from those obtainable from any other aldoses of either the D- or L-series. (c) Wohl degradation of glucose followed by nitric acid oxidation gives an active C_5-diacid; hence formulas II and V are eliminated (also VI). (d) Of the remaining formulas, III and VIII, III is correct because the 2-epimer of glucose, IV, gives an active C_6-diacid whereas the epimer of VIII, VII, gives an inactive C_6-diacid.

Deduction of formula of glucose

Photosynthesis. — Carbohydrates arise in plants from fixation of carbon dioxide and absorption of water. The energy required is supplied in the form of solar energy absorbed by the plant. Photosynthesis can be expressed by a simple equation established in 1804 by de Saussure, who found that the amount of carbon dioxide absorbed by green plants is the molecular equivalent of the oxygen expired. The combination of carbon dioxide and water to form car-

14.10

$$CO_2 + H_2O \xrightarrow{\text{Sunlight}} (CH_2O) + O_2$$
$$\longrightarrow \text{Hexose} \longrightarrow \text{Polysaccharide}$$

bohydrate and oxygen is an endothermic reaction; burning of a carbohydrate or derivative is a reversal of photosynthesis and the liberation of heat represents a tapping of stored radiant energy.

Storage of radiant energy

Fischer's Syntheses of Sugars. — Although formaldehyde is now known not to be involved in photosynthesis, as the above equation suggested, several attempts were made to synthesize sugars from

$$
\begin{array}{ccc}
CH_2{=}O & & CHO \\
| & & | \\
CH_2{=}O & \xrightarrow{\;OH^-\;} & CHOH \xrightarrow{\;n\,CH_2{=}O\;} \text{Complex mixture} \\
| & & | \\
CH_2{=}O & & CH_2OH
\end{array}
$$

formaldehyde. Aldol-like condensation does occur, but without restraint, and gives a complex mixture nonfermentable by yeast. Fischer achieved the synthesis of natural sugars (1890) by a condensation of two three-carbon components that cannot proceed beyond the hexose stage. As noted earlier (7.18), oxidation of glycerol gives a mixture of two components, glyceraldehyde and dihydroxyacetone, which are interconvertible in the presence of base through a common enediol (Lobry de Bruyn[5]-van Ekenstein[6] rearrangement). Fischer found that these two components undergo aldol condensation to a

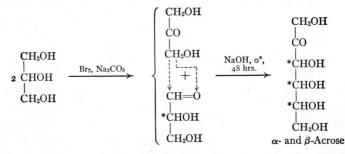

2-ketohexose mixture from which two pure *dl*-products were isolated as the osazones. The hexose chain is formed as the result of aldol addition of dihydroxyacetone, through the activated α-hydrogen atom, to the carbonyl group of glyceraldehyde. Fischer's synthesis is thus a reversal of the subsequently established fission step in the alcoholic fermentation of fructose (7.11). The ketohexose formed has three asymmetric carbon atoms, and hence eight optically active forms are possible. However, the aldehydic reaction component has an asymmetric carbon atom, and this exercises a control over the mode of addition to the carbonyl group and eliminates the element of chance. The glyceraldehyde involved in the synthesis is the *dl*-form, but because of the principle of asymmetric synthesis (12.18) each enantiomer directs the aldol addition in a specific steric sense, with the result that only half of the theoretically possible isomers are produced. The synthesis thus affords two substances of different physical properties, α- and β-acrose, each of which consists of a *dl*-mixture of enantiomers.

Asymmetric synthesis

[5] C. A. Lobry de Bruyn, 1857–1904; b. Leedenwarden, Netherlands; Ph.D. Leiden; Amsterdam; *Ber.*, **37**, 4824 (1904); *J. Chem. Soc.*, **87**, 570 (1905)

[6] W. Alberda van Ekenstein, 1858–1937; b. Gröningen, Netherlands; Amsterdam

The overall yield of α-acrosazone is about 1.5%. α-Acrosazone on hydrolysis affords the sugar-ketone (ose-one) α-acrosone, and this on reduction is attacked preferentially at the more reactive aldehydic

$$
\begin{array}{ccccc}
\text{CH=NNHC}_6\text{H}_5 & & \text{CHO} & & \text{CH}_2\text{OH} \\
| & & | & & | \\
\text{C=NNHC}_6\text{H}_5 & \xrightarrow{\text{2 H}_2\text{O}} & \text{C=O} & \xrightarrow{\text{Zn—HCl}} & \text{C=O} \\
| & & | & & | \\
(\text{CHOH})_3 & & (\text{CHOH})_3 & & (\text{CHOH})_3 \\
| & & | & & | \\
\text{CH}_2\text{OH} & & \text{CH}_2\text{OH} & & \text{CH}_2\text{OH} \\
\alpha\text{-Acrosazone} & & \alpha\text{-Acrosone} & & \alpha\text{-Acrose}
\end{array}
$$

function and yields the *dl*-2-ketose α-acrose. Fischer examined the fermentation of α-acrose by yeast and characterized the unattacked sugar as L-fructose; in this way he established that α-acrose is, in fact, the desired DL-fructose. To obtain a derivative suitable for resolution, Fischer reduced the DL-ketose by the alkaline sodium amalgam procedure by which he had previously found that D-glucose is converted, through the enediol, into D-mannitol, and obtained the expected DL-mannitol. The transference to the mannose series, how-

$$
\begin{array}{ccccccc}
\text{CH}_2\text{OH} & & \text{CH}_2\text{OH} & & \text{CO}_2\text{H} & & \\
| & & | & & | & & \\
\text{C=O} & \xrightarrow{\text{Na—Hg}} & \text{HOCH} & \xrightarrow{\text{Oxid.}} & \text{HOCH} & \xrightarrow{\text{Morphine}} & \\
| & & | & & | & & \\
(\text{CHOH})_3 & & \text{HOCH} & & \text{HOCH} & & \\
| & & | & & | & & \\
\text{CH}_2\text{OH} & & \text{HCOH} & & \text{HCOH} & & \\
& & | & & | & & \\
& & \text{HCOH} & & \text{HCOH} & & \\
& & | & & | & & \\
& & \text{CH}_2\text{OH} & & \text{CH}_2\text{OH} & & \\
\text{DL-Fructose} & & \text{D-Mannitol} & & \text{D-Mannonic acid} & & \\
(\alpha\text{-acrose}) & & (+\text{L-Mannitol}) & & (+\text{L-form}) & &
\end{array}
$$

$$
\left.\begin{array}{l}
d\text{-Morphine salt} \\
l\text{-Morphine salt}
\end{array}\right\} \xrightarrow{\text{Fractional cryst.}} \begin{array}{l}
\nearrow \text{D-Mannonic acid} \\
\searrow \text{L-Mannonic acid}
\end{array}
$$

ever, was advantageous, for the next step was oxidation to a hexuronic acid; the configuration of mannose is such that oxidation at either terminal primary alcoholic group gives the same product, DL-mannonic acid, which was resolved by fractional crystallization of the morphine salt to the optically active components. D-Mannonic acid was converted into the epimeric acid, D-gluconic acid, which has the

$$
\begin{array}{ccccccc}
\text{COOH} & & \text{COOH} & & \text{CO}— & & \text{CHO} \\
| & & | & & | & & | \\
\text{HOCH} & & \text{HCOH} & & \text{HCOH} & & \text{HCOH} \\
| & & | & & | & & | \\
\text{HOCH} & \xrightarrow{\text{Pyridine, 140}°} & \text{HOCH} & \xrightarrow{\text{HCl}} & \text{HOCH} \Big|_\text{O} & \xrightarrow{\text{Na—Hg}} & \text{HOCH} \\
| & & | & & | & & | \\
\text{HCOH} & & \text{HCOH} & & \text{HC}— & & \text{HCOH} \\
| & & | & & | & & | \\
\text{HCOH} & & \text{HCOH} & & \text{HCOH} & & \text{HCOH} \\
| & & | & & | & & | \\
\text{CH}_2\text{OH} & & \text{CH}_2\text{OH} & & \text{CH}_2\text{OH} & & \text{CH}_2\text{OH} \\
\text{D-Mannonic} & & \text{D-Gluconic} & & \gamma\text{-Lactone} & & \text{D-Glucose} \\
\text{acid} & & \text{acid} & & &
\end{array}
$$

stereochemical configuration of D-glucose, by a reaction discovered by Fischer in 1890. Epimerization induced by heating in pyridine results in inversion of the carbon atom adjacent to the carboxylic acid group (through the enol, 12.17). Conversion of D-gluconic acid into D-glucose is accomplished by reduction of the readily formed γ-lactone. D-Glucose was then converted into synthetic D-fructose through the osazone and osone, by the procedures described above.

14.12

Oxide Structure. — Although glucose enters into some reactions common to aldehydes, such as addition of hydrogen cyanide, reaction with phenylhydrazine, and reduction of Fehling's solution, it reacts with bisulfite to a much lesser extent than ordinary aldehydes react. A further peculiarity is that a freshly prepared solution of glucose shows a rotation of $[\alpha]_D + 113°$, which gradually decreases on standing to a value of $+52°$. This change, first observed in 1846, is known as **mutarotation.** It is not the result of decomposition, for after mutarotation to a constant value material can be recovered that has all the properties of the original D-glucose and shows a specific rotation in a fresh solution of $+113°$. Fischer attributed the change to reversible hydration, but this explanation became untenable when Tanret[7] (1895) prepared an isomeric crystalline D-glucose by crystallization of the highly rotatory form from a concentrated aqueous solution at an elevated temperature (110°). The new form, named β-glucose, shows an initial rotation of $[\alpha]_D + 19°$, which changes slowly to the equilibrium value of $+52°$. The ordinary or α-form of glucose is obtained by crystallization from alcohol–water. The two forms have been shown to be cyclic hemiacetals resulting from addition of one of the hydroxyl groups to the aldehydic carbonyl group; such an addition produces another center of asymmetry at C_1 and hence allows formation of two oxidic forms of glucose. Mutarotation of the sugar therefore is attributable to isomerization of one cyclic form into the other, probably by opening of the oxide ring to give the free aldehyde, and closure in the alternate steric sense by addition of the alcoholic

*α- and β-
Cyclic forms*

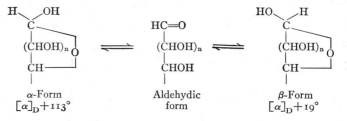

hydroxyl to the carbonyl group. An aged solution of glucose thus contains α- and β-glucose in mobile equilibrium with the aldehydic

*Equilibrium in
solution*

[7] Charles Tanret, 1847–1917; b. Joinville s. Marne; Paris pharmacist

form. Since the oxidic forms lack a carbonyl group, the response of glucose solutions to hydrogen cyanide, phenylhydrazine, and Fehling's solution must be due to the aldehydic form present in the equilibrium mixture; as this form enters into combination and is removed from the equilibrium mixture, more is formed at the expense of the oxides, and eventually the entire material is converted into the derivative of the aldehydic form. The equilibrium concentration of the reactive species is less than 0.01%, and hence conditions are unfavorable for reversible addition of sodium bisulfite, and equilibrium is reached at a point of low conversion.

The point of attachment of the oxide ring to the carbon chain was established in investigations of the more stable 1-methyl ethers of α- and β-glucose, known as α- and β-methylglucoside. Treatment of

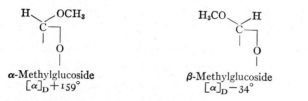

α-Methylglucoside
$[\alpha]_D + 159°$

β-Methylglucoside
$[\alpha]_D - 34°$

α- and β-
Methylglucoside

glucose with methanol and hydrogen chloride affords chiefly α-methyl-glucoside (Fischer, 1893), along with a smaller amount of the β-isomer (van Ekenstein, 1894). The methylglucosides do not react with carbonyl reagents and do not exhibit mutarotation, since the labile glucosidic hydrogen atom is replaced by methyl.

A cyclic ether of glucose is called a glucoside, and a cyclic derivative of mannose is called a mannoside; the generic name for a cyclic sugar derivative is glycoside. A glycoside having the six-membered ring of pyran is called a pyranoside and one corresponding to furan a furanoside. The furanoside structure was regarded as the more

14.13

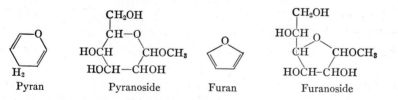

Pyran   Pyranoside   Furan   Furanoside

Pyranose (6) and furanose (5) rings

likely for the glucose derivatives until 1926 when both Haworth[8] and Hirst[9] presented evidence that methylglucoside is a pyranoside. That of Hirst is based upon the products of oxidation of tetramethyl-glucose. Methylglucoside can be methylated with methyl iodide

[8] Sir Walter Norman Haworth, 1883–1950; b. Chorley, Lancashire; Ph.D. Göttingen (Wallach); D.Sc. Manchester (Perkin, Jr.); Birmingham; Nobel Prize 1937; *J. Chem. Soc.*, 2790 (1951)

[9] Edmund Langley Hirst; b. 1898; D.Sc. Birmingham (Haworth); Birmingham, Bristol, Edinburgh

and silver oxide (Purdie,[10] 1903) or with dimethyl sulfate in an alkaline medium (Haworth, 1915) to form a pentamethyl derivative in which four of the methyl groups are present in stable ether linkage. The glucosidic methyl group is hydrolyzed readily by dilute acids but not by alkali (cf., acetals) with formation of tetramethylglucose. Hirst oxidized tetramethylglucose with nitric acid and obtained in good

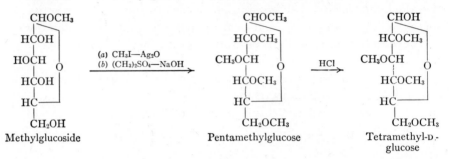

Proof of pyranoside structure

yield two acids, xylotrimethoxyglutaric acid and *d*-dimethoxysuccinic acid, both of which were isolated and identified as the diamides. Formation of these two acids shows that cleavage occurs at each side

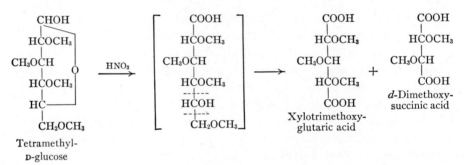

of C_5 and hence that this is the site of the one free hydroxyl group and hence the location of the oxide ring. Methylglucoside is thus characterized as a pyranoside, and glucose as a pyranose. The other hexoses in their normal forms have been shown to be pyranoses.

14.14   **Configuration and Conformation.** — A water-soluble *cis* glycol added to a solution of boric acid increases the electrical conductivity of the solution because it forms an ionic complex with the inorganic acid:

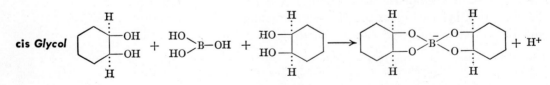

[10] Thomas Purdie, 1843–1916; b. Biggar, Scotland; Ph.D. Würzburg; St. Andrews Univ.; *J. Chem. Soc.*, **111**, 359 (1917)

The α-form of glucose, α-D-glucopyranose, produces such an increase in conductivity, and the conductivity decreases with time as the α-form is converted to an equilibrium mixture. The β-form has little initial effect, but the conductivity gradually increases. The α-form thus contains a *cis* glycol grouping, and, since the hydroxyls at C_2-C_3 and at C_3-C_4 are *trans*, the glycosidic hydroxyl at C_1, defined as an anomeric hydroxyl, must be *cis* to the hydroxyl at C_2, as in formula II. Formula III is assigned to the β-form, the full name of which is

Anomeric hydroxyl

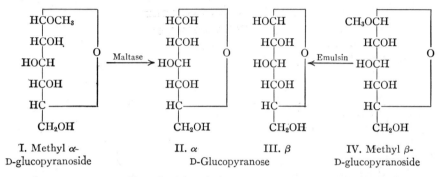

I. Methyl α-
D-glucopyranoside

II. α
D-Glucopyranose

III. β

IV. Methyl β-
D-glucopyranoside

Enzymatic hydrolysis

β-D-glucopyranose. Correlation of the two pyranoses with the glycosides, α- and β-methyl-D-glucopyranoside, was achieved through stereospecific enzyme reactions. Fischer had noted that the α-methyl derivative I is hydrolyzed by the enzyme maltase, which has no effect on the β-methyl derivative IV, whereas the enzyme emulsin hydrolyzes the β- but not the α-methyl derivative. E. F. Armstrong[11] (1903) followed the enzymatic hydrolysis by polarimetric analysis and proved that α-methyl-D-glucopyranoside is hydrolyzed to α-glucose, whereas the β-methyl derivative is hydrolyzed to β-glucose.

Stereochemical relationships are appreciated best by translation of formulas of the type I–IV into hexagons (W. N. Haworth, 1929). The operation can be done somewhat laboriously with Fischer tetrahedral projections but easily with models, and the result, for α-glucose, is formula V. The anomeric hydroxyl at C_1 is α, or down, as indicated

Haworth formulas; conformation

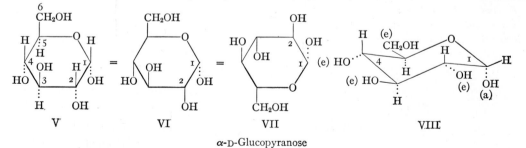

V   VI   VII   VIII

α-D-Glucopyranose

[11] Edward Frankland Armstrong, 1878–1945 (son of H. E. Armstrong); Dir. South Metropol. Gas Co., London; *Nature*, **157**, 154 (1946)

by the dotted bond, and the C_2-OH being *cis* to it is also α, or down. The rest of the formula is easily derived by remembering that the hydroxyls at 2,3 and at 3,4 are *trans* to each other and that C_4-OH is *trans* to C_5-CH_2OH. The formula can be simplified (VI) by omitting the hydrogen atoms and indicating the configuration of just the anomeric hydroxyl, in this case α (dotted bond). For showing attachment to another sugar, it is sometimes necessary to invert the formula; VI then becomes VII, and the α-orientation at C_1 is still clear from the dotted bond even though the hydroxyl group is now pointing upward.

Formula VIII shows the preferred conformation of α-glucose, established by study of cuprammonium complex formation (R. E. Reeves,[12] 1949). The hydroxyls at C_2, C_3, C_4 and the C_5-CH_2OH group are all in the stable equatorial orientation and only the anomeric hydroxyl is axial. In β-glucose (IX) the anomeric hydroxyl is equatorial, and hence this anomer would be expected to have the greater stability. That this is the case is shown by the specific rota-

All-equatorial form the more stable

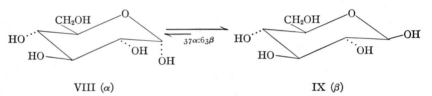

VIII (α)   IX (β)

tions of the α (+113°) and β (+19°) forms and of the equilibrium mixture (+52°). The stable, all-equatorial conformation of β-glucose may account for the widespread occurrence of β-glucosides in nature. Glucose is the only one of the eight D-aldohexoses in which the all-equatorial arrangement is possible.

Fructose is known in only one crystalline form, probably the pyranose X. That fructose exhibits mutarotation ($-132°$ $\longrightarrow$ $-92°$)

Fructo-pyranose and furanose

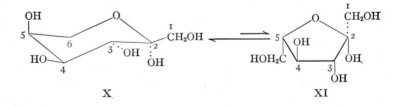

X   XI

is attributed to an equilibrium with fructofuranose, XI. Although XI has not been isolated, this is the form in which fructose occurs in sucrose and in all other natural fructosides. The significance of the dotted and full bonds at C_2 is as follows. In the cyclization of fruc-

[12] Richard E. Reeves, b. 1912 Lincoln, Nebraska; Ph.D. Yale (R. J. Anderson); U. S. Dept. Agric., Louisiana State Univ. School Med.

tose (1), addition of the C$_5$-hydroxyl to the 2-keto group produces a
C$_2$-hydroxyl of orientation the opposite of that of the anomeric C$_1$-
hydroxyl of α-glucose (3), and hence it is described as β-oriented and

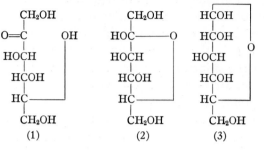

(1)   (2)   (3)

represented in XI as connected by a full-line bond. Since the five-
membered oxide ring is probably planar, a furanose or a furanoside is
under some strain from eclipsed interactions.

Molecular rotation relationships. — When an alcohol R$_1$R$_2$CHOH
is to be compared in optical properties with its derivatives, for example
the acetate, benzoate, or methyl ether, compensation for incidental
variation in molecular weight is made by comparisons based on
molecular rotation, M$_D$, calculated as follows:

14.15

$$M_D = \frac{[\alpha]_D \times Mol.\ Wt.}{100}$$

Calculation

Thus for α-D-glucose: $[\alpha]_D = +122.2°$ W (water solution; extrapolated
to zero time) and M$_D = (+122.2 \times 180.16)/100 = +202.1$. Whereas
octaacetylsucrose, α$_D + 59.6°$ Chf (chloroform), differs considerably
from octastearylsucrose, $[\alpha]_D + 16.6°$ Chf, in specific rotation, the
molecular rotations M$_D + 404$ and $+411$ are the same within the
limits of error of polarimetry.

van't Hoff in 1898 deduced the principle that the molecular rotation of a compound containing several centers of asymmetry is the
algebraic sum of the individual rotatory contributions of the component rotatory centers, or rotophores. Since experimental data
were not available for calculation of individual rotatory effects, the
idea was illustrated by supposing the superposition of a molecule
composed of $+A+B+C$ centers with the epimer made up of $-A$
$+B+C$ rotophores; since the fragment $+B+C$ is common to both
molecules, the difference between them is $+2A$. The van't Hoff
principle of additivity is thus often described as the "principle of
optical superposition."

Data now at hand show that the principle is valid only if the rotophores are all separated by one or more nonasymmetric atoms, for
example, RCHOHCH$_2$CHOHCH$_2$CHOHR′. If two rotophores are

Principle of
additivity
(optical
superposition)

contiguous, comparisons are vitiated by an as yet undeterminable vicinal effect of each center on the rotatory contribution of the other.

Although few comparisons in the sugar series are free from some distortion due to vicinal effects, Hudson discerned a general trend in the molecular rotation of α- and β-forms of sugars and of their methylglycosides, that is, pairs of sugars epimeric at C_1. A first rule states that in such a pair the α-form is invariably more strongly dextrorotatory than the β-form. Vicinal effects may alter the magnitude of the difference, $M_D^\alpha - M_D^\beta$, but not the sign of the difference, as illustrated by the following examples:

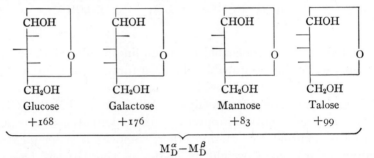

Glucose	Galactose	Mannose	Talose
+168	+176	+83	+99

$$M_D^\alpha - M_D^\beta$$

Comparisons of glucose with galactose and of mannose with talose are not vitiated by differences at the center adjacent to C_1, and substantially the same value for $M_D^\alpha - M_D^\beta$ is found for the two members of each pair. That the two values are considerably different is a consequence of vicinal effects which, however, are not sufficiently large in this or other instances to change the sign of $M_D^\alpha - M_D^\beta$. Whenever both C_1-anomers are available for characterization, Hudson's rule can be used to determine which is α and which is β.

Another rule applies to the relationship between an aldonic acid and its γ-lactone: a γ-lactone in which the oxide ring, as represented in the conventional projection formula, lies to the right is more dextro-

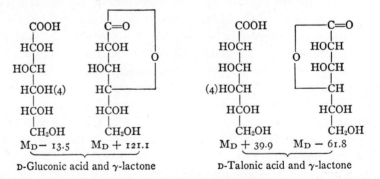

$M_D - 13.5$	$M_D + 121.1$	$M_D + 39.9$	$M_D - 61.8$
D-Gluconic acid and γ-lactone		D-Talonic acid and γ-lactone	

rotatory than the parent acid, and if the ring lies to the left the lactone is more levorotatory. An illustration of the rule is the contrasting relationships of D-gluconic acid and of D-talonic acid to their γ-lactones. With but few exceptions, lactones of the γ-gluconic type are levorotatory.

GLYCOSIDES

Plant glycosides are acetals, comparable to methylglucosides, and are derived from combination of various hydroxy compounds with various sugars. They are designated specifically as glucosides, mannosides, galactosides, etc., and the group as a whole is described by the generic name glycoside. When a sugar is combined with a non-sugar, the latter is described as an aglycone. When the second group is also a sugar unit, the combination is a di-, tri-, or polysaccharide. The glycosides are hydrolyzed by mineral acids to the sugar and the aglycone; for instance arbutin, a β-D-glucoside obtained from the bearberry (*Arctostaphylos uva-ursi*), yields glucose and hydroquinone on hydrolysis:

Arbutin

$\xrightarrow{H^+}$ C$_6$H$_{12}$O$_6$ + HO—⟨⟩—OH

D-Glucose

Hydroquinone

Hydrolyzed to sugar and aglycone

Usually an enzyme that can accomplish the hydrolysis occurs in the same plant, though in different cells. When the plant tissues are macerated the enzyme comes into contact with the glycoside and hydrolysis results. Although some enzymes can act on only one substance (substrate), many are not specific in activity. The widely distributed emulsin and maltase both hydrolyze many glycosides, but the differentiation first noted by Fischer, namely that the former acts on β-glucosides and the latter on α-glucosides, is true for α- and β-glycosides generally, and is frequently used as a proof of the type of glycoside linkage. Most natural glycosides possess the β-configuration.

DISACCHARIDES

Disaccharides can be regarded as glycosides in which the aglycone is a second monosaccharide unit. They resemble monosaccharides in that they are very soluble in water, and some have a sweet taste. Only three occur as such in nature, sucrose (cane sugar), lactose (milk sugar), and maltose, and the latter is found free only occasionally.

Sucrose. — Sucrose on hydrolysis with acids or the enzyme invertase (plants, yeast, animals) yields D-glucose and D-fructose in equal amounts. Sucrose does not reduce Fehling's solution or form derivatives with phenylhydrazine, and hence the two sugar units are linked through the glycosidic hydroxyl group of each sugar and contain no free or potential carbonyl groups. Unlike the majority of sugars, sucrose crystallizes readily, probably because it does not isomerize in solution (no mutarotation). The ring structure of the two component units was established (Haworth, 1916) by hydrolyzing completely methylated sucrose, I. One product was the usual tetramethyl-D-glucose, but the other was a tetramethylfructose derivative. Its

Structure by methylation and cleavage

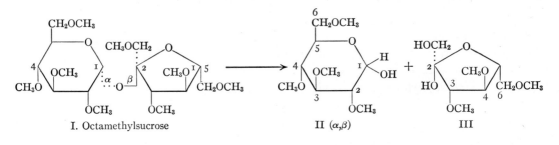

I. Octamethylsucrose   II (α,β)   III

structure was not established until ten years later, when it was found to contain a furanose ring (III). No combined fructose has ever been found to have the normal pyranose structure. The glucose unit has the α-configuration, since sucrose is hydrolyzed by maltase (an α-glucosidase); the configuration of the fructose unit is considered to be β. Recombination of the two units was first effected through the action of an enzyme on a mixture of glucose 1-phosphate and fructose (Hassid); a chemical synthesis is described in Part II.

14.18   Lactose. — Lactose occurs in the milk of mammals; human milk contains 5–8%, cow's milk, 4–6%. It is produced commercially from the latter source as a by-product in the manufacture of cheese. Lactose is a reducing sugar, forms an osazone, and can be obtained in crystalline α- and β-forms, $[\alpha]_D + 90°$ and $[\alpha]_D + 35°$. It is hydrolyzed by dilute mineral acid or by emulsin to glucose and its 4-epimer, galactose. Since the acid obtained on bromine oxidation of lactose is hydrolyzed to galactose and gluconic acid, the reducing group must be in the glucose unit, and hence lactose is a galactoside and not a

A reducing β-glycoside

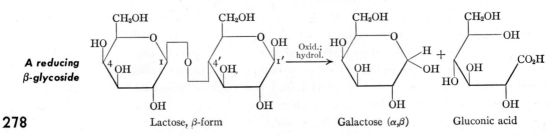

Lactose, β-form   Galactose (α,β)   Gluconic acid

glucoside. Hydrolysis by emulsin shows the sugar to be a β-galacto-
side, and methylation experiments show the 1β-galactosido link to be
joined to the 4′-hydroxyl of glucose. If the hexose units are written
in the usual way with the oxidic oxygen up, connection has to be
made between the 1β-glucosidic link, which is up, and the 4′-OH, which
is down. This can be done with the run-around glycosidic link shown
in the formula; the alternate, less convenient representation requires
inversion of one of the hexagons.

Maltose. — Maltose is obtained in about 80% yield by enzymatic
(amylase) degradation of starch. Since the disaccharide yields only

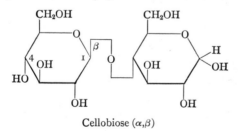

Maltose

D-glucose on hydrolysis with acids or maltase, an α-glucosidase, it is
evidently a glucose-α-glucoside. It is a reducing sugar, and hence
contains one potential aldehydic group. Methylation studies established the structure as that of glucose-4-α-glucoside.

*A reducing
α-glycoside*

Cellobiose. — Cellobiose can be obtained by hydrolysis of cellulose. It is a reducing sugar consisting of two glucose units and hydrolyzable by emulsin, a β-glucosidase; thus it is a glucose-β-glucoside.
Methylation studies have shown that cellobiose is related to maltose
in the same way that β-methylglucoside is related to the α-isomer.

Cellobiose (α,β)

*A reducing
β-glycoside*

POLYSACCHARIDES

Polysaccharides belong to two general groups: those that are
insoluble and form the skeletal structure of plants and of some animals;
and those that constitute reserve sources of simple sugars, which are
liberated as required by the action of enzymes present in the organism.
Both types are high molecular weight polymers, often built up from a
single pentose or hexose unit. In this respect they differ from the

proteins, which are high molecular weight substances containing several different units.

Cellulose. — Cellulose is the most widely distributed skeletal polysaccharide. It constitutes approximately half of the cell-wall material of wood and other plant products. Cotton is almost pure cellulose and, together with bast from flax, is the preferred source of cellulose for use as fiber. Wood cellulose, the raw material for the pulp and paper industry, occurs in association with lignin, a nonpolysaccharide which is separated by treating wood with an alkali bisulfite to form water-soluble lignosulfonates.

Cellulose on drastic hydrolysis affords glucose. Under milder conditions mixtures are formed from which cellobiose, cellotriose, and cellotetrose have been isolated; hence cellulose has the structure shown. The most stable conformation is that in which the three sub-

Structure

Conformation

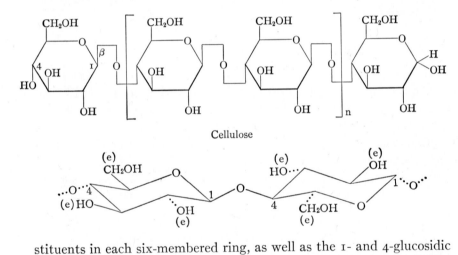

Cellulose

stituents in each six-membered ring, as well as the 1- and 4-glucosidic linkages, are all equatorial. The average molecular weight of cellulose is 400,000, corresponding to 2500 glucose units. X-ray analysis indicates that cellulose fiber is made up of micelles, or bundles of parallel oriented chains probably held together by hydrogen bonding. The diameter of a micellar unit is about 40Å, corresponding to 100–200 cellulose chains; the length is at least 600Å, corresponding to 200 glucose units. The mechanical strength and chemical stability are considered to result from micellar structure.

Micellar structure of fiber

Man and other carnivorous animals are unable to utilize cellulose, since they lack enzymes required for hydrolysis. Many microorganisms, some protozoa, and the snail can decompose cellulose. Digestion of cellulose by ruminants (cud-chewing animals) is due to the presence of microorganisms within the specially constructed alimentary system.

Cellulose Derivatives in Technology. — The silkworm, which exists on a diet consisting largely of cellulose from mulberry leaves, produces a viscous solution of the nitrogen-containing protein fibroin. The protein is secreted from two glands, each of which communicates by a duct with a tiny orifice (spinneret) located near the lip. After a drop is attached to an object, the silkworm draws a thread by moving its head and forefeet. The two filaments are cemented by a sticky protein, a silk glue. Cellulose, with three hydroxyl groups per C_6-unit, is as insoluble in organic solvents as it is in water, and processes for making silk substitutes from wood pulp cellulose involve conversion to a less hydroxylic derivative that can be dissolved in an organic solvent to give a viscous solution capable of being extruded under pressure through a die containing capillary orifices to produce a number of filaments that can be twisted together to form a thread. The nitrocellulose process, the first known for making artificial silk, was discovered by Count Hilaire de Chardonnet in 1855. Cellulose is nitrated in the presence of sulfuric acid under conditions such as to

$$[C_6H_7O_2(OH)_3]_n \xrightarrow{\text{HNO}_3,\ \text{H}_2\text{SO}_4} [C_6H_7O_2(OH)(ONO_2)_2]_n + H_2O$$
$$\text{Cellulose dinitrate}$$

give material approximating the dinitrate and known as pyroxylin; exhaustive nitration gives the trinitrate ester, guncotton. Pyroxylin dissolves in a mixture of alcohol and ether to form a viscous solution, collodion, which is forced through the orifices of a die into an atmosphere of dry air to evaporate the solvent. The nitrate groups are then removed by passage through a bath of sodium hydrosulfide solution. The denitrated thread of regenerated but somewhat altered cellulose resembles silk in appearance but is of rather poor quality.

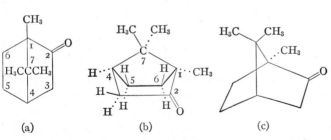

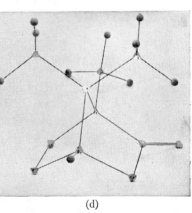

(a)   (b)   (c)   (d)

A second use for pyroxylin is in production of the cellulose nitrate plastic celluloid (cellulose + oid), which is cellulose dinitrate plasticized with about 20% of camphor. Camphor, $C_{10}H_{16}O$, is a terpene ketone,

281

and the structure (a) can be seen to contain two units of isoprene, $CH_2=C(CH_3)CH=CH_2$, by severance of bonds 1,7, 3,4, and 5,6. Formula (b) shows that the cyclohexanone ring is locked in the boat conformation by the C_7-*gem*-dimethyl bridge linked to bow (C_1) and stern (C_4). Formula (c) is a projection of (b) after this has been turned to an angle of about 45° to bring C_4 to the front and C_1 to the rear as in the model (d); (c) is the formula preferred for interpretation of interesting rearrangements characteristic of terpene chemistry. Natural camphor, m.p. 179°, $\alpha D + 44°$, comes from a tree indigenous to the island of Formosa, and *dl*-material is synthesized from the terpene hydrocarbons α- and β-pinene ($C_{10}H_{16}$), the chief constituents of turpentine from pine resin. The two solids pyroxylin and camphor are gelatinized with alcohol, which promotes plastic flow during molding and is removed in a curing operation.

Nitrocellulose lacquers

Modified pyroxylin has an important use in the production of quick-drying lacquer paints for automobiles, which dry by evaporation of the solvent. The modification required is obtained by partial depolymerization, effected by heating pyroxylin under pressure with very dilute acid, to increase the solubility in organic solvents and reduce the viscosity of the solutions. Butyl acetate is the preferred solvent.

Cellulose acetate

Acetylation of the hydroxyl groups of cellulose also increases solubility in organic solvents and thermoplasticity, and material corresponding approximately to the diacetate is employed as a fiber (acetate rayon) and as a molding plastic. Acetone is used as a solvent for spinning, and the extruded filaments are dried in warm air. In the viscose process for making rayon, wood pulp is compounded with sodium hydroxide to give a salt, alkali cellulose, which reacts with

Viscose rayon

$$[C_6H_{10}O_5]_n \xrightarrow{\text{NaOH}} [(C_6H_{10}O_5)_2 \cdot \text{NaOH}]_n \xrightarrow{\text{CS}_2} \left[(C_6H_9O_4)_2 \cdot \text{OH} \cdot \text{OC} \begin{matrix} \nearrow S \\ \searrow SNa \end{matrix} \right]_n + n\ H_2O$$

Alkali cellulose · · · Cellulose xanthate

carbon disulfide to yield a xanthate. This derivative forms a viscous colloidal solution in dilute aqueous alkali, which is ripened, filtered, and extruded through a die into a bath of dilute sulfuric acid. The acid regenerates cellulose, and the fibers are then bleached and dried.

14.23
Reserve carbohydrates

Starch and Glycogen. — Starch is the reserve carbohydrate of plants and glycogen plays a corresponding role in animals; it occurs particularly in liver and muscle. Both polysaccharides on complete hydrolysis with mineral acid yield glucose, and both are hydrolyzed partially to maltose by the enzyme amylase. The maltose units arise from chains resembling cellulose chains but with the glucose units joined at the 1- and 4-positions by α- rather than β-glycosidic links.

Joined to these chains are branches containing glucose units linked at positions 1 and 6. Hydrolysis with amylase is incomplete because the linkages between the 1α-position of one unit and the 6-position of

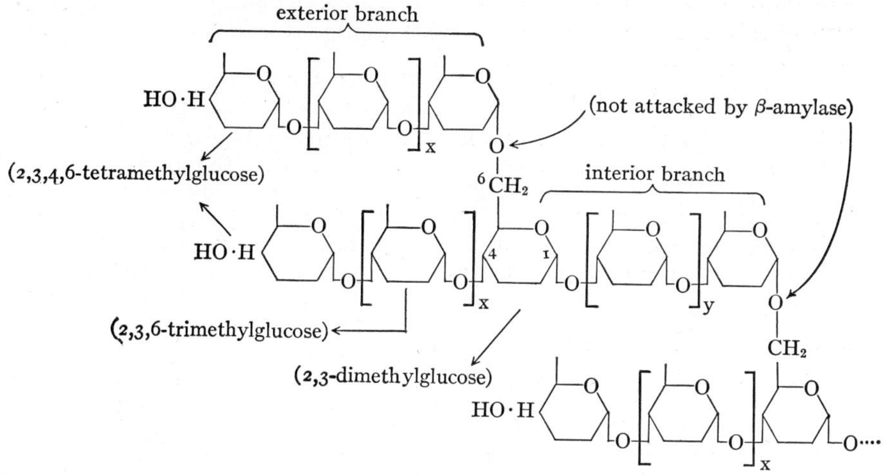

Chains of
α-glucosido
units with branches

Starch and glycogen

another are resistant to attack by the enzyme. The structure shown is based upon methylation and degradation to methylated sugars. The two polysaccharides differ only in the position and extent of branching.

SUMMARY

Classification of carbohydrates: mono-, di-, polysaccharides. Sugar = -ose. Aldo- and keto-pentoses, hexoses. Inversion of sucrose.

Proof of structures of glucose and fructose. Ability to reduce Fehling's solution characteristic of α-hydroxy ketones as well as of aldehydes. Acetylation reveals 5 OH-groups. Carbon skeleton and position of carbonyl group established by formation of cyanohydrin, hydrolysis, reduction of hydroxyl group, identification of resulting acid.

Configurations of natural hexoses: glucose, mannose, galactose, fructose (E. Fischer, 1896). Configuration of glucose at C_5 correlated with that of D-tartaric acid and of D-glyceraldehyde (OH to the right, H to the left). Natural hexoses all belong to the D-series, even levorotatory fructose, or D-(–)-fructose. Of the sixteen aldohexoses, only the three natural ones are fermentable; fructose, only natural ketohexose, also fermentable.

Osazones (Fischer, 1884). Reaction of a reducing sugar with three molecules of phenylhydrazine to give a crystalline yellow osazone sparingly soluble in water and easily isolated. Disproportionation mechanism. Reaction destroys asymmetry at C_2,

hence glucose and mannose give same osazone, which is formed also from fructose. Fischer's discovery of mannose (formed in alkaline reduction by partial epimerization of glucose at C_2; isolated, after reoxidation of mannitol, as the phenylhydrazone).

Cyanohydrin synthesis (Kiliani). Addition of HCN to aldose and hydrolysis gives an acid that forms γ-lactone reducible with Na—Hg to a new aldose. Thus aldopentose ⟶ aldohexose. One of the two possible isomers predominates because of asymmetric synthesis.

Reduction of glucose under nonisomerizing conditions gives sorbitol. NaOBr attacks aldehydic group ⟶ gluconic acid. HNO_3 attacks both terminal groups ⟶ glucosaccharic acid (dibasic). Indirect method preserves —CHO and gives glucuronic acid (utilized by animal organism for detoxication of hydroxy compounds).

Wohl degradation (1893). Aldose ⟶ oxime ⟶ cyanohydrin ⟶ lower aldose. Glucose ⟶ arabinose ⟶ erythrose. Erythrose with HNO_3 ⟶ mesotartaric acid. On similar degradation galactose ⟶ D-(–)-tartaric acid.

D-Tetroses. Erythrose on HNO_3 oxidation gives optically inactive C_4-diacid (*meso*, plane of symmetry). Threose gives active acid (no symmetry). D-Pentoses (RAXL): ribose and arabinose (C_2-epimers related to erythrose); xylose and lyxose (C_2-epimers related to threose). Deduction of configurations from activity or inactivity of derivable C_5- and C_4-diacids.

D-Aldohexoses. Mnemonic and system for deriving names and formulas. Deduction of configuration of D-glucose (III): (*a*) oxidation to C_6-diacids (III $\longrightarrow$ active acid); (*b*) C_6-diacid from III different from that from L-glucose; (*c*) Wohl degradation of III and oxidation gives active C_5-diacid; (*d*) C_2-epimer of III gives active C_6-diacid.

Photosynthesis of carbohydrates in green plants from $CO_2 + H_2O$. Endothermic; utilization of solar energy absorbed by green pigment chlorophyll.

Fischer's synthesis of D-glucose. Oxidation of glycerol gives glyceraldehyde + dihydroxyacetone; these undergo aldol condensation to a ketohexose mixture (limitation of isomers by principle of asymmetric synthesis); α- and β-acrose isolated through osazones; α-acrosazone hydrolyzed to α-acrosone and this reduced at aldehydic group to give α-acrose; this shown to be DL-fructose by action of yeast to give unfermented residue of L-fructose. Reduction of α-acrose to DL-mannitol, oxidation to an acid that on resolution with morphine affords D-mannonic acid; epimerization at C_2 with pyridine at 140° to D-gluconic acid; lactonization; reduction with Na–Hg to D-glucose, identical with natural sugar.

Oxide structure. Glucose fails to respond to some reagents for aldehydes and exhibits mutarotation ($[\alpha]_D + 113°$ for fresh solution, $+52°$ for aged solution). Existence of two forms: α-glucose (ordinary, initial $[\alpha]_D + 113°$) and β-glucose (crystallization from water at 110°, initial $[\alpha]_D + 19°$). Addition of OH group to carbonyl group to give cyclic hemiacetal with new center of asymmetry at C_1.

α- and β-Methylglucoside from glucose + CH_3OH + HCl (α-predominates). Generic name: glycoside. Nonreducing, no reaction with phenylhydrazine, no mutarotation. Possible forms: pyranoside (6-ring), furanoside (5-ring). Proof of pyranose structure: methylglucoside $\longrightarrow$ pentamethyl derivative; acid hydrolysis removes glycosidic 1-OCH_3 and gives tetramethylglucose in which OCH_3 groups are shown to be at 2, 3, 4, and 6; hence the oxide link extends to C_5.

α-Glucose (α-D-glucopyranose) shown to be C_1-C_2 *cis*-glycol from conductivity of boric acid solution (complex). The methyl pyranosides related to the pyranoses by enzymatic hydrolysis: maltase splits α, emulsin β.

Haworth hexagon formula for α-D-glucopyranose and abbreviation: write dotted (α) or full (β) bonds for just the anomeric linkage to OH at C_1. Conformations: β-form the more stable since all OH groups and CH_2OH are equatorial. D-Fructose probably a pyranoside, which in solution mutarotates through equilibrium with furanoside form.

Molecular rotation relationships. $M_D = ([\alpha] \times \text{Mol. Wt.})/100$. van't Hoff principle of additivity. Vicinal effects. Hudson's rule that α-form is more dextrorotatory than β-form. Lactone rule: if the oxide ring lies to the right, the γ-lactone is more dextrorotatory than the parent acid.

Glycosides

Hydroxy component (aglycone) combined with a sugar (mono-, di-, trisaccharide). Hydrolyzed by acids; also by enzymes occurring in same plant. Example: arbutin (hydroquinone + glucose).

Disaccharides

Sucrose. Nonreducing, no osazone, no mutarotation (therefore crystallizes readily). Structure: pyranose form of α-glucose (α-glucopyranoside) linked at C_1 to furanose form of β-fructose (β-fructofuranoside) at C_2: 1α-glucosido-[1,5]-2-fructoside-[2,5]. Inertness due to utilization of glycosidic OH groups of both components. Proof of structure: octamethylsucrose hydrolyzed to 2,3,4,6-tetramethylglucose and 1,3,4,6-tetramethylfructose. Stable form of fructose has pyranose structure, but combined fructose always occurs in the furanose form.

Lactose. Galactose, in glycosidic form, linked to glucose at C_4: 1β-galactosido-[1,5]-4-glucose. The glucose part has a free or potential carbonyl group, and hence lactose is a reducing sugar and forms an osazone.

Maltose. Corresponds to lactose except that the β-galactosido group is replaced by an α-glucosido group. A reducing sugar hydrolyzable to two molecules of glucose.

Cellobiose. Corresponds to lactose except that the galactosido group is replaced by a β-glucosido group (β-isomer of maltose).

Cellulose. Pure forms: cotton, filter paper. From wood by extraction of lignin with sulfite. Hydrolyzed with difficulty by acids to glucose. Partial hydrolysis yields cellobiose, cellotriose, cellotetrose and thus reveals structure: β-glucosido units linked head-to-tail at positions 1 and 4. Molecular weight, 400,000. Indicates chains of about 2500 glucose units. X-ray pattern shows that fiber contains bundles of parallel oriented chains (micelles).

Technological products. Nitrocellulose rayon. Celluloid: pyroxylin plasticized with camphor (a terpene ketone). Modified (depolymerized) nitrocellulose lacquers. Acetate rayon. Viscose rayon.

Starch and glycogen. Chains of α-glucoside units arranged as in maltose, with branches linked at C_1 and C_6. Reserve carbohydrates.

PROBLEMS

1. A certain pentose, which forms a tetraacetate, is condensed with hydrogen cyanide and the product is hydrolyzed and reduced with HI–P. The resulting acid is identical with one synthesized from $CH_3CH_2CH_2I$ and $CH_3CH(CO_2C_2H_5)_2$. What is the structure of the pentose?

2. Rhamnose is a methylpentose of structure

    (a) $CH_3CHOHCHOHCHOHCHOHCHO$

Suggest an oxidation test that would distinguish between structure (a) and an isomeric structure

    (b) $HOCH_2CH_2CHOHCHOHCHOHCHO$.

3. What test would distinguish between a 2-desoxyhexose (a) and a 3-desoxyhexose (b)?

    (a) $HOCH_2CHOHCHOHCHOHCH_2CHO$
    (b) $HOCH_2CHOHCHOHCH_2CHOHCHO$

4. What tests would distinguish between the isomers (a), (b), and (c)?

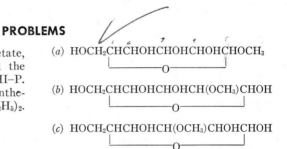

    (a) $HOCH_2CHCHOHCHOHCHOHCHOCH_3$

    (b) $HOCH_2CHCHOHCHOHCH(OCH_3)CHOH$

    (c) $HOCH_2CHCHOHCH(OCH_3)CHOHCHOH$

5. A hexose on catalytic hydrogenation in neutral solution gives a mixture of two products identified as sorbitol (14.6) and the alcohol derived from galactose. What is the hexose?

6. Two optically active D-aldotetroses, A and B, give the same osazone, but on oxidation with nitric acid A gives an optically active C_4-dibasic acid and B gives an optically inactive C_4-dibasic acid. Identify A and B.

7. How could D-galactose be distinguished from its 2-epimer, D-talose?

READING REFERENCES

C. S. Hudson, "Emil Fischer's Discovery of the Configuration of Glucose," *J. Chem. Educ.*, **18**, 353 (1941)

M. L. Wolfrom, A. L. Raymond, and E. Heuser, "The Carbohydrates," in H. Gilman, *Organic Chemistry*, II, 2nd Ed., 1532–1719, Wiley, New York (1943)

K. H. Meyer, "The Chemistry of Glycogen," *Advances in Enzymology*, **3**, 109 (1943)

W. N. Haworth, "Starch," *J. Chem. Soc.*, 543 (1946)

E. L. Hirst, "The Occurrence and Significance of the Pentose Sugars in Nature, and Their Relationship to the Hexoses," *J. Chem. Soc.*, 522 (1949)

J. Honeyman, *An Introduction to the Chemistry of Carbohydrates*, Oxford Univ. Press (1948)

E. G. V. Percival, *Structural Carbohydrate Chemistry*, Muller, London (1950)

W. W. Pigman and R. M. Goepp, Jr., *Chemistry of the Carbohydrates*, Academic Press, New York (1948) *Advances in Carbohydrates*, Academic Press 1945–

15.1

Constituents of plant or animal tissue that are insoluble in water but soluble in ether or other water-immiscible organic solvent are known as lipids. The most abundantly occurring lipids are animal fats (tallow, lard) and vegetable oils (olive, castor). These substances, which are either oils or low-melting solids with a greasy feel, are glycerides in which glycerol is esterified with two or three higher fatty acids, such as stearic (C_{18}) and palmitic (C_{16}) acid. Hydrolysis

Saponification of a fat

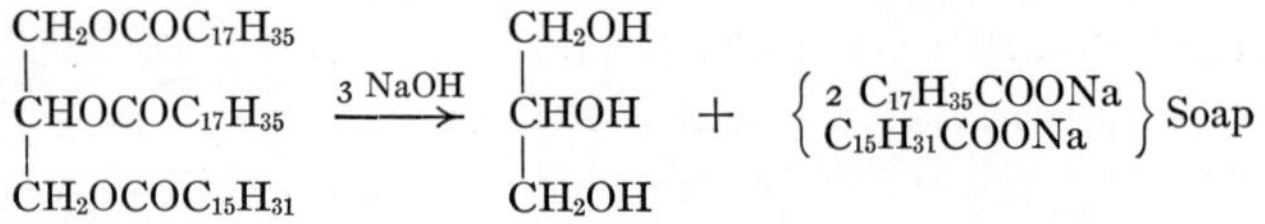

$$
\begin{array}{l}
CH_2OCOC_{17}H_{35} \\
| \\
CHOCOC_{17}H_{35} \\
| \\
CH_2OCOC_{15}H_{31} \\
\text{Typical glyceride}
\end{array}
\xrightarrow{\text{3 NaOH}}
\begin{array}{l}
CH_2OH \\
| \\
CHOH \\
| \\
CH_2OH
\end{array}
+
\left\{
\begin{array}{l}
2\ C_{17}H_{35}COONa \\
C_{15}H_{31}COONa
\end{array}
\right\}
\text{Soap}
$$

of a glyceride with hot aqueous alkali is called saponification (L. *sapo*, soap) because one product, a mixture of the sodium salts of the component fatty acids, is a soap. Saponification reverses the solubility relations, since at suitable dilution the products are soluble in water and not extractable with ether.

15.2

The tissues of brain and spinal cord contain complex structural units constructed from protein, cholesterol, and phospholipids of a type exemplified by the lecithins. A lecithin is a glyceride containing two, usually different, fatty acid residues (e.g., stearic acid and its unsaturated derivative oleic), and a phosphocholine group, which on

Lecithin, a phospholipid

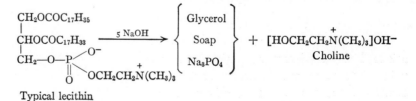

Typical lecithin

saponification affords inorganic phosphate and the quaternary base choline.

Nonsaponifiable lipids. — When brain tissue is saponified, the phospholipids, fats, and proteins are converted largely into water-soluble, ether-insoluble products and extraction of the alkaline mixture with ether affords a nonsaponifiable lipid fraction of which cholesterol, $C_{27}H_{45}OH$, is the main component. Cholesterol, a crystalline solid

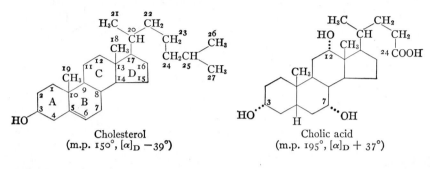

Cholesterol
(m.p. 150°, $[\alpha]_D -39°$)

Cholic acid
(m.p. 195°, $[\alpha]_D + 37°$)

of fairly high melting point, contains a secondary alcoholic group at the C_3 position in ring A, the hydroxyl group being oriented to the front (β), as are the angular methyl groups at C_{10} and C_{13} and the side chain at C_{17}. Ring B contains a double bond; the conformation of this ring is shown in the partial formula of section 13.8. Cholesterol results from similar saponification and extraction of all body tissues, including blood, which normally contains about 200 mg. of total cholesterol per 100 ml. Some 27% of the blood cholesterol is present as such and the rest is esterified with higher fatty acids such as stearic, oleic, palmitic. The total cholesterol in a man weighing 170 lbs. amounts to about 250 g. It is derived in part by biosynthesis in the body and, in carnivorous animals, from the diet. Egg yolk is a rich source of cholesterol; the water-insoluble lipid is emulsified by the lecithin present.

Bile acids are the next most abundant steroids of the animal organism. Bile contains about 6% of a mixture of conjugate acids of the type $RCONHCH_2CO_2H$, which on saponification and acidification yields a mixture of bile acids, RCO_2H, of which cholic acid is the major component. The formula given above shows that this acid has three α-oriented hydroxyl groups and a side chain like that of cholesterol but shortened by three carbon atoms and terminating in a carboxyl group. Physiologically active steroids, which function as hormones in control of normal processes of growth, are secreted by specific organs in such extremely small amounts that their isolation has required processing the nonsaponifiable fraction of tons of tissue. The gonads produce the sex hormones testosterone (C_{19}), progesterone

(C_{21}), and estradiol (C_{18}); the cortex of the adrenal gland produces adrenal cortical hormones such as cortisone (C_{21}). The nonsaponifi-

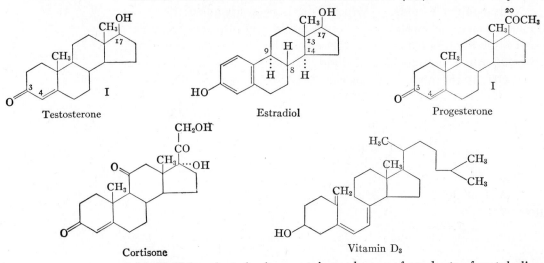

Testosterone   Estradiol   Progesterone

Cortisone   Vitamin D$_3$

able lipid fraction of urine contains a shower of products of metabolism of steroid hormones. One of the vitamins, that is, growth factors derived in whole or in part from thé diet, is a sterol related to choles-terol, namely vitamin D$_3$, which has been isolated from fish liver oils.

A steroid vitamin

The body requires only 5γ of this vitamin; dietary deficiency leads to onset of rickets, a disease characterized by softening of the bone.

15.5

Isoprenoid types

Several other nonsaponifiable lipids that occur in trace amounts in specific tissues have in common the feature that the structures are divisible in whole or in part into isoprene units (compare rubber, 4.32; camphor, 14.22). An isoprene unit is represented conveniently by the formula (1), or the abbreviation (2), in which one terminal carbon can be designated a head position (h) and the other a tail (t). Squal-ene, an unsaturated hydrocarbon of the formula $C_{30}H_{50}$ found in shark liver oil, contains six isoprene units joined thus: t—h, t—h, t—t, h—t, h—t. The structural formula as written suggests the

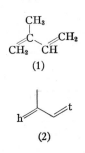

(1)

(2)

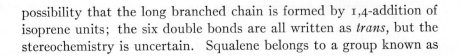

Isoprene units

Squalene

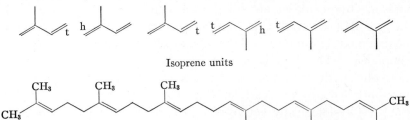

possibility that the long branched chain is formed by 1,4-addition of isoprene units; the six double bonds are all written as *trans*, but the stereochemistry is uncertain. Squalene belongs to a group known as carotenoids after the prominent member β-carotene, a pigment which occurs in the carrot, in green leaves, and in blood, and which owes its color (dilute solutions yellow) to the presence of eleven conjugated double bonds. β-Carotene, $C_{40}H_{56}$, is oxidized in the liver and suffers fission at its central link to produce vitamin A, $C_{20}H_{30}O$, a factor isolated from fish liver oils which plays a role in photoreception in the retina. It is a primary allylic alcohol derived from four isoprene units joined tail to head.

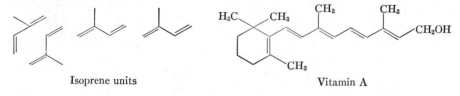

Isoprene units   Vitamin A

α-Tocopherol, a vitamin E factor which counteracts sterility in rats but which is not known to be essential to man, has been isolated from the nonsaponifiable lipid fractions of wheat germ oil and of liver. Synthesis is accomplished by condensation of trimethylhydroquinone

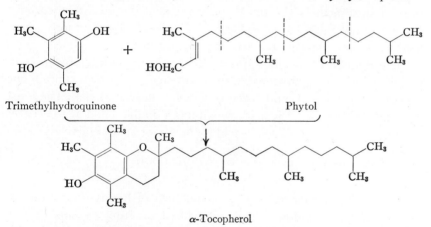

Trimethylhydroquinone   Phytol

α-Tocopherol

with phytol, an allylic, isoprenoid alcohol ($C_{20}H_{40}O$) which is liberated on saponification of an ester grouping of chlorophyll, the pigment of green plants. Vitamin K_1 also contains a phytyl group, which in this

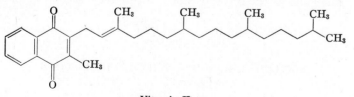

Vitamin K_1

case is linked to a quinone ring. It is likewise synthesized from phytol, and it is used in therapy to promote normal clotting of the blood, for example, in newborn babies subject to bleeding to death from a pin prick because they have not yet acquired adequate antihemorrhagic factor from the diet.

GLYCERIDE FATS AND OILS

15.7

Component Fatty Acids. — Saponification of a fat of either animal or plant source gives a mixture of fatty acids, saturated and unsaturated. All the acids have a straight chain containing an even number of carbon atoms; odd-carbon and branched-chain acids are not components of natural fats. The most abundant saturated acids are those in the series C_{12}-C_{18}. Stearic and palmitic acid occur abun-

Common saturated acid components

Acid	Formula	M.p.
Lauric	n-$C_{11}H_{23}CO_2H$	44°
Myristic	n-$C_{13}H_{27}CO_2H$	58°
Palmitic	n-$C_{15}H_{31}CO_2H$	63°
Stearic	n-$C_{17}H_{35}CO_2H$	70°

dantly in beef and pork fat glycerides, and the latter but not the former acid is a major constituent of palm oil (43%) and occurs in almost all fats. Lauric acid is the most abundant acid derived from coconut oil (48%) and related oils. Myristic acid is usually a minor component; it can be isolated readily from the nutmeg.

15.8

Unsaturated acids (C_{18})

The three most common unsaturated acids from fats are C_{18}-compounds which are hydrogenable to stearic acid and which contain one (oleic), two (linoleic), and three (linolenic) double bonds. The most abundant of these is oleic acid, which has a double bond at the center of the 18-carbon chain. Oleic acid is the major acid of olive oil (83%)

$$CH_3(CH_2)_7 \overset{10}{C}H = \overset{9}{C}H(CH_2)_7COOH$$
Oleic acid (m.p. 13°, 16°)

and is also the major acid of the depot fats of herbivorous animals: mutton and beef tallow (48%), neat's-foot oil from ox hoof (80%). As noted earlier (12.21), the natural acid, a liquid, has the *cis* configuration and is less stable than the solid *trans* form (elaidic acid). Linoleic acid and linolenic acid conform to the oleic pattern in having one double bond at the 9,10-position; both have a second double bond

Two and three nonconjugated double bonds

$$CH_3CH_2CH_2CH_2CH_2\overset{13}{C}H = \overset{12}{C}HCH_2\overset{10}{C}H = \overset{9}{C}H(CH_2)_7COOH$$
Linoleic acid (m.p. −5°)

$$CH_3CH_2\overset{16}{C}H = \overset{15}{C}HCH_2\overset{13}{C}H = \overset{12}{C}HCH_2\overset{10}{C}H = \overset{9}{C}H(CH_2)_7COOH$$
Linolenic acid (m.p. −11°)

at C_{12}-C_{13}, and linolenic acid has a third one at C_{15}-C_{16}; the hydrocarbon half of the chain is thus divided into three three-carbon units. The double bonds in these two acids all have the *cis* configuration.

The positions of the double bonds in an unsaturated acid usually are determined by identification of products of oxidative degradation. For example, oleic acid (*cis*) can be converted by oxidation with very dilute permanganate in the cold into a *vic*-diol; the product is the *erythro* diol (14.8) resulting from *cis* addition, and the same substance is formed by hydroxylation with osmium tetroxide. Hydroxylation by reaction with hydrogen peroxide in formic acid solution and hydrolysis proceeds by *trans* addition and gives the *threo* diol. Cleavage of either diol with periodic acid or with lead tetraacetate gives the C_9-aldehyde and the C_9-aldehyde acid in excellent yields.

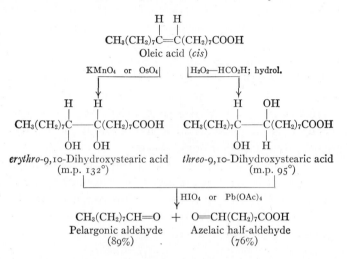

$$\overset{\displaystyle H \quad H}{\underset{\displaystyle ||}{\text{CH}_3(\text{CH}_2)_7\text{C}=\text{C}(\text{CH}_2)_7\text{COOH}}}$$

Oleic acid (*cis*)

KMnO₄ or OsO₄ | | H₂O₂—HCO₂H; hydrol.

$$\text{CH}_3(\text{CH}_2)_7\overset{\displaystyle H}{\underset{\displaystyle \text{OH}}{\text{C}}}\text{---}\overset{\displaystyle H}{\underset{\displaystyle \text{OH}}{\text{C}}}(\text{CH}_2)_7\text{COOH}$$

erythro-9,10-Dihydroxystearic acid (m.p. 132°)

$$\text{CH}_3(\text{CH}_2)_7\overset{\displaystyle H}{\underset{\displaystyle \text{OH}}{\text{C}}}\text{---}\overset{\displaystyle \text{OH}}{\underset{\displaystyle H}{\text{C}}}(\text{CH}_2)_7\text{COOH}$$

threo-9,10-Dihydroxystearic acid (m.p. 95°)

HIO₄ or Pb(OAc)₄

$$\text{CH}_3(\text{CH}_2)_7\text{CH}{=}\text{O} \quad + \quad \text{O}{=}\text{CH}(\text{CH}_2)_7\text{COOH}$$

Pelargonic aldehyde (89%)   Azelaic half-aldehyde (76%)

Natural and Hydrogenated Fats. — The degree of unsaturation is the most important factor in determining the physical as well as the chemical properties of both glycerides and fatty acids. Oleic acid is a liquid melting about 55° below the substance of which it is the 9,10-dehydro derivative, and melting points drop progressively on introduction of one and two more double bonds. Synthetic tristearin, that is, the tristearyl ester of glycerol, is a solid of melting point (71°) close to that of stearic acid (70°), whereas triolein, like oleic acid, is liquid at room temperature. Mixtures of glycerides do not show the usual melting point depressions but melt at temperatures intermediate between the melting points of the components. The animal fats tallow and lard are preferable to the more abundant and less expensive vegetable oils for manufacture of soap and for use in certain foods largely because they are solids (m.p. range 36–47°) rather than liquids, and the difference lies in the extent of unsaturation. The degree of unsaturation of a fat is measured by the iodine value, which is the number of grams of iodine that combine with one hundred grams of fat. Test solutions employ iodine monochloride (ICl), iodine mono-

15.9

Degree of un-saturation determines m.p.

Iodine value

bromide (IBr), or iodomercuric chloride (I_2HgCl_2), all of which are more reactive than iodine alone. Iodine values of samples of beef tallow are in the range 32–47; for peanut oil the range is 85–90, for whale oil it is 110–150.

The extent of unsaturation of fat may be markedly influenced by the temperature at which biosynthesis occurs. Warm-blooded animals tend to produce solid fats that are fluid at, or only a little above, body temperature. Variation may occur in fats from different parts of the organism. Neat's-foot oil, from the hoofs of cattle, has a higher iodine number than fats derived from other locations. A gradation is noted in the subcutaneous fat of the pig, the outer layers of which are progressively unsaturated. The striking influence of climate on the composition of linseed oil is shown by the following comparison: an iodine value of 190 has been reported for linseed oil from seed grown in the cold climate of Switzerland, and a value of 93 for oil from seed of the same stock grown in a Berlin greenhouse at a temperature of 25–30°. The degree of unsaturation is also dependent on the type of fat in the diet. The iodine value of lard of corn-fed hogs is 69–72, of peanut-fed hogs, 90–100.

Since the principal unsaturated acyl components of fats are convertible to stearyl groups by catalytic hydrogenation, unsaturation in a natural fat or oil can be reduced to any stage desired by hydrogenation (Ni catalyst). Since hydrogenation progressively raises the melting point, the process is described as one of hardening; abundant, highly unsaturated vegetable oils (peanut, cottonseed, soybean) are hardened by hydrogenation to more valuable products for use in making soap or to lard substitutes for use as cooking greases. Whale oil (iodine number 110–150) is partially hydrogenated to reduce the most highly reactive unsaturated centers and so eliminate odor and produce more stable oils for use as salad oil and in the compounding of cosmetics. Lard is often hydrogenated to improve keeping qualities, since development of rancidity is associated with unsaturation.

Hardening of fats

15.10

Multiple nonconjugated double bonds

Drying Oils. — Drying oils are mixed glycerides of highly unsaturated fatty acids and may be classified in two groups according to the nature of unsaturation. One group includes linseed oil (Argentina) and perilla oil (Japan). Both oils have iodine numbers in the range 170–210, and in both the major acid components, which together account for 85% of the total acids, are linoleic and linolenic acid, in which the double bonds are not conjugated but separated by methylene groups. A second group includes tung oil (China) and oiticica oil (Brazil). These have iodine values in the range 140–180 and are thus not so highly unsaturated as the first group, but the double bonds in the characteristic component acids are conjugated.

The major acid of tung oil (80% of total acids) is eleostearic acid, an isomer of linolenic acid in which the usual 9,10-double bond is con-

$$CH_3CH_2CH_2CH_2\overset{14}{C}H{=}\overset{13}{C}H\overset{12}{C}H{=}\overset{11}{C}H\overset{10}{C}H{=}\overset{9}{C}H(CH_2)_7COOH$$

Eleostearic acid (m.p. 49°)

jugated with the other two. In oiticica oil the major acid (74%) is licanic acid, the 4-keto derivative of eleostearic acid.

$$CH_3CH_2CH_2CH_2\overset{14}{C}H{=}\overset{13}{C}H\overset{12}{C}H{=}\overset{11}{C}H\overset{10}{C}H{=}\overset{9}{C}HCH_2CH_2CH_2CH_2\overset{4}{C}OCH_2CH_2COOH$$

Licanic acid (m.p. 75°)

The four oils named possess the ability, when spread on a surface and exposed to air, to slowly form dry, tough, and durable films. Mixtures with insoluble pigments are used as paints; varnishes are mixtures of drying oils with resins. The drying of these oils is not dependent upon evaporation of a solvent, as with modified nitro-cellulose lacquers (14.22), but involves oxidative polymerization. Although the nature of the reactions remains to be clarified, the process appears to be initiated by reaction with molecular oxygen to form a hydroperoxide. In linoleic and linolenic acid residues, a methylene group flanked by two activating double bonds (a) presents a point of vulnerability to attack by oxygen to give either the corresponding

$$-CH{=}CHCHCH{=}CH{-} \xleftarrow{\text{O}_2} -CH{=}CHCH_2CH{=}CH{-} \xrightarrow{\text{O}_2}$$
$$\underset{OOH}{|}$$

(b) (a)

$$-CH{=}CHCH{=}CHCH{-}$$
$$\underset{OOH}{|}$$

(c)

hydroperoxide (b) or, more probably, that (c) resulting from an allylic shift in the course of the reaction with formation of a conjugated system. In eleostearic and licanic acid the methylene groups adjacent to the two ends of the conjugated triene system appear to be more highly activated and hence more vulnerable to oxidation, for tung and oiticica oil dry more rapidly than linseed and perilla oil and are generally superior to these oils. Raw linseed oil dries only slowly, but the performance is improved by boiling the oil with lead oxide. Boiled linseed oil contains suspended lead salts which give it a muddy appearance, and modern boiled oils are made by incorporation into the oil at a more moderate temperature of a metal-containing oxidation catalyst, or drier, such as the cobalt or manganese soap (salt) of naphthenic acid. Oilcloth is made by applying several coats of linseed-oil paint to a woven canvas; linoleum is made by cementing cork particles with thickened linseed oil and rosin.

Castor Oil. — The split acid of oil from the castor bean contains small amounts of oleic and linoleic acid along with the characteristic component (88%) ricinoleic acid, or 12-hydroxyoleic acid. Castor oil is noted for retention of viscosity at high temperature, possibly because the protruding hydroxyl group impedes flow of molecules past one another, and is used as a motor lubricant. A minor fraction of an annual production of some 75,000 tons is used as a purgative. The oil is a source of four useful chemicals; *n*-heptaldehyde and undecylenic acid result from pyrolysis of castor oil (7.7), and pyrolytic decomposition of sodium ricinoleate (a) affords capryl alcohol and

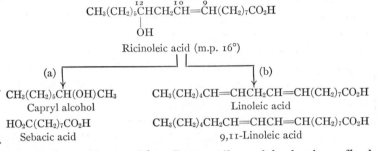

Source of other chemicals

sebacic acid (as sodium salt). Castor oil on dehydration affords a drying oil of quality intermediate between those of tung and linseed oil; the dehydration (b) proceeds in part to give acid residues in which the two double bonds are conjugated.

15.12

Soaps. — Natural or hardened fats are saponified with a solution of sodium hydroxide in an open kettle having at the bottom closed coils for indirect heating and perforated coils for direct heating through which steam can be passed at a rate to maintain agitation and ebullition. When the reaction is complete, salt is added to precipitate thick curds of the soap (common-ion effect). The aqueous layer containing glycerol is drawn off and concentrated to glycerol, which is refined by distillation in vacuum. The crude curds contain glycerol, alkali, and salt; the impurities are removed by boiling with sufficient water to form a homogeneous liquid, followed by reprecipitation of the soap with salt. In this way the soap is given several washings for recovery of glycerol and removal of impurities; then it is boiled with sufficient water to give a smooth mixture, which on

Manufacture of kettle soap

standing separates into a homogeneous upper layer of kettle soap. Kettle soap contains 69–70% soap, 0.2–0.5% salt, and about 30% water; some is sold as such or after addition of perfume or dye for household purposes. Sand, sodium carbonate, and inert fillers are added for scouring soaps; cresol or other antiseptic for medicated soaps. Powdered soaps are prepared by mixing kettle soap with builders or alkaline detergents (sodium silicate, sodium carbonate)

and with an emulsifying agent (tetrasodium pyrophosphate); the
hot mixture is then spray-dried. Toilet soaps are made from kettle
soap dried to a content of 85–90% and milled with perfume to thin
shavings, which are then compacted in bars that are cut and pressed
into cakes; transparent soaps are made by dissolving partly dried
soap in alcohol. The specific gravity of ordinary soap is about 1.05,
but by blowing air into hot molten kettle soap the specific gravity
can be lowered to 0.8–0.9 (floating soap).

Floating soap

Tallow (depot fat of cattle and sheep) is the most important soap
stock. Soap made from tallow alone has excellent detergent and
water-softening properties but must be used in hot water (tallow
yields mainly C_{16}- and C_{18}-acids, whose soaps are only slightly soluble
in water). The nut oils, coconut, babassu, and palm kernel oil, are
widely used in conjunction with tallow; their value lies in the high
content of C_{12}- and C_{14}-acids, the soaps of which are firm and also
readily soluble. Very unsaturated components cannot be used for soap
since they are subject to oxidation.

Preferred fats

Detergency is a complicated phenomenon that is not entirely
understood. One important factor undoubtedly is the orientation
of the molecules. Langmuir (1916–17) showed that a drop of fatty
oil when placed on a clean surface of water spreads rapidly until it
covers a definite area, when it spreads no farther. The area occupied
by equivalent weights of homologous fatty acids from C_{16} to C_{26} is
identical, though the depth of the film increases with increasing chain
length. These films consist of monomolecular layers, in which the
—COONa group is dipped in water, and the hydrocarbon part directed
away from water. This behavior is a property of substances that
contain both a hydrophilic and a lipophilic group, but the effect of
each must be properly balanced or the molecule will be in one phase
more than the other. Langmuir found that ricinoleic acid lies almost
flat on the surface, an effect ascribable to the presence of a second
hydrophilic group in the center of the molecule. Sodium ricinoleate
is an inferior detergent. The most striking characteristic of soap solutions is the reduction of surface tension (gas–liquid system) or of interfacial tension (liquid–liquid system). The surface tension of pure
water is 73 dynes/cm.; that of solutions of sodium oleate or linoleate
is about 25 dynes/cm. Substances that lower surface or interfacial
tension are known as surface-active compounds. Such compounds
all contain a hydrophilic and a hydrophobic group, preferably at
opposite ends of the molecule, which may be a long chain as in soap
or a complicated ring system.

*Nature of
detergent action*

*Hydrophilic-
lipophilic
balance*

Satisfactory detergency is first noted with the laurates and myris-
tates, which are often employed in soaps intended for use in sea water,

since they are more soluble in salt solution than the higher soaps. Soaps of fatty acids above C_{22} are unsuitable for detergents, since they are practically insoluble in water at room temperature. Detergency generally consists in removal of oil or grease or of solid particles dispersed in oil, and photographic studies have shown that, in the initial stages, the oil is displaced from fiber by soap solution (wetting action) to form large globules that can be detached by jarring and finally dispersed (emulsified) in the aqueous solution. Emulsions consist of fine droplets of one liquid dispersed in an immiscible liquid. The particles are kept from coalescing by a protective film of an emulsifier.

Oil-water emulsions

15.13   **Synthetic Surface-Active Agents.** — Surface-active compounds, including substances of value as detergents, wetting agents, and emulsifiers, are manufactured in a variety of types. Each has a lipophilic part, usually a fairly large hydrocarbon residue, and a hydrophilic functional group to provide distribution into the aqueous phase of a water-oil mixture. The latter function is usually an ionic group of fixed character, and the proper lipophilic-hydrophilic balance is attained by adjustment of the size of the hydrocarbon moiety. Since the field is highly competitive, the price of commercial products is kept at a minimum by use of fatty acid mixtures from fats and of alkane mixtures from petroleum, and actually mixtures probably function better than pure individual components because of coemulsifying action. Detergents of one type are made by hydrogenolysis of fat to a mixture of alcohols, which is converted into a mixture of sodium sulfate esters; the nut oils give superior detergents because of the high content of the C_{12}-sulfate I, derived from lauric acid. Being salts

Lipophilic-hydrophilic balance

Types

$$CH_3(CH_2)_{11}OSO_3^-Na^+ \qquad CH_3(CH_2)_{16}COOCH_2\overset{\displaystyle CH_2OH}{\underset{\displaystyle CH_2OH}{\vert \atop C \atop \vert}}-CH_2OH$$

I   II

of strong acids, the sodium sulfate esters are more stable than soap in solutions of low pH. Surface-active agents of another type are exemplified by a mixture of which the chief component is monostearoyl pentaerythritol, II; here the hydrophilic function is not ionic but is a triol grouping.

Surface-active agents of two types utilize the sodium sulfonate group, —SO_3Na, for distribution into the aqueous phase. In one, the alkane mixture (RH) of a petroleum fraction of appropriate molecular weight is converted by reaction with sulfur dioxide and chlorine into the sulfonyl chloride derivative and this is saponified to the sodium sulfonate III. In the other, a petroleum fraction is chlorinated to an alkyl chloride mixture, RCl, and this is condensed with an aromatic

$$RH \xrightarrow{SO_2,\ Cl_2} RSO_2Cl \xrightarrow{NaOH} \underset{III}{RSO_3Na}$$

IV   V

hydrocarbon such as naphthalene under catalysis from aluminum chloride (Friedel-Crafts reaction, 18.8) to produce a mixture of isomers and homologs roughly represented by formula IV. Sulfonation and conversion to the sodium sulfonates gives a surface-active preparation V.

SUMMARY

Term lipid designates water-insoluble, oil-soluble plant or animal product. Fats are mixed glycerides, e.g., of stearic (C_{18}) and palmitic (C_{16}) acid; saponification (alkaline hydrolysis) gives soap + glycerol. Lecithin, a phosphatide, saponified to glycerol, fatty acids, phosphate, and choline.

Nonsaponifiable lipids. (a) Steroids. Cholesterol (C_{27}, one β-OH, one double bond), abundant constituent of animal tissues. Bile acids, e.g., cholic acid (C_{24}, three α-OH). Sex hormones C_{18}, C_{19}, C_{21}; cortisone (C_{21}, adrenal gland). Vitamin D_3 (antirachitic). (b) Isoprenoid types. Squalene (C_{30}, six isoprene units linked t—h, t—h, t—t, h—t, h—t). Vitamin A (C_{20}, four isoprene units, an allylic alcohol). Tocopherol (trimethylhydroquinone + phytol, a C_{20} alcohol from chlorophyll). Vitamin K_1, a quinone with a phytyl chain.

Fatty acids of glycerides. All straight-chain, even number of carbons. Saturated: lauric (C_{12}), myristic (C_{14}), palmitic (C_{16}), stearic (C_{18}). Unsaturated (all hydrogenable to stearic, all *cis*): oleic (double bond at center), linoleic and linolenic (2 and 3 nonconjugated double bonds). Structures established by oxidation to diols (*cis* or *trans*) and glycol cleavage.

Natural fats. M.p. determined by degree of unsaturation (measured by iodine value). Cheap vegetable and whale oils converted to more valuable solid fats or more saturated oils by hydrogenation (hardening).

Drying oils. Linseed and perilla oil rich in linoleic and linolenic (multiple nonconjugated double bonds). Superior to these are tung and oiticica oil, rich in eleostearic acid (conjugated triene system) or its 4-keto derivative licanic acid. Drying involves oxidative polymerization initiated by attack of oxygen at an allylic CH_2 group to form a hydroperoxide. Linseed oil improved by boiling with lead oxide or incorporation of cobalt or manganese naphthenate as drier (oxidation catalyst).

Castor oil. Major acid: ricinoleic = 12-hydroxyoleic. Lubricant; source of n-$C_6H_{13}CHO$, $CH_2{=}CH(CH_2)_8CO_2H$, $CH_3(CH_2)_5CH(OH)CH_3$, $HO_2C(CH_2)_7CO_2H$. Dehydration to synthetic drying oil.

Soaps. Method of production of sodium soaps; recovery of glycerol. C_{12}–C_{14} acids (nut oils) improve quality (better water-solubility). Detergency dependent upon reduction in surface tension and orientation at oil-water interface; Langmuir surface films.

Synthetic surface-active compounds. Combination of a hydrophilic group (—OSO_3Na, —SO_3Na, several OH groups) with a lipophilic hydrocarbon group (C_{12}–C_{14}). Mixtures.

READING REFERENCES

F. D. Snell, "Soap and Glycerol," *J. Chem. Educ.*, **19**, 172 (1942)

T. P. Hilditch, *The Industrial Chemistry of the Fats and Waxes*, Van Nostrand, New York (1941)

T. P. Hilditch, *The Chemical Constitution of Natural Fats*, Chapman and Hall, London (1947)

A. W. Ralston, *Fatty Acids and Their Derivatives*, Wiley, New York (1948)

O. H. Wurster, "Hydrogenation of Fats," *Ind. Eng. Chem.*, **32**, 1193 (1940)

F. D. Snell, "Surface-Active Agents," *Ind. Eng. Chem.*, **35**, 107 (1943)

R. L. Kenyon, D. V. Stingley, and H. P. Young, "Chemicals from Fats," *Ind. Eng. Chem.*, **42**, 202 (1950)

chapter 16

PROTEINS

*Fibrous proteins
(water-insoluble)*

*Globular proteins
(soluble)*

Proteins (Gr. *proteios*, primary) derive their name from their great importance in all living tissues. Proteins differ from carbohydrates and fats in elementary composition, for in addition to carbon, hydrogen, and oxygen, they invariably contain nitrogen (16–18%) and usually sulfur. Proteins of one type, the fibrous proteins, are insoluble in water and serve as structural materials for animals much as cellulose serves for plants. Fibroin, the protein of silk, is an example. Others are collagen, the protein of connective tissue, which yields gelatin when boiled with water; keratin, the protein of epithelial tissue, of hair, wool, horn, feathers, nails; elastin, the protein of elastic connective tissue. A second broad group is that of the globular proteins, characterized by solubility in water or in aqueous solutions of acids, bases, or salts. Examples are egg albumin (white of egg), casein (from milk), and plasma proteins. Centrifugation of blood that has been treated with citrate solution or with heparin to prevent

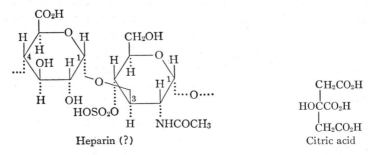

Heparin (?) Citric acid

Blood plasma

clotting causes settling of the heavier red blood corpuscles and separation of a yellowish, opalescent supernatant liquid that constitutes blood plasma and is an approximately 7% solution of plasma proteins in water at a pH close to 7.0. If the plasma is siphoned off and the sludge of corpuscles stirred with a little ether, the ether reduces the surface tension of the liquid external to the cells but does not penetrate the cell membranes and hence does not alter the pressure within the cells; the result is that the cells burst. A further centrifugation causes the ruptured cell membranes to settle and gives a rich red solution of the globular protein hemoglobin. This is the protein responsible for transportation of oxygen from the lungs to all body tissues. The mechanism of animal respiration can be demonstrated with the solution of hemoglobin prepared as described: when the solution is shaken with oxygen it becomes bright red (arterial blood), and when it is evacuated at the suction pump it becomes bluish red (venous blood). Hemoglobin is an example of a conjugated protein, and it contrasts with the above-mentioned substances, which are simple proteins. Hemoglobin is a conjugate of a protein proper, globin, and a much smaller nonproteinic C_{34}-component, heme. The component heme that is attached to the protein is known as a prosthetic group (Gr. *prosthetos*, put on). Actually heme, which contains iron, is responsible for the red color of blood and is essential for its function as oxygen carrier.

Hemoglobin = heme conjugated with globin

Blood plasma, prepared by the procedure described, contains the following globular proteins: albumins, globins (insoluble in pure water but soluble in 5% salt solution), lipoproteins (containing up to 75% lipids), fibrinogen, and prothrombin. Whole blood that is not protected with citrate or heparin as it is drawn clots on standing for a few minutes as the result of conversion of the soluble fibrinogen, under the influence of prothrombin, into an insoluble, fibrous protein fibrin, strands of which form the enmeshing structure of the clot. Centrifugation of clotted blood gives a residual mixture of fibrin and red blood corpuscles and a supernatant solution known as blood serum. Serum differs from plasma in that it contains no fibrinogen.

Blood serum

16.2

Proteins consist of giant molecules of molecular weights ranging from about 12,000 to several million units. Those proteins that are soluble in water form colloidal solutions. Chemical characterization is limited by the extreme sensitivity of the substances; treatment with an acid, a base, or an organic solvent is liable to produce a fundamental change described as denaturation, which is attended with loss of originally characteristic properties, such as water solubility or specific biological activity. Mild heating usually results in denaturation with loss in solubility, as illustrated by the familiar phenomenon of the change induced by hot water on egg white. As in most instances, the denaturation of egg albumin is irreversible.

All proteins can be hydrolyzed by the action of aqueous solutions of mineral acids at the boiling point, and they all afford mixtures of α-amino acids of the type $RCH(NH_2)CO_2H$. Analytical evidence shows that the carboxyl and α-amino groups represented in the type formula are not present as such in the protein but that they are liberated in equal amounts on hydrolysis. Thus the building units are joined together through the peptide link, —CO·NH—, between the carboxyl group of one amino acid and the amino group of another, and the process of protein hydrolysis can be represented in part as the cleavage of a polypeptide chain:

Polypeptide structure

$$\overset{R}{\underset{|}{}} \quad \overset{R'}{\underset{|}{}} \quad \overset{R''}{\underset{|}{}}$$
$$-(NH\dot{C}HCO)_n-(NH\dot{C}HCO)_{n'}-(NH\dot{C}HCO)_{n''}- \quad \xrightarrow{\text{Hydrol.}}$$

$$n\,H_2NCH(R)CO_2H \;+\; n'\,H_2NCH(R')CO_2H \;+\; n''\,H_2NCH(R'')CO_2H$$

AMINO ACIDS

16.3

Component Acids of Proteins. — Glycine, $H_2NCH_2CO_2H$, the simplest amino acid derived from proteins, was the first component to be discovered. Braconnot (1820), investigating the hydrolysis of gelatin to see if this material, like cellulose, would yield a sugar, isolated a substance which he called glycine because it had a sweet taste (Gr. *glykys*, sweet), and eighteen years elapsed before the supposed "sugar of gelatin" was found to contain nitrogen. Subsequent investigations of protein hydrolyzates have led to recognition of twenty acid components of established structure; several other acids are indicated as probable components. All known components are α-amino acids, and with the sole exception of glycine the α-carbon atom is asymmetric. Thus one group includes the following homologs: alanine, $CH_3CH(NH_2)CO_2H$; valine, $(CH_3)_2CHCH(NH_2)CO_2H$; leucine, $(CH_3)_2CHCH_2CH(NH_2)CO_2H$. Valine is the isopropyl homolog of alanine and leucine is the isobutyl homolog, and most of the other component acids are alanine derivatives: $RCH_2CH(NH_2)CO_2H$.

Type $R\underset{\underset{NH_2}{|}}{CH}CO_2H$

These substances are neutral amino acids, since each contains the same number of amino and carboxyl groups. They are amphoteric and at suitable pH can ionize as either acids or bases. The pH at which acidic ionization balances basic ionization is called the isoelectric point; for neutral amino acids the values range from 4.8 to 6.3. The electrically neutral form predominating at the isoelectric point is a dipolar ion carrying both a positive and a negative charge. The ionic

Isoelectric point

Inner salt structure

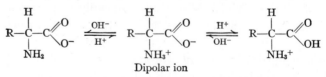

Dipolar ion

structure explains the fact that the acids are relatively infusible and nonvolatile.

The list of common amino acids given in Table I includes conventional symbols and isoelectric points. The first five members of the neutral group differ in the size and structure of the alkyl side chain, $RCH(NH_2)CO_2H$. Proline can be regarded as a cyclized

TABLE I

COMMON AMINO ACIDS FROM PROTEINS

A. NEUTRAL AMINO ACIDS			
Name	Symbol	Formula	Isoelectric point
Glycine	Gly	$CH_2(NH_2)COOH$	5.97
Alanine	Ala	$CH_3CH(NH_2)COOH$	6.00
Valine	Val	$(CH_3)_2CHCH(NH_2)COOH$	5.96
Leucine	Leu	$(CH_3)_2CHCH_2CH(NH_2)COOH$	6.02
Isoleucine	Ileu	$CH_3CH_2CH(CH_3)CH(NH_2)COOH$	5.98
Proline	Pro		6.30
Phenylalanine	Phe	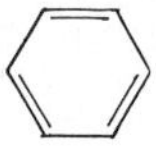	5.48
Tyrosine	Tyr	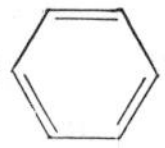	5.66
Tryptophan	Try	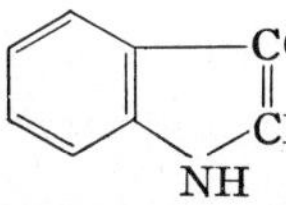	5.89
Cysteine	CySH	$HSCH_2CH(NH_2)COOH$	5.05
Cystine	CyS·SCy	$[-SCH_2CH(NH_2)COOH]_2$	4.8
Methionine	Met	$CH_3SCH_2CH_2CH(NH_2)COOH$	5.74
Serine	Ser	$HOCH_2CH(NH_2)COOH$	5.68
Threonine	Thre	$CH_3CH(OH)CH(NH_2)COOH$	
B. ACIDIC AMINO ACIDS			
Aspartic acid	Asp	$HOOCCH_2CH(NH_2)COOH$	2.77
Glutamic acid	Glu	$HOOC(CH_2)_2CH(NH_2)COOH$	3.22
C. BASIC AMINO ACIDS			
Lysine	Lys	$NH_2(CH_2)_4CH(NH_2)COOH$	9.74
Arginine	Arg	$NH_2C(=NH)NH(CH_2)_3CH(NH_2)COOH$	10.76

Pyrrolidine ring

Indole system = benzene ring fused to a pyrrole ring

Guanidyl group =
H_2NCNH-
‖
NH

n-alkyl-α-amino acid. In phenylalanine, $C_6H_5CH_2CH(NH_2)COOH$, a phenyl group is joined to an alanyl residue; tyrosine is the p-hydroxy derivative of phenylalanine. Tryptophan is similar except that the aromatic group attached to an alanyl residue is the bicyclic indole group, which contains a five-membered, nitrogen-containing pyrrole ring fused to a benzene ring.

Cysteine is the β-thiol or β-sulfhydryl derivative of alanine. It is readily oxidized to the disulfide cystine, which can be reconverted

$$2\,HSCH_2CHCO_2H \underset{red.}{\overset{oxid.}{\rightleftarrows}} \begin{array}{c} NH_2 \\ | \\ SCH_2CHCO_2H \\ | \\ SCH_2CHCO_2H \\ | \\ NH_2 \end{array}$$

Cysteine (HSCH₂CHCO₂H with NH₂) — Cystine

into cysteine by reduction. Methionine contains the thiomethyl group (CH_3S); it is derived not from cysteine but from the next higher homolog, homocysteine, which itself is not a protein component. Serine is the oxygen analog of cysteine, and threonine is the β-methyl homolog of serine; threonine contains two asymmetric carbon atoms.

$$CH_3SCH_2CH_2CHCO_2H \qquad HOCH_2CHCO_2H \qquad CH_3CHCHCO_2H$$

Methionine (NH_2) — Serine (NH_2) — Threonine (HO NH_2)

Typical neutral amino acids, such as glycine and alanine, are soluble in water and insoluble in organic solvents. However, solubility of acids of the type $RCH(NH_2)CO_2H$ varies markedly with the nature and size of the side chain R, as can be seen from Table II.

TABLE II

SOLUBILITIES

Acid	Mol. wt.	g./100 ml.[25]	
		Water	Abs. ethanol
Glycine	75.07	25.0	0.06
Alanine	89.09	16.7	
Valine	117.15	8.8	
Leucine	131.17	2.4	0.07
Isoleucine	131.17	4.1	
Proline	115.13	162	67
Cystine	240.30	0.006	

In the series glycine, alanine, valine, leucine, and isoleucine solubility in water decreases markedly with increasing size of the alkyl group, as reflected in the molecular weight; isoleucine is nearly twice as soluble as leucine. Leucine, which contains the large, lipophilic isobutyl group, can be extracted with hot butanol from a mixture of this acid with glycine. For some unknown reason the cyclic structure of proline confers on the molecule extraordinary solubility in both water and ethanol, as compared with valine, which has nearly the same molecular weight. The solubility of cystine in water is abnormally low: 0.006 g./100 ml. (25°). Such properties undoubtedly are important determinants of the lipophilic-hydrophilic balance of specific proteins.

Aspartic and glutamic acid are acidic, since they contain a second

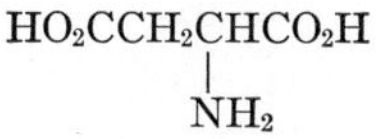

$$HO_2CCH_2CHCO_2H$$
$$|$$
$$NH_2$$
Aspartic acid

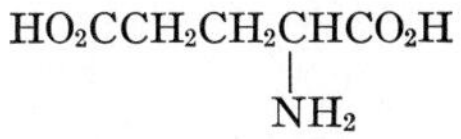

$$HO_2CCH_2CH_2CHCO_2H$$
$$|$$
$$NH_2$$
Glutamic acid

carboxyl group not paired with a basic function; the isoelectric values are 2.8 and 3.2, respectively. These amino derivatives of succinic and glutaric acid occur in proteins to some extent as the monoamides, asparagine and glutamine:

$$H_2NCOCH_2CH(NH_2)CO_2H$$
Asparagine, Asp(NH₂)

$$H_2NCOCH_2CH_2CH(NH_2)CO_2H$$
Glutamine, Glu(NH₂)

Acids of a third type, illustrated by lysine, contain two amino groups

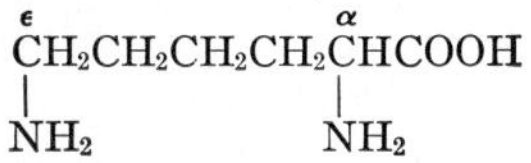

$$\overset{\epsilon}{C}H_2CH_2CH_2CH_2\overset{\alpha}{C}HCOOH$$
$$| \qquad\qquad |$$
$$NH_2 \qquad\quad NH_2$$
Lysine

and only one carboxyl group and are basic (isoelectric point 9.7). A second important basic amino acid is arginine, the δ-guanidyl derivative of α-aminovaleric acid; guanidine is the imide of urea and is very strongly basic. The guanidyl group renders arginine the most basic protein component (isoelectric point 10.8).

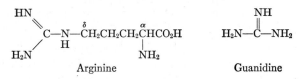

Arginine

Guanidine

Configuration. — The α-carbon atom of all the amino acids except glycine is asymmetric, and it is noteworthy that all the natural acids derived from proteins have the same configuration at this center, regardless of the sign of rotation. Natural alanine has been related to L-(+)-lactic acid, and hence all the acids from proteins belong to the L-series (K. Freudenberg,[1] 1924); since natural alanine is dextrorotatory, it is fully described as L-(+)-alanine. A natural amino acid

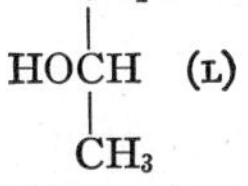

$$CO_2H$$
$$|$$
$$HOCH \quad (L)$$
$$|$$
$$CH_3$$
L-(+)-Lactic acid

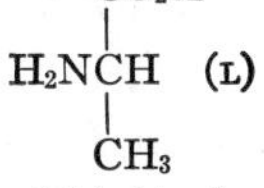

$$CO_2H$$
$$|$$
$$H_2NCH \quad (L)$$
$$|$$
$$CH_3$$
L-(+)-Alanine

that contains a second center of asymmetry is designated L to indicate the correspondence in the configuration of the α-carbon atom with

[1] Karl Freudenberg, b. 1886 Weinheim/Baden, Germany; Ph.D. Berlin (E. Fischer); Heidelberg

that of L-alanine, and the enantiomer is designated D. The diastereo-isomers of these substances are designated by the prefixes L-allo and D-allo, the letter denoting the configuration of the α-carbon atom; for example natural threonine was so named because of its relationship to D-threose; in the amino acid the prefix L- refers to the configuration

$$
\begin{array}{ccc}
\text{CO}_2\text{H} & \text{CHO} & \text{CO}_2\text{H} \\
| & | & | \\
\text{H}_2\text{NCH} \ \ (\text{L}) & \text{HOCH} & \text{H}_2\text{NCH} \ \ (\text{L}) \\
| & | & | \\
\text{HCOH} & \text{HCOH} \ \ (\text{D}) & \text{HOCH} \\
| & | & | \\
\text{CH}_3 & \text{CH}_2\text{OH} & \text{CH}_3 \\
\text{L-}(-)\text{-Threonine} & \text{D-Threose} & \text{L-Allothreonine} \\
\text{(natural)} & &
\end{array}
$$

of the α-carbon atom, whereas in the carbohydrate the prefix D- refers to the carbon atom β to the aldehyde function.

16.8   **Isolation of Amino Acids.** — For hydrolysis of a protein with the object of isolating component acids, the material is usually refluxed with hydrochloric acid (20%) or sulfuric acid (35%). Hydrolysis with hot alkali is less useful because it leads to extensive racemization of most of the products. Enzymatic hydrolysis is sometimes employed because it is less destructive to sensitive amino acids, but the reaction is slow and never complete.

All proteins afford hydrolyzates that are complex mixtures of some ten to eighteen individual amino acids and separation obviously is difficult. Because they are dipolar, saltlike, amino acids are not dis-tillable. However, Emil Fischer introduced in 1901 the technique of

esterification of a protein hydrolyzate and fractional distillation of mixtures of esters of the type $RCH(NH_2)CO_2CH_3$ derived from the neutral amino acids present. Since the component acids have rather low molecular weights, the increment of 14 units between homologs produces a fair spread in boiling point adequate for separation. The technique of ester distillation led to the discovery of valine, proline, and γ-hydroxyproline. Selective precipitation reactions have also been useful. For example, tryptophan was first isolated from a

hydrolyzate by precipitation with mercuric sulfate, and arginine by precipitation with phosphotungstic acid. The latter reagent is specific for the basic amino acids and precipitates both arginine and lysine, if present.

16.9   **Synthesis of Amino Acids.** — Methods of synthesis, apart from initial interest for completion of evidence of structure, have been investigated extensively with the object of making acids available where required as dietary supplements; poultry feed, for example, is enriched in lysine. Although the initial product of a synthesis is a racemic mixture, resolution usually can be accomplished without

difficulty. A general method consists in selective enzymatic hydrolysis
of the L-form of a DL-acetylamino acid (Greenstein,[2] 1948). Currently,
some of the amino acids are still more readily available by isolation
than by synthesis. A few of many known synthetic methods are
illustrated in the following paragraphs.

One route to α-amino derivatives of available acids consists in
introduction of an α-chloro or α-bromo substituent by catalyzed halogenation and amination of the halo acid with a large excess of ammonia. The preparation of DL-alanine by this method has been
described (11.4). The Gabriel synthesis (11.8), in which an α-halo
ester is condensed with potassium phthalimide and the product then
hydrolyzed, accomplishes the same objective more efficiently because
the possibility of side reactions leading to secondary amines is excluded.

The Strecker[3] synthesis (1850) combines the addition of hydrogen
cyanide to an aldehyde and the condensation of the addition product
with ammonia. When hydrogen cyanide is added to the carbonyl
group of an aldehyde in the presence of ammonia, the latter reagent
acts on the initially formed cyanohydrin with replacement of the
hydroxyl by an amino group and formation of an aminonitrile, which
affords an amino acid on hydrolysis.

$$CH_3CHO \xrightarrow{NH_3,\ HCN} \underset{\substack{| \\ NH_2}}{CH_3CHC\equiv N} \xrightarrow{2\,H_2O} \underset{\substack{| \\ NH_2}}{CH_3CHCOOH}$$

Acetaldehyde · · · · · · · · Aminonitrile · · · · · Alanine

Several variations of the malonic ester synthesis have been employed. The following synthesis of methionine illustrates a combination of the phthalimide and the malonic ester synthesis that has
proved useful in several instances.

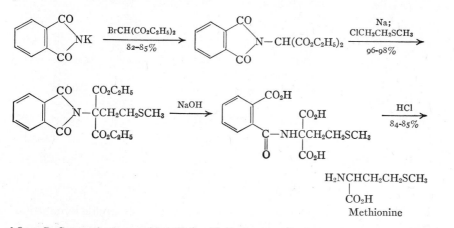

[2] Jesse P. Greenstein, b. 1902 New York; Ph.D. Brown; Nat. Cancer Inst.
[3] Adolph Strecker, 1822–71; assistant to Liebig at Tübingen

305

In another variation, the reactivity of the methylene group of malonic ester is utilized in a condensation with nitrous acid to give an oximino derivative reducible to the key intermediate aminomalonic ester. This amino ester is stabilized by benzoylation, and then a substituent group is introduced by reaction of the sodio derivative with an appropriate halide. The method is illustrated by the synthesis of glutamic acid.

Through amino-malonic ester

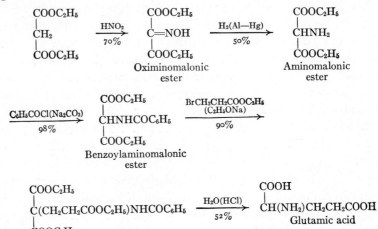

$$\begin{array}{c} COOC_2H_5 \\ | \\ CH_2 \\ | \\ COOC_2H_5 \end{array} \xrightarrow[70\%]{HNO_2} \begin{array}{c} COOC_2H_5 \\ | \\ C=NOH \\ | \\ COOC_2H_5 \end{array} \xrightarrow[50\%]{H_2(Al-Hg)} \begin{array}{c} COOC_2H_5 \\ | \\ CHNH_2 \\ | \\ COOC_2H_5 \end{array}$$

Oximinomalonic ester   Aminomalonic ester

$$\xrightarrow[98\%]{C_6H_5COCl(Na_2CO_3)} \begin{array}{c} COOC_2H_5 \\ | \\ CHNHCOC_6H_5 \\ | \\ COOC_2H_5 \end{array} \xrightarrow[90\%]{\substack{BrCH_2CH_2COOC_2H_5 \\ (C_2H_5ONa)}}$$

Benzoylaminomalonic ester

$$\begin{array}{c} COOC_2H_5 \\ | \\ C(CH_2CH_2COOC_2H_5)NHCOC_6H_5 \\ | \\ COOC_2H_5 \end{array} \xrightarrow[52\%]{H_2O(HCl)} \begin{array}{c} COOH \\ | \\ CH(NH_2)CH_2CH_2COOH \end{array}$$

Glutamic acid

Amino acids containing an aromatic group, for example phenylalanine, tyrosine, or tryptophan, are available by syntheses involving aldehyde condensations. An appropriate aromatic aldehyde is condensed with a reagent having an activated methylene group flanked

Aldehyde condensations

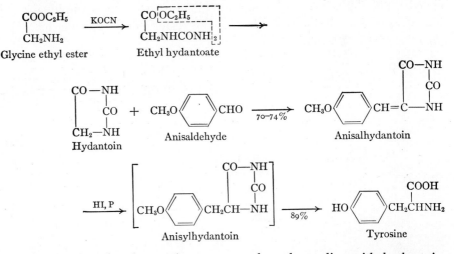

$$\begin{array}{c} COOC_2H_5 \\ | \\ CH_2NH_2 \end{array} \xrightarrow{KOCN} \begin{array}{c} CO\overline{OC_2H_5} \\ | \\ CH_2NHCONH_2 \end{array} \longrightarrow$$

Glycine ethyl ester   Ethyl hydantoate

Hydantoin + Anisaldehyde $\xrightarrow{70-74\%}$ Anisalhydantoin

$\xrightarrow{HI, P}$ [Anisylhydantoin] $\xrightarrow{89\%}$ Tyrosine

by a carbonyl and an amino group, such as the cyclic ureide hydantoin. The condensation of anisaldehyde with hydantoin gives an unsaturated substance convertible into tyrosine by reduction of the unsaturated linkage followed by simultaneous hydrolysis of the ureide grouping and the methoxyl group.

PROTEINS

H₂NCHCO—NHCHCO—NHCHCO—NHCHCO—NHCH₂CO—NHCHCO—(NHCHCO)ₙ—NHCHCO₂H

| | | | | | | | |
CH₂C₆H₅   CH₃   CH₂   (CH₂)₂   CH₂   (CH₂)₄   R   CH₂
                 | | | | |
                 CO₂H   CONH₂   SH   NH₂   OH
Phe   Ala   Asp   Glu(NH₂) CySH   Lys   Ser

16.10

The hypothetical protein formulated has phenylalanine as the amino-terminal unit, conventionally written to the left, and serine as the carboxyl-terminal unit. The substance is amphoteric, since it contains two basic groups (terminal —NH₂ and ε-NH₂ of Lys) and two acidic groups (terminal —CO₂H, and Asp-CO₂H). The sulfhydryl group (CySH) confers reducing properties, and the groups —SH, —OH, —COOH, and —NH₂ tend to promote water-solubility, whereas the hydrocarbon chains of Phe and Ala have the opposite effect. In diacids (Asp, Glu), the α-carboxyl group is utilized for formation of the peptide link, and in units having two basic functions (Lys, Arg) the α-amino function is the one so utilized. Analytical characterization of the hypothetical protein might include Van Slyke determination of the nitrogen liberated on reaction with nitrous acid, here derived from the groups: terminal —NH₂, Glu(NH₂), ε-NH₂ of Lys. Hydrolysis of the protein would liberate ammonia equivalent to the Glu(NH₂) present.

Isolation and Purification. — Most proteins are extremely prone to undergo irreversible alteration, or denaturation, and hence isolation of homogeneous individual components of protein mixtures in native form presents considerable difficulty. Since the solubility is at a minimum at the isoelectric point, adjustment of the pH to a particular value may favor separation of one component and retention of others when either a salt or a solvent such as ethanol is added in controlled amount. A method favored for slow addition of ammonium sulfate for isoelectric salting out of a protein is to rotate a cellophane bag of solid ammonium sulfate in the buffered protein solution; the electrolyte diffuses through the membrane and eventually causes precipitation of protein. If the precipitate, consisting of protein contaminated with the salt, is put in a bag and dialyzed against distilled water the ammonium sulfate is eliminated and the protein dissolves and can then be reprecipitated as before. Crystallization of proteins has been effected by suitable repetition of the process.

The purity of a given preparation is best evaluated by two physical methods. One is determination of the molecular weight by the

*Isoelectric
precipitation*

CHAPTER 16

*Ultracentrifuge
determination
of mol. wt.*

Electrophoresis

16.11

*Paper
chromatography*

Rf value

ultracentrifuge method (Svedberg [4]). When a protein solution contained in a small cell is centrifuged at very high speeds, the molecules move under the centrifugal pull toward the outer edge to an extent dependent upon their molecular weight, and the molecular weight can be determined either from the sedimentation equilibrium or from the rate of sedimentation. It is possible also to tell whether the molecules are all of the same molecular weight. The second method is that of electrophoresis (Tiselius [5]). Proteins move in an electric field at a rate determined by the size and shape of the molecule and by the number and kind of ionized groups. Material that appears homogeneous by the criterion of solubility may contain components that differ in the rate of electrophoretic travel.

Amino Acid Analysis. — Early data on the nature and proportion of the amino acid components of different proteins based upon yields of materials isolated by techniques of extraction, precipitation, and distillation have been supplemented by new techniques for assay of hydrolyzates. Some are based upon chromatographic adsorption. The method of paperstrip chromatography is applicable to minute amounts of material and furnishes significant qualitative and quantitative data (Martin [6] and Synge, [7] 1944). The components of a hydrolyzate are partitioned between water adsorbed on cellulose, and so held in a stationary phase, and an only partially water-soluble organic solvent such as butanol or phenol, which is caused to travel the length of the strip by either ascending or descending flow and constitutes a moving phase. The more lipophilic the component acid, the more it tends to travel with the organic solvent; the more hydrophilic, the greater is the tendency to be retained in the stationary water phase. The rate of flow (Rf) of acids of the same type increases with increasing molecular weight, and even homologs differing by a single methylene group travel at sufficiently different rates to be easily differentiated. At the end of the chromatogram the paper is dried and sprayed with ninhydrin to bring out spots revealing the positions of the component acids, since this reagent, indane-1,2,3-trione-2-hydrate, oxidizes

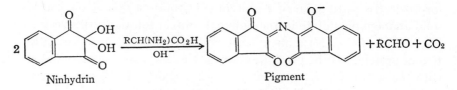

Ninhydrin   Pigment

[4] The Svedberg, b. 1884 Sweden; Uppsala; Nobel Prize 1926
[5] Arne Tiselius, b. 1902 Stockholm; Uppsala; Nobel Prize 1948
[6] Arthur John Porter Martin, b. 1910 England; Nat. Inst. Med. Res., Mill Hill, London; Nobel Prize 1952
[7] Richard Lawrence Millington Synge, b. 1914 Liverpool; Ph.D. Cambridge (Pirie); Rowett Res. Inst., Bucksburn, Scotland; Nobel Prize 1952

amino acids to RCHO, NH_3, and CO_2 and affords a dihydride that combines with the ammonia to produce a pigment. The ratio of the distance traveled by the amino acid to the distance of solvent travel is the Rf value, a constant characteristic of the specific acid. In an elaboration of the method the hydrolyzate is placed at the corner of a sheet of paper, a chromatogram is developed by allowing solvent to flow in the direction of the *x*-axis, and then another solvent is caused to flow in the direction of the *y*-axis; a greater spread is thus achieved. Highly efficient methods have been developed for chromatographic fractionation on starch columns (Moore[8] and Stein, 1948) or on ion-exchange resins (Moore and Stein, 1951). These can be applied to 2–3 g. of protein, and with use of different solvents the constituents can be separated with quantitative recoveries. The rate of solvent flow must be very low, and successful separation may require operation for more than a week.

Another method of quantitative analysis is microbiological assay (Snell,[9] 1946). A given microorganism requires certain amino acids for growth, and the rate of growth in a medium containing all but one essential acid provides an index of the amount of that component present in a test sample. Thus arginine in a hydrolyzate can be determined by the effect on growth of *Lactobacillus casei;* the concentration is determined by comparison with the effect of a standard sample at various concentrations.

The isotope dilution method (Rittenberg,[10] 1940) is theoretically applicable to any amino acid. A labeled acid of known isotopic content, for example isotopic glutamic acid, is added in known amount to the mixture to be analyzed, and glutamic acid is then isolated by the usual procedure. Since the chemical properties of the natural acid and the labeled acid are the same, the isolated material is a representative sample of added acid and acid originally present; the percent recovery is thus unimportant. The amount of acid in the hydrolyzate is calculated from the isotopic analysis of the isolated acid. If the added isotopic synthetic acid is racemic, the hydrolyzate acid is racemized before isolation, or the pure L-form is separated from the isolated racemic acid. The degree of accuracy is independent of the method of isolation, the yield, and the concentration in the hydrolyzate.

Amino Acid Sequence. — When a protein has been isolated in a state of demonstrated purity, its molecular weight established (range

Proteins

Two-dimensional chromatography

Columns of starch and of ion-exchange resins

16.12 *Microbiological method*

Isotope dilution method

16.13

[8] Stanford Moore, b. 1913 Chicago; Ph.D. Wisconsin; Rockefeller Inst.
[9] Esmond E. Snell, b. 1914 Salt Lake City; Ph.D. Wisconsin (Peterson); Univ. Wisconsin and Univ. Texas
[10] David Rittenberg, b. 1906 New York; Ph.D. Columbia (Urey); Dept. Biochem., Coll. of Phys. and Surg., Columbia

about 12,000 to 1 million), and the percentages of the component amino acids determined, the problem arises as to the sequence of amino acids in the polypeptide chain. Sanger[11] (1945) introduced a method for identification of the amino acid unit at one end of the chain, namely that having a free α-amino group. This amino group reacts with 2,4-dinitrofluorobenzene, $FC_6H_3(NO_2)_2$, to form a labeled unit, and on acid hydrolysis the terminal unit is liberated as its bright

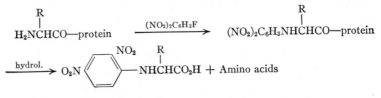

yellow 2,4-dinitrophenyl derivative, which by paper chromatography is easily separated from the accompanying unlabeled amino acids and identified. Nonterminal lysine units are attacked but are recognizable from the fact that the dinitrophenyl group is on the ε- rather than the α-amino group. For determination of the sequence within the chain, the protein is subjected to partial hydrolysis to give a mixture of di- and tripeptides, whose structures can be investigated by end-group analysis. If all dipeptides in the hydrolyzate can be characterized, a unique solution can be established for the sequence in the protein (example: II.14).

16.14

Peptides. — Peptides, arbitrarily defined as protein-like substances of molecular weight less than 10,000, are considerably more stable than proteins and are not subject to denaturation. Gluta-

Glutathione

thione, a tripeptide which occurs in nearly all living cells, participates in biological oxidation-reductions by reversible change from the sulfhydryl form (G—SH) to the disulfide form (GS—SG). It has been characterized as γ-L-glutamyl-L-cysteinylglycine, a structure that can be represented with conventional symbols (Table I): γ-L-Glu—L-CySH—Gly.

D-Amino acids

A variety of peptides isolated from bacteria and other lower plants are characterized by the presence of one or more unusual amino acid units, the D-isomer of a common amino acid or a component which is not an amino acid. A peptide found in the capsules of *Bacillus anthracis* and *B. subtilis* is composed solely of D-glutamic acid and the peptide bonds are formed mainly through the γ-amino groups; L-glutamic acid units are normally bound through the α-amino groups. Several related peptides possessing antibiotic properties have been isolated from a strain of soil microorganism, *B. brevis*

[11] Frederick Sanger, b. 1918 Gloucestershire, England; Ph.D. Cambridge; Cambridge Univ.

(Dubos, 1940). One, gramicidin-S (S = Soviet; the substance was first described by Russian scientists), is a cyclic decapeptide containing two repeating five-unit chains. Three of the five amino acids are common amino acids, L-valine, L-leucine, and L-proline; the fourth is D-phenylalanine and the fifth is the uncommon amino acid ornithine, $H_2NCH_2CH_2CH_2CH(NH_2)CO_2H$ (symbol Orn). Bacitracin-A, isolated from *B. subtilis*, appears to be a cyclic hexapeptide with three side chains, and the probable structure is that formulated (Craig, 1954).

Ileu-CySH-Leu-Glu-Ileu-Lys-Orn-Ileu
| |
Asp-Asp-His-Phe

Synthesis of Polypeptides. — In the period 1901–07 Fischer investigated the synthesis of polypeptides to see if substances could be produced having properties characteristic of proteins. Dipeptides were found to be readily available by conversion of an amino acid ester to a cyclic derivative, a diketopiperazine, which on partial hydrolysis

$$2\ H_2NCH_2CO_2C_2H_5 \xrightarrow{\text{NaOH}} \begin{array}{c} NHCH_2CO \\ | \quad\quad | \\ COCH_2NH \end{array} \xrightarrow{\text{HCl}} H_2NCH_2CO\text{—}NHCH_2CO_2H$$

Diketopiperazine   Glycylglycine

affords a dipeptide, for example, glycylglycine. Fischer's most successful method for building longer chains is illustrated for the synthesis of leucylglycylglycine. Isocaproic acid is brominated in the α-position

$(CH_3)_2CHCH_2CHBrCOCl\ +\ H_2NCH_2CO\text{—}NHCH_2COOC_2H_5 \xrightarrow[76\%]{}$
α-Bromoisocaproyl   Glycylglycine ester
chloride

$C_4H_9CHBrCO\text{—}NHCH_2CO\text{—}NHCH_2COOC_2H_5 \xrightarrow[100\%]{\text{NaOH}}$
α-Bromoisocaproylglycylglycine ester

$C_4H_9CHBrCO\text{—}NHCH_2CO\text{—}NHCH_2COOH \xrightarrow[63\%]{NH_3}$

$\begin{array}{c} CH_3 \\ \quad\searrow \\ \quad\quad CHCH_2CH(NH_2)CO\text{—}NHCH_2CO\text{—}NHCH_2COOH \\ \quad\nearrow \\ CH_3 \end{array}$

Leucylglycylglycine

and the product converted to the acid chloride with phosphorus trichloride. The halogen of the acid chloride group is more reactive than that in the α-position and hence condenses preferentially with the amino group of a second component to form a new peptide link. Cautious treatment with cold alkali effects selective hydrolysis of the ester group, which is more reactive than the peptide links, and treatment with ammonia (amination) replaces the α-bromo substituent by an amino group. By extension of this method Fischer synthesized an octadecapeptide: leucyltriglycylleucyltriglycylleucyloctaglycylglycine.

Such substances proved useful as models for studying enzymatic degradation and chemical reactions of proteins, but they lack non-terminal components carrying functional groups and they are optically inactive, since the process of α-halogenation and amination gives *dl*-products. L-Amino acids are available as starting materials for polypeptide synthesis by isolation from proteins and by synthesis and resolution. Optically active polypeptides would thus be available by the linking of the carboxyl group of one acid (A) to the amino group of another (B). The difficulty is that the amino group of component A must be protected in order to prepare a reactive acid chloride or anhydride derivative of the carboxyl function. If the amino group is protected by acetylation or benzoylation, the acid can be transformed to the acid chloride and linked to component B, but the resulting product, for example $CH_3CONHCH_2CONHCH_2CO_2H$, has two comparable amide groups and the protecting N-acyl group cannot be removed by hydrolysis without destruction of the peptide link. In 1932 Bergmann[12] introduced the carbobenzoxy synthesis, a method of polypeptide synthesis in which an amino group is masked by an acyl group removable by reduction rather than hydrolysis. Carbobenzoxy chloride, prepared from benzyl alcohol and phosgene (a), reacts with an amine in the presence of alkali (Schotten-Baumann reaction) to give a protected derivative (b) from which the amino group can be regenerated when desired by catalytic hydrogenation (c) without disturbance of peptide linkages. The unsaturated phenyl

Carbobenzoxy synthesis

(a) $C_6H_5CH_2OH$ + $ClCOCl$ $\longrightarrow$ $C_6H_5CH_2OCOCl$ + HCl

(b) $C_6H_5CH_2OCOCl$ + H_2NR $\xrightarrow{NaOH}$ $C_6H_5CH_2OCONHR$ + $NaCl$ + H_2O

(c) ⬡—CH₂|OCONHR $\xrightarrow{H_2, Pt}$ ⬡—CH_3 + CO_2 + H_2NR

group activates the carbon–oxygen linkage and so promotes reductive fission to toluene and a carbamic acid, which undergoes spontaneous decarboxylation: $RNHCOOH \longrightarrow RNH_2 + CO_2$. For synthesis of a peptide, an amino acid is converted into the N-carbobenzoxy deriva-

$$C_6H_5CH_2OCOCl + H_2NCHRCO_2H \xrightarrow{-HCl} \underset{I}{C_6H_5CH_2OCONHCHRCO_2H} \longrightarrow$$

$$\underset{II}{C_6H_5CH_2OCONHCHRCOCl} \xrightarrow{+H_2NCHR'CO_2H} \underset{III}{C_6H_5CH_2OCONHCHRCONHCHR'CO_2H} \xrightarrow{H_2,Pt}$$

$$C_6H_5CH_3 + CO_2 + \underset{IV}{H_2NCHRCONHCHR'CO_2H}$$

[12] Max Bergmann, 1886–1944; b. Fürth, Germany; Ph.D. Berlin; KWI für Lederforsch., Dresden; since 1933 Rockefeller Inst. Med. Res.; *J. Chem. Soc.*, 716 (1945)

tive I, and the corresponding acid chloride II is condensed with a second amino acid to give the N-carbobenzoxy derivative of a dipeptide (III), which on catalytic hydrogenation is cleaved to the dipeptide (IV). In the first of many applications of the carbobenzoxy method, the synthesis of L-glutamyl-L-glutamic acid, coupling of the two component acids was accomplished by use of the anhydride of carbobenzoxy-L-glutamic acid.

$$HOOCCH_2CH_2CHCOOH \quad \xrightarrow[90\%]{C_6H_5CH_2OCOCl(MgO)} \quad HOOCCH_2CH_2CHCOOH \quad \xrightarrow[84\%]{Ac_2O}$$
$$\qquad\qquad | \qquad\qquad\qquad\qquad\qquad\qquad\qquad\qquad\qquad\qquad | $$
$$\qquad\qquad NH_2 \qquad\qquad\qquad\qquad\qquad\qquad\qquad\quad C_6H_5CH_2OCONH$$

L-Glutamic acid   Carbobenzoxy-L-glutamic acid

$$O=CCH_2CH_2CHC=O \quad + \quad NH_2CHCH_2CH_2COOC_2H_5 \quad \xrightarrow{53\%}$$
$$| \qquad\qquad\qquad\qquad\qquad\qquad\qquad\qquad | $$
$$C_6H_5CH_2OCONH \qquad\qquad\qquad\qquad COOC_2H_5$$

Anhydride   Glutamic acid diethyl ester

$$HOOCCH_2CH_2CHCO-NHCHCH_2CH_2COOC_2H_5 \quad \xrightarrow[80\%]{H_2O(NaOH)}$$
$$| \qquad\qquad\qquad\qquad | $$
$$C_6H_5CH_2OCONH \qquad\qquad COOC_2H_5$$

$$HOOCCH_2CH_2CHCO-NHCHCH_2CH_2COOH \quad \xrightarrow[quant.]{H_2(Pd)}$$
$$| \qquad\qquad\qquad\qquad | $$
$$C_6H_5CH_2OCONH \qquad\qquad COOH$$

Carbobenzoxy dipeptide

$$HOOCCH_2CH_2CHCO-NHCHCH_2CH_2COOH \quad + \quad C_6H_5CH_3 \quad + \quad CO_2$$
$$| \qquad\qquad\qquad\qquad | $$
$$NH_2 \qquad\qquad\qquad COOH$$

L-Glutamyl-L-glutamic acid

Of a number of other blocking groups proposed, the phthalyl group has proved particularly useful (Sheehan,[13] 1949). Condensation of phthalylglycyl chloride (I) with an amino acid gives a phthalylglycyl derivative (II) of excellent crystallizing properties, from which the

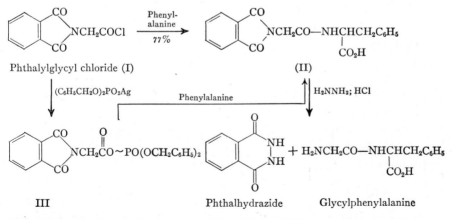

Phthalylglycyl chloride (I)   (II)

III   Phthalhydrazide   Glycylphenylalanine

[13] John C. Sheehan, b. 1915 Battle Creek, Mich.; Ph.D. Michigan (Bachmann); Merck and Co., Mass. Inst. Techn.

free amino group can be liberated by treatment with alcoholic hydrazine followed by hydrochloric acid. Cleavage to phthalylhydrazide and the dipeptide proceeds more readily than hydrogenolysis of the carbobenzoxy group, which sometimes requires several days. The dipeptide is obtained as the hydrochloride; the free amine can be liberated by passage over a basic ion-exchange resin. Glycyl-DL-phenylalanine and glycyl-L-cysteine have been prepared by this method in overall yields of 60–61%. Sheehan has also reported preparation from phthalylglycyl chloride (I) and silver dibenzyl phosphate of the derivative III (91% yield), which contains an energy-rich phosphate bond (curved line, anhydride type) and in aqueous solution at pH 7.4 acylates phenylalanine to give II in good yield.

16.17

Mixed anhydride synthesis

A useful method of peptide synthesis developed independently in 1950–51 by the research groups of T. Wieland (Germany), R. A. Boissonnas (Switzerland), and J. R. Vaughan (U.S.A.) operates on the principle that the mixed anhydride of a carboxylic acid with an alkyl acid carbonate ($HOCO_2R$) is an efficient reagent for acylation of an amine. The amino group of an amino acid is protected as the carbobenzoxy (Cb) or phthalyl (Ph) derivative, which is treated in an inert solvent (tetrahydrofuran) with enough triethylamine to form the salt and then with ethyl chlorocarbonate ($ClCO_2C_2H_5$). The mixed anhydride need not be isolated, and on addition of an amino

$$\underset{\overset{|}{NHCb}}{RCHCO_2H} \xrightarrow{N(C_2H_5)_3} \underset{\overset{|}{NHCb}}{RCHCO_2\overset{-}{N}\overset{+}{H}(C_2H_5)_3} \xrightarrow[-(C_2H_5)_3\overset{+}{N}HCl^-]{ClCO_2C_2H_5}$$

$$\underset{\overset{|}{NHCb}}{RCH\overset{O}{\overset{||}{C}}O\overset{O}{\overset{||}{C}}OC_2H_5} \xrightarrow[-CO_2]{H_2NCHR'CO_2CH_3} \underset{\overset{|}{NHCb}\;\overset{|}{R'}}{RCHCONHCHCO_2CH_3} + C_2H_5OH$$

acid, usually as ester, carbon dioxide is evolved and the N-protected dipeptide is obtained, usually in excellent yield and high optical purity. The ester group is eliminated with dilute acid and the blocking group by an appropriate standard procedure. The simplicity and versatility of the method are demonstrated by its use for synthesis of an octapeptide in which each unit is different.

16.18

Cures diabetes

Insulin. — This hormone secreted by the pancreas is required for normal metabolism of carbohydrates, and deficiency of the substance leads to the disease diabetes mellitus, characterized by increased blood glucose, excretion of sugar and acetone bodies (CH_3COCH_3, $CH_3COCH_2CO_2H$) in the urine, and depletion of glycogen normally stored in liver and muscle. A procedure for preparation of concentrated active extracts suitable for treatment of diabetic patients was developed in 1921 by Banting[14] and Macleod[15] by use of special techniques to protect the hormone from destruction by enzymes present in the gland. Crystalline insulin was isolated in 1926 by Abel by isoelectric precipitation and found to contain 0.52% zinc. In very dilute solution at pH 2–3, insulin has the relatively low molecular weight of 12,000. The hormone has a high content of cystine, and it appears that the molecule is built up of four parallel polypeptide chains bound together in a three-dimensional sheaf by four disulfide linkages of cystine (Sanger). On oxidation with performic acid the disulfide linkages are severed, with conversion of the sulfur atoms to sulfonic acid groups ($-SO_3H$), and the molecule is cleaved to four peptides, two having glycyl end groups and two having phenylalanyl end groups. By the procedure described (16.13), Sanger worked out the amino acid sequence of both chains.

Adrenocorticotropic Hormone (ACTH). — Hormones of the anterior pituitary lobe are proteins that act indirectly at a distant site by stimulating other hormones in various endocrine glands. Particular interest attaches to ACTH because of its therapeutic action in rheumatoid arthritis and other diseases associated with hypofunction of the adrenal gland. The hormone consists of a mixture of related proteins of molecular weight about 20,000. The complete amino acid sequence of one of the physiologically active components, β-corticotropin, has been worked out (American Cyanamide, 1955). In the symbolized formula the unit containing the terminal amino group is on the left (serine) and that carrying the terminal carboxyl group is on the right (phenylalanine); the symbol $Glu(NH_2)$ stands for the amide glutamine.

Ser-Tyr-Ser-Met-Glu-His-Phe-Arg-Try-Gly-Lys-Pro-Val-Gly-Lys-Lys-Arg-Arg-Pro-Val-Lys-Val-Tyr-Pro-Asp-Gly-Ala-Glu-Asp-Glu-Leu-Ala-Glu(NH_2)-Ala-Phe-Pro-Leu-Glu-Phe

Thyroglobin. — This hormone of the thyroid gland is a protein whose primary function is to increase metabolic activity of cells. The syndrome resulting from thyroglobin deficiency, myxedema, is characterized by dry skin, swollen connective tissue, high blood cholesterol, and lowered rate of basal metabolism. Dramatic cures are obtained by administration of the hormone. This protein is characterized by the presence of an unusual amino acid containing iodine, thyroxine.

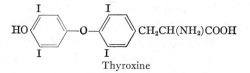

Thyroxine

---

[14] Sir Frederick Banting, 1891–1941; Univ. Toronto; Nobel Prize 1923
[15] John J. R. Macleod, 1877–1935; Univ. Toronto; Aberdeen; Nobel Prize 1923

Fibroin. — This fibrous (insoluble) protein of silk is made up largely of four neutral amino acids, two with hydroxyl groups and two without. X-ray analysis reveals an identity period of 7Å along the fiber axis corresponding to that expected for a pair of neutral units such as that formulated. The synthetic fiber nylon, a comparable

Silk protein

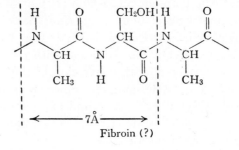

Fibroin (?)

polyamide, is made by condensation polymerization of a mixture of adipic acid and hexamethylenediamine, both of which are made from

Resembles nylon

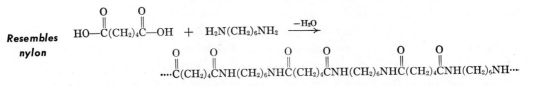

phenol. This starting material is converted through cyclohexanol into cyclohexanone and then on oxidation into adipic acid, a part of which is converted into the desired diamine.

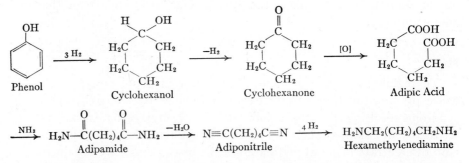

Phenol   Cyclohexanol   Cyclohexanone   Adipic Acid

Adipamide   Adiponitrile   Hexamethylenediamine

16.22   **Hemoglobin.** — The solid content of the red blood corpuscles of mammals contains on the average 32% of the conjugated protein hemoglobin. This protein is easily isolated in crystalline form from the solution prepared as described above by separation and hemolysis of red blood cells. The solution is shaken with oxygen to produce the oxygenated form, oxyhemoglobin, treated with alcohol, and kept at −20° until deep red crystals separate. Values for the percentage composition vary slightly for different animal species, but a typical empirical formula is $(C_{738}H_{1166}O_{208}N_{203}S_2Fe)_n$. Iron is the element present in smallest equivalent amount, and since at least one atom of the element must be present the iron content fixes the minimal molecular weight. Values calculated on this basis are in the range 16,500–17,000. Ultracentrifuge determinations give an average molecular weight of 65,500, or four times the minimal value; hence n in the formula has a value of four.

On careful treatment with hydrochloric acid the conjugated protein is cleaved into the fragments hemin (4%) and globin (96%). Hemin has the formula $C_{34}H_{32}O_4N_4FeCl$; the iron corresponds to the total present in hemoglobin and the chlorine atom is derived from the hydrochloric acid used for cleavage. Hemin is the chloride of the parent substance heme, $C_{34}H_{32}O_4N_4FeOH$, which is the oxidized form (ferric) of the true prosthetic group of the conjugate. Although far simpler than the original protein, the hemin molecule presents a structure that is both unusual and elaborate, as can be seen from the formula, and the problem of elucidating the structure was solved

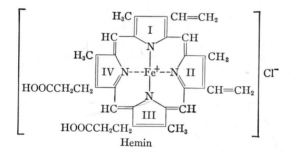

Hemin

eventually only as the result of exhaustive researches extending over a period of forty years (Nencki, Piloty, Küster, Willstätter,[16] H. Fischer[17]).

The four heterocyclic five-membered rings present in hemin are pyrrole nuclei; they are substituted with methyl, vinyl, and propionic acid groups and are bridged by unsaturated carbons constituting methine groups. The iron is considered to be bound to all four nitrogens, by either primary valences or coordinated links. Hemin (hemin chloride) on hydrolysis with dilute alkali affords the halogen-free hydroxide heme (hemin hydroxide). Methods are available for removal and reintroduction of the iron; the iron-free substances having the characteristic system of four linked pyrrole rings are known as

---

[16] Richard Willstätter, 1872–1942; b. Karlsruhe, Germany; Ph.D. Munich (Einhorn); Zurich, Berlin, Munich; Nobel Prize 1930; *J. Chem. Soc.*, 999 (1953)
[17] Hans Fischer, 1881–1945; b. Höchst/Main; Ph.D. Marburg (Zincke), M.D. Munich; Techn. Hochschule, Munich; Nobel Prize 1930

porphyrins and the iron-containing derivatives as hemes. A key substance is etioporphyrin ($C_{32}H_{38}N_4$), obtained by degradation of hemin involving elimination of iron, decarboxylation, and reduction of the vinyl groups; it is a tetra-methyltetraethylporphyrin. Isolation of the same etioporphyrin as a degradation product of the green plant pigment chlorophyll (which contains magnesium) establishes a close structural relationship between the leaf and blood pigments.

Etioporphyrin relates hemin and chlorophyll

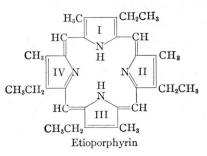
Etioporphyrin

The first insight into the porphyrin structure resulted from development of degradative methods by which the large molecule of hemin could be broken into mixtures of smaller fragments that could be isolated and characterized. Thus drastic reduction with hydrogen iodide and red phosphorus gives a mixture of four pyrroles variously

Products of reductive fission

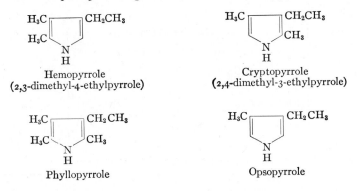

Hemopyrrole
(**2,3**-dimethyl-4-ethylpyrrole)

Cryptopyrrole
(**2,4**-dimethyl-3-ethylpyrrole)

Phyllopyrrole

Opsopyrrole

substituted with methyl and ethyl groups as shown in the formulas. Oxidative degradation also proved of value in providing the further fragment hematinic acid, a maleic imide derivative carrying a methyl and a propionic acid group as substituents, which corresponds to the arrangement in two of the four original rings. Structures of the various fragments not only provided information concerning the substituents but gave a basis for tentative formulation of the porphyrin system, and eventually it became feasible to approach the problem from the synthetic route. Attempts to link pyrrole nuclei together by synthesis derived assistance from the fact that porphyrins exhibit very characteristic line spectra observable with a simple visual instrument, and synthetic experiments initiated by Hans Fischer were rewarded with the discovery that the combination of four pyrrole rings, condensed with bridging methine groups to form a system of conjugated double bonds

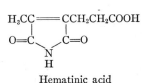
Hematinic acid

of no less than eighteen atoms, possesses such remarkable stability that it is formed, if in low yield, in unusual reactions consisting in condensation of even approximate moieties of the final molecule. Fischer achieved the synthesis of deuteroporphyrin in 1928 by the succinic acid fusion of the two pyrromethene bases shown in the formulas. Elimination of two molecules of hydrogen bromide links the two parts by methylene bridges and must produce initially a dihydroporphyrin structure, but the tendency to form the fully

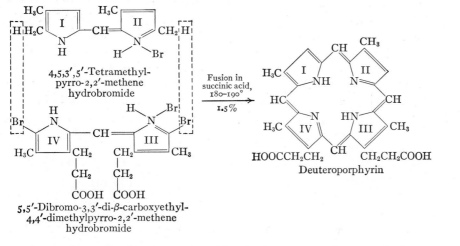

4,5,3′,5′-Tetramethyl-
pyrro-2,2′-methene
hydrobromide

Fusion in
succinic acid,
180–190°
1.5%

Deuteroporphyrin

5,5′-Dibromo-3,3′-di-β-carboxyethyl-
4,4′-dimethylpyrro-2,2′-methene
hydrobromide

unsaturated porphyrin structure evidently is so great that two hydrogen atoms are eliminated during the condensation.

Fischer's researches culminated in 1930 in synthesis of hemin itself. The two free nuclear positions in deuteroporphyrin were substituted with acetyl groups by the action of acetic anhydride and stannic chloride, and the new substituents were transformed into vinyl groups by the sequence of reactions: $-COCH_3 \longrightarrow -CH(OH)CH_3 \longrightarrow -CH=CH_2$. Introduction of iron afforded hemin.

Enzymes. — In 1897 Buchner[18] established that a cell-free aqueous solution prepared by grinding yeast with sand and filtering the solution through a fine-pore filter contains substances capable of promoting fermentation of sugars to alcohol and carbon dioxide (7.11). Biochemical studies by many subsequent investigators revealed the many steps in the complicated but efficient process and showed that each is controlled by a specific catalyst, an enzyme. In 1926 Sumner[19] succeeded for the first time in isolating an enzyme in pure, crystalline form and characterized it as a protein. This enzyme, urease, acts on

[18] Eduard Buchner, 1860–1917; b. Munich; Ph.D. Munich (Curtius); Breslau, Würzburg; Nobel Prize 1907
[19] James B. Sumner, 1887–1955, b. Canton, Mass.; Ph.D. Harvard; N. Y. State Agr. Coll., Cornell; Nobel Prize 1946

urea and promotes its decomposition to carbon dioxide and ammonia. Many other enzymes have since been isolated, and they are all proteins. Some promote hydrolysis (and resynthesis) of esters and are called hydrolases, and others catalyze hydrolysis of proteins and are called proteolytic enzymes; enzymes of these two types are completely proteinoid in make-up and are called simple proteins.

Enzymes that control processes of oxidation (oxidases) and of reduction (reductases) are conjugated proteins containing a prosthetic group, comparable to heme of hemoglobin, in which the capacity for oxidation-reduction resides. In one, a yellow enzyme, the prosthetic group attached to protein is flavin adenine dinucleotide FAD, in the formula of which the component parts are indicated. The term dinu-

*Prosthetic group
of an oxidase-
reductase*

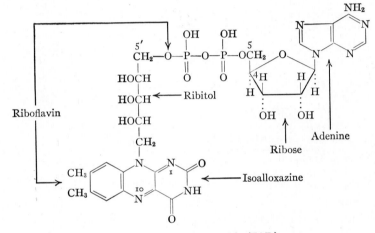

Flavin adenine dinucleotide (**FAD**)

cleotide means that the substance is a diphosphate (pyrophosphate) ester. The isoalloxazine group is responsible for the yellow color and functions as hydrogen acceptor; hydrogen adds 1,4 to the unsaturated system extending between N_1 and N_{10} to form a colorless dihydride, from which the pigment is regenerated by oxidation. Isoalloxazine itself is insoluble in water, but the hydroxyl groups of the two sugar units, fortified by those of the pyrophosphate unit, render the molecule soluble. The acidic pyrophosphate group is balanced by the basic group of adenine.

16.24   **Nucleoproteins.** — Nucleoproteins are conjugated proteins in which the nonprotein prosthetic group is a complex acid of high molecular weight (10,000–23,000) known as a nucleic acid. The name is derived from the fact that these proteins were first recognized as invariable constituents of all cell nuclei. Yeast nucleic acid is split into an approximately equimolecular mixture of four simpler substances, which are nucleotides (phosphate esters). Each nucleotide

on more drastic hydrolysis is converted into three components: a
heterocyclic base, a sugar, and phosphoric acid. One of the four
nucleotides of yeast nucleic acid is yeast adenylic acid, which has been
identified as the 3'-phosphate ester of adenosine; it is converted by
alkaline hydrolysis into adenosine, which is cleaved into its components by acid hydrolysis. Adenosine, a D-riboside of the base

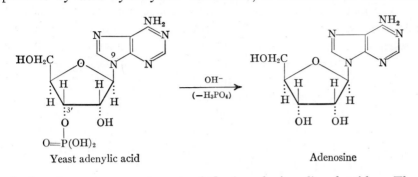

Yeast adenylic acid   Adenosine

adenine, is a component part of flavin adenine dinucleotide. The
other three nucleotides of yeast adenylic acid differ in that adenine is
replaced by other heterocyclic bases.

Coenzyme A. — This substance is the prosthetic group of an
enzyme first recognized as a catalyst required for biological acetylation
(Lipmann,[20] 1947) and it was named accordingly (A = Acetylation).
Investigations of structure (Lipmann, Lynen,[21] Baddiley[22]) established
that coenzyme A is composed of an adenylic acid residue (1) linked
through a pyrophosphate group (2) to a unit of pantothenic acid (3),

16.25

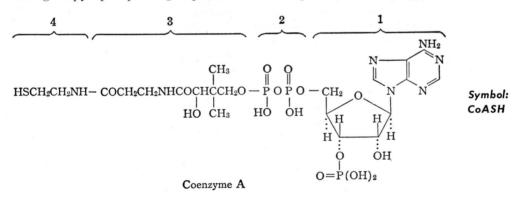

Coenzyme A

Symbol:
CoASH

a growth factor of yeast, which is joined by a peptide link to β-mer-
captoethanolamine (4). The terminal sulfhydryl group is important
for the biological functions of the coenzyme, represented by the

[20] Fritz Lipmann, b. 1899 Königsberg, Germany; Ph.D. Berlin; Rockefeller Inst., Mass.
  Gen. Hospital and Harvard; Nobel Prize 1953
[21] Feodor Lynen, b. 1911 Munich; Ph.D. Munich (Wieland); Munich
[22] James Baddiley, b. 1918 Manchester; Ph.D. and D.Sc. Manchester (Todd); Durham

symbol CoASH, because the S-acetyl derivative, CoASCOCH₃, serves as acetyl donor.

16.26

Virus Proteins. — A virus is a submicroscopic infective agent that will pass through a filter capable of removing all known living cells. Viruses are capable of autocatalytic growth and multiplication in living tissues. One, tobacco mosaic virus, present in filtered juice of plants infected with a disease known as tobacco mosaic, was isolated by Stanley[23] (1935) in crystalline form and found to be a protein of the nucleoprotein type; nucleoproteins alone are endowed with the capacity for reproduction. The molecular weight is unusually high (40 million); the nucleic acid portion amounts to about 6% of the total weight. The crystalline protein is highly infectious and its virus activity exactly parallels the range of pH stability. The substance is able to reproduce itself in the tobacco leaf, and amounts of 2-3 g. of virus protein have been isolated from plants inoculated with as little as 1 microgram of the protein.

Self-reproduction of protein

SUMMARY

Fibrous proteins (water-insoluble): fibroin (silk), collagen (boiling water ⟶ gelatin), keratin (skin, wool), elastin. Globular proteins (water-soluble at proper pH): egg albumin, casein, hemoglobin (conjugated, contains the prosthetic group heme). Plasma proteins: albumins, globins, lipoproteins, fibrinogen, prothrombin. Serum from clotted blood lacks fibrinogen, which in clotting is converted to fibrin.

Polypeptide nature of proteins; hydrolysis to amino acids; reformation from amino acids of plant proteins.

Amino Acids

Neutral: glycine, and its homologs alanine, valine, leucine, isoleucine; phenylalanine and tyrosine (p-OH); proline (5-ring); tryptophan (β-indoloalanine); cysteine (β-SH-alanine), cystine (disulfide), and methionine (S-methylhomocysteine); serine (β-OH-alanine) and threonine (β-CH₃-serine). Acidic: aspartic (α-NH₂-succinic) and glutamic (α-NH₂-glutaric); also their monoamides asparagine and glutamine. Basic: lysine (α,ε-di-NH₂-caproic) and arginine (α-NH₂-δ-guanidyl-valeric).

Isoelectric point (pH of charge balance, dipolar ion form predominates): alanine type, 6.0; aspartic acid type, about 2.0; lysine, 9.7; arginine, 10.8. Solubilities: leucine more lipophilic than glycine; proline unusually soluble in both water and ethanol; cystine of abnormally low water solubility. Configuration: all belong to L-series (NH₂ to left), related to L(+)-lactic acid.

Isolation. Hydrolysis with acids or with enzymes. Ester-distillation of neutral components. Precipitation with HgSO₄ (tryptophan), with phosphotungstic acid (basic amino acids).

Synthesis. Enzymatic resolution through N-acetyl deriv. Amination of α-halo acids. Gabriel synthesis. Strecker synthesis (RCHO ⟶ RCH(NH₂)CN ⟶ RCH(NH₂)CO₂H). Malonic ester synthesis. Aldehyde condensations.

Proteins

Isolation. Isoelectric salting out or precipitation with ethanol. Slow addition of (NH₄)₂SO₄ by dialysis to promote crystallization.

Amino acid analysis. Paper chromatography (color reaction with ninhydrin). Microbiological assay (specific acids required for normal growth). Isotope dilution method.

Amino acid sequence. End-group analysis by

[23] Wendell M. Stanley, b. 1904, Ridgeville, Ind.; Ph.D. Illinois (R. Adams); Rockefeller Inst.; Virus Lab., U. Calif.; Nobel Prize 1946

reaction with 2,4-dinitrofluorobenzene and hydrolysis.

Peptides. Glutathione = γ-L-Glu—L-CySH—Gly. Gramicidin-S (one unnatural D-amino acid). Bacitracin-A (cyclic, contains uncommon ornithine, histidine).

Polypeptide synthesis. Glycine ester $\longrightarrow$ diketopiperazine $\longrightarrow$ glycylglycine. Fischer's α-halo acid chloride synthesis (halogen replaced by NH_2 in last step). A peptide with 18 amino acid units. Carbobenzoxy synthesis ($C_6H_5CH_2OCO$—, or Cb—, masking group removable from N by hydrogenation). Example:

$$CbNHCHRCO_2H \longrightarrow CbNHCHRCOCl \longrightarrow$$
$$CbNHCHRCONHCHR'CO_2H \longrightarrow$$
$$H_2NCHRCONHCHR'CO_2H.$$

Phthalyl (Ph) synthesis: mask —NH_2 by conversion to —NPh, form the acid chloride, condense with $H_2NCHRCO_2H$, and remove phthalyl group with hydrazine. Mixed anhydride synthesis: conversion of $CbNHCHRCO_2H$ through reaction of its trimethylamine salt with $ClCO_2C_2H_5$ to the anhydride $CbNHCHRCO \cdot O \cdot COC_2H_5$, which reacts with $H_2NCHR'CO_2CH_3$ to give

$$CbNHCHRCONHCHR'CO_2CH_3.$$

Insulin: hormone of pancreas, controls carbohydrate metabolism, used for treatment of diabetes. Mol. wt. only 12,000. Four polypeptide chains bound into a sheaf by disulfide links of cystine; these cleaved by oxidation to —SO_3H.

Adrenocorticotropic hormone (ACTH). Amino acid sequence of 39 component acids determined.

Thyroglobin. Characteristic acid is thyroxine (4 iodine atoms).

Fibroin of silk composed chiefly of neutral amino acids. Resemblance to nylon, copolymer of adipic acid and hexamethylene diamine (both components produced from phenol).

Hemoglobin. Easily crystallized in oxygenated form: oxyhemoglobin (HbO_2). Iron analysis indicates minimal molecular weight of 16,500; actual molecular weight (ultracentrifuge) $4 \times 16,500 = 66,000$. Split by HCl to hemin ($C_{34}H_{32}O_4N_4FeCl$) and globin (globular protein, 96% of whole). Actual prosthetic group is heme. Hemin made of four pyrrole rings joined by methine links (—CH=). Degradation by reduction to alkylated pyrroles and oxidation to hematinic acid. Identity of deuteroporphyrin from hemin and from chlorophyll. Synthesis of hemin by Hans Fischer (1930).

Enzymes. Isolated in crystalline form (Sumner). Are all proteins. Hydrolases (split esters) and proteolytic enzymes are all-protein. Oxidases-reductases contain a prosthetic (attached) group containing an oxido-reduction function. Prosthetic group of yellow enzyme is flavin adenine dinucleotide, which has a reducible, pigmented group solubilized by ribose units and a pyrodiphosphate group whose acidity is balanced by a basic group (adenine).

Coenzyme A is a prosthetic group which, with a protein, catalyzes acetylations. Complex structure containing an adenylic acid unit, peptide links, and terminating in sulfhydryl group. Symbol: CoASH. The acetyl derivative, $CoASCOCH_3$, a donor of acetyl groups.

Virus proteins. Tobacco mosaic virus isolated in crystalline condition and found to be a nucleoprotein (Stanley, 1935). Molecular weight 40 million. Capable of reproduction in suitable environment.

READING REFERENCES

C. L. A. Schmidt, *The Chemistry of the Amino Acids and Proteins*, C. C. Thomas, Baltimore (1938)

E. J. Cohn and J. T. Edsall, *Proteins, Amino Acids and Peptides*, Reinhold, New York (1943)

H. T. Clarke, "Natural Amino Acids," in H. Gilman, *Organic Chemistry*, II, 2nd Ed., 1079–1165, Wiley, New York (1943)

H. B. Vickery and C. L. A. Schmidt, "The History of the Discovery of the Amino Acids," *Chem. Rev.*, **9**, 169 (1931)

R. J. Block, "The Isolation and Synthesis of the Naturally Occurring α-Amino Acids," *Chem. Rev.*, **38**, 501 (1946)

M. V. Tracey, *Proteins and Life*, Pilot Press, London (1948)

M. L. Anson and J. T. Edsall, *Advances in Protein Chemistry*, Academic Press (1944–)

H. Neurath and K. Bailey, *The Proteins*, Vol. 1, Academic Press (1953)

F. Haurowitz, *Chemistry and Biology of Proteins*, Academic Press (1950)

METABOLISM AND
BIOSYNTHESIS

*Digestive
hydrolysis
of polysaccharides
and proteins*

Whereas hexoses in the diet are absorbed through the intestinal wall and transported in the blood in aqueous solution to tissues where they are either oxidized to supply energy or stored as glycogen, pentoses are absorbed but not utilized and are excreted in the urine. The disaccharides sucrose, lactose, and maltose are hydrolyzed to absorbable hexoses by enzymes of the stomach or the intestines, and enzymes of the alimentary tract effect partial hydrolysis of the polysaccharide starch to smaller units capable of being absorbed and utilized. Other digestive enzymes hydrolyze dietary proteins to amino acids capable of being absorbed and carried in the blood in aqueous solution.

*Lipids
emulsified
by bile salts*

Dietary lipids, being water-insoluble, are dependent for absorption on the emulsifying action of bile salts. These are sodium salts of conjugate bile acids (15.4), e.g., $RCONHCH_2CO_2Na$, where R is a large, predominantly hydrocarbon group; and they are typical surface-active emulsifying agents. The lipid factor vitamin K_1 (15.6), for example, is not absorbed from the diet when the flow of bile is impeded by an obstructive tumor, and removal of the tumor by surgery may result in death by hemorrhage unless vitamin K_1 is administered, along with bile salts to promote its absorption, in order to maintain a level of prothrombin adequate for normal clotting of blood. Under normal functioning of the organism, only specific dietary constituents are absorbed from the gut.

*Selectivity
of absorption*

The remarkable selectivity of the intestinal membrane is demonstrated by the fact that whereas cholesterol is absorbed, plant sterols differing substantially only in the presence of an additional methyl or ethyl group are excreted in the feces. Rabbits, being herbivorous, acquire body cholesterol only by biosynthesis, and when given excess cholesterol in the diet develop atherosclerotic-like lesions containing deposited sterol; plant sterols of the normal diet do not affect the animals because they are not absorbed.

There are some suggestions that glycerides undergo hydrolysis and resynthesis in the course of their passage through the intestinal membrane. Once absorbed the water-insoluble fats are dependent upon plasma proteins for transportation in the blood stream. Lipoproteins seem to be specific fat carriers, since they all contain protein, phospholipid (15.2), and cholesterol (15.3), but some are rich in glycerides (75%) and some are poor in fatty components; the former may function as fat donors, and the latter as fat acceptors.

Combustion of fat in the body is the richest source of energy, as is evident from the following heats of combustion, given as kg.-cal. per gram of substance burned: fat, 9.5; protein, 4.4; glycogen, 4.2. Thus in intravenous feeding of patients unable to take food orally, a fat emulsion (emulsifier: lecithin) is more efficient than a solution of amino acids or of glucose.

Dynamic State of Body Constituents. — Investigations with isotopically labeled chemicals initiated by Schoenheimer[1] in 1935 and extended by others, particularly by Rittenberg and by Bloch,[2] have established that fats, proteins, carbohydrates, and steroids of the body are in a dynamic state of synthesis and degradation. For example, when fat labeled with deuterium by catalytic deuteration of linseed oil is fed to mice maintained at constant body weight, deuterium is incorporated in the depot fat of the animals within a few days. Thus glycerides are constantly removed from the storage site and replaced by new ones. Furthermore, labeled acetic acid given to animals produces fats bearing the isotopic label in the acid residues, and hence the body can synthesize higher fatty acids from a two-carbon precursor. Acetate is also one demonstrated precursor of the complicated molecule of cholesterol; isotopic acetate injected into mice gives rise to labeled cholesterol in a matter of a few minutes. Proteins and carbohydrates are also constantly synthesized and metabolically degraded. Although fats, proteins, and carbohydrates are of widely different chemical types, the pathways of biosynthesis are all interrelated and the substances all interconvertible.

Fat Metabolism. — Discovery of coenzyme A (16.25) was followed shortly by recognition that this factor plays a key role in biosynthesis of fatty acids, now known to follow the path formulated. The C—S linkage of the acetyl derivative of the coenzyme is very reactive, and

[1] Rudolf Schoenheimer, 1898–1941; b. Berlin; Ph.D. Berlin; Dept. Biochem., Coll. of Phys. and Surg., Columbia
[2] Konrad E. Bloch, b. 1912 Neisse, Germany; Ph.D. Columbia (Schoenheimer); Chicago, Harvard

$$\underbrace{CH_3C-SCoA \quad + \quad H-CH_2CSCoA}_{(1)} \rightleftharpoons HSCoA \quad + \quad CH_3C-CH_2CSCoA$$

$$\overset{\|}{O} \qquad\qquad \overset{\|}{O} \qquad\qquad\qquad\qquad \overset{\|}{O}\;\; \overset{\|}{O}$$

$$(1) \qquad\qquad\qquad\qquad (2) \qquad\qquad\qquad\qquad (3)$$

$$CH_3CH_2CH_2COSCoA \overset{2\,H}{\rightleftharpoons} CH_3CH=CHCOSCoA \overset{H_2O}{\rightleftharpoons} CH_3CH(OH)CH_2COSCoA \overset{H_2}{\Updownarrow}$$

$$(6) \qquad\qquad\qquad\qquad (5) \qquad\qquad\qquad\qquad (4)$$

$$\overset{CH_3COSCoA}{\Updownarrow}$$

$$HSCoA \quad + \quad CH_3CH_2CH_2COCH_2COSCoA \rightleftharpoons Etc.$$

$$(7)$$

the first step is condensation of two molecules of acetyl CoA (1) by elimination of CoASH (2) and formation of acetoacetyl CoA (3). Reduction of the carbonyl group (4), dehydration (5), and hydrogenation gives *n*-butyryl CoA (6). The cycle is repeated by condensation of (6) with another molecule of acetyl CoA to give (7), followed by reduction, dehydration, and hydrogenation with formation of a six-carbon acyl unit. In animals the cycle is repeated until full chain-length is reached, and it is now understandable why the chains are always normal and of even-carbon content. Bacteria that carry the cycle only to the butyric acid stage were of use in isolation of enzymes that control the early steps of the cycle. All the reactions are reversible, and degradation of fat occurs by reversal of the above sequence. In the normal organism intermediates in the cycle are all bound through the coenzyme to protein and are not isolable from the lipid fraction. In diabetes, however, metabolism is abnormal, and products of incomplete oxidation known as ketone bodies accumulate in the blood and urine (ketonuria). They include products from the cycle: aceto-

*Acetone
bodies*

acetic acid (and its decomposition product acetone) and β-hydroxybutyric acid.

17.4

Carbohydrate. — The conversion of liver glycogen to hexoses and the reverse process of synthesis of glycogen from glucose involve either cleavage or formation of glycosidic links, and occur anaerobically (in absence of oxygen). The overall metabolic conversion of hexose to carbon dioxide and water, as a source of muscular energy, requires oxygen but comprises two sets of reactions, one of which occurs anaerobically in muscle tissue and converts hexose into three-carbon fragments, while the other completes the degradation aerobically.

*Metabolism
in muscle to
pyruvic and
lactic acids*

The degradation occurring during muscular activity follows the exact pathway of the fermentation of fructose to ethanol, formulated earlier (7.11), down as far as formation of pyruvic acid, which results from fission of the hexose chain by reverse aldol condensation, dehydration of glyceraldehyde (as phosphate ester), and ketonization.

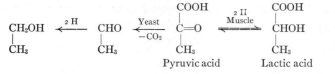

Yeast contains an enzyme, carboxylase, which effects irreversible decarboxylation of pyruvic acid to acetaldehyde, which, in fermentation, is then reduced enzymatically to ethanol. Carboxylase is absent from muscle tissue, and in this case the pyruvic acid is reduced reversibly by an enzyme hydrogen donor to lactic acid. As in fermentation, a reduction in the terminal step balances an earlier oxidation step and the overall process involves no oxygen uptake.

The reduction to lactic acid is reversible, and pyruvic acid in the presence of muscle tissue is subject to rapid oxidation by oxygen to carbon dioxide and water. The net result is expressed by the equation $CH_3COCO_2H + \frac{5}{2} O_2 \longrightarrow 3 CO_2 + 2 H_2O$, but various observations suggested the participation of several intermediary metabolites. Szent-Györgyi[3] noted that addition of traces of either fumaric, succinic, malic, or oxalacetic acid greatly increases the rate of oxygen consumption by muscle tissue, and Krebs[4] noted the similar catalytic effect of α-ketoglutaric and citric acid. The suggestion that all these substances are participating metabolites eventually was firmly established. The first step was for long suspected of involving conversion of pyruvic acid to an "active acetate" unit, and this eventually was identified as acetyl coenzyme A. The next step is addition of acetyl

CoASCOCH₃ + COCO₂H ⟶ HOCCO₂H $\xrightarrow{H_2O}$ HOCCO₂H

(structures: Acetyl CoA, Oxalacetic acid, Citric acid)

$$CoASCOCH_3 + \begin{array}{c} COCO_2H \\ | \\ CH_2CO_2H \end{array} \longrightarrow \begin{array}{c} CH_2COSCoA \\ | \\ HOCCO_2H \\ | \\ CH_2CO_2H \end{array} \xrightarrow{H_2O} \begin{array}{c} CH_2CO_2H \\ | \\ HOCCO_2H \\ | \\ CH_2CO_2H \end{array}$$

Acetyl CoA   Oxalacetic acid   Citric acid

CoA to the carbonyl group of oxalacetic acid to form a derivative which on hydrolysis yields citric acid. Coenzyme A thus plays a key role in carbohydrate metabolism as well as in the metabolism of fats (17.3) and may participate in the demonstrated interconversion of carbohydrates and fats. The relationship of oxalacetic and citric acid to other metabolites participating in the oxidation of pyruvic acid was interpreted by Krebs in terms of an elaborate cycle of changes in which various catalytic acids are involved as intermediates that are continuously synthesized and destroyed. The Krebs cycle

[3] Albert Szent-Györgyi, b. 1893 Budapest; M.D. Budapest, Ph.D. Cambridge; Marine Biol. Lab., Woods Hole, Mass.; Nobel Prize 1937
[4] Hans Adolf Krebs, b. 1900 Hildesheim, Germany, Ph.D. Hamburg; Sheffield, Oxford; Nobel Prize 1953

as presently conceived is formulated in the chart. Most of the steps are reversible, and each is catalyzed by a specific enzyme. After the formation from pyruvic acid of acetyl coenzyme A and its reaction

KREBS CYCLE

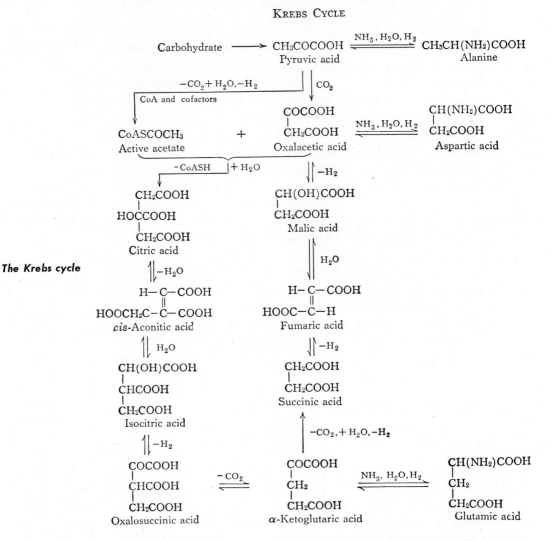

The Krebs cycle

with oxalacetic acid to form citric acid, this is dehydrated to an unsaturated acid which adds water in the reverse sense to give isocitric acid. Isocitric acid undergoes dehydrogenation to oxalosuccinic acid which, being a β-keto acid, readily loses carbon dioxide to form α-ketoglutaric acid. Oxidative decarboxylation then gives succinic acid, and the cycle is completed by dehydrogenation to fumaric acid, addition of water (malic acid), and dehydrogenation to oxalacetic acid. The net balance in the Krebs cycle is that the three moles of carbon dioxide formed by metabolic oxidation of pyruvic acid come from decarboxylation of three intermediates (pyruvic, oxalosuccinic, and α-ketoglutaric acid), and the $\frac{5}{2}$ moles of oxygen expended are utilized for oxidation of five moles of hydrogen derived from five dehydrogenative steps. The significance of the three amino acids listed in the right-hand column of the chart is discussed in the next section.

Proteins. — Plants are able to synthesize amino acids from inorganic nitrate and carbohydrate and convert them into proteins. The animal organism is able to synthesize certain of the amino acids required in amounts adequate for normal growth but not others, and the latter, called essential amino acids, are derived from the enzymatic hydrolysis of plant proteins. Eight amino acids are essential dietary constituents for man; the rat requires these same acids and two more; specific bacteria can synthesize acids inaccessible to animals by synthesis. The discussion that follows is limited to syntheses that occur in the animal organism.

One process of importance in biosynthesis is transamination, which involves interconversion of α-keto and α-amino acids through utilization by the former of the amino group of the latter:

$$\underset{H_2NCHCO_2H}{\overset{R}{\cdot}} \;+\; \underset{O=CCO_2H}{\overset{R'}{\cdot}} \;\underset{\xrightarrow{\hspace{1cm}}}{\overset{Enzyme}{\rightleftharpoons}}\; \underset{O=CCO_2H}{\overset{R}{\cdot}} \;+\; \underset{H_2NCHCO_2H}{\overset{R'}{\cdot}}$$

Schoenheimer demonstrated transamination by showing that isotopic nitrogen of dietary glycine or leucine is incorporated into almost all the other amino acids, particularly into the dicarboxylic acids. Three of the metabolites of the Krebs cycle, pyruvic, oxalacetic, and α-ketoglutaric acid, are α-keto acids which, by transamination, can afford the amino acids alanine, aspartic acid, glutamic acid (17.5). These acids are not essential dietary constituents and evidently are synthesized from the intermediates of carbohydrate metabolism. The reverse process is demonstrated by the fact that alanine, aspartic acid, and glutamic acid, and only these amino acids, are oxidized rapidly in muscle. Serine appears also to be formed by transamination; the probable precursor, supplied by carbohydrate metabolism, is β-hydroxypyruvic acid:

$$HOCH_2COCO_2H \longrightarrow HOCH_2CH(NH_2)CO_2H$$

Transthiolation, replacement of —OH by —SH, is involved in the biogenesis of cysteine. Nutritional and isotopic investigations have shown that the carbon chain arises from serine and the sulfur atom from methionine. The process probably involves demethylation of methionine to homocysteine and condensation of this with serine to

HOOCCH(NH₂)CH₂OH   +   HSCH₂CH₂CH(NH₂)COOH $\xrightarrow{-H_2O}$

Serine   Homocysteine

HOOCCH(NH₂)CH₂—S—CH₂CH₂CH(NH₂)COOH $\xrightarrow{H_3PO_4}$

Cystathionine

HOOCCH(NH₂)CH₂SH   +   (HO)₂OPOCH₂CH₂CH(NH₂)COOH

Cysteine   Phosphohomoserine

form cystathionine, which is cleaved by phosphorolysis to cysteine and the phosphate ester of homoserine.

17.8   Serine has also been shown by isotopic tracer technique to be interconvertible with glycine, a change requiring a one-carbon unit:

$$CH_2(NH_2)CO_2H \ + \ C_1\text{-unit} \ \rightleftharpoons \ HOCH_2CH(NH_2)CO_2H$$

Theoretically, addition of glycine to the carbonyl group of formaldehyde could give serine, but formaldehyde as such is not utilized. Instead, a substance known as citrovorum factor has been implicated

Donor of
C₁-units

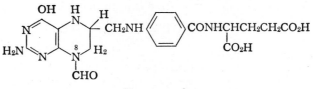

Citrovorum factor

in the reaction. This substance has a formyl group at position 8 capable of being transferred to a suitable substrate and it does promote formation of serine from glycine in the presence of formic acid. It functions as donor of C_1-units and is thus analogous to coenzyme A, donor of C_2-units. Glycine and cysteine are thus derivable from carbohydrate via serine.

17.9   Metabolic interconversion of glutamic acid and proline has been demonstrated both by isotope experiments and by use of mutant strains of microorganisms. The transformation has been shown to proceed by reduction of the γ-carboxyl group of glutamic acid (1) to

Glutamic acid
and proline

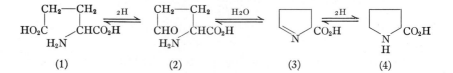

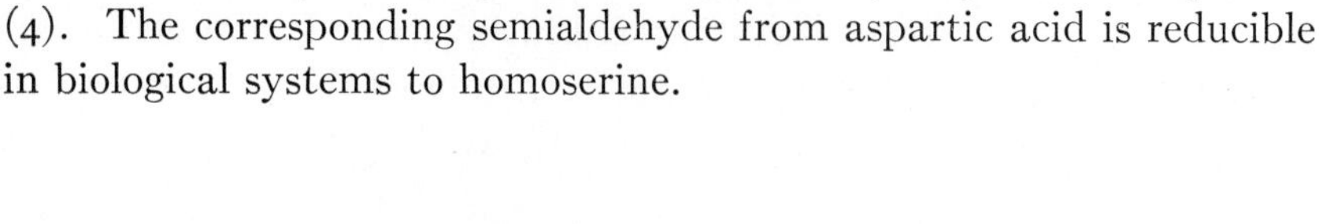

(1)   (2)   (3)   (4)

the γ-semialdehyde (2), cyclization (3), and hydrogenation to proline (4). The corresponding semialdehyde from aspartic acid is reducible in biological systems to homoserine.

SUMMARY

Polysaccharides and proteins hydrolyzed by digestive enzymes to absorbable sugars and amino acids. Lipid absorption promoted by emulsifying bile salts (example of vitamin K_1). Selectivity of absorption: cholesterol absorbed, plant sterols rejected. Fats transported in blood by proteins, probably by lipoproteins (protein, phospholipid, cholesterol, fat). Fats a richer source of body energy than proteins or carbohydrates.

Fats, proteins, carbohydrates, cholesterol all in dynamic state of synthesis and degradation. Deuterium-labeled fat incorporated into depot fat. Labeled acetate gives labeled fats and labeled cholesterol.

Role of coenzyme A in condensation of C_2-units in synthesis of fatty acids: 2 acetyl CoA $\longrightarrow$ acetoacetyl CoA; reduction of carbonyl group, dehydration, and hydrogenation to n-butyryl CoA, and repetition of cycle. Explains why acids are even-carbon and normal. Intermediate acetone bodies isolable in diabetes.

Glycogen $\rightleftharpoons$ hexoses(anaerobic). Anaerobic metabolism of fructose through glyceraldehyde and pyruvic acid to lactic acid. Aerobic reduction of pyruvic acid to lactic acid. Aerobic oxidation of pyruvic acid to CO_2 and H_2O. Identification of intermediary metabolites. Role of coenzyme A in conversion of pyruvic acid and oxalacetic acid to citric acid: formation of acetyl CoA and its addition to carbonyl group. Krebs cycle. Reversibility of steps. Oxygen-hydrogen-CO_2 balance.

Proteins. Amino acids not available by biosynthesis in animals are essential dietary constituents. Transamination correlates alanine, aspartic acid, and glutamic acid with metabolites of the Krebs cycle. β-Hydroxypyruvic acid the probable precursor of serine. Transthiolation interrelates serine and cysteine. Glycine + citrovorum factor + formic acid $\longrightarrow$ serine. Glutamic acid converted through γ-semialdehyde to proline.

READING REFERENCES

R. Schoenheimer, *The Dynamic State of Body Constituents*, Harvard University Press (1942)

A. W. D. Avison and J. D. Hawkins, "The Role of Phosphoric Esters in Biological Reactions," *Quart. Rev.*, **5**, 171 (1951)

S. Ochoa, "Enzymatic Mechanisms in the Citric Acid Cycle," *Adv. in Enzymology*, **15**, 183 (1954)

F. Lynen and S. Ochoa, "Enzymes of Fatty Acid Metabolism," *Biochimica et Biophysica Acta*, **12**, 299 (1953)

F. Lipmann, "Development of the Acetylation Problem, a Personal Account," *Science*, **120**, 855 (1954)

AROMATIC STRUCTURE AND SUBSTITUTION

18.1

Benzene, discovery

The first known members of the series, eventually called aromatic because of the fragrance characteristic of some of them, bear names that reflect their natural origin: benzoic acid and benzyl alcohol from gum benzoin, toluene from tolu balsam, xylene from wood tar (Gr. *xylon*, wood), salicylic acid from a glucoside in the bark and leaves of the willow (*Salicaceae*). Benzene itself was discovered in 1825 by Michael Faraday, who isolated the substance from an oily condensate deposited from compressed illuminating gas. He established that it is composed of equal numbers of carbon and hydrogen atoms and named it carbureted hydrogen. Mitscherlich (1834) found that benzoic acid can be converted by dry distillation with lime into an identical hydrocarbon, which he further characterized by vapor density measurements as having the formula C_6H_6. As a convenient name indicating the relationship to derivatives designated as benzoic, benzoyl, and benzyl because they had been obtained from gum benzoin, Mitscherlich coined the German word benzin, but Liebig, editor of the important "Liebig's Annalen," criticized the name as implying a relationship to strychnine and quinine and recommended a change to

Name

benzol, based on oleum, or the German *Öl*, oil. Laurent (1837) proposed the alternate name pheno from the Greek "I bear light," in recognition of the discovery of the hydrocarbon in illuminating gas, and this gained usage in the form of the name phenyl for the C_6H_5 group. The name benzol became established in the German literature, but in England and France the ending eventually was changed to -ene to avoid confusion with the systematic designation of alcohols.

Aromatics from coal tar

In 1845 Hofmann found that benzene can be isolated by redistillation of the tar resulting as a by-product of the conversion of coal into coke for use in metallurgy. In the next decade some progress was made on the technological production from coal tar of benzene and other aromatic compounds, which were destined to constitute key starting materials for a variety of syntheses. The first synthetic dye, one derived from coal tar, was discovered in 1856 by Perkin,[1] a young English student of Hofmann. The discovery was the result of fortunate circumstance coupled with industry and vision. Perkin's dye mauveine initiated the development of what has now become a dominant factor in world economics: the synthetic organic chemical industry. The initial spectacular advances were based on empirical findings, but the young industry could hardly have enjoyed normal growth for long without guidance in the form of an elucidation of the chemical nature of benzene. The Kekulé theory of valence announced in 1859 accounted for most known compounds of the methane series but did not at first appear applicable to benzene and derivatives, since the formula C_6H_6 indicates a highly unsaturated molecule and yet benzene behaves like a saturated compound. The characteristic reactions are not additions but substitutions, for example, $C_6H_6 + HONO_2 \longrightarrow H_2O + C_6H_5NO_2$ (nitrobenzene).

In 1865 it occurred to Kekulé that the structure of the hydrocarbon should be deducible from the number of its substitution products, just as the structure of propane follows from the fact that the hydrocarbon affords two mono-, four di-, and five trichloro derivatives. From an evaluation of the still fragmentary and partly erroneous data on hand, Kekulé concluded that benzene must have a structure allowing for only a single product of monosubstitution and for three disubstitution products, and saw that these relationships can be accounted for only on the basis of a cyclic formula. A ring of six carbon atoms, each carrying a hydrogen atom, would explain the equivalence of all six possible positions for monosubstitution and account for the existence of three di derivatives. The possibilities for di- and trisubstitution are shown with outline formulas. As new

Kekulé deduced cyclic structure

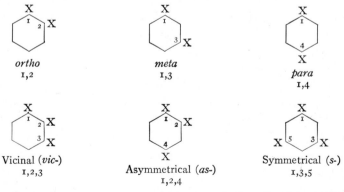

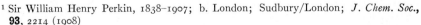

Three di and three tri derivatives

[1] Sir William Henry Perkin, 1838–1907; b. London; Sudbury/London; *J. Chem. Soc.*, **93**, 2214 (1908)

compounds were prepared and characterized and old ones reinvestigated, abundant evidence soon accumulated that left no doubt of the correctness of this part of Kekulé's theory, for the number of isomers in different series invariably corresponded with the predicted number.

Confirmation of another nature came from correlation of benzene derivatives with compounds of the cyclohexane series. Baeyer, in a classical investigation of the reduction of benzenedicarboxylic acids (1887–92), isolated hexahydro derivatives that could be identified by synthesis. The *para* isomer, for example, afforded both the *cis* and *trans* forms of the reduced acid, and these were synthesized by Perkin, Jr.[2] (1892) by an adaptation of the malonic ester synthesis, as formu-

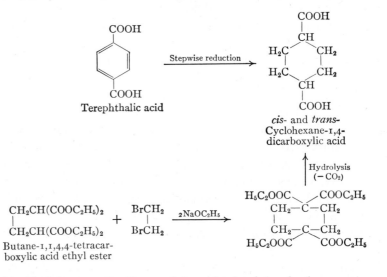

Terephthalic acid

cis- and *trans*-Cyclohexane-1,4-dicarboxylic acid

Butane-1,1,4,4-tetracarboxylic acid ethyl ester

lated. Cyclohexane itself was later obtained by hydrogenation of benzene (Sabatier and Senderens, 1901). Independent evidence came from the field of physics. The interesting substance mellitic acid of the formula $C_6(COOH)_6$, occurring in a mineral found in brown coal, can be converted into and obtained from known derivatives of benzene, and it also can be produced by oxidation of graphite or amorphous carbon with nitric acid. X-ray crystallographic analysis (Debye and Scherrer, 1917) established that graphite is made up of a series of interconnected honeycombs of six-membered carbon rings (in graphite the rings appear to be planar, whereas the diamond molecule, characterized by the X-ray studies of W. H. and W. L. Bragg, contains puckered rings corresponding to the chair form of cyclohexane). Since graphite is correlated with benzene, benzene must have a six-membered ring structure.

[2] William Henry Perkin, Jr., 1860–1929; b. Sudbury/London; Edinburgh, Manchester, Oxford; Nature, **124**, 263 (1929)

To dispose of the remaining valences, Kekulé proposed the familiar benzene formula with three double bonds. His proposal started a storm of controversy, criticism, and counterproposal that extended for seventy years. Although the discussions of this period form an interesting chapter in the history of science, they are without impact on modern thought because the mystery of the inert character of the benzene ring was resolved with the development in 1930–35 of the theory of resonance. This theory (4.33), supplemented by the orbital theory (4.34), accounts adequately for the known facts. That *o*-xylene is actually neither (a) nor (b) but a resonance hybrid of the two is demonstrated by the results of quantitative ozonization studies (Wibaut,[3] 1941). The hydrocarbon affords the following three frag-

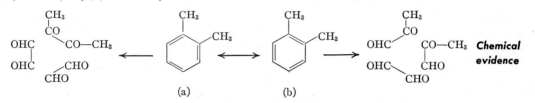

(a)   (b)

Chemical evidence

ments: glyoxal (OHC·CHO = A), diacetyl (CH₃COCOCH₃ = B), and methylglyoxal (CH₃COCHO = C). Fragments A and B can come from one Kekulé structure (a) in the ratio of two to one, and A and C from the other structure (b), but neither structure alone can give all three substances. Wibaut found that the three products are formed in the relative amounts calculated for an equal contribution of each form. Ozonization of 1,2,4-trimethylbenzene also indicated a 50:50 ratio of the contributing structures.

Whereas ordinary open-chain conjugated polyenes are reactive and prone to add reagents at the ends of the conjugated system, 1,6-diphenylhexatriene-1,3,5 (1) contains a triene system of stability approaching that of benzene, for the hydrocarbon is unusually resistant to oxidation by alkaline permanganate and does not add hydrogen

18.3

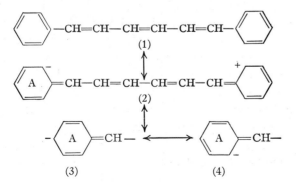

(1)

(2)

(3)   (4)

Resonance stabilization of triene system

[3] Johan Pieter Wibaut, b. 1886 Middelburg, Netherlands; D.Sc. Amsterdam; Amsterdam

bromide (Kuhn,[4] 1928). Here the triene system is conjugated at the two ends, and hence resonance is possible not only by charge separation analogous to that illustrated for butadiene (4.30) but also by distribution of charge into *ortho* and *para* positions of the benzene rings. Thus one resonance structure is shown in (2), and two others involving ring A are shown in the partial formulas (3) and (4). Comparable resonance accounts for the fact, noted earlier (10.16), that the 2,4-dinitrophenylhydrazones of α,β-unsaturated carbonyl compounds are markedly deeper in color than those of corresponding saturated ones. In structure (a) the dinitrophenyl group, which is the light-absorbing

*Color
intensification*

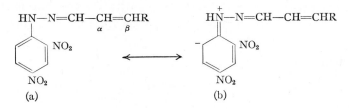

(a)   (b)

center responsible for the color, is not conjugated with the —N=CH— bond and hence not subject to influence by the α,β-bond with which it is conjugated; full conjugation is achieved, however, in resonance structures such as (b).

18.4

In the pre-resonance era, when the stability of the benzene ring seemed attributable to the symmetrical, closed conjugated system of the Kekulé formula, Willstätter, Waser, and Heidelberger [5] completed a long and difficult synthesis of cyclooctatetraene in order to determine if this hydrocarbon of comparable type possesses comparable aromaticity. The hydrocarbon proved to be too unstable for any but brief study, but it was characterized as wholly unlike benzene and comparable in reactivity in addition and polymerization processes to ordinary open-chain dienes. Willstätter's original synthesis has been confirmed (Cope,[6] 1948); in the meantime Reppe at the I. G. Farbenindustrie found that by operating at a suitably high pressure (in tetrahydrofuran in the presence of a nickel catalyst) acetylene can be polymerized to cyclooctatetraene. The method is suitable for large-scale production. A third method of preparation (Cope, 1948) utilizes as the initial step the dimerization of chloroprene to a cyclooctadiene. Samples prepared by both processes are identical with Willstätter's material, and hence his observation of the high reactivity of cyclo-

Cyclooctatetraene

*Polymerization
of acetylene*

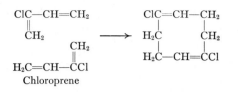

Chloroprene

octatetraene is confirmed. Cyclooctatetraene is particularly prone
to undergo reactions leading to aromatic compounds, two examples
of which are shown in the formulas. All four bonds are reducible by

Lacks aromaticity

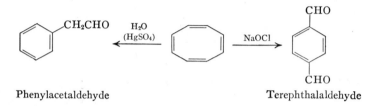

Phenylacetaldehyde   Terephthalaldehyde

hydrogen (cyclooctane, m.p. 13°); in a neutral medium the reaction
proceeds very slowly after addition of three moles of hydrogen. Thus
cyclooctene, b.p. 142°, can be prepared in about 90% yield by hydrogenation with palladium catalyst in methanol. Oxidation of cyclooctene with chromic acid leads to suberic acid (64% yield).

Thus the eight-membered conjugated system does not possess the
aromatic characteristics of the six-membered system. This relationship, anomalous on the basis of classical concepts, is understandable
in terms of the resonance theory. Whereas the planar cyclohexatriene
ring is practically strain-free, the cyclooctatetraene ring would be
under significant strain if all eight carbon atoms were in a plane, and
physical evidence indicates that, in analogy with saturated large-ring
hydrocarbons and ketones, the ring assumes a puckered and largely
strain-free configuration. Alternate nonplanar, or puckered structures
can be visualized, comparable to the two Kekulé forms of benzene,
but the transformation of one form into the other would require
movement of certain carbon atoms from one side of the median plane
of the molecule to the other. Since resonance can occur only when
interconversion of the contributing structures entails no migration or
movement of atomic centers but merely electron shifts, cyclooctatetraene is incapable of achieving stabilization through resonance.

*Inhibition of
resonance
in nonplanar ring*

Orientation of Substituents. — Some early inferences regarding
structures of aromatic compounds were speculative but nevertheless
correct. Thus mesitylene, a trimethylbenzene resulting from condensation of three molecules of acetone under the influence of concentrated sulfuric acid, was regarded by Baeyer as the symmetrical
or 1,3,5-derivative because of the manner of its formation, and Laden-

18.5

CHAPTER 18

Mesitylene

Phthalic acid

Salicylic acid

burg [7] (1874) proved this structure by demonstrating, through inter-conversions of nitro and amino derivatives of the hydrocarbon, that any two of the positions not occupied by methyl groups are equivalent; this relationship is consistent with the 1,3,5-structure but not with the alternate 1,2,3- or 1,2,4-formulation. In mesitylene each methyl group is *meta* to the other two groups, and since the hydrocarbon can be degraded to one of the xylenes that is convertible by oxidation into isophthalic acid (one of the three benzenedicarboxylic acids), the xylene and the acid must have the *meta*, or 1,3-structure. Victor Meyer [8] (1870) correlated one of the hydroxybenzoic acids with isophthalic acid and so characterized it as a *meta* derivative. Since phthalic acid is the only benzenedicarboxylic acid found to form a cyclic anhydride, it was inferred to have the *ortho* structure. Salicylic acid was also classified as an *ortho* compound because of the formation of cyclic derivatives. Through a rather elaborate series of transformations, Ladenburg was able to characterize as *para* isomers certain key compounds of the dimethyl, dicarboxy, and hydroxycarboxy series, and these served as points of reference for elucidation of the structures of other compounds.

Other early inferences were less secure, and in some instances erroneous. In 1874 Körner [9] proposed and experimentally exploited a method that is free from any uncertainty. Körner's absolute method consists in establishment of the number of isomeric substitution products of a given kind derivable from a substance under investigation. The three xylenes, for example, offer different opportunities for monosubstitution. The *ortho* isomer can give rise to two derivatives containing the group A, for this can be placed at either the 3-

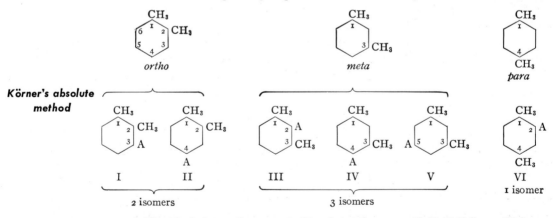

Körner's absolute method

[7] Albert Ladenburg, 1842–1911; b. Mannheim, Germany; Ph.D. Heidelberg; Kiel
[8] Victor Meyer, 1848–97; b. Berlin; Geneva, Zurich ETH, Heidelberg; Ber., **30**, 2157 (1897); T. E. Thorpe, "Victor Meyer Memorial Lecture," *J. Chem. Soc.*, **77**, 169 (1900)
[9] Wilhelm Körner, 1839–1925; b. Kassel, Germany; Giessen, Milan; *J. Chem. Soc.*, **127**, 2975 (1925)

or 4-position, as shown in the outline formulas I and II. If A is introduced at position 5, the structure is identical with II, and substitution at position 6 is equivalent to that at 3; the formula stands for a symmetrical ring, and the identity of the pairs of structures can be seen by rotating or inverting one ring. The rule for numbering is the obvious one of starting with a substituted position and counting in a direction that gives the simplest set of numbers, and hence if a bromine atom were located at either position 3 or 6, as formula I is written, the substance would be named 1,2-dimethyl-3-bromobenzene. The structure of the *meta* compound permits three different orientations of the A-substituted derivative, III–V, whereas in the *para* isomer, all available nuclear positions are identical, and only one monosubstitution product (VI) is possible. Thus the *ortho, meta,* and *para* compounds can be differentiated by establishing which one leads to two mononitro, monobromo, or other derivatives, which gives three isomers, and which but one.

Application of the principle is not easy, for the derivatives are not all obtainable by direct substitution, and even when the direct method can be employed, mixtures often result and care is required to secure pure substances. In experiments characterized by scrupulous attention to purity of the products, Körner established the structures of the dibromobenzenes by determining the number of mononitro derivatives and of the tribromobenzenes derivable from each isomer; this research also fixed the structures of the tribromo compounds. Griess (1874) characterized the isomeric diaminobenzenes (phenylenediamines) by eliminating the carboxyl group from each member of the series of six diaminobenzoic acids by distillation with lime. Two of these gave the same isomer, m.p. 103°, three gave another, m.p. 63°, and the sixth afforded a further diamino compound, m.p. 140°.

Mechanism of Aromatic Substitutions. — The characteristic reactions of benzene are substitutions, for example, reaction of the hydrocarbon with bromine under catalysis by ferric bromide to form bromobenzene:

$$\text{1. } C_6H_6 \;+\; Br_2 \;\xrightarrow{\;FeBr_3\;}\; C_6H_5Br \;+\; HBr$$

A long entertained postulate, advanced in the attempt to reconcile the behavior of benzene with that of typical alkenes, was that of addition of bromine to one of the double bonds in the Kekulé structure to produce a hypothetical dibromide, which then loses the elements of hydrogen bromide under catalysis by ferric bromide to form bromobenzene. The more reactive hydrocarbon phenanthrene does form an isolable, crystalline dibromide in the absence of catalyst, and under the influence of ferric bromide this does indeed yield the sub-

18.6

stitution product, 9-bromophenanthrene. Price,[10] however, determined the rates of the addition and substitution reactions (1936) and found that the dibromide is formed in a relatively slow, reversible

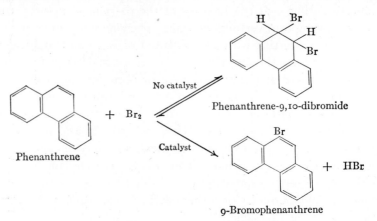

Addition-
elimination
hypothesis
disproved

18.7
Electrophilic
attack by Br⁺

reaction and that, when treated with a catalytic amount of ferric bromide, it does not yield bromophenanthrene directly but reverts to phenanthrene and bromine, which then enter into an independent, catalyzed substitution reaction.

Aromatic substitutions are now regarded as a replacement of a hydrogen atom of the intact unsaturated nucleus as the result of attack by an electrophilic agent. Substitution by bromine is promoted by catalysts such as ferric bromide and iodine which can combine with bromine to form a positively charged bromonium ion linked to an anion which can act as acceptor for the hydrogen atom to be displaced: $Br^+FeBr_4^-$ and $Br^+[IBr_4]^-$. Kinetic studies show that the reaction proceeds in two steps, the first of which controls the rate. This consists in attack of one double bond by the bromonium ion to

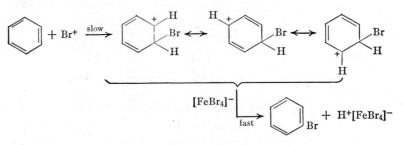

give a carbonium ion in which the charge is distributed among three structures. The second step is elimination of a proton with restoration of the aromatic ring. The first step is the same as that in addition

[10] Charles C. Price; b. 1913 Passaic, N. J.; Ph.D. Harvard (Fieser); Notre Dame, Pennsylvania

340

of bromine to an olefin (4.16). The reason this is not followed by re-action of the carbonium ion with bromide ion to give a dibromide, if a proton acceptor is available, is that the dibromide lacks the resonance stabilization of the aromatic ring of bromobenzene. Addition does occur in the absence of ion-forming catalysts, for pure benzene and bromine react under photocatalysis to give a mixture of stereoisomeric benzene hexabromides; intermediate products have not been isolated.

A second useful substitution is the Friedel[11]-Crafts[12] reaction, dis-covered in 1877 and widely used for synthesis of hydrocarbons of mixed type: aromatic-aliphatic, or Ar-R. For example, benzene reacts with methyl chloride in the presence of a catalytic amount of anhydrous aluminum chloride to give toluene (2). Still more useful is the Friedel-Crafts ketone synthesis (3), in which the same catalyst

2. C_6H_6 + CH_3Cl $\xrightarrow{AlCl_3}$ $C_6H_5CH_3$ + HCl

3. C_6H_6 + CH_3COCl $\xrightarrow{AlCl_3}$ $C_6H_5COCH_3$ + HCl

promotes reaction of an aromatic hydrocarbon with an acid chloride to give an acyl-substituted product. The Friedel-Crafts reaction is also catalyzed by ferric bromide, and the mechanism is doubtless the same as that of bromination, namely, initial attack by the cation of an ionic complex: $CH_3{}^+AlCl_4{}^-$, $CH_3\overset{+}{C}OAlCl_4{}^-$.

The only other generally applicable aromatic substitutions are nitration (4) and sulfonation (5). Nitration has been shown (Ingold,

4. C_6H_6 + $HONO_2$ $\longrightarrow$ $C_6H_5NO_2$ + H_2O
Nitrobenzene

5. C_6H_6 + $HOSO_3H$ $\longrightarrow$ $C_6H_5SO_3H$ + H_2O
Benzenesulfonic acid

Hughes) to involve the nitronium ion, $NO_2{}^+$, and the reaction is often conducted in sulfuric acid solution, for this acid promotes formation of the required electrophilic agent by the reaction:

HNO_3 + $2 H_2SO_4$ $\rightleftharpoons$ $NO_2{}^+$ + H_3O^+ + $2 HSO_4{}^-$

Nitration thus follows a course analogous to bromination (1). Studies

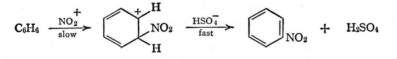

[11] Charles Friedel, 1832–99; b. Strasbourg, France; Paris; *Ber.*, **32**, 3721 (1899); *Bull. Soc. Chim.*, [4], **51**, 1493 (1932); *J. Chem. Educ.*, **26**, 3 (1949)
[12] James M. Crafts, 1838–1917; b. Boston; Ph.D. Harvard; Mass. Inst. Techn.

of sulfonation are less extensive but indicate that sulfur trioxide is the active species and that the reaction is analogous to nitration:

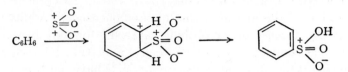

$C_6H_6 \longrightarrow$

18.10

Control of Substitutions. — Each of the five substitutions cited can be controlled over a wide range of intensity of reaction to meet requirements of specific aromatic reactants. Some nitrations can be accomplished with dilute nitric acid, others with concentrated acid (71%) or with fuming acid (90%), and some require nitric-sulfuric acid mixtures (mixed acid). Some nitrations are conducted to advantage in acetic acid solution, and the reaction can be intensified in acetic anhydride solution, in which case the effective agent is acetyl nitrate, CH_3COONO_2. From the reaction temperature, strength of acid, and requirement for an accessory dehydrating agent, a given nitration is said to proceed very easily, readily, or with difficulty. The same is true of halogenations and of Friedel-Crafts substitutions, where the controlling factors are the nature and amount of catalyst and the reaction temperature. The intensity of sulfonation is controllable over a rather wide range by regulation of the temperature (0° to about 360°) and of the concentration of acid (dilute acid to oleum).

18.11

Directive Influence of Substituent Groups. — The different substitution reactions are influenced in the same way by substituents in the benzene ring, which exert a profound control over both the orientation and the ease of substitution. Phenol can be nitrated so easily that dilute nitric acid suffices at room temperature (mixture of *ortho*

*op-Product,
with ease*

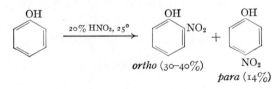

ortho (30–40%)   para (14%)

and *para* isomers), whereas in order to nitrate nitrobenzene efficiently the substance must be warmed with a mixture of fuming nitric acid and concentrated sulfuric acid; in this case orientation is exclusively

*m-Product,
with difficulty*

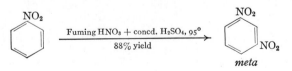

meta

342

in the *meta* position.   Control over the direction of substitution is described as a directive influence, though promotion or retardation of substitution is no less important.

The direction of substitution and the activation or deactivation exerted by various groups are determined by a combination of an inductive effect and a resonance effect.   Since substitutions involve attack by a positive ion or fragment, a group in which the key atom attached to the ring is positively charged or positively polarized repels the attacking electrophilic agent and decreases susceptibility to substitution.   Thus the electron-attracting positive pole of the trimethylammonium group, $-\overset{+}{N}(CH_3)_3$, induces a general drift of electrons in its direction and so decreases the electron density at all positions in the ring as to effect a marked deactivation for substitution. The nitro group, since the key atom carries a positive charge, operates similarly.   Conversely, an electron-releasing group displaces electrons into the ring and increases electron density at the available carbon centers and thus activates them for electrophilic attack.   Relative inductive effects of substituents in the benzene ring other than ionic ones can be estimated from the dipole moment data given in the

DIPOLE MOMENTS

ELECTRON-ATTRACTING		ELECTRON-RELEASING	
Substituent	Dipole moment	Substituent	Dipole moment
$-NO_2$	3.97	$-N(CH_3)_2$	1.58
$-CN$	3.90	$-NH_2$	1.52
$-COCH_3$	2.93	$-OH$	1.61
$-CHO$	2.75	$-OCOCH_3$	1.52
$-COOC_2H_5$	1.91	$-OCH_3$	1.16
$-Cl$	1.56	$-CH_3$	0.41
$-Br$	1.53		
$-I$	1.30		
$-COOH$	1.0		

tables.   The nitro group is powerfully electron-attracting and carboxyl is weakly so; amino and hydroxyl groups are potently electron-releasing and methyl is very weakly so.   The order of these inductive effects is in some cases entirely different from that inferred from the effect of α-substituents on the ionization of acids (9.3).   The reason is that groups in which the key atom carries unshared electrons are, in consequence of resonance, linked to the ring by a bond that has partial double-bond character and hence is quite different from the single bond linking an α-substituent in an acid.   Dipole moments reveal the character of groups as they function when linked to a resonant aromatic system.

Nitrobenzene is regarded as a resonance hybrid involving four structures; since resonance is possible only when a transition from one form to another involves no movement of atoms, the atoms in all the structures lie in a single plane. The effect of resonance in

Resonance effect

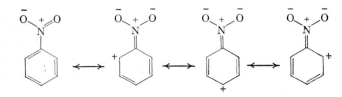

nitrobenzene is to set up positive centers at the *ortho* and *para* positions, and hence to render these sites particularly inaccessible to electrophilic agents; the *meta* carbon atoms are deactivated by induction, along with the rest, but at least offer better points for attack than *ortho-para* positions. Thus nitrobenzene is nitrated with difficulty because of inductive repulsion of $\overset{+}{N}O_2$ and the orientation is *meta* in consequence of resonance. Similar interpretations can be made of the weaker directive influences of less potently electron-attracting carbonyl functions (a), since initial charge separation (b)

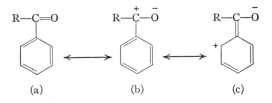

(a)   (b)   (c)

is promoted by distribution of the positive charge into the ring, as in (c).

Although in aliphatic compounds the hydroxyl group is electron-attracting, the dipole moment data show that hydroxyl attached to a benzene ring is strongly electron-releasing. Thus the high susceptibility of phenol to electrophilic substitution is attributable to an inductive effect. Resonance is possible, since a pair of unshared

Resonance in phenol and in phenoxide ion

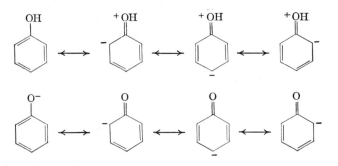

electrons is available on oxygen to move in and form a double bond, with charge separation. Distribution of the negative charge among three centers increases the electron density at these positions and results in *ortho-para* substitution. Replacement of the phenolic hydrogen by methyl or by acetyl produces some diminution in the inductive activation but does not influence the direction of substitution as determined by resonance. The negative pole of the phenoxide ion has a powerful inductive effect and renders the ring even more susceptible to electrophilic substitution than that of nonionized phenol; resonance again controls *ortho-para* orientation. The nonionized amino group, like hydroxyl, has a key atom with unshared electrons and the inductive and resonance effects in amines are like those in phenols.

Halogen substituents present a special case. Resonance establishes electron-rich centers at *ortho-para* positions and determines the course

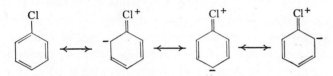

*op–Directing but
deactivating*

of substitution. However, unlike other *ortho-para* directing groups, aromatic halogen like aliphatic halogen is electron-attracting and so the inductive effect deactivates the ring, and chlorobenzene is nitrated less readily than benzene.

The trimethylammonium group presents an open problem. This is the most powerfully deactivating group known and it directs substitution exclusively to the *meta* position. The explanation advanced in the case of nitrobenzene is not applicable because of the requirement that one valence of pentavalent nitrogen retain its polar character. Thus in the ion $C_6H_5\overset{+}{N}(CH_3)_3$ the charge is not free to shift to a position in the ring; the ionic nitrogen has a shell of eight electrons and is incapable of sharing another pair with carbon. The best explanation advanced is that in the trimethylanilinium ion the power-

18.13

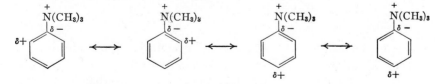

*Postulated
resonance*

ful positive pole induces a fractional negative charge on the adjacent carbon of the ring that is balanced by a fractional positive charge that can appear at positions 2, 4, and 6, which are thereby rendered inaccessible for electrophilic attack.

345

The methyl group in toluene is weakly electron-releasing and produces an enhancement of reactivity, which however is minor as compared to the effect of a hydroxyl or amino group. That methyl also directs *ortho-para* presents a problem in interpretation, but a minor one, since the directive effect is feeble. Resonance of the type formulated above is impossible, and the C–C bond distance connecting the group to the nucleus is the same as that of an aliphatic single-carbon link. Resonance by a postulated process known as hyperconjugation, or no-bond resonance, has been advanced in explanation.

Hyperconjugation

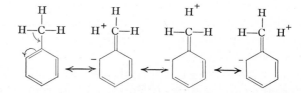

The electrons of each of the three CH bonds in turn are considered to participate in displacements in the same way as unshared electrons of oxygen, nitrogen, or halogen participate, but to a lesser extent. The formulation is not intended to imply complete separation of a proton, for the charged atom must remain within bonding distance of the carbon.

18.14

op-Directors; activators (except halogen)

Groups of the two main types discussed are summarized in the

$$—N(CH_3)_2 \quad —NH_2 \quad —OH \qquad —OCH_3 \quad —NHCOCH_3 \quad —OCOCH_3$$

<u>(very powerful)</u>

$$—CH_3 \qquad —Cl, Br, I \qquad —C_6H_5 \qquad —CH_2COOH \qquad —CH{=}CHCOOH$$

two sets of formulations, and they are arranged in the order of approximate relative effectiveness in controlling the direction of substitution. With the exception of halogen, the activating or deactivating efficacy follows the same order.

m-Directors; deactivators

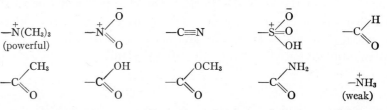

18.15

Meta Substitutions. — The rules of orientation are useful in predictions of the chief products of substitution reactions, but they indicate the predominant, rather than the exclusive products. Careful quantitative studies have been made by the Netherlands school (Holleman,[13] Wibaut) and others to determine, often by physical

[13] Arnold Frederick Holleman, 1858–1953; b. Oisterwyk, Netherlands; Ph.D. Leiden (Franchimont); Amsterdam

methods of analysis, the exact proportion of the isomers formed, even in small amounts, in various substitutions, usually nitration. The results are conveniently summarized by affixing to the formula of a substance undergoing a given substitution figures representing the proportions of the different isomers found in the total substitution product; the percentages established by analysis should not be confused with the percentage yields that can be secured in practice, and usually are distinctly higher. Thus in actual preparative work *m*-dinitrobenzene can be obtained in 88% yield by nitration of nitrobenzene, but analysis of the total nitrated material has shown that the *meta* isomer constitutes 93% of the whole and that the *ortho* and *para* isomers are present to the extent of 6% and 1%, respectively, as indicated in the abbreviated summary. The *ortho* and *para* isomers are produced in such small amounts that they are easily eliminated during crystallization. The trimethylammonium group is even more potent than the nitro group because it affords exclusive *meta* substitution, and carboxyl is weaker than nitro because it allows considerable *ortho-para* substitution. That positively charged or unsaturated groups direct an entering group to the *meta* position by deactivating all the positions, with particular suppression of attack at the electron-rich *ortho* and *para* carbon atoms, is illustrated by nitration of *p*-nitrobenzoic acid. The only positions available are *ortho* to either a carboxyl or a nitro group, and it is understandable that the reaction should proceed with difficulty; the suppression of *ortho* substitution is greater for the

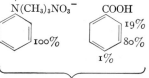

Nitration

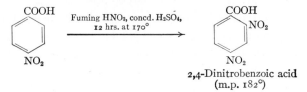

2,4-Dinitrobenzoic acid
(m.p. 182°)

nitro substituent, and the group introduced takes a place *ortho* to the weaker carboxyl.

The deactivating influence of *meta* directing groups controls the course of substitution of polynuclear compounds. In 4-nitrodiphenyl,

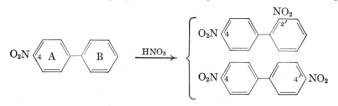

for example, one of the benzene rings (A) is deactivated whereas the other is not, and substitution occurs in the *ortho* (2′-) and *para* (4′-)

positions of the unsubstituted ring (B). The same is true of derivatives of diphenylmethane, $C_6H_5CH_2C_6H_5$, and dibenzyl, $C_6H_5(CH_2)_2C_6H_5$, which are attacked preferentially at the *ortho* and *para* positions of

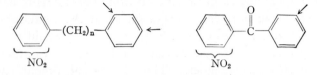

the ring containing no nitro or other *meta* directing groups. A nitro or similar derivative of benzophenone undergoes reaction at the *meta* position of the unsubstituted ring.

18.16   *Ortho-Para* **Substitutions.** — The relative effectiveness of various *ortho-para* directing groups cannot be gauged well from the extent to which *meta* substitution is allowed, for this occurs to a negligible extent (1–4%), but is established by results of competition between two groups in the same molecule, preferably in the *para* positions. In *p*-aminophenol substitution occurs preferentially in the position *ortho* to the amino group, which therefore is more influential than hydroxyl.

Competition between groups

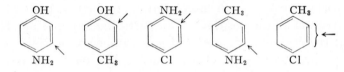

If either the amino or hydroxyl group is pitted against methyl or other alkyl group or against halogen, substitution is dominated by the —NH_2 or —OH group. The dimethylamino, amino, and hydroxyl groups so far surpass all other groups of the *ortho-para* type that amines and phenols undergo special substitutions not applicable to other aromatic compounds. The other *ortho-para* directing groups included in the list given above are arranged in the approximate order of effectiveness, as judged by competition reactions, but in this category of second-order effectiveness the differences are relatively slight. There is so little difference between methyl and halogen, for example, that the *p*-halotoluenes ordinarily afford mixtures of the two possible monosubstitution products.

Groups of type I activate both *ortho* and *para* positions, but the ratio of *ortho* and *para* substitution varies over a rather wide range, as illustrated by the following summary:

op-Ratio variable

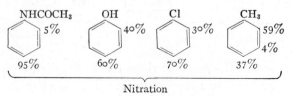

Nitration

Para substitution generally predominates over *ortho* substitution. The results cited for toluene constitute an exception, but in this case the *ortho-para* ratio is sensitive to conditions and varies from 3:2 to 2:3 according to the nitrating agent; it will be noted also that the methyl group is one of the most weakly effective members of the series and permits some *meta* substitution.

Temperature and Steric Effects. — The examples cited thus far refer largely to nitrations, though the data on the *ortho-para* ratio include some halogenations. Nitration and halogenation can be described as normal substitutions since they are irreversible and not subject to variation in the proportion of isomers with reaction temperature or with steric factors. Sulfonation and Friedel-Crafts alkylation are both reversible reactions that are subject to the effects noted. In alkylation of toluene with methyl chloride catalyzed by aluminum chloride, a group initially introduced *ortho* to a second methyl group may undergo displacement to a more remote site under the influence of either an increased amount of catalyst or an elevated temperature. At a low temperature or with a mild catalyst there is a considerable predominance of attack in the *para* position rather than in the more hindered site adjacent to the methyl group. Friedel-Crafts acylation is not reversible but is nevertheless subject to hindrance, and the aluminum chloride-catalyzed reaction of acetyl chloride with toluene yields solely the *para* acetyl derivatives. The results contrast markedly with those of nitration (18.16).

A similar tendency is observable in sulfonations, as is evident from the comparative data on nitration and sulfonation of chlorobenzene and of toluene. In each case the reversible sulfonation gives a distinctly lower proportion of the *ortho* isomer than nitration (or halogenation). Avoidance of the *ortho* position in reversible reactions appears attributable to steric hindrance, or a spatial blocking of the adjacent *ortho* sites. A further indication of steric effects is that *ortho* substitution is particularly suppressed when the directing group is bulky; thus *t*-butylbenzene is sulfonated exclusively in the *para* position, whereas under comparable conditions toluene affords a significant amount of the *ortho* isomer. The conditions of sulfonation are important, and a comparison of the results obtained with toluene at 0° and at 100° shows that the proportion of *ortho* substitution decreases with increasing temperature. Thus in reactions of the abnormal reversible type there is a definite preference for *para* over *ortho* substitution, particularly with a space-consuming directing group or at elevated temperatures.

Mono- and Polysubstitutions. — The contrast between the effect of *meta* directing groups in deactivating the benzene ring for substitu-

18.17
Nitration, bromination irreversible, normal

Sulfonation, Friedel-Crafts alkylation reversible, subject to ortho effect

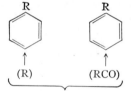

Friedel-Crafts reaction

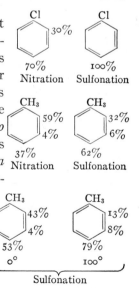

Sulfonation

18.18

349

tions and the substitution-promoting influence of *ortho-para* directors has important practical consequences. When benzene is nitrated, the reaction comes to a sharp stopping point with introduction of one nitro group, for the resistance of the nucleus to substitution is so increased that a second group can be introduced only under much more drastic conditions. The mononitro derivative is thus obtainable in high yield and without contamination by polynitro compounds. Since the group introduced on sulfonation is of the same type, hydrocarbons of the benzene series can be converted easily into monosulfonic acids, and forcing conditions are required for introduction of a second group *meta* to the first. In the Friedel-Crafts ketone synthesis, the maximum intensity obtainable is such that the reaction is limited to monosubstitution. Halogen atoms in the benzene ring possess the unique character of directing substituents into the *ortho* and *para* positions but of exerting a weak deactivating influence. Thus dibromination of benzene requires more severe treatment than monobromination, and the successive stages of polysubstitution are attainable in discrete steps. Friedel-Crafts alkylation is the one instance in which the group introduced facilitates further substitution. Toluene is distinctly more susceptible than benzene to nitration and sulfonation; also it undergoes methylation more readily than the parent hydrocarbon, and hence when benzene is condensed with methyl chloride in the presence of aluminum chloride, the product initially formed inevitably consumes some of the reagent before the starting material is exhausted, with formation of polysubstitution products.

18.19

Reactions of Polysubstituted Compounds. — When more than one group is present in a substance undergoing substitution, the relative location and nature of the groups may exert either an antagonistic or a reinforcing influence on the course of the reaction. In mesitylene each of the three equivalent positions is under the substitution-facilitating influence of one *para*-methyl and two *ortho*-methyl groups, and consequently the hydrocarbon undergoes ready substitution even though the only position attacked is hindered by two adjacent methyl groups. Among the xylenes, the order of reactivity as indicated by sulfonation and desulfonation reactions is: *m* > *o* > *p*. The superior reactivity of *m*-xylene can be attributed to the reinforcing influence of the strong *para* and moderate *ortho* direction to the 4-position, the site of the sulfonation; both methyl groups exert a moderate activat-

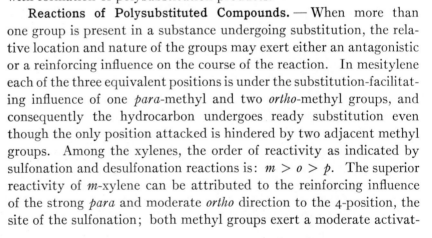

ing influence at position 2, but this position is well blocked, particularly to a reaction notably subject to steric hindrance. Of the two positions available in *o*-xylene, one (4) is under the strong *para* influence of a methyl group, and the other (3) is *ortho* activated and moderately hindered; hence sulfonation occurs at the former position. In *p*-xylene the only position available corresponds to the less reactive 3-position of *o*-xylene, and consequently the hydrocarbon is the least readily sulfonated of the three isomers.

p-Nitrophenol contains groups of different types, but these are not antagonistic. The nitro group deactivates position 3 very strongly but influences the *meta* position 2 only moderately in an adverse

sense, and since the latter position is under the *ortho* influence of the powerful hydroxyl group, it is the exclusive site of monosubstitution, for example, on nitration or bromination. In *o*-nitrophenol the expected sites of substitution are positions 4 and 6, which are *para* and *ortho*, respectively, to the hydroxyl and *meta* to the nitro group. Since *para* orientation ordinarily is stronger than *ortho*, predominant attack at position 4 would be anticipated. Actually sulfonation gives the 4-sulfonic acid exclusively; bromination affords the 4-monobromo compound along with the 4,6-dibromo derivative; and nitration gives chiefly 2,4-dinitrophenol, along with a small amount of the isomeric 2,6-dinitrophenol.

SUMMARY

Faraday (1825): isolation of benzene from illuminating gas (*pheno*, bear light). Mitscherlich (1834): benzene from benzoic acid (from gum benzoin, origin of name). Perkin (1856): first synthetic dye from coal tar products. Kekulé (1865): cyclic structure deduced from number of substitution products, one mono, three di, three tri. Confirmation: (a) hexahydroterephthalic acids (Baeyer) identical with synthetic *cis* and *trans* cyclohexane-1,4-dicarboxylic acids (Perkin, Jr.); (b) graphite, shown by X-ray analysis to contain C_6-rings, on HNO_3 oxidation yields mellitic acid (benzenehexacarboxylic acid). Controversy over bond structure resolved by resonance theory. Ozonization of *o*-xylene establishes exactly equal contribution of two resonance structures. Stability of diphenylhexatriene due to distribution of charges in *op*-positions of ring. Comparable resonance explains color of 2,4-dinitrophenylhydrazones.

Cyclooctatetraene. Willstätter synthesis (1913). Reppe synthesis by polymerization of acetylene under pressure. Cope synthesis from chloroprene. Is very reactive and lacking in aromaticity. Explanation: eight-carbon system is nonplanar and hence incapable of resonance stabilization.

Orientation of substituents. Early inferences: mesitylene = 1,3,5-trimethylbenzene (from 3 moles of acetone); phthalic acid is *ortho* (anhydride); salicylic acid is *ortho* (ring formation). Körner's absolute method (1874). Number of possible mono derivatives: *ortho* 2, *meta* 3, *para* 1.

Ferric-bromide catalyzed bromination. Hypothesis of addition of Br_2 and elimination of HBr tested in the case of phenanthrene and found invalid (1936). Accepted mechanism of bromination: attack by Br^+ of $Br^+FeBr_4^-$ to give resonance-stabilized carbonium ion, acceptance of proton by $FeBr_4^-$.

Friedel-Crafts alkylation and acylation involve attack by cations: CH_3^+ and CH_3CO^+. Nitration: attack by $\overset{+}{N}O_2$, formed from $HNO_3 + 2\,H_2SO_4$. Sulfonation: attack by SO_3, which contains two semipolar bonds.

Control of substitutions: temperature, strength of acid, use of mixed acid, solvent; in Friedel-Crafts reaction and halogenation, nature and amount of catalyst. Phenol nitrated easily to o- and p-derivatives, nitrobenzene nitrated less readily than benzene to m-derivative.

Inductive effect: positively charged or other electron-attracting group decreases electron density in ring and hence decreases susceptibility to electrophilic attack; electron-releasing group has the opposite inductive effect. Dipole moments (see 18.11) as measure of inductive effects (these differ from those inferred from ionization constants of acids because some aromatic groups are linked by hybrid bond).

Resonance structures of nitrobenzene with op positions carrying positive charge and hence particularly inaccessible to electrophilic attack. Resonance in compounds with carbonyl-containing directing groups. In phenol, phenoxide ion, and aniline op positions carry negative charge and hence are vulnerable to attack. Halogen atoms op-directing (resonance), but deactivating (induction).

The trimethylanilinium ion incapable of comparable resonance, may be polarized in a sense rendering op positions inaccessible. Weak op direction of methyl group and postulate of hyperconjugation (no-bond resonance). Summary of two types of groups (18.14).

Meta substitutions require forcing conditions; all positions in ring are deactivated (induction), particularly those *ortho* and *para* (resonance). $-\overset{+}{N}(CH_3)_3$ most powerful (100% *meta* nitration), $-NO_2$ next (93% *meta*), $-CO_2H$ weaker (80% *meta*). p-Nitrobenzoic acid, nitrated with great difficulty, is substituted *ortho* to less powerful carboxyl group. 4-Nitrodiphenyl is substituted in ring not deactivated by nitro group.

Ortho-para substitutions. Competitions between groups in p-positions establish order: $NH_2 > OH >$ halogen or alkyl. Some variation in o/p ratio in nitrations.

Nitration and bromination irreversible and ratio of products is independent of temperature and steric hindrance effects noted in sulfonation and Friedel-Crafts alkylation, both reversible. Entering group avoids hindered o-position. p-Product predominates in F.-C. alkylation at low temperature, in F.-C. acylations, in sulfonation as compared to nitration.

Mono- vs. polysubstitution. Nitration, sulfonation, Friedel-Crafts acylation stops with monosubstitution because of deactivating effect of m-directing group introduced. In Friedel-Crafts alkylation op-directing group introduced has activating effect and hence polysubstitution occurs.

Combined directive effect of two or more groups. Reinforcing effect of methyl groups in mesitylene. Explanation of order of reactivity of the xylenes: $m > o > p.$ p-Nitrophenol $\longrightarrow$ 2-derivative; o-nitrophenol $\longrightarrow$ 4- and 6-derivatives.

PROBLEMS

1. Suggest a synthesis of cyclohexane-1,3-dicarboxylic acid similar to that of the 1,4-isomer achieved by Perkin (18.1). How can the tetracarboxylic acid esters required for these two syntheses be obtained?

2. Calculate the molecular ratio of the reaction products expected to result from ozonization of 1,2,4-trimethylbenzene on the theory of a resonance system.

3. Could Körner's absolute method of determining structures be applied to the three isomeric trimethylbenzenes?

4. Write formulas for the six diaminobenzoic acids, and explain the significance of the results obtained by Griess on decarboxylation of these substances (18.5).

5. Predict the chief products of the following reactions:
   (a) Nitration of resorcinol dimethyl ether (1,3-dimethoxybenzene)
   (b) Monobromination of $p\text{-}CH_3CONHC_6H_4OCOCH_3$
   (c) Sulfonation of p-cymene, $p\text{-}CH_3C_6H_4CH(CH_3)_2$

(d) Sulfonation of p-methylacetophenone, p-CH$_3$C$_6$H$_4$COCH$_3$

(e) Nitration of phenol-p-sulfonic acid

(f) Condensation of 1,2,4-trimethylbenzene with acetyl chloride in the presence of aluminum chloride

(g) Nitration of m-dichlorobenzene

(h) Friedel-Crafts condensation of succinic anhydride with desoxybenzoin, C$_6$H$_5$COCH$_2$C$_6$H$_5$

(i) Nitration of diphenylmethane-p-carboxylic acid

(j) Friedel-Crafts methylation of p-chlorodiphenylmethane

(k) Mononitration of 4-methyl-4'-hydroxydiphenyl

READING REFERENCES

F. R. Japp, "Kekulé Memorial Lecture," *J. Chem. Soc.*, **73**, 97 (1898)

W. H. Perkin, "Baeyer Memorial Lecture," *J. Chem. Soc.*, **123**, 1520 (1923)

L. Pauling, "The Significance of Resonance to the Nature of the Chemical Bond and the Structure of Molecules," in H. Gilman, *Organic Chemistry*, II, 2nd Ed., 1970–1979, Wiley, New York (1943)

A. F. Holleman, "Some Factors Influencing Substitution in the Benzene Ring," *Chem. Rev.*, **1**, 187–230 (1924)

P. D. Bartlett, "The Electronic Theory of Aromatic Substitutions," in H. Gilman, *Organic Chemistry*, I, 2nd Ed., 205–213, Wiley, New York (1943)

H. B. Watson, *Modern Theories of Organic Chemistry*, Oxford University Press (1941)

CHAPTER
19
AROMATIC HYDROCARBONS

19.1

From Coal Tar. — Pyrolysis of bituminous coal at temperatures in the range 1000–1300° in a retort without access of air converts the bulk of the material into coke, a hard porous residuum of carbon and ash, and affords coal gas and a mixture of less volatile products separating as a condensate of black viscous coal tar and a water layer containing ammonia. **Coal gas** is refined by passage through tar and ammonia scrubbers and through oil-absorption tanks for recovery of **light oil,** which consists principally of benzene (60%) and toluene (15%). The weight of **coal tar** amounts to some 3% of the coal, and on redistillation about 40% of the tar is obtained as aromatic fractions boiling at temperatures up to 360° (the residue is pitch). Each fraction is further refined by extraction with alkali to separate the weakly acidic phenols and with acid to separate nitrogen bases and is then fractionated further.

Benzene, toluene, and a mixture of the three xylenes are available in quantity from commercial processing of coal tar; naphthalene is the most abundant single constituent (11%). A large number of other hydrocarbons have been isolated from this source, including the tricyclic isomers phenanthrene and anthracene, and the tetracyclic

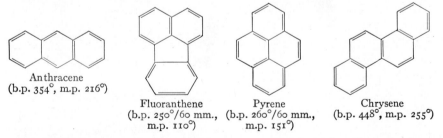

Anthracene
(b.p. 354°, m.p. 216°)

Fluoranthene
(b.p. 250°/60 mm., m.p. 110°)

Pyrene
(b.p. 260°/60 mm., m.p. 151°)

Chrysene
(b.p. 448°, m.p. 255°)

hydrocarbons formulated. Anthracene was valued in the early days of coal-tar technology as the starting material for production of alizarin, the first natural dye prepared synthetically (1868), and it gained new importance with the discovery of the indanthrone vat dyes (1901), also obtainable from this hydrocarbon.

The benzene and toluene found in light oil can be separated effectively by fractional distillation, but each is accompanied by a small amount of a heterocyclic analog of nearly the same boiling point and comparable aromaticity. Thus coal-tar benzene, unless specially processed, contains a trace of thiophene. The resemblance to benzene is so marked that the presence of the substance in coal-tar benzene remained unsuspected till an incident in one of Victor Meyer's lectures provided a clue leading to the discovery of the sulfur compound (1882). Meyer periodically demonstrated to his students a supposedly characteristic color test for benzene, which consists in shaking a sample with concentrated sulfuric acid and a crystal of isatin, but on one occasion he applied the test in expectation of proving that benzoic acid on decarboxylation gives benzene. The beautiful blue color failed to appear, since the color reaction is specific for thiophene and not for benzene. In thiophene stabilization cannot be achieved as in benzene by resonance involving chiefly two equivalent Kekulé structures. Yet the difference between the calculated and observed heats of combustion points to a resonance stabilization of 29 kg.-cal./mole, as compared with 39 kg.-cal./mole for benzene. Furthermore the interatomic distance between the carbon and the hetero atom is somewhat less than normal and hence indicative of a certain degree of double-bond character. Actually the hetero atom is responsible for a

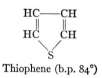

Thiophene (b.p. 84°)

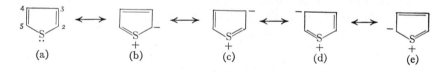

(a)   (b)   (c)   (d)   (e)

Resonance stabilization

resonance effect by virtue of displacement of a pair of its unshared electrons. Thus five resonance structures can be written. Structures (b) to (e) involve a formal separation of charge, and resonance stabilization in such a system is not so great as that acquired from resonance involving exactly equivalent structures, as in benzene. Structures (c) and (d) probably represent excited structures of minor contribution as compared to (b) and (e), where the conjugation extends between the two ionic charges. That (b) and (e) are indeed prominent contributors is suggested by the preponderance of α-substitutions in electrophilic reactions, for the centers of high electron density are at the α- and α'-positions in these structures.

Pyridine
(b.p. 115°)

α-Picoline
(b.p. 129°)

Quinoline
(b.p. 238°)

Isoquinoline
(b.p. 242°, m.p. 25°)

355

The basic fraction of coal tar affords practical amounts of pyridine and its methyl homologs, α-, β-, and γ-picoline; smaller amounts are obtained of the bicyclic analogs of naphthalene, quinoline, and isoquinoline. The resonance energy of pyridine is 43 kg.-cal./mole, significantly higher than that of benzene. In this heterocycle the possibility for resonance extends beyond the two identical Kekulé structures (a) and (b) to three additional structures (c–e), in which

Pyridine superaromatic

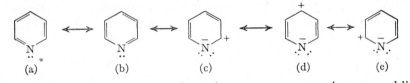

(a)   (b)   (c)   (d)   (e)

the relatively electron-attracting nitrogen atom acquires an additional pair of electrons from a carbon atom in the α- or γ-position, which thereby becomes positively charged. Reactions with electrophilic reagents involve the pyridinium ion, and this offers the same opportunity for resonance. Thus electrophilic substitution occurs only at the β-position. Actually, such substitution is realizable only under forcing conditions. Bromination can be accomplished only in the vapor phase at a temperature of about 300°, and sulfonation and nitration can be effected only under forcing conditions. Attempted Friedel-Crafts reactions are invariably negative. Thus pyridine corresponds in aromaticity to nitrobenzene rather than to benzene.

19.4   **Properties.** — Rather pleasant aromatic odors are distinguishing characteristics of benzene (b.p. 80°), toluene, the xylenes, and of naphthalene, a solid (m.p. 80°). The liquid hydrocarbons are lighter than and insoluble in water, and their vapors are toxic and highly flammable. Benzene burns with a luminous, sooty flame, and its heat of combustion is 8.79 kg.-cal./ml. (cyclohexane, 8.68). Boiling points increase with increasing molecular weight, and an additional methyl group produces an increment in boiling point of about 30° when one, two, or three methyls are substituted into benzene (b.p. 80°), regardless of the position, as well as in the series benzene, toluene, ethylbenzene, n-propylbenzene. In contrast to boiling points, melting points reflect a structural characteristic: symmetry or lack of symmetry. p-Xylene freezes at 13°; the o- and m-isomers at −28° and −54°. The symmetrical 1,2,4,5-tetramethylbenzene, durene, melts at 80°, whereas its isomers are liquids. Hexamethylbenzene is symmetrical and melts at 166°.

PREPARATION AND SYNTHESIS

19.5

From Aliphatic and Alicyclic Compounds. — Instances of the synthesis of aromatic hydrocarbons from aliphatic starting materials are rare. A reaction of interest, though without practical application, is the partial conversion of acetylene into benzene at a high temperature (Berthelot, 1866). A demonstration of the stable character and ease

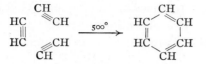

of formation of the benzene ring is the smooth production of *p*-cymene by the action of dehydrating agents on camphor. The bridge linkage carrying the *gem*-dimethyl group is severed in the process of molecular

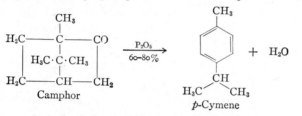

rearrangement, but the substance is formed nevertheless in high yield. *p*-Cymene can be obtained from several other natural isoprenoids (terpenes); it occurs along with these substances in many essential oils and is available in this country from spruce turpentine.

Acetone on treatment with concentrated sulfuric acid undergoes trimeric aldolization and dehydration with production of mesitylene

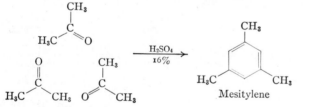

(low yield). 1,3,5-Triphenylbenzene is formed similarly from acetophenone, $C_6H_5COCH_3$. The reaction has been applied to the synthesis

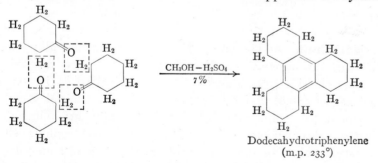

Dodecahydrotriphenylene
(m.p. 233°)

of the interesting tetracyclic hydrocarbon dodecahydrotriphenylene from cyclohexanone; the product crystallizes from the reaction mixture in large, sparlike needles.

357

Wurtz-Fittig Synthesis. — The method of Wurtz for the coupling of two alkyl groups by interaction of an alkyl halide with sodium was applied by Fittig in 1864 to the synthesis of hydrocarbons containing an alkyl group linked to an aromatic ring, or aryl group (Ar). Hydrocarbons of this type were first obtained in this way. The method, the Wurtz-Fittig reaction, is represented as follows:

$$\text{ArX} + \text{RX} + 2\,\text{Na} \longrightarrow \text{Ar·R} + 2\,\text{NaX}$$

Although Wurtz condensation of two different alkyl halides by interaction with sodium gives difficultly separable mixtures of paraffinic hydrocarbons, Fittig's adaptation of the reaction to the preparation of compounds of mixed types can be applied successfully because the reaction products are easily separable. In the production of hydrocarbons of the type Ar·R, the by-products are the paraffinic hydrocarbon R·R and the aromatic hydrocarbon Ar·Ar, and the difference in the boiling points is so profound that separation can be accomplished. For example, if methyl bromide is condensed with bromobenzene in the presence of two equivalents of sodium with the object of preparing toluene (b.p. 111°), the by-products are ethane and diphenyl (b.p. 254°). The reaction is illustrated (1) by the synthesis of *p*-xylene from either *p*-dibromobenzene or *p*-bromotoluene, and (2) by a particularly favorable synthesis of a mixed alkyl-aryl hydrocarbon requiring little excess alkyl halide.

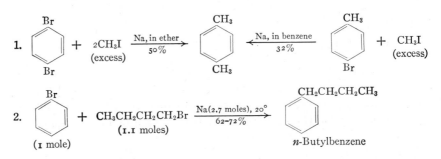

Yields rather low

Friedel-Crafts Alkylation. — The reaction of an alkyl halide (RX) with an aromatic hydrocarbon (ArH) under catalysis by aluminum chloride to produce an aralkyl derivative (ArR) was discussed earlier (18.8) and interpreted as involving initial attack by the cation of the complex $R^+AlCl_4^-$. Since the alkyl group introduced is electron-releasing and activates the ring for electrophilic attack, the reaction cannot be stopped sharply at the stage of monosubstitution, and yields are poor. Nevertheless, the reaction has uses because of its simplicity, for example for the synthesis of the di- and triphenyl derivatives of methane.

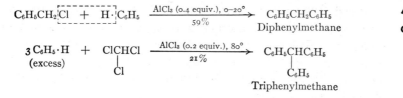

The reaction provides a practicable method for the synthesis of durene, 1,2,4,5-tetramethylbenzene, because this symmetrically substituted hydrocarbon has a higher melting point and lower solubility than any of its isomers or than the tri- and pentamethylbenzenes that invariably accompany it in the reaction of benzene with four equivalents of methyl chloride, and hence can be separated from the reaction mixture by freezing and purified by recrystallization. The

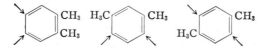

Durene

preparation is modified to advantage by treatment of the xylene mixture from coal tar with two equivalents of methyl chloride in the presence of aluminum chloride, for each of the three isomers can afford durene on dimethylation, though a mixture of tri-, tetra-, and pentamethylbenzenes also results. A practicable procedure (L. I.

Smith,[1] 1926) consists in passing methyl chloride (2.3 moles) under slight pressure into technical xylene (1 mole) and aluminum chloride (0.4 mole) at 95°, separating the crude tri-, tetra-, and pentamethyl-benzene fractions by distillation, freezing the durene from the middle fraction, and crystallizing it three times from alcohol. The yield of pure durene is 10–11%.

Although aluminum chloride has been the most frequently used catalyst, several other catalysts are available, of varying degree of activity below that of aluminum chloride, and hence condensation can be moderated by use of these milder agents. Suitable catalysts, listed in the order of decreasing potency, are as follows:

$$AlCl_3 > HF > H_2SO_4 \ (96\%) > FeCl_3 > SnCl_4 > BF_3 > ZnCl_2$$

The reagents are Lewis acids or mineral acids. The control that is possible through the choice and amount of catalyst and regulation of the temperature is important in polysubstitutions, for under mild

[1] Lee Irwin Smith, b. 1891 Indianapolis; Ph.D. Harvard (Kohler); Minnesota

conditions the entering groups tend to become oriented in *ortho* and *para* positions, whereas under forcing conditions *meta* orientation obtains. Thus trisubstitution can be directed to afford chiefly either the 1,2,4- or the 1,3,5-derivative. Substitution in the *meta* position is favored by use of a considerable amount (usually 2 equivalents) of aluminum chloride, the most active catalyst, or of a high reaction temperature. The effect of temperature is seen in the fact that the

Influence of conditions

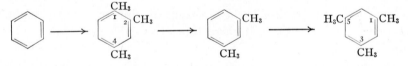

reaction of benzene with three moles of methyl chloride gives chiefly 1,2,4-trimethylbenzene when conducted at 0°, but yields chiefly the 1,3,5-isomer when carried out at 100°. The proportion of catalyst is even more important. Durene is formed in a series of *ortho* and *para* substitutions, and the procedure for its preparation cited above calls for use of 0.4 equivalent of aluminum chloride at 95°. If the amount of catalyst is increased to 2 equivalents of $AlCl_3$, the *meta* derivative mesitylene can be obtained in yields up to 63% in a reaction conducted at 100° (J. F. Norris,[2] 1938–39). A likely explanation of the variation in the course of the reaction with conditions is that the Friedel-Crafts reaction is reversible. If an alkylbenzene is treated with aluminum chloride in the absence of an alkylating agent, it is converted in part into a mixture of higher and lower substitution products; alkyl groups evidently are severed from one molecule and transposed to another. Furthermore, 1,2,4-trimethylbenzene rearranges to mesitylene in the presence of aluminum chloride. There-

Mesitylene

Mechanism

fore production of 1,3,5-derivatives under forcing conditions may be the result of an initial *ortho-para* substitution followed by elimination of one group and affixture in a more secure position.

Another peculiarity of the Friedel-Crafts reaction is that the hydrocarbon group of the alkyl halide frequently suffers rearrangement. Thus *n*-propyl bromide and isopropyl bromide on reaction with benzene in the presence of aluminum chloride both yield isopropylbenzene, or cumene (Gustavson, 1878); normal halides invariably give rise

[2] James F. Norris, 1871–1940; b. Baltimore; Ph.D. Johns Hopkins Univ.; Mass. Inst. Techn.

in whole or in part to hydrocarbons having secondary groups regardless of the catalyst. The apparent abnormality was clarified by

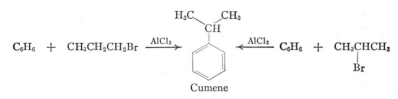

Cumene

Kekulé's observation (1879) that *n*-propyl bromide is isomerized to
isopropyl bromide by contact with aluminum chloride, probably because the reagent catalyzes formation of a carbonium ion capable of
isomerizing to an ion stabilized by electron-release from two alkyl

$$CH_3CH_2CH_2Br \xrightarrow{-Br^-} [CH_3CH_2\overset{+}{C}H_2 \longrightarrow CH_3\overset{+}{C}HCH_3] \xrightarrow{Br^-} CH_3CHBrCH_3$$

groups. The structure of the Friedel-Crafts reaction product is predictable from the Markownikoff rule of addition. Isobutyl chloride,
for example, affords *t*-butylbenzene as the result of isomerization:

$$(CH_3)_2CHCH_2Cl \xrightarrow{-Cl^-} [(CH_3)_2CH\overset{+}{C}H_2 \longrightarrow (CH_3)_2\overset{+}{C}CH_3] \xrightarrow{C_6H_6} (CH_3)_3CC_6H_5$$

Friedel-Crafts Acylation. — This reaction, already briefly discussed (18.8), is illustrated by the synthesis of acetophenone with
use of acetic anhydride, which is just as effective as acetyl chloride,
and of benzophenone from an aroyl chloride; in each case excess
benzene is used as solvent. The reaction proceeds exothermally for

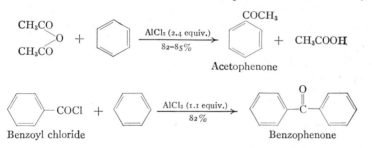

Benzoyl chloride   Benzophenone

a time and is completed by brief refluxing. The mixture is then cooled
and treated cautiously with ice and hydrochloric acid to decompose an
aluminum chloride complex and bring aluminum salts into the aqueous
phase; the ketonic reaction product is then recovered from the washed
and dried organic layer by distillation of the solvent.

Whereas Friedel-Crafts alkylation requires only a catalytic
amount of aluminum chloride, in an acylation the acid chloride or
anhydride forms a complex in which each carbonyl group present is
bound as a complex with one mole of aluminum chloride, and the
reagent is required in slight excess over the theoretical molar ratio to

provide for catalysis. In the case of an acid chloride, in the first step (a) aluminum chloride functions as a Lewis acid and accepts a pair

(a) $C_6H_5\overset{\text{Cl}}{\underset{}{C}}=\overset{..}{\underset{..}{O}}:\ +\ \overset{\text{Cl}}{\underset{\text{Cl}}{Al}}:\text{Cl}\ \rightleftharpoons\ C_6H_5\overset{\text{Cl}}{\underset{}{C}}=\overset{+}{\underset{..}{O}}:\overset{\text{Cl}}{\underset{\text{Cl}}{Al}}:\overset{-}{\text{Cl}}$

(b) $C_6H_5\overset{\text{Cl}}{\underset{}{C}}=\overset{+}{\underset{..}{O}}:\overset{\text{Cl}}{\underset{\text{Cl}}{Al}}:\overset{-}{\text{Cl}}\ \rightleftharpoons\ C_6H_5\overset{+}{C}=O\ +\ \text{Cl}:\overset{\text{Cl}}{\underset{\text{Cl}}{Al}}:\text{Cl}$

The active agent:

$C_6H_5\overset{+}{C}=O$

(c) $C_6H_5\overset{+}{C}=O\ +\ C_6H_6\ \longrightarrow\ C_6H_5\overset{C_6H_5}{\underset{}{C}}=O\ +\ H^+$

(d) $(C_6H_5)_2C=O\ +\ AlCl_4^-\ \rightleftharpoons\ (C_6H_5)_2C=\overset{+}{\underset{..}{O}}:\overset{\text{Cl}}{\underset{\text{Cl}}{Al}}:\overset{-}{\text{Cl}}\ +\ Cl^-$

(e) $(C_6H_5)_2C=\overset{+}{\underset{..}{O}}:\overset{-}{AlCl_3}\ +\ H_2O\ \longrightarrow\ (C_6H_5)_2C=O\ +\ Al(OH)Cl_2\ +\ HCl$

of electrons from the ketonic oxygen atom to form a coordinate covalent complex. This complex dissociates (b) to a certain extent to give the benzoyl cation, which is the effective agent in electrophilic attack of benzene (c), with expulsion of a proton. The reaction product, benzophenone, combines with the ion $AlCl_4^-$ to form a second coordinate covalent complex (d) which, at the end of the reaction, is decomposed by water (e). Complex formation thus binds an equivalent quantity of the metal halide. When an anhydride is employed as acylating agent, sufficient aluminum chloride must be used to allow for oxonium-salt formation at both carbonyl groups.

A useful application of the synthetic method is the preparation of keto acids by interaction of an aromatic hydrocarbon with one of the readily available cyclic anhydrides, as illustrated in the examples.

γ-Keto acids from cyclic anhydrides

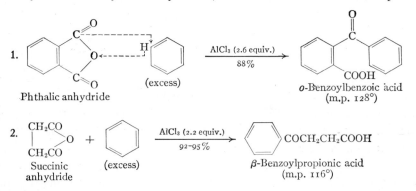

1. Phthalic anhydride (excess) AlCl₃ (2.6 equiv.) 88% → o-Benzoylbenzoic acid (m.p. 128°)

2. Succinic anhydride (excess) AlCl₃ (2.2 equiv.) 92–95% → β-Benzoylpropionic acid (m.p. 116°)

The γ-keto acids of the aromatic and mixed aliphatic-aromatic types that are obtainable in this way constitute important intermediates for further syntheses. If toluene is employed in place of benzene, the orientation of the substituent is almost exclusively in the position *para* to the methyl group.

The reactions proceed very smoothly and stop abruptly with introduction of a single acyl group, since the inductive effect of the electron-attracting acyl group introduced inhibits further electrophilic attack. Acetophenone is indifferent to further treatment with acetyl chloride or acetic anhydride in the presence of aluminum chloride even under forcing conditions. All other *meta*-directing groups similarly inhibit Friedel-Crafts acylations, as well as alkylations; for example, C_6H_5CHO, $C_6H_5CO_2CH_3$, C_6H_5CN, and $C_6H_5NO_2$ are completely inert to this form of substitution. Nitrobenzene has such a marked and specific solvent power for aluminum chloride (with which it forms an oxonium-salt complex) that it is frequently employed as a solvent for Friedel-Crafts condensations with other aromatic compounds.

m-Directors inhibit reaction

A useful application of the reaction is the synthesis of cyclic ketones by intramolecular Friedel-Crafts cyclization between an aromatic ring and an acid chloride group in an attached side chain, as illustrated by the preparation of α-tetralone. Five- and six-mem-

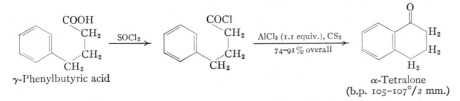

γ-Phenylbutyric acid   α-Tetralone (b.p. 105–107°/2 mm.)

bered ring ketones are generally obtainable in good yield by this method. One of the alternate procedures that is often effective consists in treatment of the free acid with liquid hydrogen fluoride, for example:

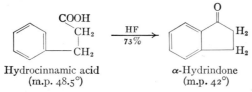

Hydrocinnamic acid (m.p. 48.5°)   α-Hydrindone (m.p. 42°)

Clemmensen Reduction. — This method of reducing the aromatic-aliphatic ketones produced by the Friedel-Crafts reaction consists in refluxing a ketone with amalgamated zinc and hydrochloric acid.

19.9

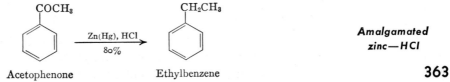

Acetophenone   Ethylbenzene

Amalgamated zinc—HCl

Acetophenone, for example, is reduced to ethylbenzene. The reaction apparently does not proceed through initial reduction to a carbinol, for carbinols that might constitute intermediates are stable under the conditions used. With substances sparingly soluble in aqueous hydrochloric acid, improved results sometimes are obtained by addition of a water-miscible organic solvent such as ethanol, acetic acid, or dioxane. Particularly favorable results are obtained by addition of the water-insoluble solvent toluene (Martin, 1936), vigorous stirring, and the use for amalgamation of zinc that has been freshly melted and poured into water (Sherman, 1948). The ketone is retained largely in the upper toluene layer and is distributed into the aqueous solution of hydrochloric acid in contact with the zinc at so high a dilution that the side reaction of bimolecular reduction is largely suppressed.

Alternate methods

The Clemmensen and Wolff-Kishner (10.17) methods of reduction supplement each other; Clemmensen reduction is inapplicable to acid-sensitive compounds, and the Wolff-Kishner method cannot be used with compounds sensitive to alkali or containing other functional groups that react with hydrazine. Formation of an ethylenethioketal and desulfurization with Raney nickel (10.18) is useful in research but the reagents are too expensive for commercial application.

Clemmensen or Wolff-Kishner reduction is applicable to the γ-keto acids and cyclic ketones obtainable by the Friedel-Crafts processes of condensations with succinic anhydride (succinoylation) and of intramolecular cyclization.

Useful applications

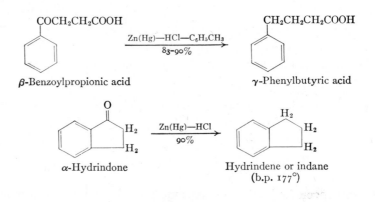

β-Benzoylpropionic acid → γ-Phenylbutyric acid

α-Hydrindone → Hydrindene or indane (b.p. 177°)

19.10   **Dehydrogenation of Hydroaromatic Hydrocarbons.** — Hydro derivatives of aromatic compounds are called hydroaromatic: cyclohexane, cyclohexanol, 1,2,3,4-tetrahydronaphthalene (tetralin), perhydronaphthalene (decalin). Alicyclic substances containing six-membered rings but having carbon substituents that block conversion to the aromatic state unless they are eliminated (e.g., camphor and 1,1-dimethylcyclohexane) are not classified as hydroaromatic. Hydroaromatic compounds can be aromatized by dehydrogenation. The chief experimental methods, illustrated for a general case, include

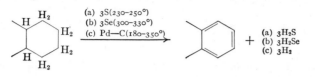

dehydrogenation with sulfur at a rather low temperature (Vesterberg, 1903), dehydrogenation with the less active and often less destructive selenium at distinctly higher temperatures (Diels, 1927), and catalytic dehydrogenation (Zelinsky, 1911). Dehydrogenation over a 10% palladium charcoal catalyst, prepared by reduction of palladium chloride in an alkaline suspension of activated carbon (Norit) with formaldehyde, often proceeds very smoothly. If the substance to be dehydrogenated is heated with about one tenth part of palladium charcoal to about 310–320°, hydrogen is evolved steadily and the material is soon aromatized.

Dehydrogenation has particular significance owing to the generally applicable methods available for the synthesis of hydroaromatic compounds. For example, α-tetralone, obtainable readily by reactions

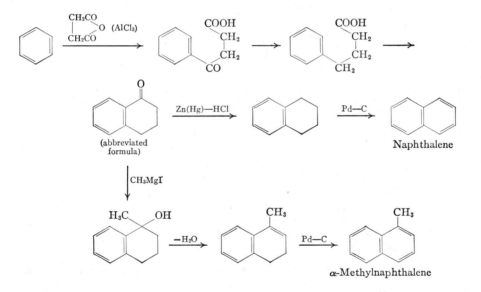

Typical synthesis

discussed in the preceding sections, can be converted into naphthalene by Clemmensen reduction to tetralin and dehydrogenation, or it can be condensed with methylmagnesium iodide and the resulting carbinol then dehydrated to a methyldihydronaphthalene that is dehydrogenated to α-methylnaphthalene.

CHAPTER 19

19.11

Grignard Syntheses. — The Grignard reaction can be applied in numerous ways to the synthesis of mixed aromatic-aliphatic hydrocarbons, containing both saturated and unsaturated side chains. One

Aryl Grignard reagents   1.

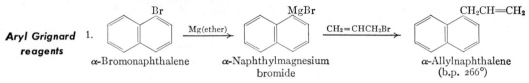

α-Bromonaphthalene   α-Naphthylmagnesium bromide   α-Allylnaphthalene (b.p. 266°)

type of synthesis, illustrated in examples (1), (2), and (3), utilizes the aryl Grignard reagents easily prepared by interaction of aromatic bromides or iodides with magnesium.

2.

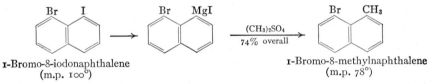

C₆H₅MgBr   +   CH₃COC₆H₅

Phenylmagnesium bromide   Acetophenone

α,α-Diphenylethylene (b.p. 275°)

A generally useful reaction consists in the introduction of a nuclear methyl group by interaction of an aryl Grignard reagent with dimethyl sulfate. The net result is equivalent to a Wurtz-Fittig synthesis, but methylation of a Grignard reagent often proceeds more smoothly and is applicable to more selective synthetic operations, as illustrated in example (3).

3.

1-Bromo-8-iodonaphthalene (m.p. 100°)

1-Bromo-8-methylnaphthalene (m.p. 78°)

Aromatic ketones

Other elaborations of the Grignard reaction involve addition of an alkylmagnesium halide to an aromatic carbonyl compound, as illustrated by the synthesis of *p*-cymene (4). The terminal step of reduction of the double bond in the side chain has been accomplished most

4.

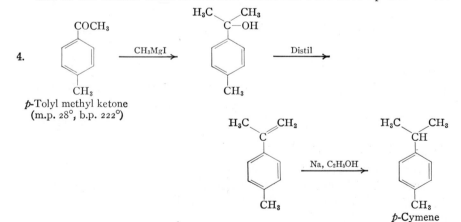

p-Tolyl methyl ketone (m.p. 28°, b.p. 222°)

p-Cymene

366

satisfactorily in comparable cases by catalytic hydrogenation in the presence of platinum, for there is no difficulty in stopping short of hydrogenation of the nucleus (much slower), but it is of interest that a double bond conjugated with the aromatic ring can be reduced with sodium and absolute ethanol.

Hydrolysis of Sulfonates. — Since sulfonation is reversible, a hydrocarbon often can be regenerated from the sulfonic acid or the alkali sulfonate ($ArSO_3Na$). Desulfonation usually proceeds best in an aqueous solution of dilute sulfuric acid at temperatures of 135–200°, and can be carried out by heating the reagents in a sealed tube or by passing superheated steam into the solution of the sulfonic acid or sulfonate; the hydrocarbon steam distils from the reaction mixture as it is formed. Desulfonation is valuable in the isolation of pure

$$ArSO_3H(Na) + H_2O \xrightarrow{\text{dil. H}_2\text{SO}_4 \text{ (heat)}} ArH + H_2SO_4(NaHSO_4)$$

hydrocarbons from the isomer mixtures derived from coal tar or petroleum that cannot be separated by fractional distillation. The mixture can be sulfonated and the sulfonic acids converted into the solid water-soluble sodium or potassium salts, which are fractionally crystallized; hydrolysis of the isolated sulfonates then affords the liquid or solid hydrocarbons.

*Separation
of xylenes*

The xylene fraction from coal tar usually contains some 50–60% of *m*-xylene and 10–25% each of the *ortho* and *para* isomers, along with some ethylbenzene. Separations have been worked out that utilize differences in the ease of sulfonation and desulfonation. *m*-Xylene is the most reactive of the three isomers (18.19) and slowly dissolves in 80% sulfuric acid at room temperature as the result of conversion into the derivative I; *o*- and *p*-xylene are not attacked on being shaken

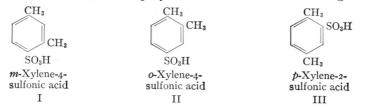

m-Xylene-4-sulfonic acid	*o*-Xylene-4-sulfonic acid	*p*-Xylene-2-sulfonic acid
I	II	III

with 80% acid but undergo sulfonation with 84% acid to give the sulfonic acids II and III, respectively. Other experiments show that *o*-xylene is slightly more reactive than the *para* isomer.

Another use of the reversible sulfonation reaction is the introduction of blocking groups that permit special orientations, as in the example shown:

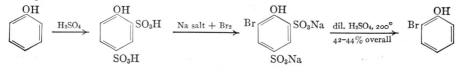

Decarboxylation. — A degradative method sometimes useful consists in heating the sodium salt of a carboxylic acid with soda lime to effect decarboxylation. As noted previously, the first thiophene-free benzene was prepared by this method. The carboxyl group eliminated may also be located in a side chain, as in a laboratory preparation of

$$C_6H_5CH{=}CHCOOH \xrightarrow[\text{38-41\%}]{\text{Distil}} C_6H_5CH{=}CH_2$$

Cinnamic acid   Styrene

styrene. A carboxyl group located on an unsaturated carbon atom is readily eliminated, and the reaction proceeds at a temperature close to the boiling point of styrene (146°) and requires no basic catalyst. Elimination of a carboxyl group attached to an aromatic nucleus is accomplished only under more drastic conditions, and a usually satisfactory procedure consists in heating the acid with copper-chromium catalyst in quinoline solution (J. R. Johnson, 1930). A practicable

Furan

application is the preparation of furan, a heterocyclic oxygen compound exhibiting aromatic characteristics to a moderate degree (resonance energy, 24 kg.-cal.). Furfural, available on a technical scale by the processing of corncobs, is converted in part by the Cannizzaro reaction into 2-furoic acid, which is decarboxylated.

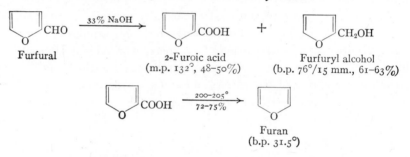

Furfural   2-Furoic acid   Furfuryl alcohol
             (m.p. 132°, 48–50%)   (b.p. 76°/15 mm., 61–63%)

Furan
(b.p. 31.5°)

19.14   **Zinc-Dust Distillation of Phenols.** — Phenols are often convertible into the parent hydrocarbons by interaction with zinc dust at a red heat; presumably the oxygen is eliminated as zinc oxide. The reaction is carried out either by distilling the phenol through a hard-glass tube of zinc dust heated to a dull glow in a furnace, or by heating a

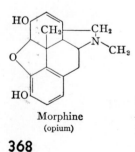

Morphine
(opium)

gram or two of the phenol with 25–50 g. of zinc dust in a sealed-off Pyrex flask until the glass begins to soften. The degradative reaction has little preparative value, but is useful in investigation of substances of unknown structure because it affords a means of establishing the nature of the parent hydrocarbon. Thus the alkaloid morphine was first recognized as a phenanthrene derivative by degradation to phenanthrene on zinc-dust distillation; this method also provided the first clue that the natural dye alizarin is an anthracene derivative.

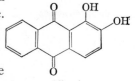

Alizarin

PROPERTIES

Oxidation of Alkylbenzenes. — A characteristic reaction of toluene is oxidation to benzoic acid, accomplished by heating with dilute nitric

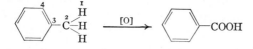

acid in a sealed tube, by refluxing with potassium dichromate and sulfuric acid, or by the action of alkaline potassium permanganate at 95° (nearly quantitative yield). The reaction not only illustrates the stability of the benzene ring, which survives the oxidation, but points to vulnerability of a methyl group attached to the aromatic nucleus not found in methane. The difference is attributable to activation of the hydrogen atoms of the methyl group by the unsaturated aromatic nucleus, and the reactivity, as compared with that of methane, is seen also in the ready chlorination of toluene in sunlight to benzyl chloride, $C_6H_5CH_2Cl$, and in the oxidation with lead tetraacetate to benzyl acetate, $C_6H_5CH_2OCOCH_3$ (low yield). The xylenes are convertible into the corresponding phthalic acids, and mesitylene affords 1,3,5-benzenetricarboxylic acid. Ethyl, *n*-butyl, and still larger side chains are also easily degraded to carboxyl groups by oxidation, as the result of initial attack at the activated position adjacent to the benzene ring. The *t*-butyl group, which has no hydrogen atom in the activated position, is stable to oxidation.

Diphenylmethane is oxidized readily to benzophenone. In triphenylmethane the lone methane hydrogen atom is activated by all

19.15

Activation of side chain

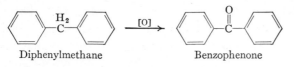

Diphenylmethane   Benzophenone

three phenyl groups, and its lability is manifested in the very ready oxidation to triphenylcarbinol. Thus the reaction has been effected

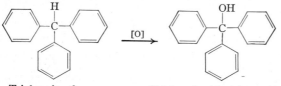

Triphenylmethane   Triphenylcarbinol (m.p. 162°)

by passing air into a solution of the hydrocarbon in carbon disulfide in the presence of a trace of aluminum chloride.

Free Radicals. — In the early part of the nineteenth century many attempts were made to prepare methyl, ethyl, and comparable radicals in a free state, in analogy with the isolation of sodium from sodium chloride. A likely approach appeared to consist in abstraction of the halogen of a halogen compound by interaction with a metal, and prior to 1864, when Cannizzaro demonstrated the applicability of the Avogadro principle for the establishment of true molecular weights (1811), several substances were prepared that were thought to be radicals: Gay-Lussac's "CN" (1815) proved to be cyanogen, $(CN)_2$; Bunsen's supposed radical cacodyl, resulting from the action of zinc on cacodyl chloride, $(CH_3)_2AsCl$, became recognized as the normal-valence compound $(CH_3)_2As—As(CH_3)_2$; Frankland's "ethyl" (1850), obtained from ethyl iodide and zinc, as well as the hydrocarbons produced by the Kolbe electrolysis of acid salts (1849), proved to have twice the expected molecular weight.

An authentic free radical was first prepared by Gomberg in 1900. Gomberg [3] had synthesized tetraphenylmethane (m.p. 285°) and was interested to observe that the tetranitro derivative of this hydrocarbon, which has no hydrogen on the methane carbon atom, gave no color reaction with alcoholic potassium hydroxide and thereby contrasted with trinitrotriphenylmethane. To determine whether the difference is general, Gomberg sought to synthesize hexaphenylethane by the following coupling reaction:

$$2(C_6H_5)_3CCl + 2 Ag \longrightarrow (C_6H_5)_3C—C(C_6H_5)_3 + 2 AgCl$$

Triphenylchloro-
methane (m.p. 113°)   Hexaphenylethane

The product was a high-melting, sparingly soluble, white solid resembling tetraphenylmethane in physical properties and in its inert character. Analysis, however, showed that it was no hydrocarbon but an oxygen-containing compound $(C_{38}H_{30}O_2)$. The experiment was then repeated with exclusion of air by shaking a solution of triphenylchloromethane in benzene with finely divided silver in an atmosphere of carbon dioxide. A yellow solution resulted which, on evaporation in the absence of air, deposited colorless crystals of a hydrocarbon having the composition expected for hexaphenylethane but exhibiting remarkable reactivity. Solutions in benzene or carbon disulfide absorb oxygen with avidity, with separation of the white oxygen compound, and in the absence of oxygen, they absorb chlorine, bromine, and iodine. When the colorless hydrocarbon is first dissolved

[3] Moses Gomberg, 1866–1947; b. Elisabetgrad, Russia; Ph.D. Michigan (Prescott); Michigan; *J. Am. Chem. Soc.*, **69**, 2921 (1947)

in a solvent, the solution is momentarily colorless, but within a few seconds becomes tinged with yellow, and the color soon deepens. The change is reversible, for on evaporation of the solution, the colorless hydrocarbon is recovered. Gomberg interpreted the results as follows: "The experimental evidence . . . forces me to the conclusion that we have to deal here with a free radical triphenylmethyl $(C_6H_5)_3C$—. The action of zinc results, as it seems to me, in a mere abstraction of the halogen:

$$2(C_6H_5)_3C\text{—Cl} + Zn \longrightarrow 2(C_6H_5)_3C\text{—} + ZnCl_2$$

Now, as a result of the removal of the halogen atom from triphenylchloromethane, the fourth valence of the methane is bound either to take up the complicated group $(C_6H_5)_3C$— or remain as such, with carbon as trivalent. Apparently the latter is what happens."

Molecular weight determinations established that the colorless solid is hexaphenylethane and that in solution it dissociates to colored triphenylmethyl radicals to a point of equilibrium. The free radical

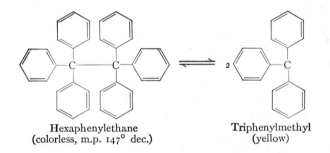

Hexaphenylethane (colorless, m.p. 147° dec.)
Triphenylmethyl (yellow)

combines with halogens to produce triphenylmethyl halides, and with oxygen to form the colorless peroxide, $(C_6H_5)_3C$—$O \cdot O$—$C(C_6H_5)_3$, with disturbance of the equilibrium and eventually complete conversion. Many other hexaarylethanes and related compounds subsequently have been examined, and the degree of dissociation determined from the molecular weights observed at the boiling points and freezing points of various solvents. The point of equilibrium between the ethane and the radical at any temperature can be determined by measurement either of the molecular extinction coefficients of the colored solutions or of the paramagnetic susceptibilities of solutions containing the paramagnetic free radical (attracted by a magnet) and the diamagnetic ethane (not attracted). Values found for the dissociation of hexaphenylethane in benzene at 20° are: 3.6% in a 4% solution, 9.6% in a 0.5% solution, 25.8% in a 0.055% solution. An increase in temperature favors dissociation; for example, a 0.07% solution in benzene contains 18% of the free radical at 13° and 42%

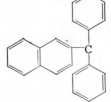

Tri-*p*-biphenylmethyl
74% (deep violet)

Tri-*o*-anisylmethyl
95–100% (orange)

Other radicals

Diphenyl-α-naphthylmethyl
28–31% (deep red-brown)

Diphenyl-β-naphthylmethyl
7–9% (wine red)

at 43°. Some of the more striking variations in the extent of dissociation with changes in the nature of the aryl groups are illustrated in the formulas, which include the percent of the radical present at equilibrium in benzene at 5° in approximately 0.08 molar solution; such a solution contains about 3% of triphenylmethyl.

An empirical correlation of the dissociation of hexaphenylethane with other phenomena, such as the susceptibility of triphenylmethane to oxidation, is that the bond connecting the two ethane carbon atoms is activated by all six phenyl groups, and indeed thermochemical studies have shown that this bond is weaker than that in ethane by about 30 kg.-cal. (Bent, 1936). Steric hindrance between the two clusters of benzene rings may contribute to weakening the linkage. However the dissociation to radicals is determined less by weakening of the ethane linkage than by stabilization of the free radical through resonance. The triphenylmethyl radical contains an unpaired electron, and the paramagnetic property is due to the presence of the odd

$$(C_6H_5)_3C : C(C_6H_5)_3 \rightleftharpoons 2(C_6H_5)_3C \cdot$$

electron that is not compensated magnetically. This odd electron does not remain on the methane carbon atom but appears also at the *ortho* and *para* positions in all three phenyl groups, as shown in the formulas for one of the rings. In all, there are ten electron structures that contribute to the resonance state. Chemical evidence of reso-

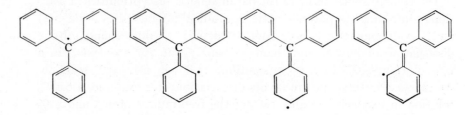

nance is that under certain conditions triphenylmethyl dimerizes to the hydrocarbon formulated by condensation of one radical into a *p*-position of another. This stable and unreactive hydrocarbon (m.p. 234°) was initially mistaken for hexaphenylethane.

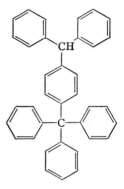

The triphenylmethyl group can enter into the formation of both positive and negative ions. Colorless solutions of triphenylcarbinol in alcohol or acetic acid become intensely colored on addition of mineral acids owing to formation of ionized halochromic salts:

$$(C_6H_5)_3COH + HX \longrightarrow [(C_6H_5)_3C]^+ + X^- + H_2O$$

On the other hand, addition of finely powdered sodium to a solution of the triphenylmethyl radical in ether-benzene or in liquid ammonia produces intensely red solutions of the ionic but nevertheless ether-soluble triphenylmethylsodium:

$$(C_6H_5)_3C + Na \longrightarrow [(C_6H_5)_3C]^- + Na^+$$

The relationship of the two ions to the radical is shown in the following electronic formulas:

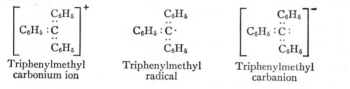

Triphenylmethyl carbonium ion	Triphenylmethyl radical	Triphenylmethyl carbanion

Cation and anion

SUMMARY

Aromatics from coal tar. Hydrocarbons: benzene, toluene, xylenes, naphthalene, phenanthrene, anthracene. Thiophene (S): accidental discovery, resonance energy 29 kg.-cal. (benzene, 30 kg.-cal.). Nitrogen bases: pyridine, picolines (methylpyridines), quinoline and isoquinoline (naphthalene analogs). Pyridine more aromatic than benzene: resonance energy 43 kg.-cal.

Boiling points: benzene 80° (mol. wt. 78); 30° rise for each added methyl group, regardless of position. Melting points: highest for isomers of greatest symmetry (*p*-xylene 13°, durene 80°, hexamethylbenzene 166°).

Preparation and Synthesis

Formation from aliphatics. (*a*) Acetylene ⟶ benzene (no preparative value). (*b*) Camphor ⟶ *p*-cymene (demonstrates stability of aromatic structure). (*c*) Acetone ⟶ mesitylene; cyclohexanone ⟶ dodecahydrotriphenylene.

Wurtz-Fittig synthesis: ArX + RX + 2 Na ⟶ Ar·R. By-products Ar·R and R·R of such different types and b.p.'s that separation is possible. Yields fair (e.g. *n*-butylbenzene from bromobenzene).

Friedel-Crafts alkylation: di- or triphenylmethane from benzyl chloride or chloroform and benzene; durene (sym. isomer of high m.p., separable from mixture by crystallization) from benzene or from xylene mixture. Chief catalysts in order of potency: $AlCl_3 > HF > H_2SO_4 > SnCl_4 > BF_3 > ZnCl_2$. *o,p*-Alkylation under mild conditions (low temp., minimum catalysis). Benzene ⟶ 1,2,4-trialkylbenzene. *m*-Alkylation under forcing conditions. Benzene ⟶ mesitylene or 1,3,5-triethylbenzene. Theory: 1,2,4-derivative is formed initially and the 1-methyl group (*ortho*) rearranges to a less hindered position (*meta*). Primary alkyl groups rearrange to secondary or tertiary (formation and isomerization of carbonium ion).

Friedel-Crafts acylation with acid chlorides or anhydrides. Need 1 equivalent of $AlCl_3$ per carbonyl group, since RCOCl forms coordinate covalent complex with AlCl₃ (Lewis acid) that dissociates to $C_6H_5\overset{+}{C}=O$, the active electrophilic agent that attacks benzene. Resulting ketone also forms complex, which is decomposed on addition of water. Applicability limited to aromatic compounds containing no unsaturated groups (COR, CO₂R, CN, NO₂, SO₃H). Nitrobenzene useful as solvent (inert; dissolves AlCl₃ by complex formation). Ring closure of γ-phenylbutyric acid by intramolecular Friedel-Crafts reaction on acid chloride (or by treating free acid with liquid HF).

Clemmensen reduction: amalgamated zinc and concd. HCl. Improvements of Martin (add layer of toluene) and of Sherman (use freshly poured zinc, stir mechanically).

Dehydrogenation of hydroaromatics: S at 240°, Se at 315°, Pd-C at 180°. Examples: synthesis of naphthalene and of α-methylnaphthalene.

Grignard syntheses, for example condensation of ArMgBr with CH₂=CHCH₂Br, with an aldehyde or ketone, or with (CH₃)₂SO₄.

Hydrolysis of sulfonates (dil. H₂SO₄ at 135–200°). Useful for isolation and separation: fractional crystallization of sulfonate mixture, desulfonation; partial sulfonation of xylene mixture (reactivity: m-xylene > o-xylene > p-xylene). Synthetic use: block 2 and 4 positions of phenol by sulfonation, brominate at position 6, remove the SO₃H groups.

Decarboxylation of acids. Benzoic acid ⟶ benzene; cinnamic acid ⟶ styrene (goes more readily because COOH is on ethylenic double bond). Furfural (from corncobs) ⟶ furoic acid (by Cannizzaro reaction) ⟶ furan (resonance energy 24 kg.-cal.).

Zinc-dust distillation: phenolic substance ⟶ hydrocarbon. Use in characterization of natural products.

Properties

Oxidation of alkyl side chains. $C_6H_5CH_3 \longrightarrow C_6H_5CO_2H$ (activation by unsaturated phenyl group). Oxidation of $(C_6H_5)_2CH_2$, $(C_6H_5)_3CH$, polyalkylbenzenes.

Free radicals. Gomberg's triphenylmethyl (1900). Reactivity (O₂ gives peroxide); color of solutions. Hexaphenylethane 3% dissociated (0.08 M solution at 5°); dissociation increased to 74–95% by replacement of phenyl groups by o-methoxyphenyl or p-biphenyl groups. Theory of resonance stabilization of the radicals. Evidence of the Chichibabin hydrocarbon. Conversion of triphenylcarbinol with HX into triphenylmethyl carbonium ion and of triphenylmethyl with Na into triphenylmethyl carbanion.

PROBLEMS

1. Suggest methods for the Friedel-Crafts synthesis of (a) t-butylbenzene, (b) p-di-t-butylbenzene.
2. How could p-$(CH_3)_3CC_6H_4CO_2H$ be synthesized starting with toluene?
3. Devise a synthesis of p-$(CH_3)_2CHC_6H_4CO_2H$ starting with benzene.
4. What products would you expect to result from the following reactions?
   (a) $C_6H_6 + (CH_3)_2C=CH_2 + HF$
   (b) $C_6H_5CH_2CH_3 + (CH_3)_2CHCl + BF_3$
   (c) $C_6H_5CH_2CH_3 + 2\ CH_3CH_2Cl + AlCl_3$ (2 equivalents, no cooling)
   (d) $C_6H_5CH_3 + CH_3COCl + AlCl_3$ (1 equivalent)
5. Indicate syntheses of n-butylbenzene utilizing any aliphatic components desired and starting with: (a) benzene, (b) bromobenzene, (c) benzaldehyde.
6. Work out a synthesis of α-phenylnaphthalene starting with benzene and succinic anhydride.
7. Devise a synthesis of β-methylnaphthalene from toluene and succinic anhydride.
8. Give two ways of preparing α-methylnaphthalene from α-bromonaphthalene.
9. Suggest a synthesis of $C_6H_5(CH_2)_5COOH$, starting with bromobenzene and cyclohexanone.

READING REFERENCES

E. L. Martin, "The Clemmensen Reduction," in R. Adams, *Organic Reactions*, I, 155–209, Wiley, New York (1942)

M. Gomberg, "The Existence of Free Radicals," *J. Am. Chem. Soc.*, **36**, 1144–1170 (1914)

W. E. Bachmann, "Free Radicals," in H. Gilman, *Organic Chemistry*, I, 2nd Ed., 581–630, Wiley, New York (1943)

W. A. Waters, "Some Recent Developments in the Chemistry of Free Radicals," *J. Chem. Soc.*, 409 (1946)

M. E. Cameron, "Victor Meyer and the Thiophene Compounds," *J. Chem. Educ.*, **26**, 521 (1949)

NITRO COMPOUNDS AND SULFONIC ACIDS

NITRO COMPOUNDS

Nitration, conducted with nitric acid alone or in combination with acetic acid, acetic anhydride, or sulfuric acid, provides an efficient method for preparation of mono-, di-, and trinitro derivatives of use as solvents, explosives, dyes, and analytical reagents, or important as intermediates for primary amines, into which they are convertible by reduction. Introduction of a (polarized) nitro group produces an increase in boiling point out of proportion to the increase in molecular weight, amounting to 120–130° for the nitro derivatives of benzene and toluene. Nitrobenzene (b.p. 210°) has about the same molecular weight (123.11) as mesitylene (120.19), but the boiling point is higher by 46°. Nitro compounds are heavier than water, and unless they contain a solubilizing group, they are insoluble in water. They dissolve in cold concentrated sulfuric acid, usually without permanent change, as the result of formation of oxonium salts. Technical preparations of nitrobenzene, trinitrobenzene, and trinitrotoluene usually are yellowish, but the purified substances are colorless.

High boiling points

Nitrobenzene. — Nitrobenzene can be produced on a technical scale in yields up to 98% by nitration of benzene with mixed acid at 50–55°. It is a colorless hygroscopic liquid, immiscible with water and volatile with steam, D_4^{25} 1.197. It has a characteristic sweetish odor and was once called oil of mirbane because the smell is reminiscent of that of oil of bitter almonds. Nitrobenzene has remarkable solvent power for organic compounds and is employed as a crystallizing solvent for substances that are practically insoluble in more usual solvents, though it has the disadvantage of being somewhat difficult to remove from crystals owing to low volatility and of acting as a mild oxidizing agent at temperatures near the boiling point. It also dissolves anhy-

A useful solvent

drous aluminum chloride as the result of complex formation, and is a useful solvent for the Friedel-Crafts reaction.

Nitrobenzene is toxic and is taken into the body both by inhalation of the vapor and by absorption through the skin. It produces chronic intoxication and turns the blood a chocolate brown color owing to either oxidation of hemoglobin to methemoglobin (ferric) or formation of a complex, Hb—nitrobenzene. The substance is excreted in part as *p*-aminophenol. The methyl homologs are not poisonous, apparently because a mechanism is available for their elimination from the system. Thus *p*-nitrotoluene is oxidized in the body to *p*-nitrobenzoic acid, which presumably is excreted in conjugation with glycine.

Nitration of nitrobenzene under rather drastic conditions affords *m*-dinitrobenzene; reaction with fuming sulfuric acid gives *m*-nitrobenzenesulfonic acid with only traces of the *ortho* and *para* isomers; and the chief product of catalyzed chlorination is *m*-nitrochlorobenzene. When warmed with powdered potassium hydroxide, nitrobenzene undergoes a reaction that contrasts with these normal *meta* substitutions; the material is converted in part into a mixture of the oxidation products *o*- and *p*-nitrophenol, in which the former predominates, and in part into a product of reduction, azoxybenzene.

Nucleophilic substitution

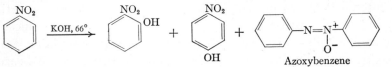

The reaction proceeds in the absence of oxygen and is a disproportionation; it is of little practical value but of theoretical significance. Unlike the characteristic *meta* substitutions, where the nucleus is attacked by an electrophilic positive ion or fragment, hydroxylation induced by hydroxide anion represents nucleophilic attack, and the fact that the hydroxyl group enters the *ortho* and *para* positions substantiates the general theory of aromatic substitutions; resonance in nitrobenzene renders these positions centers of low electron density, or of a relatively positive character.

20.3   **Nitrotoluenes.** — The mixtures of *o*- and *p*-nitrotoluene resulting in nearly theoretical yield from nitration of toluene can be separated sharply on a technical scale by fractional distillation in vacuum, for the isomers differ more than usual in boiling point (b.p. 222° and 238°, respectively).

Dinitrobenzenes. — The *ortho* and *para* isomers are obtainable in two steps from the appropriate nitroaniline, which can be oxidized with Caro's acid (H_2SO_5) to the nitroso compound, as in the example.
20.4   The nitroso derivative is then oxidized with dilute nitric acid or with nitric acid containing hydrogen peroxide.

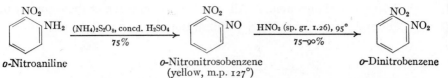

o-Nitroaniline   o-Nitronitrosobenzene
(yellow, m.p. 127°)   o-Dinitrobenzene

The *ortho* and *para* isomers differ decidedly in chemical behavior from the product of normal nitration, *m*-dinitrobenzene, the nitro groups of which are reducible but are otherwise inert. In *o*- and *p*-dinitrobenzene one nitro group labilizes the other, as indicated by the fact that one of the groups is easily displaced by hydroxyl, methoxyl, amino, or halo groups, as illustrated. This activation is another manifestation of the general phenomenon illustrated above in the

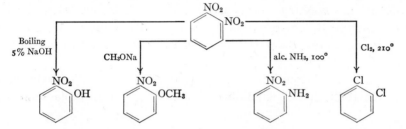

ortho-para hydroxylation of nitro compounds by interaction with alkali. The key atom of the nitro group is positively polarized and by the resonance effect establishes positive centers at the *ortho* and *para* positions; a second positively polarized group located at such a center presents a situation of incompatibility and hence is easily displaced by a group of the opposite character. The nucleophilic displacement induced by alkali can be pictured as an attack by an anion

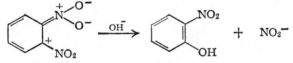

*Nucleophilic
displacement*

at a positive carbon atom in one of the resonance structures with expulsion of nitrite ion. *m*-Dinitrobenzene represents a state of electronic compatibility of the substituent groups and is inert to alcoholic ammonia even at 250°. On the other hand, it is susceptible to nucleophilic attack at the relatively electron-poor centers *ortho* and *para* to the two nitro groups, and can be partially hydroxylated by the action of powdered potassium hydroxide or by oxidation with potassium ferricyanide in alkaline solution.

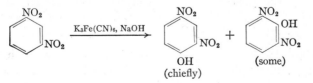

377

Nitrochlorobenzenes. — All three mononitrochlorobenzenes can be obtained from benzene by combination of the reactions of nitration

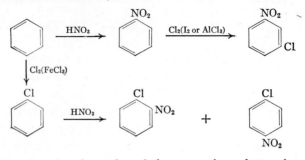

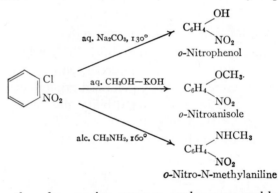

and halogenation, for the order of the operations determines the final orientation. *m*-Nitrochlorobenzene is obtained by nitration of benzene followed by chlorination, but if the order is reversed a mixture results containing about two parts of the *para* isomer to one of the *ortho*.

The halogen atom in *o*- or *p*-nitrochlorobenzene is distinctly more reactive than that in chlorobenzene, and is readily replaceable by

Labile halogen

hydroxyl, methoxyl, or amino groups; under comparably mild conditions chlorobenzene remains unattacked. The reactions illustrated for *o*-nitrochlorobenzene are paralleled in the *para* series, but no comparable reactivity of the halogen atom is discoverable in the *meta* isomer, for the chlorine atom in *m*-nitrochlorobenzene has the same normal inert character as that of chlorobenzene; for example the *meta* compound is inert to amines even in the temperature range 180–190°. The labilizing influence of the nitro group on halogen in the *ortho* or *para*, but not in the *meta*, position can be attributed to the incompatibility of the positive, or electron-poor, centers set up through resonance and to the electron-attracting character of the halogen atom; hence the susceptibility of such halogen atoms to nucleophilic displacement by anionic reagents is understandable. The chlorine atom of 2,4-dinitrochlorobenzene is even more labile in the same sense, as illustrated by the smooth reaction of the substance with aniline to give a diphenylamine derivative. A comparable reaction with alcoholic ammonia occurs even at room temperature.

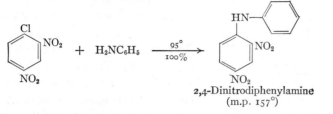

2,4-Dinitrodiphenylamine
(m.p. 157°)

2,4,6-Trinitrotoluene (TNT, m.p. 81°). — The preparation of this important high explosive is accomplished by nitration of toluene with mixed acid, usually in three steps, with utilization of the spent acid from trinitration for the dinitration, and of the spent acid from dinitration for mononitration. The main end product, the 2,4,6-trinitro derivative (VI), is formed through the intermediates II–V. Monosubstitution gives the *ortho* and *para* isomers in a ratio varying some-

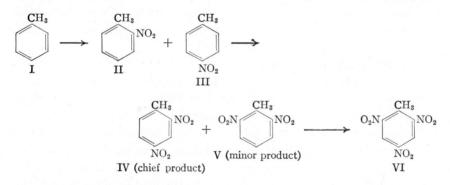

IV (chief product) V (minor product) VI

what with temperature, and the mixture contains a small amount (4%) of *m*-nitrotoluene. In the next step the *p*-nitro compound III yields exclusively 2,4-dinitrotoluene (IV) by substitution *ortho* to the methyl and *meta* to the nitro group; in the *o*-nitro isomer II, comparable positions are available at 4 and 6 but substitution occurs preponderantly at the point of the stronger *para* direction by the methyl group, and gives the same 2,4-isomer; 2,6-dinitrotoluene (V, m.p. 65°) is produced in only minor amounts. Both dinitro compounds are converted on further nitration into the same trinitro derivative VI, or TNT. On a technical scale, overall yields of purified TNT up to 85% are realized.

1,3,5-Trinitrobenzene (TNB, m.p. 122°). — The marked deactivating influence of nitro groups is well illustrated by the difficulty of preparing trinitrobenzene by direct nitration. One procedure calls for heating 60 g. of *m*-dinitrobenzene with 1 kg. of fuming sulfuric acid and $\frac{1}{2}$ kg. of fuming nitric acid (sp. gr. 1.52) at 100–110° for five days; the yield is 45%. No practicable procedure has been found for preparing trinitrobenzene from benzene, though the substance has greater explosive power than trinitrotoluene. Trinitrotoluene is the commonly used high explosive because it can be prepared readily by direct nitration of the hydrocarbon, thanks to the activating influence of the methyl group in counteracting, to a sufficient extent, the influence of the nitro groups. The methyl group in TNT thus is required for the production, and not for the functioning, of the substance. The usual laboratory preparation of trinitrobenzene is indirect and consists in the degradation of trinitrotoluene by oxidation in concentrated

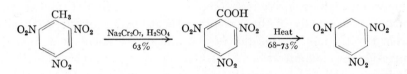

sulfuric acid solution with sodium dichromate. The product, 2,4,6-trinitrobenzoic acid, loses carbon dioxide with such readiness that decarboxylation is accomplished by heating a suspension in water to the boiling point.

20.8   **Picric Acid (m.p. 122°).** — Picric acid, the 2,4,6-trinitro derivative of phenol, cannot be prepared satisfactorily by the action of nitric acid because phenol is so sensitive to oxidation that much of the material is destroyed rather than nitrated. A satisfactory procedure consists in first sulfonating phenol to the 2,4-disulfonic acid and then adding nitric acid to the reaction mixture. The unsaturated sulfonic acid groups provide protection against the oxidizing action of nitric acid, and since sulfonation is reversible, the acid groups are smoothly

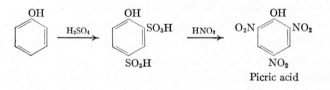

Picric acid

replaced by nitro groups. The process is simple and a yield of 70% is obtainable. A still more economical method utilizes chlorobenzene as the starting material; this can be converted efficiently into the 2,4-dinitro derivative, which, by virtue of its highly labile halogen, is readily hydrolyzed to the dinitrophenol; the latter is then nitrated. Chlorobenzene is a cheaper starting material than phenol, and in a modern process phenol is made from chlorobenzene in a reaction requiring a high temperature and pressure because of the inert char-

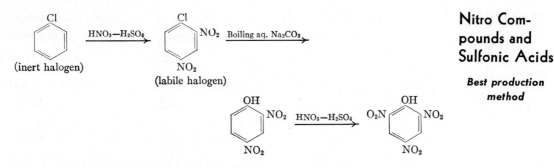

acter of the halogen. In the picric acid process, replacement of halogen
by hydroxyl is accomplished at a stage where it proceeds under mild
conditions.

Picric acid is formed by the action of nitric acid on a number of
organic substances containing a benzene ring, often as a result of extensive oxidative degradation, displacement of attached groups by
nitro substituents, and hydrolysis of a nitrogen substituent with
formation of a hydroxyl group. Thus the substance arises from the

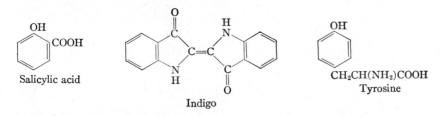

Salicylic acid · Indigo · Tyrosine

action of nitric acid on salicylic acid or on indigo, and was first obtained from the latter source (1771). Picric acid is characterized by
a bitter taste and strongly acidic nature as well as by a yellow color.
It was observed to be formed by the action of nitric acid on silk
(1799), the specific source probably being the tyrosine units in the
protein. Dumas (1836) established the correct composition and introduced the present name (Gr. *pikros*, bitter), and Laurent (1841) recognized the substance as a trinitro derivative of phenol and prepared it
from the parent compound. Picric acid was found to stain proteins
yellow and was introduced as a dye for silk in 1849, the first instance
of the use of an artificial dye. Application as an explosive was announced in an English patent (1871). The versatile nitro compound
also has bactericidal activity and formerly found use in the treatment
of burns, and it is employed in the laboratory for characterization of
organic bases (amine picrates) and of polynuclear hydrocarbons
(hydrocarbon-picrate complexes, 20.12). The substance has a pK_a
of 0.80 and approaches the mineral acids in acidic strength and ability
to corrode metals.

Tetryl. — The common name of this useful explosive is an abbreviation of N,2,4,6-tetranitro-N-methylaniline, and the compound

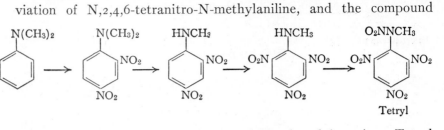

Tetryl

can be described also as methyl-2,4,6-trinitrophenylnitramine. Tetryl is prepared from N,N-dimethylaniline, which suffers loss of one methyl group by oxidation:

$$-\text{N(CH}_3)_2 \longrightarrow -\text{N(CH}_3)\text{COOH} \longrightarrow -\text{NHCH}_3 + \text{CO}_2$$

20.10

Explosives. — Among compounds with adequate explosive power, the most important factor in determining specific applications is sensitivity to shock of impact, as measured by the height from which a weight must fall for its impact to cause a small sample of the sub-

	Trinitrobenzene	
	Ammonium picrate	High explosives
Increasing	TNT	
impact	Compressed picric acid	
sensitivity	Tetryl	Boosters
↓	Lead azide	
	Mercury fulminate	Detonators

stance to explode. The relatively impact-resistant nitro compounds are classified as high explosives and are detonated by the shock of one of the primary explosives listed as detonators:

$$\overset{-}{\text{C}}\equiv\overset{+}{\text{N}}-\text{O}-\text{Hg}-\text{O}-\overset{+}{\text{N}}\equiv\overset{-}{\text{C}} \qquad \overset{-}{\text{N}}=\overset{+}{\text{N}}=\text{N}-\text{Pb}-\text{N}=\overset{+}{\text{N}}=\overset{-}{\text{N}}$$

Mercury fulminate   Lead azide

Tetryl occupies an intermediate place in the scale, and is not sensitive enough to serve as a detonator but is too easily exploded to be employed as the main charge in a shell or bomb; the intermediate character renders the substance an ideal booster. TNT is the most widely used filling for shells and air-borne demolition bombs. It is sufficiently insensitive to withstand the shock entailed in the ejection of a shell from a gun barrel under the pressure developed from ignition of a propellant charge, and can be caused to explode on operation of an impact- or time-fuse mechanism firing a detonator-booster element. It is the only explosive nitro compound that melts below 100°, and it is conveniently melted with steam and poured into shells and bombs. Cast TNT is less sensitive than crystalline or pelleted material and is not exploded by a fulminate blasting cap or a lead azide detonator, but satisfactory operation is obtained with either type of detonator in combination with a charge of tetryl representing only a fraction of the charge of TNT; the booster is exploded by the detonator and produces a wave sufficient to set off the TNT. Ammonium picrate is less sensitive to shock and finds specific use as a charge for armor-piercing shells because it withstands the shock of severe impact better than the slightly more sensitive TNT and is conserved for explosion under detonation after the shell has penetrated.

REDUCTION OF NITRO COMPOUNDS

By reduction with a sufficiently powerful reagent such as stannous chloride in hydrochloric acid solution, nitrobenzene can be converted in high yield into aniline. By use of milder reagents and by control of the acidity or alkalinity of the reaction mixture, it is possible to produce a number of substances of various intermediate stages of reduction, some of which are products of direct reduction, whereas others arise through secondary changes. Particularly comprehensive studies have been made of electrolytic reduction (Haber, 1900), where exact control is possible through adjustment of the imposed potential, current density, and hydrogen-ion concentration, and the results indicate that the sequence of primary reduction steps is as follows:

20.11

$$C_6H_5NO_2 \xrightarrow{\text{2 H}} C_6H_5NO \xrightarrow{\text{2 H}} C_6H_5NHOH \xrightarrow{\text{2 H}} C_6H_5NH_2$$

Nitrobenzene Nitrosobenzene Phenylhydroxyl- Aniline
amine

Reduction sequence

Both nitrosobenzene and phenylhydroxylamine are reactive, and under the catalytic influence of alkali they condense with elimination of a molecule of water in a manner reminiscent of aldol condensation and afford azoxybenzene. Azoxybenzene is made up of two units

$$C_6H_5\overset{\text{...}}{N}=O \; + \; H\overset{|}{N}-C_6H_5 \xrightarrow{OH^-(-H_2O)} C_6H_5-N\overset{+}{=}N-C_6H_5$$

Nitrosobenzene   OH   O⁻

Phenylhydroxylamine   Azoxybenzene

Secondary product

derived from nitrobenzene molecules linked through the nitrogen atoms, one of which carries an oxygen atom joined by a semipolar bond. This oxygen is readily removed during electrolytic reduction or by treatment with iron powder and water, with formation of azobenzene, which, in turn, can add two hydrogen atoms and form hydrazobenzene. A terminal reaction stage is reached with reductive

$$C_6H_5-N\overset{+}{=}N-C_6H_5 \xrightarrow{\text{2 H}} C_6H_5N=NC_6H_5 \longrightarrow C_6H_5N-NC_6H_5$$

O⁻   Azobenzene   H H

Azoxybenzene   Hydrazobenzene

383

fission of the bond linking the nitrogen atoms in hydrazobenzene, with formation of two molecules of aniline. Both the intermediate reduc-

Terminal step

$$C_6H_5N\!\!\mid\!\!NC_6H_5 \xrightarrow{\ 2\,H\ } C_6H_5NH_2 + H_2NC_6H_5$$
$$\overset{|}{H}\ \overset{|}{H} \qquad\qquad\qquad Aniline$$
Hydrazobenzene

tion products and the substances derived from them by secondary transformations are thus convertible into aniline.

It is of interest that although the nitro group is attacked by most reducing agents it is stable to aluminum isopropoxide. Thus nitro compounds containing carbonyl groups can be reduced selectively by the Meerwein-Ponndorf method, for example:

Meerwein-Ponndorf reduction

$$o\text{-}NO_2C_6H_4CHO \xrightarrow[90\%]{Al(OC_3H_7)_3} o\text{-}NO_2C_6H_4CH_2OH$$
$$o\text{-Nitrobenzaldehyde} \qquad\qquad o\text{-Nitrobenzyl alcohol}$$

Rearrangement Products. — Two useful products result from nitrobenzene through processes of rearrangement to the *para* position, namely *p*-aminophenol from phenylhydroxylamine and benzidine, or *p,p'*-diaminodiphenyl, from hydrazobenzene:

$$C_6H_5NHOH \xrightarrow{H^+} HOC_6H_4NH_2(p)$$

Benzidine

$$C_6H_5NHNHC_6H_5 \xrightarrow{H^+} (p)H_2NC_6H_4\cdot C_6H_4NH_2(p')$$

HYDROCARBON—POLYNITRO COMPOUND COMPLEXES

20.12

When concentrated solutions of picric acid and naphthalene in benzene or alcohol are mixed at room temperature, golden yellow needles of a substance having a higher melting point (150°) than either component and having a more pronounced yellow color than picric acid soon separate. The substance is a molecular complex containing

Picrates

equivalent amounts of the hydrocarbon and the polynitro compound, and in solution it dissociates to the components till an equilibrium is established. Benzene forms only a very labile complex that reverts to picric acid on brief exposure to air, but naphthalene, anthracene, and phenanthrene form stable complexes. These are commonly called picrates, but should not be confused with salts of the acid with amines or inorganic bases. The condensed-ring polynuclear hydrocarbons

TNB and TNT complexes

form similar molecular complexes with trinitrobenzene and trinitrotoluene, which, like the picrates, are of value in isolation, purification, and identification of hydrocarbons. Regeneration of a hydrocarbon from its purified picrate can be accomplished by extraction of the acid from a benzene or ether solution of the complex with aqueous ammonia; the neutral complexes can be split by chromatography on alumina, on which the nitro component is the more strongly adsorbed.

SULFONIC ACIDS

The arylsulfonic acids resulting from sulfonation are derivatives of sulfuric acid in which one hydroxyl is replaced by an aryl group, $ArSO_2OH$, and they resemble the parent acid in chemical and physical properties. They are comparable in acidic strength to sulfuric acid; they are very hygroscopic, liberally soluble in water, but less destructive. For this reason p-toluenesulfonic acid is preferred to sulfuric acid as catalyst for esterification, dehydration, and ketal formation. Isolation of a free acid is accomplished by moderate dilution of the sulfonation mixture with water and addition of concentrated hydrochloric acid; the solubility is decreased by the common-ion effect and the sulfonic acid crystallizes on cooling, usually as a hydrate. A minor by-product is the diaryl sulfone, $ArSO_2Ar$, but this is insoluble in water and is easily eliminated.

Free acids

Usually the free sulfonic acids are not isolated but are converted directly into the sodium or potassium salts. One procedure is to pour the sulfonation mixture into water and add excess sodium chloride. Since the arylsulfonic acid has the same acidic strength as hydrochloric acid, an equilibrium is set up, and the solubility of the sodium

$$C_6H_5SO_3H + NaCl \rightleftharpoons C_6H_5SO_3Na + HCl$$

Sodium sulfonates

sulfonate is so decreased as the result of the excess sodium-ion concentration that the substance readily crystallizes. This process of salting out with common salt can be employed also in recrystallization of the product, but sodium benzenesulfonate is so very soluble in water that a large amount of sodium chloride is required and the product is liable to be contaminated with inorganic material. A pure product is sometimes obtainable by crystallization from absolute ethanol; sodium benzenesulfonate dissolves in this solvent, though sparingly, whereas sodium chloride is insoluble. Sulfonates derived from polynuclear aromatic compounds are insoluble in methanol or ethanol, but can be prepared in salt-free condition by an alternate process that depends on the solubility of sodium acetate in methanol. The sulfonate is repeatedly salted out from aqueous solution with sodium acetate in order to replace sodium chloride as a contaminant by sodium acetate, which is then removed by repeated extraction of the dried and powdered product with boiling methanol. Another method of obtaining a sodium salt from a sulfonation reaction mixture containing excess sulfuric acid is to neutralize the diluted mixture with calcium hydroxide or with barium carbonate. The calcium or barium sulfonate can be extracted with hot water and thus separated from a residue of the inorganic sulfate, and the aqueous extract is then treated with sodium carbonate to precipitate an insoluble carbonate and give a solution that on evaporation affords the sodium salt of the sulfonic acid.

Usually sodium and ammonium sulfonates are more soluble in water than other salts; potassium salts are slightly less soluble and often crystallize better, and barium and calcium salts are distinctly less soluble. The metal salts are infusible and insoluble in ether. Amine salts, such as those formed with *p*-toluidine, are composed of two organic parts, and they are less soluble in water than the alkalimetal salts and often crystallizable from alcohol or alcohol-water mixtures; also they have characteristic melting points. The *p*-

*p-Toluidine salts
for characterization*

$$\text{ArSO}_3\text{H} \ + \ \text{CH}_3\text{C}_6\text{H}_4\text{NH}_2 \ \longrightarrow \ \text{ArSO}_3\overset{-}{\text{N}}\overset{+}{\text{H}}_3\text{C}_6\text{H}_4\text{CH}_3$$
$$\text{\textit{p}-Toluidine salt}$$

toluidine salts thus are useful derivatives for characterization, and they are easily prepared by addition of the amine and hydrochloric acid to a solution of a sodium salt:

$$\text{ArSO}_3\text{Na} \ + \ \text{NH}_2\text{C}_6\text{H}_4\text{CH}_3 \ + \ \text{HCl} \ \longrightarrow \ \text{ArSO}_3\overset{-}{\text{N}}\overset{+}{\text{H}}_3\text{C}_6\text{H}_4\text{CH}_3 \ + \ \text{NaCl}$$

The sulfonate group often is introduced to provide water solubility, particularly in the case of dyes. Another use is separation of hydrocarbon mixtures by virtue of the crystallizing properties of the sulfonates and the readily accomplished desulfonation, as illustrated for the xylenes (19.12). Chemical transformations of the aromatic sulfonates are not numerous but are useful.

20.14   **Acid Chlorides.** — Arylsulfonic acids, either free or as salts, are convertible into acid chlorides, ArSO_2Cl, by the methods applicable to preparation of the chlorides of carboxylic acids, namely by interaction with phosphorus halides. Alternate procedures for the preparation of benzenesulfonyl chloride are indicated as follows:

1. $3\ \text{C}_6\text{H}_5\text{SO}_2\text{ONa} \ + \ \text{PCl}_5 \ \xrightarrow[\text{75-80\%}]{170-180°} \ 3\ \text{C}_6\text{H}_5\text{SO}_2\text{Cl} \ + \ 2\ \text{NaCl} \ + \ \text{NaPO}_3$

2. $2\ \text{C}_6\text{H}_5\text{SO}_2\text{ONa} \ + \ \text{POCl}_3 \ \xrightarrow[\text{74-87\%}]{170-180°} \ 2\ \text{C}_6\text{H}_5\text{SO}_2\text{Cl} \ + \ \text{NaCl} \ + \ \text{NaPO}_3$

The reaction mixture is cooled and treated with water and ice, and the acid chloride separating as an oil is collected, dried, and distilled. Another method is the action of at least two equivalents of chlorosulfonic acid on benzene:

*Use of chloro-
sulfonic acid*

3. $\text{C}_6\text{H}_6 \ + \ \underset{\text{(3 equiv.)}}{2\ \text{ClSO}_2\text{OH}} \ \xrightarrow[\text{75-77\%}]{20-25°} \ \text{C}_6\text{H}_5\text{SO}_2\text{Cl} \ + \ \text{H}_2\text{SO}_4 \ + \ \text{HCl}$

If chlorosulfonic acid is not used in excess, a significant amount of diphenyl sulfone is formed as a by-product, and when an aromatic hydrocarbon is treated in carbon tetrachloride solution with just one equivalent of chlorosulfonic acid, the reaction product is the free sulfonic acid:

$$C_6H_6 \ + \ ClSO_2OH \ \longrightarrow \ C_6H_5SO_2OH \ + \ HCl$$

Production of the acid chloride with use of excess reagent probably proceeds through formation of the free acid and replacement of hydroxyl by the chlorine of chlorosulfonic acid.

Benzenesulfonyl chloride is an easily solidified liquid, m.p. 14.4°, b.p. 251.5°. It can be digested with cold water with little hydrolysis, but reacts readily with alcohols and with ammonia, as described below, and it is useful as a reagent in the Hinsberg test for characterization of amines of different types (11.10). A reagent often preferred because it is a solid is p-toluenesulfonyl chloride, m.p. 69°.

Esters. — Ester derivatives of sulfonic acids are sometimes prepared for purposes of identification, but they are lower melting and less easily prepared than the p-toluidine salts. The preparation is

1. $ArSO_3Na \ + \ (CH_3)_2SO_4 \ \xrightarrow{\text{150–160°}} \ ArSO_3CH_3 \ + \ CH_3NaSO_4$

2. $ArSO_2Cl \ + \ HOCH_3 \ \longrightarrow \ ArSO_2OCH_3 \ + \ HCl$

accomplished either (1) by heating the solid sodium salt of the acid with dimethyl or diethyl sulfate or (2) by the action of an alcohol or of a sodium alkoxide (in ether) on the acid chloride. The methyl ester of benzenesulfonic acid is a liquid that is slowly hydrolyzed by water at room temperature. The homolog, methyl p-toluenesulfonate, $CH_3C_6H_4SO_3CH_3$, melts at 28°.

Sulfonamides. — The acid chlorides react readily with ammonia or with amines to form sulfonamides. Thus benzenesulfonyl chloride affords benzenesulfonamide when shaken with aqueous ammonia or on interaction with solid ammonium carbonate. This easily prepared derivative is a neutral substance which crystallizes well from alcohol,

$$C_6H_5SO_2Cl \ + \ NH_3 \ \longrightarrow \ C_6H_5SO_2NH_2 \ + \ HCl$$
$$\text{Benzenesulfonamide}$$
$$\text{(m.p. 156°)}$$

and in general sulfonamides are satisfactory derivatives for characterization of aromatic sulfonic acids.

Chloroamides. — The action of sodium hypochlorite on a sulfonamide results in substitution of halogen for an amide hydrogen atom. p-Toluenesulfonamide is converted initially into the N-monochloro derivative, known as chloramine-T:

$$p\text{-}CH_3C_6H_4SO_2NH_2 \ + \ NaOCl \ \longrightarrow \ p\text{-}CH_3C_6H_4SO_2NHCl \ + \ NaOH$$

20.15

20.16

20.17

387

This substance slowly liberates hypochlorous acid on contact with water and is an effective antiseptic agent used for treatment of wounds. The active chlorine atom is described as positive.

Saccharin (*o*-Sulfobenzoic Acid Imide). — The cyclic imide of *o*-sulfobenzoic acid was first prepared by Remsen[1] (1879) and found to have extraordinary sweetness of taste. The substance is about

550 times as sweet as cane sugar, and the aqueous solution retains a detectable sweet taste at a dilution of 1:100,000. It is employed as a sweetening agent, particularly by diabetics incapable of tolerating sugar, and is excreted unchanged in the urine. The technical preparation is essentially that introduced by Remsen, namely oxidation of *o*-toluenesulfonamide with aqueous permanganate solution at 35°. The *o*-sulfonamidobenzoic acid initially formed undergoes spontaneous loss of water in a neutral or weakly alkaline solution with closure of the heterocyclic ring. The starting material is obtained from the mixture of *ortho* and *para* acids resulting from sulfonation

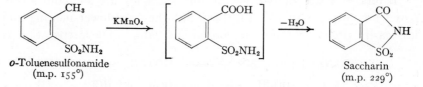

o-Toluenesulfonamide (m.p. 155°)   Saccharin (m.p. 229°)

of toluene; the acids are converted into acid chlorides by phosphorus pentachloride, the solid *p*-toluenesulfonyl chloride is largely removed by freezing, and the liquid residue containing the *ortho* compound treated with ammonia. Saccharin is sparingly soluble in cold water, but the doubly activated imino hydrogen atom is acidic, and saccharin forms a water-soluble sodium salt.

A substance of still greater sweetening power has been described by Verkade (1946); 1-*n*-propoxy-2-amino-4-nitrobenzene is 4000 times as sweet as cane sugar.

Alkali Fusion of Sulfonates. — An important use of sulfonic acids is the preparation of phenols, accomplished by fusion with molten sodium or potassium hydroxide in the temperature range 290–340°. The sulfonate group is replaced by the —ONa(K) group, and the phenol is obtained by treating the cooled melt with ice and hydrochloric acid:

$$ArSO_3Na + NaOH \longrightarrow ArONa + NaHSO_3$$
$$ArONa + HCl \longrightarrow ArOH + NaCl$$

A typical laboratory procedure is illustrated for the preparation of β-naphthol. A charge of potassium hydroxide is placed in a nickel, copper, or iron crucible, along with a small amount of water to render

---

[1] Ira Remsen, 1846–1927; b. New York; Ph.D. Göttingen; Williams Coll., Johns Hopkins Univ.

the material more easily fusible, and heated over a free flame to a temperature of about 250°. The melt is stirred with a thermometer

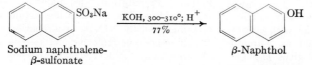

Sodium naphthalene-β-sulfonate   β-Naphthol

enclosed in a protective metal case while the fully dried and powdered sodium naphthalene-β-sulfonate is added. The solid only partly dissolves and there is no initial reaction, but as the temperature is gradually raised a critical point is reached at which the mass rapidly changes, with separation of a mobile yellow-brown layer of potassium β-naphtholate floating on an almost clear layer of alkali. The fusion is soon over, and the cooled melt is added in portions to ice and hydrochloric acid and the precipitated β-naphthol collected. The cheaper sodium hydroxide is employed where possible in technical operations, but it has less solvent action than potassium hydroxide, gives a less mobile melt, and may prove unsatisfactory. A successful compromise in some instances consists in use of mixtures of the two alkalis, as in the second example, where sodium hydroxide alone gives none of the

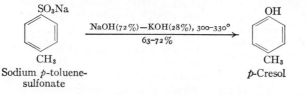

Sodium p-toluene-sulfonate   p-Cresol

desired product. A further variation, used widely in the industry and to some extent in the laboratory, is to conduct the fusion in pressure vessels with aqueous solutions of alkali. Alkali fusion is not applicable to sulfonic acids containing nitro or halo substituents.

Conversion to Nitriles. — A reaction that would appear analogous to alkali fusion is conversion of a sulfonate into a nitrile by heating with potassium cyanide or potassium ferricyanide, for example:

20.20

$$C_6H_5SO_3K \ + \ KCN \ \xrightarrow{\text{Pyrolysis}} \ C_6H_5CN \ + \ K_2SO_3$$
Benzonitrile

The nitrile reaction, however, differs in that the mixture of the dry salts remains unfused even at very high temperatures. The conditions thus are unfavorable for both chemical interaction and heat interchange. Only a small quantity of the mixture can be processed in one charge in a glass flask or retort, or else the material in the interior will not reach the pyrolysis temperature; even so the vessel usually is damaged at the temperature required to obtain the maximum amount of nitrile, which distils from the salt mixture. The yields often are poor and at best seldom exceed 50%.

Nitro compounds used as intermediates to amines, as explosives, dyes, solvents. Nitro group raises b.p. 120–130°. Soluble in H_2SO_4, oxonium salt.

Nitrobenzene, b.p. 210°, volatile with steam, high solvent power, toxic, excreted as p-amino-phenol. Under forcing conditions gives m-SO_3H, m-NO_2, and m-Cl derivatives. Reaction with KOH consists in part in nucleophilic attack by OH^- at electron-poor centers to give o- and p-nitrophenol.

Nitrotoluenes, o- and p-. Nitration of toluene, precision fractionation (16° difference in b.p.).

Dinitrobenzenes, o- and p-. From the nitroanilines by oxidation of NH_2 to NO with Caro's acid (H_2SO_5) and then oxidation with HNO_3. One of two nitro groups in o- or p-position is labile and subject to nucleophilic displacement: o-dinitrobenzene + OH^- ⟶ o-nitrophenol (labile also to CH_3ONa or NH_3). m-Dinitrobenzene not susceptible to displacement of groups but suffers nucleophilic op-substitution with KOH or alkaline ferricyanide.

Nitrochlorobenzenes. All three isomers available by combination of chlorination and nitration reactions in proper order. Halogen atom in o- and p-isomers labilized by resonance, which renders carbon atom carrying chlorine relatively positive and hence subject to nucleophilic displacement. E.g., o-nitrochlorobenzene affords o-nitrophenol on reaction with Na_2CO_3 at 130°; reacts readily with $KOCH_3$ or CH_3NH_2.

TNT. Nitration of toluene gives trinitro derivative in 85% yield under activating influence of methyl group.

TNB (1,3,5-trinitrobenzene). With no activating group present to counterbalance deactivation by groups introduced, direct nitration of benzene proceeds too poorly to be practical. TNB has superior explosive properties but is unavailable. Laboratory preparation: oxidize methyl group of TNT and decarboxylate.

Picric acid. Discovery: action of HNO_3 on indigo. Preparation: (a) phenol ⟶ 2,4-disulfonic acid (stable to oxidizing action of HNO_3), treatment with HNO_3 (sulfonation reversed); (b) chlorobenzene (chlorine inert) ⟶ 2,4-dinitrochlorobenzene (chlorine labile) ⟶ 2,4-dinitrophenol ⟶ picric acid. Specific properties: bitter taste, dyes wool yellow, bactericidal, strong acid (pK_a 0.8), forms hydrocarbon complexes.

Tetryl: N,2,4,6-tetranitro-N-methylaniline.

Explosives. TNT, TNB, and ammonium picrate are high explosives, of relatively low sensitivity to shock and requiring detonation by a small booster charge. TNT, m.p. 80.6°, melted with steam and poured into shells; cast TNT is less sensitive than pelleted material. Common boosters (intermediate impact sensitivity): pelleted picric acid, tetryl. Detonators (to set off booster charge): mercury fulminate, lead azide.

Reduction of nitro compounds. Under appropriate conditions, nitrobenzene yields the following sequence of primary reduction products: nitrosobenzene (C_6H_5NO), phenylhydroxylamine (C_6H_5NHOH), aniline. Nitrosobenzene can condense with phenylhydroxylamine to form azoxybenzene, $C_6H_5N{\overset{+}{=}}N(-O^-)C_6H_5$, which is reducible through azobenzene ($C_6H_5N\!=\!NC_6H_5$) and hydrazobenzene ($C_6H_5NHNHC_6H_5$) to aniline. Useful rearrangements: phenylhydroxylamine ⟶ p-aminophenol; hydrazobenzene ⟶ benzidine (p-$H_2NC_6H_4$—$C_6H_4NH_2$-p).

Hydrocarbon—polynitro compound complexes. Naphthalene picrate: yellow dissociable complex of higher m.p. and lower solubility than either component. Useful for identification and isolation. Chief nitro components: picric acid, TNB, TNT. Hydrocarbons that form complexes: naphthalene, anthracene, phenanthrene.

Sulfonic Acids

Arylsulfonic acids, $ArSO_2OH$, are strongly acidic (cf. H_2SO_4), hygroscopic, very soluble in water, salted out by HCl, used as acid catalysts.

Sodium sulfonates, $ArSO_3Na$, less soluble, neutral, nonhygroscopic. Isolated by partial neutralization of sulfonation mixture, addition of NaCl. Minor by-product: diphenyl sulfone, $C_6H_5SO_2C_6H_5$. Sodium sulfonates obtained salt-free by salting out with sodium acetate and extracting this substance with methanol. Calcium and barium salts less soluble. p-Toluidine salts useful for identification: crystallizable from ethanol, characteristic melting points.

Acid chlorides, $ArSO_2Cl$. Preparation: (a) $ArSO_2ONa + PCl_5$ or $POCl_3$; (b) ArH + excess $ClSO_2OH$ ⟶ $ArSO_2Cl$. Use: benzenesulfonyl chloride or p-toluenesulfonyl chloride + a primary or secondary amine (Hinsberg test).

Other derivatives. Esters: $ArSO_3Na + (CH_3)_2SO_4$, or $ArSO_2Cl + HOCH_3$ ⟶ $ArSO_2OCH_3$. Sulfonamides: $ArSO_2Cl + NH_3$ ⟶ $ArSO_2NH_2$. Chloroamides: p-$CH_3C_6H_4SO_2NH_2 + NaOCl$ ⟶ p-$CH_3C_6H_4SO_2NHCl$ (chloramine-T, antiseptic).

Saccharin = o-sulfobenzoic acid imide. Preparation from o-toluenesulfonamide. Use as sweetening agent; compare 1-n-propoxy-2-amino-4-nitrobenzene.

Alkali fusion of sulfonates ──→ phenols. Molten KOH, NaOH, or KOH-NaOH at 290–340°; acidification of cooled melt. Inapplicable to sulfonates containing nitro or halo substituents.

Nitriles: $ArSO_3K + KCN \longrightarrow ArCN$. Both salts remain unfused at high temperatures, hence heat interchange is poor and yields are low.

PROBLEMS

1. Crude TNT contains small amounts of 2,3,4- and 2,4,5-trinitrotoluene, which are objectionable contaminants. Suggest a method for their removal.
2. Suggest a method of preparing 2,4-diamino-N-methylaniline, starting with chlorobenzene.
3. Summarize examples cited of nucleophilic substitutions of nitro compounds and account for the phenomena.
4. Summarize examples cited of nucleophilic displacements.

READING REFERENCES

W. C. Lothrop and G. R. Handrick, "The Relationship between Performance and Constitution of Pure Organic Explosive Compounds," *Chem. Rev.*, **44**, 419 (1949)

J. F. Bunnett and R. E. Zahler, "Aromatic Nucleophilic Substitution Reactions," *Chem. Rev.*, **49**, 273 (1951)

chapter 21

ARYL AMINES

Aniline was first obtained in 1826 by destructive distillation of indigo (20.8) and later was isolated from a coal-tar distillate. Fritzsche (1840) introduced an improved method of preparation from indigo by heating the natural dye with concentrated alkali, established the formula, and proposed the subsequently accepted name (Spanish *añil*, Sanskrit *nēlē*, indigo, a blue dye named for the blue river Nile). A base subsequently recognized as identical with aniline was obtained (1842) by reduction of nitrobenzene; and with development of the coal-tar industry this reaction eventually became the standard method for the technical production of a key chemical on a scale mounting to several million pounds per year.

Primary aromatic amines are obtained almost entirely by nitration and reduction. A number of methods of reduction are available. Small-scale reductions are often carried out with tin and hydrochloric acid ($C_6H_5NO_2 \longrightarrow C_6H_5NH_2$, 80%), or more cleanly with a solution of stannous chloride in concentrated hydrochloric acid; the basic product is isolated from the diluted reaction mixture either by addition of enough alkali to neutralize the acid and dissolve the tin in the form of sodium stannite and sodium stannate or by precipitation of the metal as sulfide. In technical practice it is more economical to reduce the nitro compound with iron powder and water, with a small amount of hydrochloric acid as catalyst. Where proper reaction con-

1.

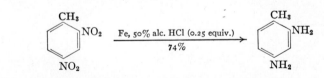

ditions have been worked out, this procedure also serves for laboratory preparations, as in the reduction of 2,4-dinitrotoluene (1). Reduction

with zinc dust and alkali is less widely employed but sometimes gives excellent results (2).

2.

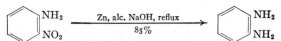

If the nitro compound contains an acetylamino or acetoxy group reduction in either an acidic or a basic medium results in hydrolysis of the acetyl groups. If retention of an acetyl group is required, as in the preparation of the monoacetyl derivative of *o*-phenylenediamine (3), the most satisfactory method is catalytic hydrogenation in a neutral medium.

3.

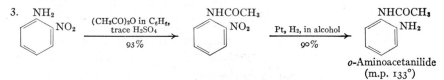

o-Aminoacetanilide
(m.p. 133°)

Selective reduction

Selective reduction of one group in a polynitro compound can be accomplished with use of the calculated amount of sodium or ammonium sulfide or hydrosulfide (example 4). The reaction can be

4.

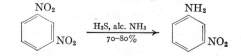

conducted by use of a weighed quantity of crystalline sodium sulfide or by dissolving the nitro compound in alcoholic ammonia and passing in hydrogen sulfide to a given gain in weight. The reagent reduces one nitro group before another, but the reaction will proceed beyond this stage unless the amount of reagent is controlled.

BASIC CHARACTER

Aniline has only weakly basic properties (pK_b 9.3) as compared with methylamine (pK_b 3.4). The diminished basicity of aromatic amines can be attributed empirically to the unsaturated aromatic nucleus, in analogy with the relationship of acetamide to ammonia. The explanation provided by the resonance theory is that the anilinium ion is incapable of resonance involving the nitrogen, for a reason already stated (18.13), whereas such resonance stabilization is possible in aniline; there is thus little driving force to promote ionization. The N-methyl derivatives of aniline and the three toluidines all have dissociation constants in the same range as the parent amine, and hence alkyl substitution in either the amino group or the nucleus has little influence on the basic strength. Introduction of a 21.2

nitro substituent, however, results in marked decrease in basicity, as can be seen from the pK_b values of the isomers: *ortho*, 13.8; *meta*, 11.4; *para*, 12.0. The feebly basic character of the nitroanilines is evidenced by the fact that the colorless salts formed with concentrated sulfuric or hydrochloric acid are hydrolyzed on dilution with moderate amounts of water to yellow, water-insoluble bases; the *ortho* isomer is precipitated most readily, the *para* compound separates next, and *m*-nitroaniline separates only on more extensive dilution. Decrease in basicity attending introduction of the nitro group at any position in the ring can be attributed to the inductive effect; the positively polarized nitro group induces a drift of electrons in the sense of withdrawal from the ring and from the amino nitrogen atom, and hence affinity of the nitrogen for protons is decreased. The effect is magnified in the polynitro compounds 2,4-dinitroaniline and picramide (2,4,6-trinitroaniline); the latter compound forms with concentrated sulfuric acid a salt scarcely more stable than the oxonium salts of ethers. Diphenylamine is very feebly basic and the salts formed with concentrated acids are readily hydrolyzed.

21.3
    Acid Salts. — Aniline dissolves readily in dilute solutions of mineral acids with formation of salts which are so soluble in water that they are not easily precipitated by excess acid. Hydrochloride salts are isolated most easily by passing dry hydrogen chloride gas into a solution of the amine in ether, for the salts are insoluble in this solvent and separate quantitatively. Salts of the higher amines are less soluble in water and can be crystallized from an aqueous medium, with use of excess acid where required to decrease solubility.

    Inner Salts. — Sulfanilic acid (p-H$_2$NC$_6$H$_4$SO$_3$H), a typical amine sulfonic acid, has properties indicative of a dipolar ion, or inner salt

Sulfanilic acid

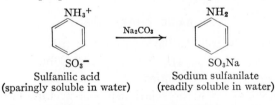

Sulfanilic acid
(sparingly soluble in water)

Sodium sulfanilate
(readily soluble in water)

structure, as shown in the formula. It is insoluble in ether and soluble in water at room temperature only to the extent of about 1%, and when heated in a capillary tube it begins to decompose at 280°. Sulfanilic acid dissolves readily when warmed with aqueous sodium carbonate solution with formation of the sodium salt, but it has so little tendency to combine with mineral acids that it can be crystallized from concentrated hydrochloric acid (anhydrous form; the commercial preparation is the monohydrate).

Acetyl Derivatives. — As in the aliphatic series, acetylation obliterates basic characteristics of aromatic amines. Acetanilide is a neutral compound no more soluble in dilute hydrochloric acid than in water. An acetyl derivative is prepared easily either by the action of acetic anhydride on the anhydrous amine or by dissolving the amine with an equivalent quantity of hydrochloric acid in water and

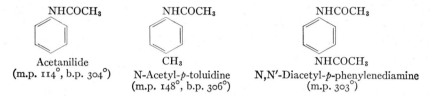

Acetanilide
(m.p. 114°, b.p. 304°)

N-Acetyl-*p*-toluidine
(m.p. 148°, b.p. 306°)

N,N′-Diacetyl-*p*-phenylenediamine
(m.p. 303°)

adding acetic anhydride, followed by enough sodium acetate to react with the hydrochloride salt and liberate the free amine. The acetyl derivatives melt at higher temperatures than the free amines and are useful derivatives for characterization. They are also useful by virtue of stability to oxidation, in contrast with free amines, and because of moderation in the substitution-facilitating influence of the amino group.

PREPARATION OF SPECIFIC AMINES

Aniline (b.p. 184°). — The standard industrial preparation of aniline involves reduction of nitrobenzene with iron chips and 30% hydrochloric acid. After the reaction is complete the mixture is neutralized with soda, and the aniline removed by distillation with steam saturated with aniline. Since aniline is slightly soluble in water (3 g. in 100 g. H_2O), sodium chloride is added to the distillate to make a 20% solution, in which aniline is completely insoluble. After separation of the two layers, pure aniline is obtained by distillation in practically quantitative yield.

21.5

Methyl- and Dimethylaniline. — Methylation of aniline by any of the standard methods of alkylation is liable to afford mixtures of the mono- and dimethyl derivatives, along with unchanged starting material, but by control of the conditions one or the other derivative can be obtained as the chief product. A technical process for production of dimethylaniline consists in heating a mixture of aniline, methanol, and concentrated sulfuric acid at 230–235° and a pressure of 25–30 atmospheres (97% yield). Small amounts of aniline and methylaniline present in technical preparations can be eliminated by adding enough acetic anhydride to react with these contaminants and distilling the unattacked tertiary amine from a residue containing the much less volatile acetyl derivatives. Technical methylaniline is produced by

21.6

heating aniline with methanol and hydrochloric acid at 180° in an autoclave. A laboratory method applicable generally to the preparation of monoalkyl derivatives of aromatic amines consists in alkylation of the arylsulfonyl, or Hinsberg, derivative of a primary amine in the form of the sodium salt (Ullmann):

$$C_6H_5NH_2 \xrightarrow{C_6H_5SO_2Cl} C_6H_5\underset{\overset{|}{H}}{N}{-}SO_2C_6H_5 \xrightarrow{NaOH}$$

$$C_6H_5\underset{\overset{|}{Na}}{N}SO_2C_6H_5 \xrightarrow{(CH_3)_2SO_4} C_6H_5\underset{\overset{|}{CH_3}}{N}SO_2C_6H_5 \xrightarrow{Hydrol.} C_6H_5\underset{\overset{|}{CH_3}}{N}H$$

A method of preparing N-alkylarylamines is catalytic hydrogenation of a mixture of a primary amine and an aldehyde; the reaction possibly proceeds through formation and reduction of the anil derivative (Schiff base) of the aldehyde:

$$ArNH_2 + O{=}CHR \longrightarrow ArN{=}CHR \xrightarrow{2 H} ArNHCH_2R$$

21.7 **Toluidines.** — The *ortho* and *para* methyl derivatives of aniline are obtained technically by reduction of the corresponding nitrotoluenes with iron powder and a catalytic amount of hydrochloric acid.

21.8 **Nitroanilines.** — Nitration of aniline with nitric acid alone is not satisfactory because the amine is subject to considerable destruction as a result of the oxidizing action of the reagent. The amine is stabilized against oxidation by dissolving it in sulfuric acid, and nitration in such a solution proceeds somewhat more smoothly and affords *Meta* *m*-nitroaniline as the chief product, though in only moderate yield, for the amine is present largely as the ionic salt and substitution occurs under the influence of the rather weakly *meta* directing ammonium group, —NH$_3$+. The reaction has no practical use since *m*-nitroaniline can be prepared more efficiently by partial reduction of *m*-dinitrobenzene with ammonium hydrosulfide.

Acetylation of aniline not only provides stabilization to oxidation but prevents formation of a *meta* directing ionic group, and acetanilide

Ortho and para

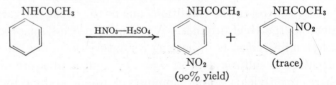

on nitration with mixed acid reacts smoothly with almost exclusive production of *p*-nitroacetanilide (m.p. 215°); a small amount of *o*-nitroacetanilide (m.p. 94°) is formed but is easily eliminated by crystallization of the much higher-melting and less soluble *para* isomer.

Acid hydrolysis of the recrystallized product affords *p*-nitroaniline in good overall yield. In a large-scale operation, a certain amount of *o*-nitroaniline can be recovered from the mother liquors of crystallization of the nitration product by hydrolysis and steam distillation (volatility ascribable to chelation). A more efficient process is indicated as follows:

o-Nitroaniline-*p*-sulfonic acid

SO₃H as blocking group

Sulfonation of acetanilide blocks the *para* position, and on reaction with nitric acid in sulfuric acid solution a nitro group is introduced at the 2-position and the acetyl group is eliminated. Hydrolysis of the sulfonic acid substituent then affords *o*-nitroaniline.

The diminished basicity of the nitroanilines has been noted (21.2). Another deviation from the behavior of aniline, shown by *o*- and *p*-nitroaniline but not by the *meta* isomer, is ready reaction with alkalis with displacement of the amino group by hydroxyl. This reaction is

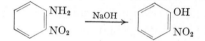

another manifestation of the sensitivity of nitro compounds to nucleophilic attack in the *ortho* and *para* positions (20.4).

Phenylenediamines. — The *ortho* and *para* diamino derivatives of benzene are obtainable by reduction of the corresponding nitroanilines; a specific procedure for the preparation of *o*-phenylenediamine (m.p. 103°) has been indicated in example 2, 21.1. *m*-Phenylenediamine (m.p. 63°) is prepared by reduction of the readily available *m*-dinitro compound.

21.9

Halogen Derivatives. — Aniline combines with bromine with such avidity that interaction of the amine with a dilute aqueous solution

21.10

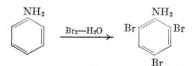

Strong activation by NH₂

of bromine affords a precipitate of the sparingly soluble 2,4,6-tribromoaniline, m.p. 118°. The reaction demonstrates the powerful substitution-facilitating influence of the amino group, for this directing group causes the three bromine atoms, which ordinarily are *op* directing, to assume positions *meta* to one another. Bromination in aqueous solution is useful for obtaining solid derivatives for identifica-

397

tion, since most aromatic amines respond with affixture of bromine at all available positions *ortho* and *para* to the amino group; thus the toluidines react to give the following products: dibromo-*o*-toluidine, m.p. 50°; tribromo-*m*-toluidine, m.p. 97°; dibromo-*p*-toluidine, m.p. 73°. Bromination of aniline proceeds so rapidly even at high dilution that an early process for extraction of bromine from sea water consisted in the addition of chlorine to liberate bromine from the sodium bromide, followed by aniline to combine with the free halogen and give a filterable precipitate.

The effect of the amino group in promoting halogenation is so powerful that the acetyl derivative is used to control the reaction to

Acetylation moderates activation

monosubstitution. Acetanilide reacts to give almost exclusively the *p*-bromo derivative, which is hydrolyzed easily to the amine. *p*-Chlo-

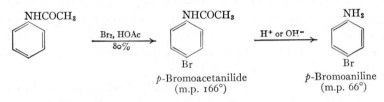

	p-Bromoacetanilide (m.p. 166°)	*p*-Bromoaniline (m.p. 66°)

roaniline is obtainable similarly; a small amount of the *ortho* compound is formed, and in technical practice the mixture is separated, after hydrolysis, by steam distillation of the *o*-chloroaniline. The *meta* isomer is prepared by reduction of *m*-nitrochlorobenzene.

21.11   **Sulfanilic Acid and Isomers.** — Sulfanilic acid, used extensively as an intermediate for dyes, is prepared by mixing equal moles of aniline and concentrated sulfuric acid and baking the resulting acid sulfate at 180° until a test portion when neutralized with sodium hydroxide no longer liberates aniline. Sulfanilic acid monohydrate crystallizes on pouring the cooled mixture into water. The reaction

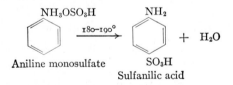

Aniline monosulfate   Sulfanilic acid

involves migration of the sulfonic acid group from the side chain to the nucleus and dehydration; experiments of Bamberger (1897) established that the initial reaction is loss of water from the sulfate with formation of phenylsulfamic acid, a dehydration comparable to the pyrolytic conversion of an ammonium salt into an amide. When phenylsulfamic acid is heated cautiously, the sulfonic acid group first migrates to the *ortho* position, giving orthanilic acid, which rearranges at 180° to sulfanilic acid. The progressive migrations to the *ortho* and then the *para* position can be attributed to α,γ-shifts. Phenylsulfamic acid affords orthanilic acid by an α,γ-shift of the sulfonic acid group to the *ortho* position, with a similar shift of hydrogen

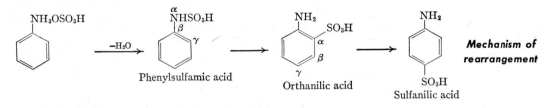

Phenylsulfamic acid — Orthanilic acid — Sulfanilic acid

in the reverse direction. Another α,γ-shift brings the acid group into the evidently more stable *para* position, and this interpretation accounts for the complete absence of the *meta* derivative from the reaction mixture. Several comparable rearrangements are known involving migration of a group from an initial position of attachment to nitrogen or to oxygen into *ortho* or *para* positions in the ring; for example, the acid-catalyzed rearrangement of phenylhydroxylamine to *p*-aminophenol (20.11).

Anisidines. — The *o*- and *p*-methoxy derivatives of aniline are prepared by reduction of the corresponding nitroanisoles (m.p. 9° and 54°), which in turn are obtainable by nitration of anisole, by the action of methyl alcoholic potassium hydroxide on the nitrochlorobenzenes, or by methylation of the nitrophenols in the form of the sodium salts with dimethyl sulfate in boiling toluene.

21.12

Diphenylamine (m.p. 54°) is prepared by heating aniline hydrochloride with a small excess of aniline (1.1 equiv.) under slight pres-

21.13

$$C_6H_5NH_3Cl + C_6H_5NH_2 \xrightarrow[82\%]{210-240°, \, 6 \, atm.} C_6H_5NHC_6H_5 + NH_4Cl$$

sure; the aniline is extracted from the resulting melt with warm dilute hydrochloric acid, and an oily layer of the feebly basic diarylamine is collected and distilled.

SPECIAL CHEMICAL PROPERTIES

Oxidation. — Primary and secondary aromatic amines are so sensitive to oxidation that they often deteriorate in storage owing to attack by oxygen. Purified aniline is a colorless oil, but on exposure to air it eventually acquires a deep reddish brown color. The extent of air oxidation, however, is not great, and practically colorless aniline can be recovered in good yield from very dark material by distillation from a trace of zinc dust. Solid amines (e.g., *p*-toluidine) are less vulnerable to air oxidation than liquid amines. Wieland (1911) discovered that diphenylamine on careful oxidation with

21.14

potassium permanganate in acetone solution is converted into tetraphenylhydrazine, apparently through formation and association of diphenylnitrogen radicals:

Free radical

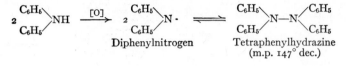

Diphenylnitrogen   Tetraphenylhydrazine
(m.p. 147° dec.)

Association of the radicals is practically complete at room temperature, for the colorless tetraphenylhydrazine gives solutions that are likewise colorless in the cold. When a solution in toluene is heated to about 70°, however, it acquires a greenish brown color attributable to the radical; the color fades on cooling, and the original hydrazine derivative is recoverable from the solution. The behavior is similar to that of hexaphenylethane (19.16), except that the diphenylnitrogen radical does not combine with oxygen (or with iodine) and is present in equilibrium with the diarylhydrazine in amounts too small to be

Evidence

determined. Evidence of dissociation to free radicals, apart from the color phenomena, is provided by interaction of the substance with triphenylmethyl to form the compound $(C_6H_5)_3C—N(C_6H_5)_2$ and with sodium to give $(C_6H_5)_2NNa$.

With use of different oxidizing agents under varying conditions, aniline is convertible into a host of oxidation products, including azobenzene, azoxybenzene, nitrobenzene, quinone, and the dye Aniline Black. Most of the reaction products appear derivable through an initial abstraction of one amino hydrogen atom with formation of a transient free radical sensitive to further attack, either at the nitrogen atom or at the *para* position of the nucleus.

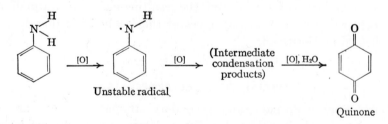

Unstable radical   (Intermediate condensation products)   Quinone

21.15

Action of Nitrous Acid on Primary Amines. — The response of aromatic amines of the three classes to nitrous acid parallels only in part the behavior of aliphatic amines (11.11). Whereas a primary alkylamine on treatment with nitrous acid in hydrochloric acid solution affords an alcohol and nitrogen, aniline hydrochloride is convertible under controlled conditions (low temperature, excess acid) into a crystalline salt of the formula $C_6H_5N_2Cl$, benzenediazonium

chloride. The product undergoes hydrolytic decomposition when
boiled with dilute acid, and hence the overall reaction resembles that

$$C_6H_5NH_3Cl \ + \ HONO \ \xrightarrow{\ 0°\ } \ C_6H_5\overset{+}{N_2}\overset{-}{Cl} \ + \ 2\,H_2O$$

$$C_6H_5\overset{+}{N_2}\overset{-}{Cl} \ + \ H_2O \ \xrightarrow{\text{dil. H}_2\text{SO}_4,\text{ heat}} \ C_6H_5OH \ + \ N_2 \ + \ HCl$$

in the aliphatic series. The diversified reactions and uses of the aryldiazonium salts are described later (21.19).

N-Nitroso Compounds. — Secondary aromatic amines, like dial-
kylamines, combine with nitrous acid to form N-nitrosoamines. The
product from methylaniline is known as either N-nitroso-N-methylaniline or methylphenylnitrosoamine; it is a bright yellow oil which

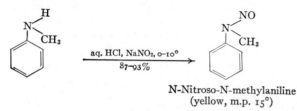

N-Nitroso-N-methylaniline
(yellow, m.p. 15°)

crystallizes on cooling and can be distilled in vacuum. The N-nitroso
derivative of N-methyl-*p*-toluidine is a yellow solid which melts at
54°; that of diphenylamine melts at 67°.

N-Nitroso-N-methylaniline readily undergoes rearrangement under
the catalytic influence of hydrochloric acid. When a solution in alcohol

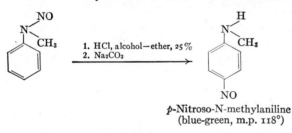

p-**Nitroso**-N-methylaniline
(blue-green, m.p. 118°)

is treated with concentrated hydrochloric acid and allowed to stand
for a time at room temperature, the substance rearranges to *p*-nitroso-
N-methylaniline, which separates as the crystalline hydrochloride
(yellow).

C-Nitroso Compounds. — Whereas tertiary aliphatic amines are
inert to nitrous acid, those of the aromatic series undergo nitrosation

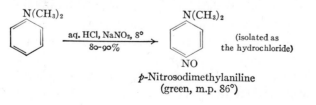

p-**Nitrosodimethylaniline**
(green, m.p. 86°)

in the nucleus with formation of C-nitroso compounds. The nitrosation reaction proceeds rapidly at 0°, usually with exclusive substitution in the *para* position, if available, or otherwise in the *ortho* position. Phenols also yield C-nitroso derivatives, in transformations characterized by the low temperature of reaction and by exclusive attack at the *para* position, whereas neither aromatic hydrocarbons nor any of their derivatives other than the free amines and phenols react with nitrous acid. C-Nitrosation is a special substitution applicable only to compounds containing the very powerful substitution-facilitating dialkylamino or hydroxyl group.

21.18 Phenyl isocyanide, $C_6H_5N{=}C$, is formed on heating aniline with chloroform and alcoholic potassium hydroxide (Hofmann, 1867).

$$C_6H_5N\overline{H_2} \;+\; H\overline{|C|Cl_3|} \xrightarrow{\text{KOH}} C_6H_5N{=}C$$
Phenyl isocyanide
(b.p. 166°)

The isocyanide (or isonitrile) is toxic, and has a penetrating, characteristic odor resembling that of hydrogen cyanide, and since the substance can be recognized by smell, its formation from a drop of aniline is used as a test (general for primary amines). It is a colorless liquid when freshly distilled, but is unstable in the presence of air and becomes discolored on brief exposure and soon resinifies. Phenyl isocyanide is formulated conventionally as containing bivalent carbon, but dipole moment data indicate the presence of one polar link,

Bivalent or negatively charged carbon

$C_6H_5\overset{+}{N}{\equiv}\overset{-}{C}$; the substance has a marked tendency to enter into reactions by which the carbon atom acquires its normal condition, even without disturbance of the unsaturation, as in the first two of the following reactions:

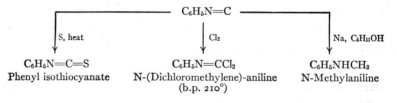

S, heat	Cl₂	Na, C₅H₁₁OH
$C_6H_5N{=}C{=}S$	$C_6H_5N{=}CCl_2$	$C_6H_5NHCH_3$
Phenyl isothiocyanate	N-(Dichloromethylene)-aniline	N-Methylaniline
	(b.p. 210°)	

DIAZONIUM SALTS

21.19 Benzenediazonium chloride, $C_6H_5N_2{}^+Cl^-$, the product of the reaction between aniline hydrochloride and nitrous acid in the presence of excess hydrochloric acid at ice-bath temperature, is an ionic salt, very soluble in water and completely insoluble in ether; in aqueous solutions it is completely dissociated. The crystalline solid is very sensitive to shock when dry and detonates violently on mild heating.

Preparation of the solid can be accomplished by employing the combination of an organic nitrite and an organic acid as the source of nitrous acid, for the diazonium salt is then the only ether-insoluble product and is precipitated from this solvent. The reaction product

$$C_6H_5N^+H_3Cl^- + n\text{-}C_4H_9ONO + CH_3COOH \xrightarrow{\text{Ether}} C_6H_5N_2^+Cl^- + CH_3COOC_4H_9$$

is sensitive and requires careful handling. Fortunately, for nearly all reactions isolation of the solid is not required, for the reactions can be carried out satisfactorily with the readily prepared aqueous solutions. Preparation of such a solution, or diazotization of an amine, is conducted as follows. The amine is dissolved in a suitable volume of water containing three equivalents of hydrochloric acid, by heating if required, and the solution is cooled well in ice, when the amine hydrochloride usually crystallizes. With control of the temperature to 0–5°, an aqueous solution of sodium nitrite is added in portions until, after allowing a few minutes for reaction, the solution gives a positive test for excess nitrous acid with starch–iodide paper. The amine hydrochloride dissolves in the process to give a clear solution of the much more soluble diazonium salt. One equivalent of hydrochloric acid is bound by the amine and provides the anion of the product, a second reacts with sodium nitrite to liberate nitrous acid, and the third maintains proper acidity required to stabilize the diazonium salt by inhibition of secondary changes. The process can be summarized as follows:

$$ArNH_2 + 3\,HCl + NaNO_2 \xrightarrow{\text{In water at } 0°} ArN_2^+Cl^- + NaCl + HCl + 2\,H_2O$$

Diazonium salts were discovered by Griess.[1] The name is based on the presence of two nitrogen atoms (Fr. *azote*, nitrogen) and on analogy to ammonium compounds with respect to saltlike characteristics. The structure and a possible mechanism of formation through the N-nitroso derivative are shown in the formulation. Addition

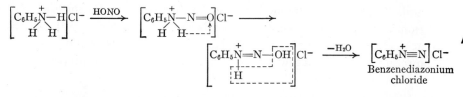

Benzenediazonium chloride

of alkali to a well-cooled solution of benzenediazonium chloride may result in initial conversion to the quaternary ammonium hydroxide, $[C_6H_5\overset{+}{N}{\equiv}N]OH^-$, which isomerizes at once to a weakly acidic substance, benzenediazoic acid, characterized as metal salts, or diazotates.

[1] Peter Griess, 1829–88; b. Kirchhosbach, Germany; assistant to Hofmann in London, chemist in an English brewery

The aryldiazoic acids, referred to also as diazo hydroxides or diazo hydrates, are comparable in structure and in acidity to nitrous acid;

$$[C_6H_5\overset{+}{N}{\equiv}N] \; + \; OH^- \; \rightleftharpoons \; \underset{\substack{\text{Benzenediazoic} \\ \text{acid}}}{C_6H_5N{=}NOH} \; \overset{KOH}{\rightleftharpoons} \; \underset{\substack{\text{Potassium benzene-} \\ \text{diazotate}}}{C_6H_5N{=}NOK}$$

they have not been isolated in crystalline form, for acidification of the alkaline solution, even with acetic acid, results largely in reversal of the equilibrium and reconversion to the diazonium salt. Potassium salts have been isolated as crystallizates from concentrated alkaline solutions and purified by precipitation from alcoholic solution with ether. Two forms have been isolated and characterized by Hantzsch[2] as geometrical isomers:

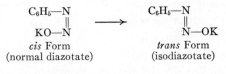

The initially produced form (normal, or *cis*) of potassium benzene-diazotate is labile, and is more reactive chemically and has a higher energy content than the *iso* form (*trans*) to which it changes rather rapidly in either the solid or the dissolved state. A freshly alkalized solution of benzenediazonium chloride thus consists principally of the alkali salt of the *cis* form of benzenediazoic acid; the *trans* form predominates in an aged solution.

Most aromatic primary amines can be diazotized by the procedure indicated. Usually a clear colorless solution of the diazonium salt results, even though the amine salt used is only sparingly soluble, but in some instances the diazonium salt crystallizes. This is the case with sulfanilic acid because of the formation of an inner salt. The substance is diazotized by bringing it into solution as the sodium salt, adding the requisite amount of sodium nitrite, and pouring the solution on a mixture of ice and concentrated hydrochloric acid; nitrous acid and the dipolar sulfanilic acid are liberated together and promptly interact, and after a few seconds the dipolar diazonium salt separates:

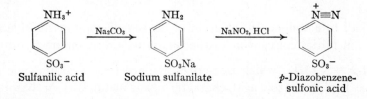

² Arthur Hantzsch, 1857–1935; b. Dresden; Ph.D. Würzburg (R. Schmitt); Leipzig; *J. Chem. Soc.*, 1051 (1936)

Hydrolysis to Phenols. — When a solution of a diazonium salt in aqueous sulfuric acid is boiled, nitrogen is evolved and the amine derivative is converted into the corresponding phenol. Usually

$$[Ar\overset{+}{N}\equiv N]\overset{-}{Cl} + HOH \longrightarrow ArOH + N_2 + HCl$$

40–50% sulfuric acid is used in order to attain a reflux temperature sufficiently high to promote reasonably rapid hydrolysis, and the strong acid may destroy the sensitive hydroxy compound. Hydrochloric acid is less satisfactory as a reagent because adequate temperatures are not obtainable and also because the diazonium salt group may be replaced in part by halogen. The crude reaction product may be deeply colored owing to contamination with azo compounds almost invariably formed as by-products, but purification can be accomplished by extraction with alkali or by steam distillation, and the pure phenol obtained in moderate yields. Since the diazonium salt need not be isolated, introduction of a hydroxyl group can be accomplished in essentially three steps: nitration, reduction to the amine, and diazotization in aqueous medium followed by hydrolysis in the same solution. The overall process is more elaborate than that of sulfonation and alkali fusion, and ordinarily the yields are not so satisfactory. The chief preparative application of the route through the diazonium derivative is in instances where the alternate method is inapplicable. Thus *m*-nitrophenol cannot be prepared through the sulfonate because of the sensitivity of nitro compounds to alkali, but is obtainable through the diazo reaction. Nuclear

Comparison with sulfonate-alkali fusion

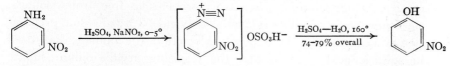

halogen substituents also are liable to be attacked by alkali at the elevated temperatures required for alkali fusion of a sulfonate, but *o*- and *p*-chlorophenol, for example, can be prepared satisfactorily from the corresponding amines by diazotization and hydrolysis.

21.21

Sandmeyer Reaction. — When an aqueous solution of benzenediazonium chloride is treated with one equivalent of potassium iodide and warmed, the benzenediazonium iodide present in the equilibrium mixture decomposes with evolution of nitrogen and formation of iodobenzene in good yield. Neither chloro- nor bromobenzene can be

$$C_6H_5NH_2 \xrightarrow{\text{aq. HCl, NaNO}_2,\ 5°} [C_6H_5\overset{+}{N}\equiv N]\overset{-}{Cl} \xrightarrow[\substack{74-76\% \\ \text{overall}}]{\text{KI, 95°}} C_6H_5I + N_2 + KCl$$

prepared by this procedure, but Sandmeyer [3] (1884) discovered that

---

[3] Traugott Sandmeyer, 1854–1922; b. Wettingen, Switzerland; assistant to Victor Meyer and Hantzsch; Geigy Co., Basel

replacement of the diazonium salt group by halogen is catalyzed markedly by cuprous salts and thereby contributed a practicable preparative method that has proved capable of wide application and of certain elaborations that can be described as Sandmeyer-type replacements. For preparation of aryl chlorides by the Sandmeyer procedure, the amine is diazotized in ice-cold solution in hydrochloric acid with sodium nitrite, and a solution of one equivalent of cuprous chloride in hydrochloric acid is added; a deep brown, sparingly soluble complex separates consisting of a double molecule of the diazonium salt and cuprous chloride, and when the suspension of this substance is warmed, decomposition sets in with evolution of nitrogen, disappearance of the solid, and separation of an oily layer containing the organic halide. Although the crude reaction mixture usually is dark colored, separation of the halide from contaminants and inorganic salts can be accomplished by steam distillation. Both *o*- and *p*-chlorotoluene can be prepared in good yield; this method also is

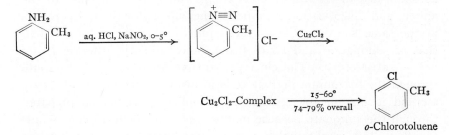

convenient for obtaining *m*-nitrochlorobenzene free from isomers, since pure *m*-nitroaniline is available (yield 68–71%). For preparation of a bromide by the Sandmeyer reaction, the amine is diazotized in sulfuric acid solution and the resulting aryldiazonium sulfate treated with a solution of cuprous bromide in excess hydrobromic acid; the complex is then decomposed by heat. *p*-Bromotoluene can be prepared from *p*-toluidine in 70–73% yield, and *o*-chlorobromobenzene is obtainable from *o*-chloroaniline with equal success. The reaction can be applied to preparation of nitriles, which result from the action of a solution of cuprous cyanide in excess potassium cyanide on a diazonium salt, as shown in the example.

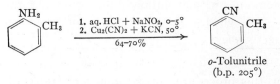

In the examples cited a molecular equivalent of the cuprous salt component is required for formation of the intermediate molecular complex. Gattermann[4] (1890) discovered that freshly precipitated copper powder (zinc dust and copper sulfate solution) can replace the cuprous salt as promoter for the replacement and is effective in catalytic amounts and at temperatures lower than those required in the Sandmeyer procedure. The most useful application of the Gattermann procedure is for joining two aromatic nuclei by interaction of a diazonium salt and a hydrocarbon under the catalytic influence of metallic copper. The yield in this instance is low, and the product is

$$C_6H_5N_2Cl \;+\; C_6H_6 \;\xrightarrow[13\%]{\text{Cu (or Zn), alcohol, } 30-40°} \; C_6H_5 \cdot C_6H_5 \;+\; N_2 \;+\; HCl$$
$$\text{Diphenyl}$$

accompanied by higher hydrocarbons of the same type (terphenyl, quaterphenyl, quinquiphenyl) formed by interaction of the diazonium salt with diphenyl.

Deamination. — Methods of reduction are available for replacement of the diazonium salt group by hydrogen, thus eliminating a primary amino substituent; the reaction is described as a deamination. The first known procedure, discovered by Griess in 1864, consists in treatment of the diazonium salt with ethanol, which serves as a hydrogen donor and becomes oxidized to acetaldehyde. An appre-

$$ArN_2Cl \;+\; CH_3CH_2OH \;\longrightarrow\; ArH \;+\; N_2 \;+\; HCl \;+\; CH_3CHO$$

ciable amount of water must be avoided or else hydrolysis will occur, but isolation of the dry diazonium salt is not always required. The utility of the deamination reaction is illustrated by the preparation of *s*-tribromobenzene, which is not accessible by direct bromination, for it contains *op* directing groups *meta* to one another. The desired orientation is achieved in the bromination of aniline under the dominating directive influence of the amino group. Thus 2,4,6-tribromoaniline is obtainable from aniline in nearly quantitative yield, and can be converted into *s*-tribromobenzene by reduction of the diazotized amine with ethanol. The moist precipitate of tribromoaniline

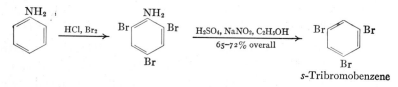

s-Tribromobenzene

is dissolved in ethanol containing some benzene as diluent and treated with concentrated sulfuric acid followed by solid sodium nitrite; the diazonium salt is reduced as formed, with evolution of nitrogen and production of the deaminated product and acetaldehyde.

[4] Ludwig Gattermann, 1860–1920; b. Goslar, Germany; Ph.D. Göttingen (Hübner); Freiburg; *Ber.*, **54A**, 115 (1921)

Deamination with ethanol gives good results with diazonium salts of several polyhalo- and polynitroamines, but with simpler compounds considerable material is converted into the corresponding ethyl ether by the side reaction:

$$ArN_2Cl + HOC_2H_5 \longrightarrow ArOC_2H_5 + N_2 + HCl$$

A superior and more convenient procedure is reduction of the diazonium salt in aqueous solution with a large excess of hypophosphorous

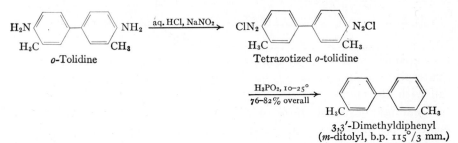

With hypophosphorous acid

o-Tolidine — Tetrazotized *o*-tolidine — 3,3'-Dimethyldiphenyl (*m*-ditolyl, b.p. 115°/3 mm.)

acid, H_3PO_2 (Mai, 1902). The reaction proceeds in the cold, and the reagent can be added to the aqueous solution of the diazotized amine. The example cited illustrates the preparation through an amine derivative of a hydrocarbon difficultly accessible by other methods.

A further example of deamination is the standard method for preparation of *m*-toluidine from *p*-toluidine. The amine is acetylated

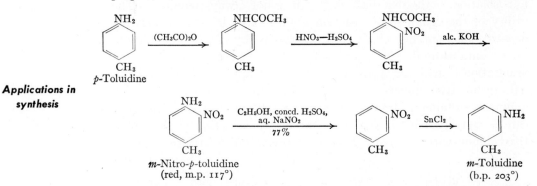

Applications in synthesis

p-Toluidine — *m*-Nitro-*p*-toluidine (red, m.p. 117°) — *m*-Toluidine (b.p. 203°)

both to prevent oxidation and to permit *ortho* orientation, a nitro group is introduced, and after deacetylation the amino substituent is eliminated. The diazonium salt is not isolated but is produced under conditions suitable for the replacement reaction; thus *m*-nitro-*p*-toluidine is suspended in alcohol, treated with concentrated sulfuric acid, and after cooling, a concentrated aqueous solution of sodium nitrite is added in portions.

Reduction to Arylhydrazines. — Reduction of a diazonium salt with excess sodium sulfite in a warm solution results in formation of

21.23

the corresponding arylhydrazine. The reaction proceeds through the diazo chloride (C_6H_5N=NCl) or diazo sulfonate (C_6H_5N=NSO_3Na) present in equilibrium with the diazonium salt. The product can be

$$[Ar\overset{+}{N}\equiv N]\overset{-}{X} \rightleftharpoons ArN=N-X \xrightarrow{4\,H} ArNHNH_3X \xrightarrow{NaOH} ArNHNH_2$$

isolated as either the hydrochloride or the free base. An efficient procedure for preparation of **phenylhydrazine** consists in diazotization of aniline in hydrochloric acid solution, reduction with sodium sulfite,

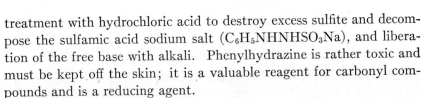

1. $HCl + NaNO_2$, o°
2. Na_2SO_3, 60–70°
3. HCl, 100°
4. NaOH

80–84%

Phenylhydrazine (m.p. 24°, b.p. 243°, pK_b 8.80)

treatment with hydrochloric acid to destroy excess sulfite and decompose the sulfamic acid sodium salt ($C_6H_5NHNHSO_3Na$), and liberation of the free base with alkali. Phenylhydrazine is rather toxic and must be kept off the skin; it is a valuable reagent for carbonyl compounds and is a reducing agent.

Coupling Reaction. — Diazonium salts react readily with phenols and aryl amines to form bright-colored azo compounds in which the two aromatic nuclei are linked through the azo grouping, —N=N—. The smoothly proceeding reaction is described as coupling. Benzenediazonium chloride couples with phenol in alkaline solution rapidly at ice-bath temperature to form p-hydroxyazobenzene (or p-benzeneazophenol). Since a diazonium salt changes in alkaline solution with

21.24

Azo compounds

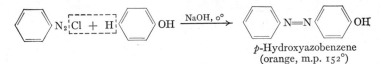

p-Hydroxyazobenzene
(orange, m.p. 152°)

eventual formation of the unreactive *trans*-diazotate, the proper procedure is to stir the solution of benzenediazonium chloride slowly into a chilled solution of phenol containing sufficient alkali to neutralize the organic and inorganic acids in the resulting mixture and maintain suitable alkalinity. Coupling occurs so rapidly as to preclude destruction of the diazo component. Dimethylaniline couples analogously in an aqueous medium that is either neutral or weakly acidified with acetic acid, and gives a yellow p-benzeneazo compound. These ex-

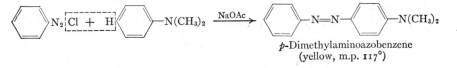

p-Dimethylaminoazobenzene
(yellow, m.p. 117°)

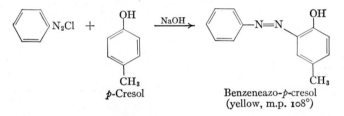

Chelate ring

 amples illustrate a reaction that is specific to phenols and to tertiary amines having available a free position *ortho* or *para* to the hydroxyl or amino group. Where a choice is open, coupling occurs practically exclusively in the *para* position. The product of coupling benzenediazonium chloride with phenol contains at most about 1% of *o*-hydroxyazobenzene (orange, m.p. 83°). The small amount of *ortho* isomer can be separated from the nonvolatile *para* compound by steam distillation; the volatility of the *ortho* isomer is ascribable to the presence of a chelate ring. Although there is a marked preference for *para* substitution, coupling occurs readily enough in the *ortho* position

p-Cresol
Benzeneazo-*p*-cresol
(yellow, m.p. 108°)

if this alone is available. The coupling reaction is spectacular because of the rapid formation of brightly colored products from colorless components. It is comparable to C-nitrosation with nitrous acid (21.17) with respect to exclusive *para* orientation and rapidity of combination in aqueous solution even at 0°. Both reactions are specific to amines and phenols and depend on the powerful directive influence of the hydroxyl and amino group. Studies of the rate of coupling in solutions of varying acidity indicate that one reacting species is always the diazonium ion and that the other, in an amine coupling (1), is the nonionized amine, and in a phenol coupling (2), is the phenoxide ion (Bartlett,[5] 1941):

Mechanism

1. ArN_2^+ + $C_6H_5N(CH_3)_2$

2. ArN_2^+ + $C_6H_5O^-$

In the pH range 2–6 the velocity of an amine coupling increases with decreasing acidity till the concentration of free amine reaches a maximum, and in a phenol coupling in the region pH 5–8 the rate of reaction increases with increasing pH because a greater proportion of the reactive phenoxide component becomes available. This interpretation not only accords with the general concept of other aromatic substitutions (18.7) but extends the evidence. Here the entering group is an actual cation, and that it is attracted to the nucleus of the phenoxide ion more strongly than to that of the phenol is a consequence of the inductive and resonance effect of the negatively charged

[5] Paul D. Bartlett, b. 1907 Ann Arbor, Mich.; Ph.D. Harvard (Conant), Nat. Res. Fellow Rockefeller Inst. (Levene); Harvard

oxygen, which results in increased electron density at the nuclear positions, particularly *ortho* and *para*. A positive charge on the nitrogen atom of an amine would have the opposite effect, and hence it is the free amine that couples.

Just as primary and secondary amines are attacked by nitrous acid in the amino group rather than in the nucleus, such amines ordinarily react with diazonium salts to give N-substitution products known as diazoamino derivatives. Thus benzenediazonium chloride and aniline combine to form diazoaminobenzene. A convenient procedure consists in dissolving two equivalents of aniline in three equivalents of hydrochloric acid and adding one equivalent of sodium nitrite, followed by two equivalents of sodium acetate. Like the

Diazoaminobenzene
(yellow, m.p. 98°)

N-nitrosoamines, diazoamino compounds rearrange under the influence of acid catalysts with transposition of the arylazo group to the *para* position in the nucleus. Thus diazoaminobenzene rearranges to

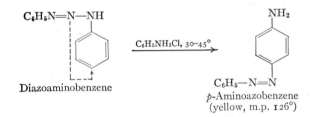

Diazoaminobenzene

C_6H_5—N=N
p-Aminoazobenzene
(yellow, m.p. 126°)

p-aminoazobenzene, the product that would have resulted from direct nuclear coupling. Such rearrangements proceed more rapidly by gentle heating in the presence of the amine hydrochloride. Test experiments indicate that the rearrangement actually involves fission of the diazoamino compound under the influence of the acidic catalyst to the diazonium salt and the amine and recombination of the components with nuclear substitution. Secondary amines, N-methylaniline for example, react similarly, and yield as the initial product the N-substituted aryldiazoamino compound, which can be rearranged to the azo compound.

A preparative use of azo compounds is for synthesis of *ortho* and *para* aminophenols and diamines, obtainable by reductive fission of the azo linkage. Thus *p*-hydroxyazobenzene is cleaved by reduction with stannous chloride or sodium hydrosulfite to *p*-aminophenol and aniline. An amino group can be introduced into the *para* position of phenol by coupling with diazotized aniline and reduction of the azo compound. Separation of the two amines resulting on reduction is

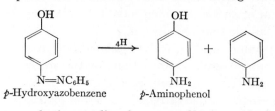

p-Hydroxyazobenzene   *p*-Aminophenol

facilitated by employing *p*-diazobenzenesulfonic acid, for the sulfanilic acid subsequently formed on reduction is easily removed as the water-soluble sodium salt:

$$p\text{-}HOC_6H_4N{=}NC_6H_4SO_3Na \xrightarrow{Na_2S_2O_4} p\text{-}HOC_6H_4NH_2 + H_2NC_6H_4SO_3Na$$

21.27   **Azo Dyes.** — The bright colors characteristic of azo compounds are due to the azo group, —N=N—, which is called a chromophore (Gr. *chroma*, color, + *phoros*, bearer). Hydroxyl and amino groups, whose presence in a coupling component facilitates preparation of azo compounds, augment the function of a chromophoric group and are called auxochromes (Gr. *auxo-*, increase). Azo compounds of adequate color and stability are useful dyes if they possess some structural feature giving them affinity for fiber. *p*-Aminoazobenzene, formulated above, is a direct dye for wool and silk (Aniline Yellow) and is held to these fibers by salt formation between the amino group of the dye and carboxyl groups of the protein (aspartic, glutamic units). Orange II is also direct to wool and silk because the sulfonate group binds the dye to basic groups of the protein (lysine, arginine). Dyes of these types have no affinity for the neutral cellulose chains of cotton and rayons. Dyes of a type known as substantive, however, are bound to cellulosic fibers by forces of adsorption or hydrogen bonding. An example is Congo Red, made by coupling doubly diazotized benzidine

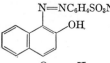

Orange II

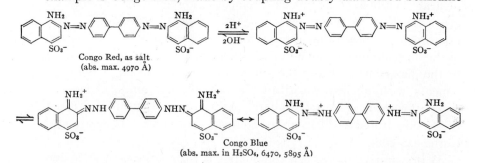

Congo Red, as salt
(abs. max. 4970 Å)

Congo Blue
(abs. max. in H₂SO₄, 6470, 5895 Å)

(20.11) with 1-aminonaphthalene-4-sulfonic acid (naphthionic acid). This substance is associated in solution (mol. wt. about 8000) and its affinity for cotton is probably a consequence of the colloidal properties. It is now used as an indicator rather than a dye because the color changes from red to blue in the presence of mineral acid. The color change is considered to be due to the formation of a resonance-stabilized, quinonoid inner salt.

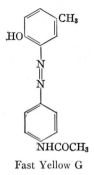

Fast Yellow G

Cellulose acetate (14.22) and nylon (16.21) are neutral substances but they differ from cellulose in having few hydroxyl groups available for hydrogen bonding, and these hydrophobic fibers are indifferent to the usual cotton dyes. They are dyed from an aqueous dispersion of a water-insoluble azo dye in the presence of a dispersing agent, when the dye apparently enters the fiber in the form of a solid solution. Dyes that have affinity for hydrophobic fibers under these conditions contain free hydroxy or amino groups; an example is Fast Yellow G.

SUMMARY

Aniline discovered as degradation product of indigo (name derived from Sanskrit word for indigo *nēlē*, referring to blue river Nile).

Methods for reduction of nitro compounds to amines: Fe + HCl (economical); $SnCl_2$ or Sn + HCl (convenient laboratory procedure); catalytic hydrogenation (to avoid hydrolysis of an acetyl group); Na_2S or $(NH_4)_2S$ (specific for partial reduction of polynitro compound, e.g. *m*-dinitrobenzene $\longrightarrow$ *m*-nitroaniline).

Boiling points abnormally high: aniline, mol. wt. 93, b.p. 184°. Basic character: aniline (pK_b 9.3) a weak base (compare CH_3NH_2, pK_b 3.4) because free aniline molecule is stabilized by resonance whereas anilinium ion is incapable of resonance (positive charge cannot leave N for redistribution in nucleus). The nitroanilines are still weaker bases because nitro group attracts electrons from ring and away from amino N and decreases affinity of N for proton. Di- and trinitroanilines extremely weak bases. Diphenylamine only feebly basic.

Amine salts. Hydrochlorides precipitated from aqueous solution by salting out with excess hydrochloric acid or from ethereal solution by gaseous HCl. Sulfanilic acid exists as inner salt or dipolar ion; insoluble in water, soluble in sodium carbonate solution as $H_2NC_6H_4SO_3Na$.

Aniline and derivatives. Produced from nitrobenzene with Fe and HCl. Acetanilide (neutral, stable to oxidation) prepared by action of acetic anhydride on aniline or by acetylation in aqueous solution. N-Methyl- and N,N-dimethylaniline made technically by heating aniline with methanol and an acid at appropriate temperature and pressure. Laboratory methods: action of dimethyl sulfate on sodium salt of benzenesulfonyl (Hinsberg) derivative of RNH_2 affords pure $RNHCH_3$; hydrogenation of a mixture of a primary amine ($ArNH_2$) and an aldehyde (RCHO) gives a secondary amine ($ArNHCH_2R$). Toluidines, *o*- and *p*-, available by reduction of *o*- and *p*-nitrotoluene.

Nitroanilines. *m*-Isomer available by partial reduction of *m*-dinitrobenzene with Na_2S (is chief product of nitration of aniline in sulfuric acid solution, but *m*-directive power of $-\overset{+}{N}H_3$ is weak and yield is only moderate). Nitration of acetanilide and hydrolysis affords *p*-nitroaniline in good yield; *o*-nitroaniline isolable from mother liquors by steam distillation (volatile because of hydrogen-bonded chelate structure).

Phenylenediamines, $C_6H_4(NH_2)_2$, available by reduction of the nitroanilines.

Halogen derivatives. Aniline brominated in water at high dilutions to sparingly soluble 2,4,6-tribromoaniline. Demonstrates powerful substitution-facilitating influence of amino group. Early use in extraction of bromine from sea water. Generality of reaction; use in identification. Moderating effect of acetylation: acetanilide $\longrightarrow$ *p*-bromoacetanilide $\longrightarrow$ *p*-bromoaniline.

Sulfanilic acid. Baking of aniline sulfate at 180° causes dehydration to phenylsulfamic acid ($C_6H_5NHSO_3H$), which rearranges to orthanilic acid by α,γ-shifts; further rearrangement affords sulfanilic acid.

Anisidines: $H_2NC_6H_4OCH_3$. Available from (a) anisole, $C_6H_5OCH_3$; (b) nitrochlorobenzenes; (c) nitrophenols.

Diphenylamine (feeble base): by heating aniline with aniline hydrochloride.

Oxidation. Diphenylamine ⟶ diphenyl-nitrogen ⟶ tetraphenylhydrazine. Intermediate free radical combines with triphenylmethyl. Aniline probably oxidized initially to free radical which affords a succession of products leading to quinone.

Nitrous acid. A primary amine ($ArNH_2$) yields a diazonium salt (ArN_2Cl), hydrolyzable to a phenol ($ArOH$) and N_2. A secondary amine, $C_6H_5NHCH_3$, gives an N-nitroso derivative, $C_6H_5N(NO)CH_3$, rearranged by acid to a C-nitroso derivative, p-$ONC_6H_4NHCH_3$. A tertiary amine, $C_6H_5N(CH_3)_2$, gives a C-nitroso derivative, p-$ONC_6H_4N(CH_3)_2$ (high yield, exclusive p-substitution).

Phenylisocyanide, $C_6H_5N{=}C$ or $C_6H_5\overset{+}{N}{\equiv}\overset{-}{C}$. From aniline, $CHCl_3$, KOH. Test for primary amines (detectable by odor).

Diazonium Salts

Benzenediazonium chloride. Ionic character, water-soluble, ether-insoluble, detonates readily when dry. Isolation: aniline hydrochloride + butyl nitrite + acetic acid; precipitation by ether. Preparation in aqueous solution (diazotization of the amine): $C_6H_5NH_2$ in water + 3 moles HCl, cool in ice, add $NaNO_2$. Structure of $C_6H_5N_2Cl$; possible mechanism of formation. Equilibrium reactions induced by alkali. Formation of benzenediazoic acid, $C_6H_5N{=}NOH$, and the potassium salt: potassium benzenediazotate (*cis* form; labile, reactive) and potassium isobenzenediazotate (*trans* form; stable, unreactive). Diazotization of sulfanilic acid to p-diazobenzenesulfonic acid.

Hydrolysis to phenols by refluxing with 45% H_2SO_4. Use where alkali fusion of a sulfonate is inapplicable, e.g. *m*-nitroaniline ⟶ *m*-nitrophenol; *p*-chloroaniline ⟶ *p*-chlorophenol.

Sandmeyer reaction. $ArN_2^+Cl^- + KI \longrightarrow ArI$. $ArN_2^+Cl^- + Cu_2Cl_2 \longrightarrow ArCl$. $ArN_2^+Br^- + Cu_2Br_2 \longrightarrow ArBr$. $ArN_2^+Cl^- + Cu_2(CN)_2 \longrightarrow ArCN$. Gattermann modification: Cu powder as catalyst. Chief use: $C_6H_5N_2^+Cl^- + C_6H_6(Cu) \longrightarrow C_6H_5 \cdot C_6H_5$ (diphenyl).

Deamination: $ArN_2^+Cl_2^- + $ reducing agent $\longrightarrow$ ArH. Reducing agents: (a) absolute ethanol (converted to CH_3CHO; usually requires dry diazonium salt; may give $ArOC_2H_5$ as by-product); (b) hypophosphorous acid, H_3PO_2 (applicable in aqueous solution). Use in synthesis: removal of an amino group required to direct substituents into specific positions. Examples: (a) preparation of *s*-tribromobenzene starting with aniline; (b) preparation of *m*-toluidine starting with *p*-toluidine (acetylate, nitrate, deacetylate, diazotize, deaminate, reduce).

Reduction to arylhydrazines: $ArN_2^+Cl^-$ reduced by $SnCl_2$ or Na_2SO_3 to $ArNHNH_2$.

Diazo coupling.

$C_6H_5N_2^+Cl^- + C_6H_5OH$ (NaOH, 0°) $\longrightarrow$
$$C_6H_5N{=}NC_6H_5OH\text{-}p$$

Reaction rapid at 0°; exclusive p-substitution; highly colored product. N,N-Dimethylaniline couples similarly in neutral or weakly acid solution. Coupling occurs in o-position if p-position is blocked (p-cresol). Active species:

(a) $ArN_2^+ + C_6H_5N(CH_3)_2$; (b) $ArN_2^+ + C_6H_5O^-$.

Coupling of $C_6H_5N_2^+Cl^-$ with aniline gives diazoaminobenzene, $C_6H_5N{=}N{-}NHC_6H_5$; rearrangement to p-aminoazobenzene, p-$H_2NC_6H_4N{=}NC_6H_5$. Secondary amines react similarly. Reductive fission of an azo compound. Use in preparation of p-aminophenols: couple a phenol with diazotized sulfanilic acid, reduce to the p-aminophenol (water-insoluble) and sulfanilic acid (soda-soluble). Difference between o-benzeneazophenols (chelated structure, alkali-insoluble, steam-volatile) and p-benzeneazophenols (no hydrogen bonding, alkali-soluble, not steam-volatile).

Azo dyes. Chromophoric azo group responsible for color. Auxochromes (OH, NH_2) enhance color. Basic direct dyes to wool and silk bound by amino groups to COOH groups of proteins; acidic dyes (SO_3Na) bound to free basic groups. Substantive dyes, e.g., Congo Red, held to cotton by hydrogen bonding. Dyes for hydrophobic fibers (cellulose acetate, nylon): small molecules with OH or NH_2 groups applied from aqueous dispersion to form solid solution.

PROBLEMS

1. Write equations for the alternate methods of preparing o- and p-anisidine mentioned in 21.12.
2. In what respects are amines subject to oxidation? Indicate two methods by which stabilization can be achieved, and explain how each modification influences substitutions.

3. Describe three instances of initial attack by a reagent on the nitrogen atom of an amine, with subsequent rearrangement into the nucleus.

4. How can *p*-bromophenol be prepared from acetanilide?

5. Indicate a sequence of reactions by which *o*-toluidine can be converted into phthalic acid.

6. Utilizing *p*-toluidine as the starting material, devise methods for the preparation of:

   (*a*) *p*-Bromobenzoic acid
   (*b*) *p*-Tolylhydrazine
   (*c*) 3,5-Dibromotoluene
   (*d*) 4,4′-Dimethyldiphenyl
   (*e*) 4-Methyl-2-aminophenol
   (*f*) N-Methyl-*p*-toluidine

7. How could N-methylaniline be converted into 4-amino-N-methylaniline?

8. Suggest methods for the preparation of the following compounds:

   (*a*) *m*-Chloroaniline   (*b*) *m*-Cresol
   (*c*) *m*-Bromochlorobenzene

9. Starting with hydrocarbons available from coal tar or by ready synthesis, suggest methods for the preparation of the following compounds:

   (*a*) 2,4,6-Trimethylphenol
   (*b*) 2-Cyano-1,4-dimethylbenzene
   (*c*) 4-Chlorobenzene-1,3-dicarboxylic acid
   (*d*) 2,5-Dimethyl-4-aminophenol
   (*e*) 3-Amino-4-methylacetophenone

READING REFERENCE

K. H. Saunders, *Aromatic Diazo-Compounds*, E. Arnold, London (1949)

PHENOLS

Phenols usually are crystalline solids, but certain alkylphenols are liquids (*m*-cresol). Phenol itself is a solid at room temperature, but the melting point (43°) is greatly depressed by small amounts of water, and liquid preparations containing 2–10% of water find some use in medicine (cauterization) and in extraction operations. Symmetrically substituted phenols are particularly high melting, as illustrated by the following examples:

Melting points and symmetry

p-Nitrophenol, m.p. 114° Hydroquinone (1,4-dihydroxybenzene), m.p. 170°
p-Cyclohexylphenol, m.p. 133° Phloroglucinol (1,3,5-trihydroxybenzene), m.p. 219°

High boiling points

The boiling points are considerably higher than those of aliphatic alcohols; thus phenol (mol. wt. 94) boils at 181°, whereas *n*-hexyl alcohol (mol. wt. 102) boils at 156°. Association in the liquid state through hydrogen bonding is, in a phenol, supplemented by association due to attraction of polarized resonance structures (18.12).

Weakly acidic

The most distinctive property of phenols is the weakly acidic character, attributable to the enolic grouping: —CH=C(OH)—. Phenol is a weak acid, pK_a 10.0, and it forms salts (phenolates) with sodium hydroxide but not with the carbonate. This behavior is typical and distinguishes phenols from carboxylic acids, which react with both alkali carbonates and bicarbonates. An aromatic substance found to be more soluble in sodium hydroxide solution than in water but showing no increased solubility in the presence of sodium carbonate is likely to be a phenol. Values for the dissociation constants of substituted phenols show little regularity, except in the series of nitro compounds. The three mononitrophenols are more acidic (pK_a 7.2–8) than the parent substance, and the effect is greatly magnified in 2,4-dinitrophenol (pK_a 4.0) and in picric acid, which is nearly as strongly acidic as a mineral acid. Stabilization of the anionic form by nitro groups is the counterpart of suppression of the basic dissociation of the amines (21.2), and likewise can be attributed to inductive and resonance effects.

PREPARATION

Generally applicable methods for preparation of phenols are **alkali fusion of a sulfonate** (20.19) and **hydrolysis of a diazonium salt** (21.20), and these two reactions render phenols available from hydrocarbons through initial sulfonation or nitration. A third method, alkaline **hydrolysis of an aryl halide,** is applied industrially to the preparation of phenol from chlorobenzene at a high temperature and pressure, and is applicable under ordinary conditions to the highly reactive polynitro halogen compounds. A fourth method consists in **dehydrogenation of a hydroaromatic ketone,** conducted either with a palladium or platinum catalyst or with sulfur or selenium. The reaction

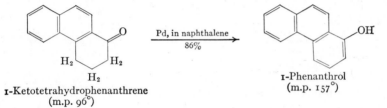

1-Ketotetrahydrophenanthrene
(m.p. 96°)

1-Phenanthrol
(m.p. 157°)

probably proceeds by removal of two hydrogen atoms with formation of an unstable keto form of dihydrobenzenoid structure, which isomerizes to the phenol:

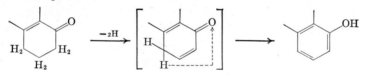

SPECIFIC PREPARATIONS

Phenol. — During World War I the phenol required for production of picric acid was produced from benzene by sulfonation and

$$C_6H_6 \xrightarrow{H_2SO_4 + 9.5\% \, SO_3, \, 50-70°} C_6H_5SO_3H(Na) \xrightarrow{NaOH, \, 320-350°} C_6H_5ONa(H)$$

alkali fusion. The overall yield was only 60–75%, and a considerable loss was entailed in the sulfonation process, which reaches equilibrium with the accumulation of water from the reaction. An innovation, announced by the Dow Chemical Company in 1928, consists in hydrolysis of chlorobenzene by a dilute aqueous solution of alkali at high temperature and pressure. Hydrolysis is conducted as a con-

$$C_6H_5Cl \xrightarrow[2000-3000 \, lbs./sq. \, in.]{6-8\% \, aq. \, NaOH, \, 300°,} C_6H_5ONa \xrightarrow{HCl} C_6H_5OH$$

tinuous process by flowing the reactants through a pipe line system capable of maintaining the required temperature and pressure and of suitable length (about one mile) to provide the period required for reaction (about twenty minutes). An inevitable side reaction results in formation of diphenyl oxide, and accumulation of this material, for which no large-scale use has arisen, would detract from the efficiency of the process. A solution of this apparent difficulty followed

Control of by-product

$$C_6H_5ONa + C_6H_5OH \rightleftharpoons C_6H_5OC_6H_5 + NaOH$$
$$\text{Diphenyl oxide}$$

from the observation that the by-product is formed in a reversible reaction and can be kept from accumulating by simply recirculating the amount necessary to meet the equilibrium requirement.

A newer process utilizes cumene, available by Friedel-Crafts alkylation of benzene with propylene. Air is blown into the liquid

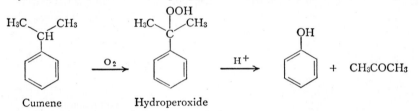

Cumene   Hydroperoxide

hydrocarbon in the presence of a trace of base (NaOH) to produce the hydroperoxide, which on acid catalysis decomposes to phenol and acetone.

22.4

Derivatives of Phenol. — The ether derivatives, **anisole**, $C_6H_5OCH_3$ (b.p. 154°), and **phenetole**, $C_6H_5OC_2H_5$ (b.p. 172°), are liquids with an aromatic fragrance, obtained conveniently by alkylation of phenol with dimethyl or diethyl sulfate in a weakly alkaline aqueous medium. A phenol often is converted into its ether to provide protection against oxidation or other undesired side reaction during transformations not involving the oxygen function, for the masking group subsequently can be removed and the hydroxyl group regenerated. Anisole can be demethylated by refluxing in acetic acid solution with 48% hydrobromic acid or by heating with hydriodic acid at 130°: $C_6H_5OCH_3 + HX \longrightarrow C_6H_5OH + CH_3X$. Aluminum chloride is a further effective dealkylating agent; the ether can be heated with aluminum chloride alone at 120°, or refluxed in benzene or carbon disulfide solution with an amount of the reagent equivalent to the number of alkoxyl groups present:

$$C_6H_5OCH_3 + AlCl_3 \longrightarrow \left[\begin{matrix} C_6H_5 \\ > \overset{+}{O} - AlCl_2 \\ CH_3 \end{matrix} \right] Cl^- \xrightarrow{\text{Heat}}$$

Ether cleavage

$$C_6H_5OAlCl_2 \xrightarrow{H_2O} C_6H_5OH + HOAlCl_2$$
$$(+CH_3Cl)$$

Phenyl acetate, $C_6H_5OCOCH_3$, is a liquid, b.p. 196°; acetyl derivatives in general are prepared by warming the phenol with excess acetic anhydride with addition of either a basic catalyst (fused sodium acetate, pyridine, triethylamine) or an acid catalyst (sulfuric acid, boron fluoride etherate). **Phenyl benzoate,** $C_6H_5COOC_6H_5$ (m.p. 71°), is obtained by shaking a weakly alkaline solution of phenol with benzoyl chloride (Schotten-Baumann reaction) or by interaction of the components in cold pyridine solution. The Schotten-Baumann procedure is applicable to the preparation of **phenyl *p*-toluenesulfonate** (m.p. 95°):

$$C_6H_5OH \;+\; p\text{-}CH_3C_6H_4SO_2Cl \longrightarrow C_6H_5OSO_2C_6H_4CH_3(p)$$

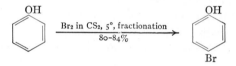

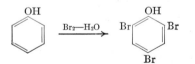

Halophenols. — Chlorination of phenol without solvent at temperatures from 40–155° affords mixtures of *o*- and *p*-chlorophenol in which the latter predominates. Pure *o*- and *p*-chlorophenol, like the *meta* isomer, are best prepared from the corresponding chloroanilines by diazotization and hydrolysis. Monobromination of phenol at low temperatures results in almost exclusive *para* substitution; the *ortho*

22.5

isomer is produced in appreciable amounts only at higher temperatures. In analogy to the behavior of aniline, phenol is converted rapidly by bromine water into the sparingly soluble tribromo derivative. The reaction is employed for the detection of phenol, since turbidity is discernible at dilutions as high as 1:100,000.

Powerful activation by OH

Nitrophenols. — Nitration of phenol with dilute aqueous nitric acid gives a mixture of the *o*- and *p*-isomers, with some predominance of the former substance (18.11), and since a sharp separation can be made by steam distillation, both isomers are obtainable satisfactorily from the reaction mixture. *o*-Nitrophenol is readily volatile with steam and is obtained from the distillate in substantially pure form, whereas the nonvolatile *p*-isomer is retained in the distillation flask along with any dinitrophenols and other contaminants and requires more extensive purification. The steam volatility of *o*-nitrophenol, as that of *o*-nitroaniline, is attributed to chelation. A method of preparing *p*-nitrophenol in better yield consists in oxidation of *p*-nitroso-

22.6

o-Nitrophenol ·

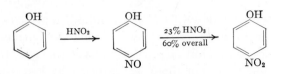

phenol with nitric acid. A satisfactory preparation of *m*-nitropheno
proceeds from *m*-nitroaniline by the diazo reaction (21.20). 2,4-
Dinitrophenol is produced as an intermediate in the preparation of
picric acid by nitration of chlorobenzene (20.8).

22.7   **Catechol.** — Catechol, or 1,2-dihydroxybenzene, occurs in many
plants and is excreted in horse urine both as such and as the sulfate
ester. Several methods are available for the preparation of this technically important compound. A technical process involves hydrolysis
of either *o*-chlorophenol or *o*-dichlorobenzene with aqueous alkali in
the presence of a catalyst under forcing conditions. In another tech-

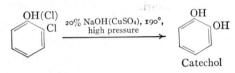

Catechol

nical process, sodium phenol-2,4-disulfonate is fused with alkali under
conditions so controlled that only the *ortho* sulfonate group is replaced
by hydroxyl; the *para* sulfonate group is then removed by hydrolysis:

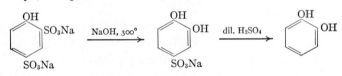

22.8   **Resorcinol.** — The *m*-dihydroxy derivative of benzene, not found
in nature, is prepared by alkali fusion of sodium *m*-benzenedisulfonate.

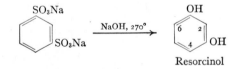

Resorcinol

High reactivity   Resorcinol is highly reactive because of the reinforcing action of the
two hydroxyl groups, and is substituted initially at the 4-position,
para to one hydroxyl and *ortho* to the other. The course of disubstitution is dependent on the nature of the reagent and on the conditions;
specific procedures afford the 4,6-dichloro and the 2,4-dinitro derivatives.

22.9   **Hydroquinone.** — Hydroquinone occurs in certain plants as the
glycoside arbutin (14.16), from which it is liberated on hydrolysis
with emulsin or sulfuric acid. A special method of preparation is
oxidation of aniline, through a succession of intermediates leading to

the yellow substance quinone, from which hydroquinone (colorless) is obtained on reduction. The reduction is reversible, and hydroqui-

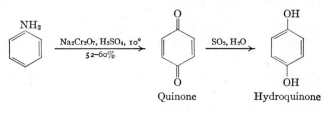

Quinone   Hydroquinone

none has reducing properties. It is employed as a photographic developer because of its ability to reduce to metallic silver the silver subhalide resulting from exposure of silver halide emulsion to light.

Has reducing properties; a developer

22.10

Pyrogallol is produced technically from the natural product gallic acid by distillation from a mixture with pumice in an atmosphere of carbon dioxide. Like other polyhydroxy acids, gallic acid undergoes

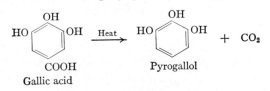

Gallic acid   Pyrogallol

decarboxylation more readily than ordinary aromatic carboxylic acids. Pyrogallol has strong reducing properties and is used as a photographic developer. It is also employed in a strongly alkaline solution as an absorbent for oxygen in gas analysis. **Pyrogallol 1,3-dimethyl ether** is obtained by methylation with methyl iodide in methanol solution in the presence of potassium hydroxide at 150–160°.

Oxygen absorbent

Phloroglucinol, or *s*-trihydroxybenzene, is an expensive chemical obtainable from *s*-triaminobenzene. The amine is available as a reduction product of the corresponding trinitro compound, which in turn is prepared from TNT (20.6), and the intermediate 2,4,6-trinitrobenzoic acid is a point of departure for the preparation of phloroglucinol. The reduction product of the trinitro compound when refluxed

22.11

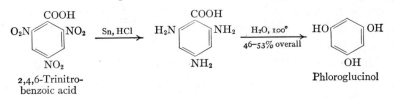

2,4,6-Trinitro-   Phloroglucinol
benzoic acid

From TNT

in a nearly neutral solution for a prolonged period undergoes hydrolysis of the amino groups to hydroxyl groups, and decarboxylation. The ready replacement of amino groups by hydroxyl and the low-temperature decarboxylation are both reactions specific to the structures in question and are probably associated with the tendency of the symmetrical triol system to react in the triketo form. Thus phloroglucinol reacts with hydroxylamine to form the trioxime of cyclohexane-1,3,5-trione.

22.12

Aminophenols. — *o*-Aminophenol is prepared by reduction of *o*-nitrophenol, for example with sodium hydrosulfite ($Na_2S_2O_4$) in alkaline solution or with zinc dust and aqueous calcium chloride solution. The *m*-isomer, a useful dye intermediate, is produced tech-

Special reaction

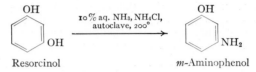

Resorcinol — *m*-Aminophenol

nically from resorcinol. Conversion of phenols into amines is applicable to the phenolic derivatives of naphthalene and other polynuclear hydrocarbons possessing enhanced reactivity, but in the benzene series useful application is limited to a few special instances. *p*-Aminophenol is employed in the production of dyes and as a photographic developer; it has strong reducing properties and is rapidly discolored in neutral or alkaline solution. Technical processes of preparation are reduction of *p*-nitrophenol with iron powder and dilute hydrochloric acid, and electrolytic reduction of nitrobenzene in sulfuric acid solution; the latter reaction proceeds through formation and rearrangement of phenylhydroxylamine. Convenient procedures for the preparation of *p*-aminophenols from phenols are based on the reduction of the *p*-nitroso or *p*-sulfobenzeneazo derivatives resulting from nitrosation or coupling with diazotized sulfanilic acid. Selective acetylation of the amino group is easily accomplished in aqueous solution. A solution of *p*-aminophenol hydrochloride in water is

Diazo coupling and reduction

$$p\text{-}HOC_6H_4NH_2 \cdot HCl + (CH_3CO)_2O + CH_3COONa \xrightarrow{\text{aq. solution, } 25^\circ} p\text{-}HOC_6H_4NHCOCH_3$$

p-Acetylaminophenol (m.p. 169°)

treated with one equivalent of acetic anhydride, followed at once by one equivalent of sodium acetate; the free amine is acetylated as it is liberated from the salt.

22.13

Carvacrol and **thymol** occur in several essential oils and probably

Natural products

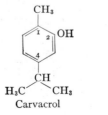

Carvacrol — Thymol

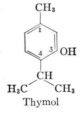

are transformation products of terpenoid constituents. A synthesis of carvacrol consists in sulfonation of *p*-cymene (1-methyl-4-isopropyl-benzene) and alkali fusion of the resulting 2-sulfonic acid.

Saligenin, *o*-HOC$_6$H$_4$CH$_2$OH, results from hydrolysis of salicin **22.14** (C$_{13}$H$_{18}$O$_7$), a bitter glucoside found in the bark of willow and poplar trees and used to some extent in medicine as an antipyretic and a tonic.

4-*n*-Hexylresorcinol, a synthetic disinfectant, is prepared by con- **22.15** densation of resorcinol with caproic acid in the presence of anhydrous

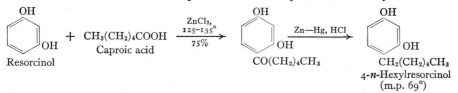

Resorcinol + Caproic acid → 4-*n*-Hexylresorcinol (m.p. 69°)

A disinfectant

zinc chloride. The condensation is a Friedel-Crafts type, but resorcinol is substituted with such ease that an acid, rather than an acid chloride, can be employed and the moderately active zinc chloride provides adequate catalysis. The completing step is Clemmensen reduction of the ketone.

REACTIONS

Typical phenols are differentiated from the majority of other **22.16** organic compounds by their characteristic weakly acidic nature, recognizable by ready solubility in alkali but not in sodium carbonate solution (exception: the more strongly acidic nitrophenols). Many phenols, like aliphatic enols, give rise to characteristic colors when treated with ferric chloride in dilute aqueous or alcoholic solution as the result of complex formation (phenol, violet; cresols, blue; cate-chol, green; resorcinol, dark violet).

Substitutions. — The facility with which phenols undergo sub- **22.17** stitution is illustrated by the ready formation of the 2,4,6-tribromo derivative (22.5), by the diazo coupling reaction (21.24), and by the nitrosation of phenols (22.6), preferentially in the *para* position, on interaction with nitrous acid at ice-bath temperature. A further instance of the substitution-facilitating influence of the hydroxyl group is mercuration, applicable specifically to phenols. Thus phenol reacts with mercuric acetate to give the *o*-acetoxymercuri derivative, which is convertible into the chloromercuri derivative by interaction

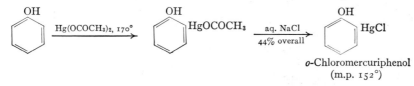

o-Chloromercuriphenol (m.p. 152°)

423

with sodium chloride. The chloromercuri group in the phenol is replaceable by iodine; for example *o*-chloromercuriphenol is converted by iodine in chloroform solution into *o*-iodophenol (m.p. 43°) in 63% yield.

22.18   **Friedel-Crafts Reaction.** — The presence of a phenolic hydroxyl group alters the behavior in the Friedel-Crafts reaction, for phenol initially reacts with the reagent with evolution of hydrogen chloride and production of an aluminum chloride salt. A phenol methyl ether

$$C_6H_5OH + AlCl_3 \longrightarrow C_6H_5OAlCl_2 + HCl$$

enters into Friedel-Crafts reactions in the normal manner if the mixture is kept at a temperature low enough to avoid cleavage of the ether group by aluminum chloride (22.4). In large-scale preparations, where uniform cooling may be difficult, some cleavage of the ether group may occur and the crude reaction product is remethylated prior to purification.

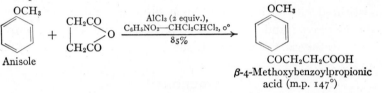

Anisole

β-4-Methoxybenzoylpropionic acid (m.p. 147°)

22.19   **Fries Reaction.** — Fries [1] discovered (1908) that an acyl derivative of a phenol when heated with aluminum chloride is converted into the isomeric *o*- or *p*-hydroxy ketone, or more often into a mixture of the two. The material is present in the reaction mixture as the aluminum chloride salt, and the hydroxy compound is liberated on hydrolysis with ice and hydrochloric acid. *m*-Hydroxy ketones have

$$C_6H_5OCOCH_3 \xrightarrow{AlCl_3(-HCl)} CH_3COC_6H_4OAlCl_2 \longrightarrow CH_3COC_6H_4OH$$

Phenyl acetate

o- and *p*-Hydroxy-acetophenone

been observed very rarely as products of the Fries reaction, and the chief variation is in the ratio of the *ortho* and *para* isomers. This ratio varies somewhat with the solvent and the amount of catalyst, *Temperature effect* and is influenced particularly by the temperature, as illustrated strikingly by the behavior of *m*-cresyl acetate, which can be converted into either of two products in good yield by adjustment of the temperature.

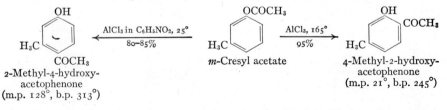

2-Methyl-4-hydroxy-acetophenone (m.p. 128°, b.p. 313°)

m-Cresyl acetate

4-Methyl-2-hydroxy-acetophenone (m.p. 21°, b.p. 245°)

[1] Karl Fries, b. 1875 Kiedrich/Rhine; Ph.D. Marburg (Zincke); Marburg, Braunschweig

The *o*-isomer predominates at elevated temperatures because it has superior stability, and stabilization of this structure and not of that of the *p*-isomer can be attributed to the presence of a chelate ring in the aluminum chloride complex produced in the reaction. This inter-

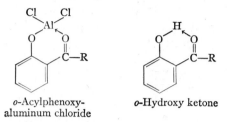

o-Acylphenoxy-
aluminum chloride

o-Hydroxy ketone

pretation is supported by the fact that free *o*-hydroxy ketones are chelated, since ordinarily chelation is stronger in a metal derivative than in the corresponding hydroxy compound. Thus the isomeric methylhydroxyacetophenones differ considerably in boiling point (68°); the (chelated) *o*-hydroxy ketone is distinctly more volatile than the fully hydroxylic *p*-isomer and it is also more soluble in ligroin.

The distinct differences in properties associated with the presence or absence of chelation facilitate separation of the mixtures ordinarily obtained in Fries reactions. The *o*-isomer often can be removed selectively by steam distillation, or the isomers can be separated adequately by fractional distillation. Thus, unlike many substitutions that afford mixtures, the Fries reaction has preparative value and offers a convenient route to both the *o*- and *p*-acyl derivatives of phenols.

Oxidation. — Phenols, like amines, are susceptible to oxidation, and the initial step consists in abstraction of the hydroxylic hydrogen atom with formation of a free radical containing univalent oxygen. Such radicals usually are so unstable and reactive that they undergo rapid transformation into secondary products, but certain hydroxy derivatives of phenanthrene afford radicals of stability comparable to triphenylmethyl (Goldschmidt, 1922). Thus 9-chloro-10-phenanthrol, on oxidation with potassium ferricyanide in alkaline solution or with lead dioxide in organic solvents, gives a colored phenanthroxyl radical that slowly associates to a colorless dimeric form till equilib-

22.20

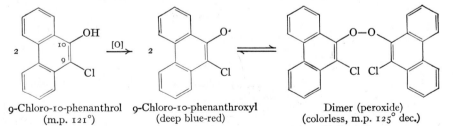

9-Chloro-10-phenanthrol
(m.p. 121°)

9-Chloro-10-phenanthroxyl
(deep blue-red)

Dimer (peroxide)
(colorless, m.p. 125° dec.)

Free radical

rium is reached; the monomer and dimer are present in about equal amounts at equilibrium in pyridine solution at room temperature. Reducing agents regenerate chlorophenanthrol.

Condensation with Aldehydes. — Phenols condense readily with aliphatic and aromatic aldehydes to give initial products that can be regarded as arising from an aldol-like addition of the phenol molecule, at a reactive *o*- or *p*-position, to the carbonyl group of the aldehyde.

$$R-C \underset{O}{\overset{H}{<}} + H \cdot C_6H_4OH \longrightarrow R-CHC_6H_4OH \; (o \text{ and } p)$$
$$\underset{\underset{OH}{|}}{}$$

With adjustment of the proportion of the reactants and the conditions, two molecules of phenol react with one of the aldehyde. The type

$$HOC_6H_4 \cdot H + RCH = O + H \cdot C_6H_4OH \longrightarrow HOC_6H_4-\underset{\underset{R}{|}}{CH}-C_6H_4OH$$

of condensation lends itself to continuation, with the resulting production of polymers, and forms the basis for the preparation of the phenol-formaldehyde resin Bakelite (Baekeland,[2] 1909). Phenol condenses with formaldehyde with introduction in *ortho* and *para* positions of the methylol group, —CH₂OH, which condenses with another molecule of phenol with loss of water and production of a methylene bridge. Further polymerization results in a three-dimensional molecule of the type illustrated in the following formulation:

Bakelite resin

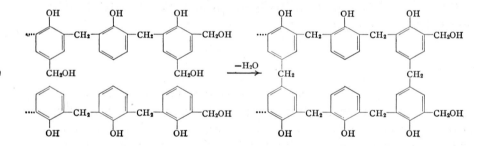

22.22   **Claisen Allylation.** — Claisen[3] discovered (1923) that phenol allyl ether when heated rearranges to *o*-allylphenol (nearly quantitative

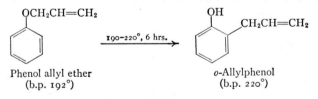

Phenol allyl ether
(b.p. 192°)

o-Allylphenol
(b.p. 220°)

[2] Leo Hendrik Baekeland, 1863–1944; b. Ghent, Belgium; Univ. Brussels, Columbia; president General Bakelite Corp.
[3] Ludwig Claisen, 1851–1930; b. Linden/Hannover, Germany; Ph.D. Bonn (Kekulé); Aachen, Kiel, Berlin; *Ber.*, **69A**, 97 (1936)

yield); the allyl group migrates from oxygen exclusively to the *o*-position in the ring. Allyl ethers are obtained by reaction of allyl bromide with a solution of the phenol in acetone containing suspended potassium carbonate to neutralize the hydrogen bromide liberated (phenol allyl ether, 86–97% yield). When the procedure is altered by use of anhydrous potassium phenolate in suspension in benzene, the chief product is the C-allyl derivative, *o*-allylphenol. Acetone, a polar solvent, favors O-allylation, and the nonpolar benzene favors direct allylation of the ring. The product of C-allylation is identical with that produced by rearrangement in this instance, but not in the general case of substituted β-alkenyl compounds. Thus the ether I

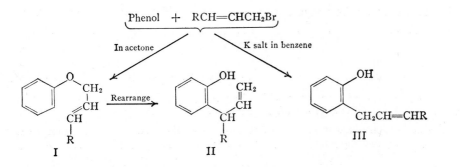

is formed by alkylation in acetone and rearranges on being heated to II, an isomer of the substance III resulting as the chief product of direct C-alkylation. An allylic rearrangement, or α,γ-shift, thus occurs in the allyl group in the course of the migration.

TROPOLONES

Some members of this group that occur in nature have been investigated extensively since early times, but the basic structure was not recognized until 1945, when Dewar in England and the Japanese chemist Tetsuo Nozoe[4] in Formosa independently noted that the heptatrienolone structure (1) should have aromatic characteristics, since two equivalent Kekulé-like structures are possible (2). Such

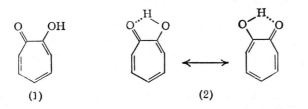

[4] Tetsuo Nozoe, b. 1902 Sendai, Japan; D.Sc. Osaka Imperial Univ.; Taihoku Imp. Univ. (Formosa), Tohoku Univ. (Japan)

427

CHAPTER 22

Stipitatic acid

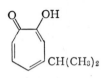

Hinokitol

natural products as stipitatic acid, a mold metabolite, and hinokitol, a constituent of the essential oil of the Japanese hinoki tree, have aromatic properties but are nonbenzenoid, and the tropolone structures suggested by Dewar and Nozoe have been established. The name is derived from that of tropane, the parent substance of the tropine alkaloids, characterized by the presence of a seven-carbon ring. Tropolones exhibit marked phenolic properties: positive ferric chloride test; pK_a values close to 7 (intermediate between phenol and acetic acid); diazo coupling; nitration and bromination. They are resistant to permanganate oxidation, and the ketonic character is masked.

SUMMARY

Phenol, m.p. 43°; symmetrically substituted derivatives high-melting. Boiling points higher because of hydrogen bonding and attraction of polarized resonance structures.

Phenol a weak acid (pK_a 10.0), soluble in alkali but not in soda solution. Nitro substituents stabilize anionic form by inductive effect and increase acidic strength: nitrophenols, pK_a 7.2–8; 2,4-dinitrophenol, pK_a 4.0; picric acid, pK_a 0.8.

Preparation

General methods: (a) alkali fusion of a sulfonate (not applicable to nitro, halo, or cyano compounds); (b) hydrolysis of a diazonium salt; (c) dehydrogenation of a hydroaromatic ketone.

Phenol. (a) Sulfonation of benzene and alkali fusion (60–75% overall). (b) Dow process: chlorobenzene + 7% aqueous alkali at 300° and high pressure; continuous process in pipe line reactor; accumulation of by-product diphenyl oxide avoided by recycling material at equilibrium concentration.

Phenol derivatives. Anisole and phenetole by alkylation in alkaline solution with $(CH_3)_2SO_4$ or $(C_2H_5)_2SO_4$. Demethylation by refluxing with HOAc—HBr (48%) or by heating with $AlCl_3$ at 120° or in refluxing benzene. Phenyl acetate by action of acetic anhydride catalyzed by NaOAc, pyridine, $(C_2H_5)_3N$, H_2SO_4, or BF_3-etherate. Phenyl benzoate by reaction with benzoyl chloride in the presence of aqueous alkali (Schotten-Baumann reaction) or pyridine.

Halophenols. Pure o-, m-, and p-chlorophenols from the chloroanilines by diazotization and hydrolysis. p-Bromophenol by bromination at low temperature. Phenol + bromine water $\longrightarrow$ tribromophenol (m.p. 95°), precipitate detectable at dilution of 1:10,000.

Nitrophenols. Nitration of phenol with dilute acid gives mixture of o- and p-nitrophenols separable by steam distillation; *ortho* isomer steam volatile because of chelation. Pure p-nitrophenol by oxidation of p-nitrosophenol. m-Nitrophenol available from m-nitroaniline.

Catechol, $C_6H_4(OH)_2$-1,2. (a) High temperature hydrolysis of o-dichlorobenzene. (b) From 2,4-disulfonate of phenol by selective alkali fusion of 2-SO_3Na and hydrolysis of 4-SO_3Na.

Resorcinol, $C_6H_4(OH)_2$-1,3. From benzene by disulfonation and alkali fusion.

Hydroquinone, $C_6H_4(OH)_2$-1,4. By oxidation of aniline to quinone, and reduction.

Pyrogallol, $C_6H_3(OH)_3$-1,2,3. Decarboxylation of gallic acid. Photographic developer. Oxygen absorbent.

Phloroglucinol, $C_6H_3(OH)_3$-1,3,5. From TNT by oxidation, reduction, and simultaneous hydrolysis and decarboxylation.

Aminophenols. *Ortho* and *para* isomers from the nitrophenols, *meta* by amination of resorcinol (specific case, not general in benzene series). p-Aminophenols available from phenols by coupling with diazotized sulfanilic acid and reduction. Acetylation in aqueous solution gives N-acetyl derivative with free OH group (addition of acetic anhydride and sodium acetate to solution of hydrochloride).

Carvacrol (2-hydroxy-p-cymene) and thymol (3-hydroxy-p-cymene) from essential oils. Carvacrol from p-cymene by sulfonation and alkali fusion. Saligenin, o-$HOC_6H_4CH_2OH$, from a natural glucoside.

4-n-Hexylresorcinol (disinfectant), acylation of resorcinol with caproic acid ($ZnCl_2$) and Clemmensen reduction.

Reactions

Facile substitution: tribromophenol formed at high dilution; low-temperature nitrosation and diazo coupling (*para* preferred); mercuration (*o*-HgOAc derivative).

Friedel-Crafts acylation of phenol methyl ethers; products subsequently demethylated with $AlCl_3$. Fries reaction: phenol $\longrightarrow$ phenyl acetate ($+ AlCl_3$) $\longrightarrow$ *o*- and *p*-hydroxyacetophenone. High temperature favors formation of *ortho* product because its $-AlCl_2$ salt is stabilized by chelation.

Chelation in free *o*-hydroxy ketone enhances volatility and makes separation of isomers easy.

Oxidation. Initial formation of free radical shown with 9-chloro-10-phenanthrol.

Condensation with aldehydes. Bakelite: three dimensional phenol-formaldehyde resin.

Claisen rearrangement: $C_6H_5OCH_2CH=CH_2$ $\longrightarrow$ *o*-$CH_2=CHCH_2C_6H_4OH$. Direct C-allylation of phenol K-salt in benzene. O $\longrightarrow$ C migration with α,γ-rearrangement in allyl group.

Tropolones

Nonbenzenoid aromatic α-hydroxy ketones with seven-carbon ring. Resonance stabilization. Phenolic properties: diazo coupling, bromination.

Tropolone structure established for several natural products.

PROBLEMS

1. Compare the effect of *o*-, *m*-, and *p*-nitro groups on the dissociation of phenol and of aniline.
2. Summarize instances of the modification in physical properties attributable to chelation.
3. Outline a series of experiments by which saligenin (22.14) could be shown to contain one phenolic hydroxyl group and one alcoholic group.
4. Suggest a method for the synthesis of 4-ethylcatechol.
5. Outline the steps involved in the synthetic production from benzene of:

   (*a*) Anisole   (*d*) *p*-Aminophenol
   (*b*) Catechol   (*e*) 4-*n*-Hexylresorcinol
   (*c*) *o*-Aminophenol

6. Cite qualitative tests that would distinguish between the following compounds:
   $C_6H_5OCH_2COOH$,   *p*-$CH_3COC_6H_4OH$,
   $C_6H_5OCOCH_3$, $C_6H_5COCH_2OH$.
7. Formulate syntheses of α- and β-naphthol starting with benzene or anisole and succinic anhydride.
8. By what sequence of reactions could *p*-aminophenol be converted into 2-bromo-4-aminophenol?

9. Neosynephrine hydrochloride, a sympathomimetic drug, is a bitter substance of the formula $C_9H_{14}O_2NCl$, and has the constants: m.p. 143°, $\alpha_D -46°$. It dissolves readily in water, and addition of bicarbonate to the solution causes separation of the base neosynephrine ($C_9H_{13}O_2N$). This base is soluble in aqueous sodium hydroxide, and on Zerewitinoff determination it gives three moles of methane. Excess acetic anhydride in pyridine converts neosynephrine (A) into a neutral compound B, $C_{15}H_{19}O_5N$, and this with dilute sodium carbonate solution gives C, $C_{13}H_{17}O_4N$, which on treatment with dimethyl sulfate and alkali gives D, $C_{14}H_{19}O_4N$. Compound D when boiled with aqueous sodium hydroxide is hydrolyzed to a basic substance E, $C_{10}H_{15}O_2N$, and on mild catalytic hydrogenation E yields F, $C_{10}H_{15}ON$. Excess methyl iodide converts F into a water-soluble salt G, $C_{12}H_{20}ONI$, which when heated with potassium hydroxide gives trimethylamine and a neutral compound H, $C_9H_{10}O$. Ozonization of H gives *m*-methoxybenzaldehyde and formaldehyde. Deduce the structure of neosynephrine.

READING REFERENCES

A. H. Blatt, "The Fries Reaction," in R. Adams, *Organic Reactions*, I, 342, Wiley, New York (1942)

D. S. Tarbell, "The Claisen Rearrangement," *Organic Reactions*, II, 1 (1944)

J. W. Cook and J. D. Loudon, "The Tropolones," *Quart. Rev.*, 5, 99 (1951)

A. W. Johnson, "Aromaticity in Seven-Membered Rings," *J. Chem. Soc.*, 1331 (1954)

ARYL HALIDES

23.1

Halogenation

*Favorable for
p-dihalides*

*Sandmeyer
reaction*

Preparation. — The benzene nucleus is readily brominated or chlorinated under catalysis by a ferric or aluminum halide, and since the substituent introduced has a deactivating inductive effect, the reactions are easily controlled to monosubstitution, if desired, or else carried to the stage of disubstitution. The *para* isomer is the predominant product and, furthermore, the *para* dihalogen compounds (Cl, Cl; Br, Br; Cl, I) are all solids, in contrast to the *o*-isomers, and hence are readily purified by crystallization. Thus *p*-dibromobenzene (m.p. 89°) is obtainable in 85% yield by bromination of benzene in the presence of ferric bromide, and chlorobenzene affords *p*-bromochlorobenzene (m.p. 67°) in yield of 88%. Dichlorination of benzene in the presence of aluminum chloride gives chiefly the solid *p*-dichloro compound (m.p. 53°), used as a moth repellent, and the residual liquid product, consisting largely of the liquid *o*-dichlorobenzene but containing some *m*- and *p*-isomers, is useful as a special solvent. The *p*-bromo derivatives of anisole and of dimethylaniline also can be made satisfactorily by direct bromination without catalyst.

The Sandmeyer reaction (21.21) affords a useful route to iodobenzene (b.p. 188°) and fluorobenzene (b.p. 85°), to *o*- and *p*-bromotoluene, and to *o*-bromochlorobenzene since the required amines are readily available. *m*-Bromotoluene can be made in this way from *p*-toluidine via *m*-toluidine (21.2), but an alternate route from the same starting material is as follows:

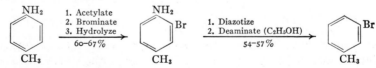

Side-Chain Halogenation. — Toluene undergoes catalyzed chlorination or bromination in the nucleus in the same manner as benzene, with orientation to about the same extent in the *ortho* and *para* positions. When, however, the catalyst is omitted and the hydrocarbon is treated with either halogen at the reflux temperature, preferably with exposure to light, the chlorine or bromine atoms enter the methyl side chain rather than the nucleus, with formation in succession of the mono-, di-, and trihalo derivatives:

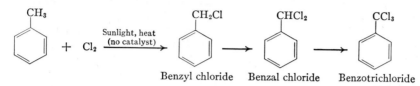

Benzyl chloride   Benzal chloride   Benzotrichloride

The conversion of toluene into benzyl chloride proceeds more readily than the chlorination of methane, since the unsaturated phenyl group activates the hydrogens of the methyl group for substitution. This influence is particularly apparent in the behavior of hydrocarbons with longer side chains, for halogenation is effected in the α-positions of the chain but not at more remote sites:

$$ArCH_2CH_2CH_3 \longrightarrow ArCHClCH_2CH_3 \longrightarrow ArCCl_2CH_2CH_3$$

Attack of activated α-position

The differentiation between nuclear and side-chain halogenation is sharply defined. In the absence of a catalyst, attack of methyl or other alkyl groups is favored by light and heat, and if a potent catalyst such as an aluminum or iron halide is present nuclear substitution occurs exclusively.

The benzyl and benzal halides and benzotrihalides are all liquids with the exception of benzyl iodide (m.p. 24°), prepared from a mixture of benzyl chloride and potassium iodide in refluxing alcohol. The halides are all highly reactive substances that undergo rapid hydrolysis in moist air, and they are potent lachrymators. Benzyl bromide and benzyl iodide cause a flow of tears, with painful swelling of the eyes, at concentrations of 0.004 mg. and 0.002 mg. per liter, respectively. ω-Chloroacetophenone (phenacyl chloride), $C_6H_5COCH_2Cl$ (m.p. 59°, b.p. 245°) is a still more powerful lachrymator, effective at a concentration of only 0.0003 mg. per liter, and has been used as a chemical warfare agent and in police work; it is dispersed by explosion in grenades, either in the solid form or in solution, and also by burning a mixture of the substance with black powder. The substance is made by chlorination of acetophenone in acetic acid solution.

Lachrymators

Chloromethylation. — The chloromethyl group, —CH_2Cl, characteristic of benzyl chloride can be introduced directly into the aromatic nucleus by a process closely akin to the Friedel-Crafts reaction. This consists in interaction with formaldehyde and hydrogen chloride in the presence of a catalyst such as zinc chloride or aluminum chloride

23.3

431

(Blanc reaction). Benzyl chloride, for example, can be prepared in good yield by passing hydrogen chloride gas into a suspension of para-formaldehyde and anhydrous zinc chloride in benzene. Paraformalde-hyde undergoes depolymerization under the influence of hydrogen

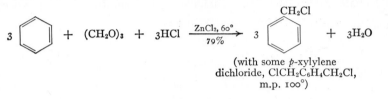

$$3 \bigcirc + (CH_2O)_3 + 3HCl \xrightarrow[79\%]{ZnCl_2,\ 60°} 3 \bigcirc^{CH_2Cl} + 3H_2O$$

(with some p-xylylene
dichloride, $ClCH_2C_6H_4CH_2Cl$,
m.p. 100°)

chloride, and in the presence of the catalyst benzene condenses with formaldehyde or the addition product with hydrogen chloride, $HOCH_2Cl$, with the ultimate production of benzyl chloride.

23.4

Reactivity. — Compounds of the benzyl halide type show greatly enhanced reactivity as compared with alkyl halides, and are similar to allyl halides (8.7). Activation in benzyl halides, as in allyl halides, is attributed to a tendency to form an intermediate carbonium ion stabilized by resonance. In the present instance resonance establishes positive centers at the *ortho* and *para* positions in the nucleus, as well as in the side chain, as shown in the formulas. In contrast with the

Analogy to allyl and to vinyl halides

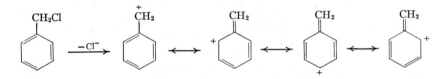

benzyl halides, the nuclear-substituted halogen derivatives of benzene are markedly less reactive than the corresponding alkyl halides and are comparable to vinyl halides. The inert character of the aryl and vinyl compounds is attributed to the opportunity for resonance in the halide molecules, rather than in a derived ion, with resulting shorten-ing of the carbon–halogen bond distance and increased firmness of binding (8.11). Labilization of ordinarily inert chlorine or bromine groups by nitro or other unsaturated groups in *ortho* or *para* positions has been noted (20.5) and interpreted as due to resonance. In the absence of such labilizing groups, aryl halides are inert to alkalis ex-cept at high temperatures and pressures (chlorobenzene ⟶ phenol, 300°, 22.3), and often can be freed from persistent impurities by steam distillation from a mixture with aqueous alkali. Chloro- and bromo-benzene depart from the behavior characteristic of alkyl halides in being unattacked by silver hydroxide, alcoholic ammonia, or sodium ethoxide even at temperatures of 100–150°. The chief reactions in-volving the halogen groups, other than the technical production of phenol from chlorobenzene, are those with specific metals and with cuprous cyanide, as detailed in the following section.

REACTIONS

Aryl halides generally enter into the **Wurtz-Fittig reaction** (19.6) under the influence of metallic sodium. Bromides and iodides of the aromatic series also combine with magnesium in the presence of ether to give **Grignard reagents;** the reaction usually is initiated somewhat less readily than when an alkyl halide is used, but arylmagnesium bromides and iodides nevertheless are obtainable without difficulty and in good yield, and are of inestimable value in synthesis. There are few limitations beyond those encountered as well in the aliphatic series (incompatible groups), though the factor of steric hindrance sometimes is important. Thus a bromine atom flanked in both *ortho* positions by substituents, one of which is a chlorine atom, may react abnormally. However, *o-* and *p-*bromochlorobenzene afford mono-Grignard derivatives satisfactorily; the *p-*compound, *p-*ClC$_6$H$_4$MgBr, is characterized by a beautiful chemiluminescence of its solutions, observable in the dark and due to slow air oxidation. *p-*Bromodimethylaniline also yields a Grignard reagent, *p-*(CH$_3$)$_2$NC$_6$H$_4$MgBr. Chlorobenzene does not react with magnesium under the usual conditions.

Aryllithium Compounds. — Either chloro- or bromobenzene, when treated in ethereal solution with two equivalents of freshly cut metallic lithium by the technique employed in preparing a Grignard reagent, reacts with the separation of lithium halide and the production of a

$$C_6H_5Br(Cl) \quad + \quad 2\,Li \quad \xrightarrow{\text{Ether}} \quad C_6H_5Li \quad + \quad LiBr(Cl)$$
Phenyllithium

solution of phenyllithium. Phenyllithium affords benzoic acid on carbonation, and adds to the carbonyl group of aldehydes, ketones, and esters, for example:

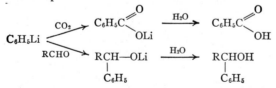

There are some differences in the behavior of aryllithium and arylmagnesium halide derivatives in the selective attack on polyfunctional carbonyl components, but in general the two are comparable, with slight advantages with respect to yields in favor of selection of the Grignard derivative where a choice is open. Thus if a bromide can be secured as a synthetic intermediate, it is usually treated with magnesium rather than with lithium, whereas if only the chloride is available, it can be utilized through conversion into the aryllithium. Occasions arise where advantage can be taken of the gradation in reactivity. Thus in 1-chloro-8-bromonaphthalene the more reactive halogen can be replaced by methyl through the Grignard derivative, and the other one converted into a lithium derivative that will link the aryl residue to another component:

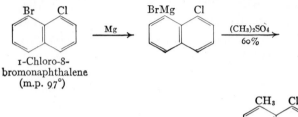

1-Chloro-8-
bromonaphthalene
(m.p. 97°)

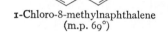

1-Chloro-8-methylnaphthalene
(m.p. 69°)

23.7

Ullmann Reaction. — The action of metallic sodium on an aryl halide results in formation of a certain amount of the expected diphenyl derivative, but the reaction does not proceed well and gives rise to several by-products. Thus *p*-bromotoluene on reaction with sodium gives a mixture containing the normal product, 4,4'-dimethyl-diphenyl, together with 3,4'-dimethyldiphenyl, dibenzyl, and *p*-benzyl-toluene. The by-products probably arise through isomerization of initially formed arylsodium (p-$CH_3C_6H_4Na$), with migration of the sodium to other positions in the nucleus and also into the side chain. Ullmann discovered that diphenyl derivatives can be prepared more satisfactorily by use of copper powder or copper bronze at an elevated temperature. The high-boiling iodobenzene affords diphenyl when refluxed with copper, but this parent hydrocarbon is made more easily by thermal dehydrogenation of benzene. The Ullmann reaction, however, is valuable for the synthesis of substituted diphenyls, for example:

Synthesis of diphenyl derivatives

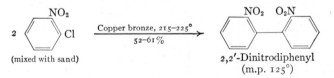

(mixed with sand)

2,2'-Dinitrodiphenyl
(m.p. 125°)

The reaction is sometimes conducted in nitrobenzene solution, with suspended copper.

23.8

Conversion to Nitriles. — Although alkyl halides react readily with potassium cyanide in aqueous alcohol, aryl halides are indifferent to this reagent. They do, however, afford nitriles on interaction with anhydrous cuprous cyanide in pyridine solution at somewhat elevated temperatures. Pyridine is required, perhaps because it not only dissolves the halide but forms a molecular complex with cuprous cyanide which separates as a crystalline solid on mixing the reagents and dissolves on heating. The reagents are employed in an anhydrous condition to obviate hydrolysis of the nitrile at the high temperature required. If the halide has a sufficiently high boiling point, a suitable reaction temperature can be obtained in an open flask, as in the following example:

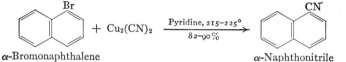

α-Bromonaphthalene   α-Naphthonitrile

When applied to a more volatile halide the reaction is conducted in a sealed tube or autoclave. Chlorides serve as satisfactorily as bromides, and the yield and purity of the products leave little to be desired.

Insecticides Containing Halogen. — The remarkably active contact insecticide known as DDT (dichlorodiphenyltrichloroethane) was introduced in 1942 by the Swiss firm J. R. Geigy. The substance is prepared by condensation of chlorobenzene with chloral hydrate in the presence of sulfuric acid, based upon the original synthesis by Zeidler (1874). Various isomers are also formed, particularly o,p'-DDT, and

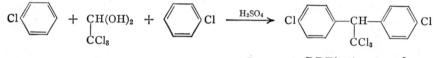

DDT(p,p', m.p. 109°)

technical preparations contain only about 70% of the p,p'-form, which is the most active isomer. The toxic effect may be due to combination of the action of the chlorobenzene unit (respiratory poison) with that of chloroform (lipid-soluble narcotic). DDT has shown spectacular success in control of diseases (typhus, malaria) that are transmitted by insect carriers. It is also used effectively in protecting agricultural crops against a variety of pests; indeed it is lethal to a wider range of insects that any other insecticide now known.

Another insecticide, known as gammexane or 666, is made by addition of three moles of chlorine to benzene. Addition, rather than substitution, is accomplished by exclusion of halogenation catalysts and of oxygen but with ultraviolet irradiation (other additions: hydrogenation, ozonization). Six of nine possible stereoisomeric benzene hexachlorides are produced and are distinguished by the prefixes α, β, γ, etc. Only the γ-isomer (m.p. 111°) has insecticidal properties and it is a minor constituent of the mixture (10–12%). The β-form (m.p. 200°) is known from X-ray studies to have the cen-

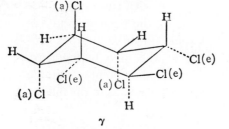

γ

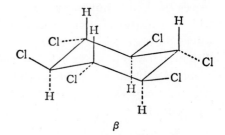

β

trosymmetrical configuration. This isomer is capable of undergoing only *cis* elimination of hydrogen chloride and it is dehydrohalogenated by sodium ethoxide at a rate 1/7000 to 1/2400 that of the other isomers, all of which can undergo *trans* elimination.

SUMMARY

Nuclear halogenation (catalysts: FeX_3, $AlCl_3$). *p*-Dihalobenzenes available by direct halogenation because they are the chief products and are solids separable by crystallization; example: *p*-dichlorobenzene (solid, moth repellent), *o*-dichlorobenzene (liquid, useful solvent). Bromination of $C_6H_5OCH_3$ and $C_6H_5N(CH_3)_2$ gives *p*-products, requires no catalyst.

Preparation by Sandmeyer reaction. Best route to *o*-bromochlorobenzene. Example of synthesis: *p*-toluidine ⟶ *m*-bromotoluene.

Side-chain halogenation (absence of catalyst): $C_6H_5CH_3$ ⟶ $C_6H_5CH_2Cl$ (benzyl chloride), $C_6H_5CHCl_2$ (benzal chloride), $C_6H_5CCl_3$ (benzotrichloride). Promotion by light. Activation by phenyl group. Lachrymatory properties, particularly of $C_6H_5CH_2Br$, $C_6H_5CH_2I$. More potent: ω-Chloroacetophenone (phenacyl chloride), $C_6H_5COCH_2Cl$.

Chloromethylation: $ArH + CH_2O + HCl(ZnCl_2)$ ⟶ $ArCH_2Cl$. Limitations of Friedel-Crafts alkylation.

Reactivity of benzyl halides attributed to stabilization of intermediate carbonium ion by resonance. Inert character of aryl halides attributed to resonance in the molecule rather than the ion, with shortening of the C—Cl bond. C_6H_5Br inert to AgOH, NH_3, C_2H_5ONa below 150°.

Reactions utilizing metals: Wurtz-Fittig; Grignard (satisfactory with ArBr, not with ArCl; thus ClC_6H_4Br ⟶ ClC_6H_5MgBr). Aryllithium compounds: $ArCl + 2\ Li$ ⟶ $ArLi$; analogous to ArMgBr in scope of reactions. Aryl chlorides inert to Mg, react with Li.

Ullmann reaction: $2\ ArX + $ copper bronze at 220° ⟶ $Ar \cdot Ar$ (diphenyl derivative).

Conversion to nitriles: $ArX + Cu_2(CN)_2$ (Py at 220°) ⟶ $ArCN$. Applicable to chlorides and bromides; yields excellent.

Insecticides. DDT from chlorobenzene and chloral hydrate in presence of H_2SO_4. Gammexane (γ-isomer; one of 9) by addition of 3 Cl_2 to benzene in light (absence of halogenation catalyst).

PROBLEMS

1. Indicate all the steps required for preparation of *p*-bromoiodobenzene from aniline.
2. What products would be expected from the action of alkali on the three products of side-chain chlorination of toluene?
3. (a) How could p-$CH_3C_6H_4CH_2OH$ be made in two steps from toluene? Would you anticipate difficulty in securing a pure product?
   (b) Suggest a synthesis of pure *p*-methylbenzyl alcohol from *p*-bromochlorobenzene.
4. Suggest a method for the preparation of 2,5-dimethylbenzyl chloride.
5. How could you convert anisole into 2-amino-4-bromoanisole?
6. Suggest a method for removal of an aromatic bromine atom (replacement by hydrogen).
7. What alternate procedures are available for the conversion of *m*-xylene, through a monohalo derivative, into 2,4-dimethylbenzoic acid?

READING REFERENCE

R. C. Fuson and C. H. McKeever, "Chloromethylation of Aromatic Compounds," in

R. Adams, *Organic Reactions*, I, 63–90, Wiley, New York (1942)

AROMATIC CARBOXYLIC ACIDS

The monocarboxylic acid derivatives of the benzene series are all crystalline solids melting above 100°; derivatives of benzoic acid substituted in the *p*-position by methyl, halo, nitro, hydroxyl, methoxyl, or amino groups melt in the neighborhood of 200°. As compared with aliphatic acids of similar molecular weight, the boiling points are slightly higher and the melting points very much higher. Benzoic acid is somewhat more acidic (pK_a 4.17) than acetic acid (pK_a 4.74), and nearly all the common substituents, other than the amino group, increase the acidic strength, particularly when in the *o*-position. A hydrophilic carboxyl group joined to the benzene nucleus tends to decrease solubility in hydrocarbons or ether and to produce some solubility in water; the monocarboxylic acids are only slightly soluble in cold water, and on the addition of sodium carbonate or bicarbonate characteristically pass into solution with liberation of carbon dioxide.

GENERAL METHODS OF PREPARATION

One route to carboxylic acids is **oxidation of carbon side chains or rings.** Thus toluene yields benzoic acid, *m*- and *p*-xylene afford isophthalic and terephthalic acid, respectively, and mesitylene and durene are convertible into the corresponding polybasic acids. On a laboratory scale the polyalkyl compounds usually are oxidized most satisfactorily either with a dilute aqueous solution of potassium permanganate at the reflux temperature or with dilute nitric acid at an elevated temperature, attained in a sealed tube or autoclave. In technical operations the most economical process is chlorination and hydrolysis: $ArCH_3 \longrightarrow ArCCl_3 \longrightarrow ArCO_2H$. Another method is **hypohalite oxidation of aceto compounds:** $ArCOCH_3 \xrightarrow{HOCl} ArCOCCl_3$ $\xrightarrow{NaOH} ArCO_2H + CHCl_3$. The required methyl ketones are readily available by the Friedel-Crafts reaction, and the combination of this

CHAPTER 24

efficient condensation with the haloform reaction often offers an excellent method of introducing a carboxyl group. An advantage over the method of oxidation of alkyl derivatives is that the hypohalite reaction is more generally applicable because the reagent is not destructive to ring systems less resistant to oxidative attack than the isolated benzene nucleus. Thus β-methylnaphthalene is oxidized in the nucleus in preference to the methyl group, but the aceto derivative undergoes hypochlorite oxidation readily:

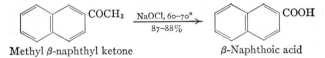

Methyl β-naphthyl ketone   β-Naphthoic acid

Carboxylic acids are also prepared by **hydrolysis of nitriles,** available from aryl halides by reaction with cuprous cyanide and pyridine, from amines by diazotization and the Sandmeyer reaction (or from the less efficient fusion of sulfonates with potassium cyanide). A further general method is **carbonation of Grignard reagents or aryllithiums.** For example, 2-bromomesitylene forms a Grignard reagent which on reaction with carbon dioxide yields mesitylenecarboxylic acid, $2,4,6\text{-}(CH_3)_3C_6H_2COOH$; carbonation of an ethereal solution of α-naphthylmagnesium bromide with dry ice affords α-naphthoic acid in 70–85% yield from the bromide.

SPECIFIC ACIDS

24.3

$C_6H_5CO_2CH_3$
C_6H_5COCl

$C_6H_5CONH_2$
Benzoyl peroxide

Perbenzoic acid

438

Benzoic acid, m.p. 122°, b.p. 249°, pK_a 4.17, is volatile with steam and easily sublimed. Solubilities (g./100 g.) are: water, 0.21; benzene, 0.82; acetone, 28.6; methanol, 36.4. It is made industrially by hydrolysis of benzotrichloride. Methyl benzoate (liq., b.p. 199°) is available by Fischer esterification, and benzoyl chloride (liq., b.p. 197°) by reaction with phosphorus pentachloride or thionyl chloride. When shaken with aqueous ammonia, the chloride is converted rapidly into benzamide, $C_6H_5CONH_2$ (m.p. 130°). Benzoyl peroxide (m.p. 105°, dec.) is made by stirring benzoyl chloride at 0° with 5% aqueous sodium peroxide, and the peroxide can be converted into perbenzoic acid by treatment with a solution of sodium methoxide in methanol at 0° in the presence of chloroform to extract the methyl benzoate formed, careful acidification of the aqueous layer, and extraction with

$$(C_6H_5COO)_2 + CH_3ONa \xrightarrow{CHCl_3,\ 0°} C_6H_5COOONa + C_6H_5COOCH_3$$

$$C_6H_5COOONa + H_2SO_4 \xrightarrow{0°} C_6H_5COOOH + NaHSO_4$$

chloroform. The dried chloroform solution is used for conversion of ethylenic compounds into oxides.

Phthalic acid is so named because the standard source has always been oxidation of the abundant coal tar constituent naphthalene (na<u>phth</u>alene + <u>ic</u>). In the modern vapor-phase method, naphthalene

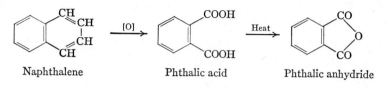

Naphthalene   Phthalic acid   Phthalic anhydride

vapor is passed with air over vanadium pentoxide catalyst on silica gel at 470°, at which temperature the acid is cyclized to the anhydride, which sublimes into the condenser in pure form. Phthalic acid (pK$_a$ 3.0) decomposes at variable temperatures in the range 200–230°, and is best identified by conversion to phthalic anhydride, which melts sharply at 132° and for which a color test is available. This consists in heating the anhydride with resorcinol and sulfuric acid to form fluorescein, a substance related to the triphenylmethane dyes and recognizable from the beautiful fluorescence of its solutions.

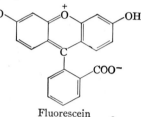

Fluorescein
(abs. max. 4935, 4600 Å)

Phthalimide is produced in industry by saturating molten phthalic anhydride with dry ammonia and heating the mixture to 170–240° under pressure. The cyclic imide can be prepared on a laboratory

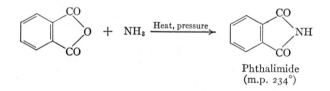

Phthalimide
(m.p. 234°)

scale by heating the anhydride with concentrated aqueous ammonia solution and eventually raising the temperature to 300°. The acidic character of phthalimide (pK$_a$ 8.30) and the use of the potassium salt in the Gabriel synthesis of primary amines have been mentioned (11.8). By careful saponification the heterocyclic ring can be opened without elimination of nitrogen; thus when a solution of phthalimide in 25% aqueous potassium hydroxide is allowed to stand in the cold for one to two hours and acidified, the acid-amide, **phthalamidic acid,** is produced.

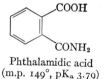

Phthalamidic acid
(m.p. 149°, pK$_a$ 3.79)

Phthalide, a γ-lactone, has been obtained by reduction of phthalic anhydride by various methods. A convenient procedure is reduction of phthalimide in aqueous sodium hydroxide solution with zinc dust activated with a small amount of copper (deposited from copper sulfate solution) at 8°; yield 67–71%. **Perphthalic acid,** which is comparable in properties and uses to perbenzoic acid but more available

439

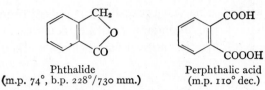

Phthalide
(m.p. 74°, b.p. 228°/730 mm.)

Perphthalic acid
(m.p. 110° dec.)

and more stable, is prepared by stirring phthalic anhydride (crystallized from benzene-ligroin to produce proper particle size) with aqueous sodium perborate at 0°, acidifying, and extracting with ether.

Anthranilic Acid. — This substance, the *o*-amino derivative of benzoic acid, is prepared in high yield by the action of sodium hypochlorite on phthalimide in alkaline solution at 80°; the ring is opened by hydrolysis and the phthalamidic acid formed undergoes the Hofmann reaction. The amino acid is largely precipitated on neutralization of the alkaline solution, and an additional amount can be recovered as the copper salt. **Methyl anthranilate,** found in oils

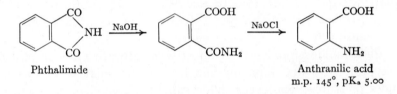

Phthalimide

Anthranilic acid
m.p. 145°, pKa 5.00

extracted from jasmine and orange leaves, is obtained by esterification with methanol and sulfuric acid as a crystalline solid of characteristic fragrance (m.p. 25°, b.p. 135°/15 mm.).

24.6
Salicylic Acid. — The *o*-hydroxy derivative of benzoic acid was obtained first in 1838 by the action of alkali on the corresponding aldehyde, probably as the result of disproportionation (Cannizzaro reaction). In 1859 Kolbe discovered a method of preparation that, in slightly modified form (Schmitt, 1885), has made the substance available in quantity at a low price. In the technical process a solution of phenol in aqueous alkali is evaporated to a dry powder, and the sodium phenolate is saturated with carbon dioxide at 4–7 atmospheres pressure and heated to 125°; free salicylic acid is liberated on acidification of an aqueous solution of the cooled melt and is obtained in close to the theoretical amount. The Kolbe reaction may proceed by addition of the aromatic component to a carbonyl group of carbon dioxide:

By Kolbe reaction

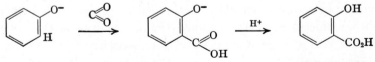

Salicylic acid
m.p. 159°, pKa 3.00

The Kolbe reaction is applicable to other phenols and usually proceeds in good yield. Carboxylation *ortho* to the phenolic hydroxyl group is the rule, but *p*-derivatives are sometimes produced as well.

Methyl salicylate occurs in many plants and was known first as the fragrant principle of wintergreen and called oil of wintergreen. It is one of three ester derivatives used in medicine, the others being **acetylsalicylic acid,** or **aspirin,** and the phenyl ester, **salol.** The methyl

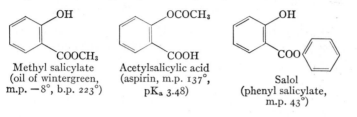

Methyl salicylate (oil of wintergreen, m.p. −8°, b.p. 223°)

Acetylsalicylic acid (aspirin, m.p. 137°, pK$_a$ 3.48)

Salol (phenyl salicylate, m.p. 43°)

ester is prepared by Fischer esterification of salicylic acid. The acetyl derivative can be prepared efficiently by acetylation with acetic anhydride with sulfuric acid as catalyst. Salol is made by condensation of salicylic acid with phenol under the influence of phosphorus oxychloride. The application of these substances in medicine is based on the fact that salicylic acid itself produces a beneficial physiological response when absorbed through the intestinal membrane, but, being rather strongly acidic, is disagreeably irritating when taken by mouth. The irritating action is eliminated by esterification of the carboxyl group with either methanol or phenol and also by acetylation, for the acetyl derivative is less acidic than the phenolic carboxylic acid. These three esters, methyl salicylate, aspirin, and salol, are not hydrolyzed to an appreciable extent on contact with the weakly acidic digestive fluids of the stomach, and pass through without harmful action; on discharge to the alkaline intestinal tract, however, the esters undergo hydrolysis, and salicylic acid is liberated.

The three **toluic acids** can be prepared by hydrolysis of the corresponding nitriles with 75% sulfuric acid; the nitrile intermediates are available from the amines (Sandmeyer reaction). *m*-Toluic acid is prepared also by partial oxidation of *m*-xylene with dilute nitric acid.

Halobenzoic Acids. — The readily available anthranilic acid provides a convenient starting material for preparation of the *o*-chloro, bromo, and iodo derivatives of benzoic acid (diazotization and Sandmeyer reaction). Another method, applicable to the *o*- and *p*-chloro and bromo acids, is permanganate oxidation of the appropriate halogen derivative of toluene. Chlorination of benzoic acid at room temperature in the presence of ferric chloride gives *m*-chlorobenzoic acid as the chief product, along with the 2,5- and 3,4-dichloro derivatives.

Nitrobenzoic Acids. — The *ortho* and *para* isomers are made by oxidation of the nitrotoluenes with potassium permanganate or potassium dichromate. *m*-Nitrobenzoic acid is the chief product of the nitration of benzoic acid and can be prepared also from benzotrichloride by virtue of the *meta* directing effect of the trichloromethyl group and the susceptibility of the side-chain substituents to hydrolysis.

POLYBASIC ACIDS

24.10

Isophthalic acid, m-$C_6H_4(COOH)_2$ (m.p. 348°), and **terephthalic acid** (*para*, sublimes at about 300°) are obtained from the xylenes by permanganate oxidation or by partial bromination in the side chains, hydrolysis, and oxidation. The difficultly fusible terephthalic acid is but sparingly soluble in water, whereas the unsymmetrical isomers are readily soluble in hot water.

Characteristic properties of the three benzenetricarboxylic acids are indicated in the notations under the formulas. The first two acids of unsymmetrical structure are very soluble in water and are extracted from aqueous solution by ether or ethyl acetate only after several

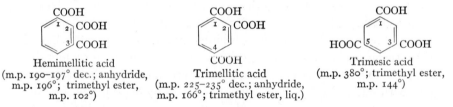

Hemimellitic acid
(m.p. 190–197° dec.; anhydride,
m.p. 196°; trimethyl ester,
m.p. 102°)

Trimellitic acid
(m.p. 225–235° dec.; anhydride,
m.p. 166°; trimethyl ester, liq.)

Trimesic acid
(m.p. 380°; trimethyl ester,
m.p. 144°)

applications of fresh solvent or with a continuous extractor. The 1,2,3- and 1,2,4-acids yield anhydrides when heated, and melt with decomposition in ill-defined temperature ranges. The 1,2,3-isomer, hemimellitic acid, is prepared most conveniently by stepwise oxidation of acenaphthene from coal tar. Trimellitic acid (1,2,4) and

Preparation by oxidative degradation

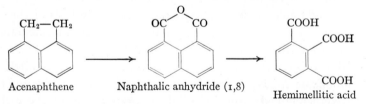

Acenaphthene   Naphthalic anhydride (1,8)   Hemimellitic acid

trimesic acid (1,3,5) result from permanganate oxidation of the corresponding trimethylbenzenes, pseudocumene and mesitylene.

Diphenic acid, the 2,2'- or *o,o'*-dicarboxy derivative of diphenyl, can be prepared by a synthesis applicable to more highly substituted members of the series. This consists in diazotization of anthranilic acid and reduction of the diazonium salt with freshly prepared cuprous ammonium hydroxide solution:

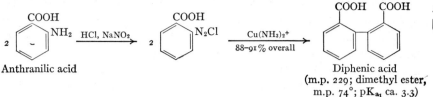

Anthranilic acid

$$2 \underset{\text{Anthranilic acid}}{\overset{\text{COOH}}{\underset{\text{NH}_2}{\bigcirc}}} \xrightarrow{\text{HCl, NaNO}_2} 2 \underset{}{\overset{\text{COOH}}{\underset{\text{N}_2\text{Cl}}{\bigcirc}}} \xrightarrow[\text{88–91\% overall}]{\text{Cu(NH}_3)_2{}^+} \underset{\substack{\text{Diphenic acid}}}{\overset{\text{COOH COOH}}{\bigcirc\bigcirc}}$$

Diphenic acid
(m.p. 229; dimethyl ester,
m.p. 74°; pK$_{a_1}$ ca. 3.3)

ARYL–SUBSTITUTED PARAFFINIC ACIDS

24.11

Phenylacetic acid can be prepared from toluene through benzyl chloride, which reacts with sodium cyanide in aqueous alcohol to give benzyl cyanide in 80–90% yield; hydrolysis of the nitrile with dilute sulfuric acid then affords phenylacetic acid (80% yield). The next member of the series, β-phenylpropionic acid, is known as **hydrocinnamic acid** because it is made most readily by reduction of its unsaturated derivative, cinnamic acid ($C_6H_5CH{=}CHCO_2H$), with sodium amalgam. **Phenylpropiolic acid,** $C_6H_5C{\equiv}CCOOH$, is made by addition of bromine to the double bond of cinnamic acid and treatment of the dibromide with alcoholic potassium hydroxide, which eliminates two molecules of hydrogen bromide.

Methods of synthesis

γ-**Phenylbutyric acid,** $C_6H_5CH_2CH_2CH_2COOH$, is prepared conveniently by the Friedel-Crafts succinoylation of benzene and Clemmensen reduction of the keto acid (19.8, 19.9). The next homolog, δ-**phenyl-n-valeric acid,** has been made by the following steps (the yields in the last two reactions are practically quantitative):

$$\underset{\text{Cinnamaldehyde}}{C_6H_5CH{=}CHCHO} + CH_2(COOH)_2 \xrightarrow[\text{70–80\%}]{\text{HOAc, 95}^\circ} \underset{\substack{\text{Cinnamalmalonic acid}\\ \text{(m.p. 208}^\circ\text{ dec.)}}}{C_6H_5CH{=}CHCH{=}C(COOH)_2} \xrightarrow{\text{H}_2,\text{ Pd}}$$

$$\underset{\substack{\omega\text{-Phenyl-}n\text{-propylmalonic}\\ \text{acid (m.p. 98}^\circ)}}{C_6H_5CH_2CH_2CH_2CH(COOH)_2} \xrightarrow{\text{Heat } (-\text{CO}_2)} \underset{\delta\text{-Phenyl-}n\text{-valeric acid}}{C_6H_5CH_2CH_2CH_2CH_2COOH}$$

A synthesis of ϵ-**phenyl-n-caproic acid** involves condensation of phenylmagnesium bromide with a cyclic ketone and oxidation of the tertiary carbinol with chromic anhydride in anhydrous acetic acid and reduction of the keto acid (Fieser and Szmuszkovicz, 1948). The carbinols from cyclopentanone, cyclohexanone, and cyclooctanone are oxidized rapidly at room temperature in yields of 75–85% and

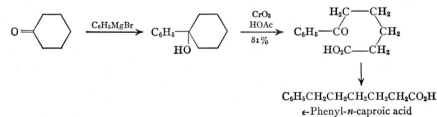

$$O{=}\bigcirc \xrightarrow{\text{C}_6\text{H}_5\text{MgBr}} \underset{\text{HO}}{C_6H_5{-}\bigcirc} \xrightarrow[\text{81\%}]{\substack{\text{CrO}_3\\ \text{HOAc}}} \underset{\substack{\text{HO}_2\text{C}{-}\text{CH}_2}}{C_6H_5{-}\overset{\text{H}_2\text{C}{-}\text{CH}_2}{\underset{}{CO}}\overset{}{\underset{}{CH_2}}}$$

$$\downarrow$$

$$\underset{\epsilon\text{-Phenyl-}n\text{-caproic acid}}{C_6H_5CH_2CH_2CH_2CH_2CH_2CO_2H}$$

afford the homologs $C_6H_5(CH_2)_nCO_2H$, where n = 4, 5, and 7. The anhydrous procedure is much faster and smoother than the classical procedure of dissolving the organic substance in acetic acid and the chromic anhydride in a little water (1 part to 10 parts of acetic acid).

ESTERIFICATION OF AROMATIC ACIDS

24.12
Steric hindrance

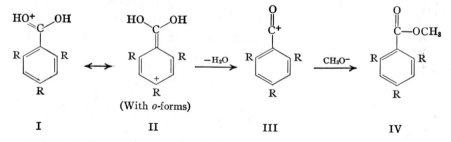

The phenomenon of steric hindrance was discovered by Victor Meyer in a study of relative rates of Fischer esterification of aromatic acids (1894). When refluxed with methanol containing 3% hydrogen chloride for 3–5 hrs., benzoic acid and *m*- and *p*-substituted benzoic acids afford the methyl esters in about 90% yield. In contrast, the acids formulated in the margin when treated in the same way yield little or no ester, and their methyl esters, obtainable by the silver salt method or with diazomethane, are very resistant to hydrolysis. Thus when both *ortho* positions are blocked by methyl, bromo, or nitro groups the steric hindrance is so great as to suppress both esterification and hydrolysis. Both *ortho-para* and *meta* directing groups exhibit this *ortho* effect, and the controlling factor is the size of the group. Thus an *o*-fluoro atom exerts considerably less hindrance than an *o*-bromo substituent. That a single substituent can exert a considerable ortho effect is shown by the fact that Fischer esterification of salicylic acid (*o*-OH) requires a reflux period five times that adequate for esterification of benzoic acid.

Newman[1] (1941) discovered that 2,4,6-trimethylbenzoic acid can be esterified by dissolving it in 100% sulfuric acid and pouring the solution into an alcohol; the reaction takes only a few minutes and the yields are excellent. Conversely, the ester is efficiently hydrolyzed by pouring a sulfuric acid solution into water. When treated in the same way, benzoic acid is not esterified and methyl benzoate is not hydrolyzed. According to Newman's interpretation, both the hindered and unhindered acid can be supposed to combine with a proton from sulfuric acid to form a conjugate acid (I), stabilized by resonance (II). The resonance structures, however, require coplanarity of all

Esterification of hindered acids

I   II   III   IV

(With *o*-forms)

---

[1] Melvin S. Newman, b. 1908 New York; Ph.D. Yale (R. J. Anderson); postdoctoral work Harvard (Fieser); Ohio State

the carbon and oxygen atoms, and, if R = methyl, interference between methyl and hydroxyl groups enhances the tendency for expulsion of water with formation of the positive acyl ion III, which can react with methanol to form the ester IV. In the absence of this steric factor (R = H), structures I and II are stable and have no tendency to lose water. The method of esterification is not successful with some esters, for example 2,4,6-tribromobenzoic acid.

SUMMARY

Aromatic carboxylic acids all solids of m.p. and b.p. higher than aliphatic acids of comparable molecular weight. Benzoic acid, pK_a 4.17; acetic acid, pK_a 4.74. Polycarboxylic acids water-soluble.

General preparative methods: oxidation of side chains or rings (direct or by chlorination and hydrolysis); $ArCOCH_3 + NaOCl$ (applicable in naphthalene series where nucleus is attacked by ordinary oxidizing agents); hydrolysis of nitriles (from halides with cuprous cyanide or from amines by Sandmeyer reaction); from Grignard derivative of ArBr or lithium derivative of ArCl.

Benzoic acid. From toluene through benzotrichloride. Ester, chloride, amide. Benzoyl peroxide: $C_6H_5COCl + Na_2O_2$ at $0°$. Perbenzoic acid: $(C_6H_5COO)_2 + CH_3ONa$ $(0°)$; acidify $(0°)$.

Phthalic acid. Anhydride prepared by vapor-phase catalytic oxidation of naphthalene. Heating with NH_3 under pressure $\longrightarrow$ phthalimide; careful hydrolysis gives phthalamidic acid (amide-acid). Phthalimide in $NaOH + Zn \longrightarrow$ phthalide (lactone).

Anthranilic acid from phthalimide + NaOCl.

Salicylic acid. Kolbe reaction: dry $C_6H_5ONa + CO_2$ under pressure. Usually gives o-carboxy phenols. Derivatives used as medicinals: methyl ester (oil of wintergreen), aspirin (acetyl derivative), salol (with $C_6H_5OH + POCl_3$). Liberation of free salicylic acid in intestine.

Toluic acids from the amines through the nitriles. Halobenzoic acids: o-acids from anthranilic acid; oxidation of halotoluenes; benzoic acid $\longrightarrow$ m-$ClC_6H_4CO_2H$. Nitrobenzoic acids: oxidation of o- and p-nitrotoluene; $C_6H_5CO_2H \longrightarrow m$-$O_2NC_6H_4CO_2H$.

Polybasic acids. Isophthalic acid (m) and terephthalic acid (p) from the xylenes. Hemimellitic acid, $C_6H_3(CO_2H)_3$-1,2,3, by oxidation of acenaphthene. Trimellitic (1,2,4-) and trimesic acid (1,3,5-) by oxidation of pseudocumene and mesitylene. Diphenic acid (diphenyl-2,2′-dicarboxylic acid) from diazotized anthranilic acid + $Cu(NH_3)_2OH$.

Aryl-substituted paraffinic acids. Phenylacetic acid from benzyl chloride through benzyl cyanide. Conversion of cinnamic acid to hydrocinnamic acid, $C_6H_5CH_2CH_2CO_2H$ (reduction), and to phenylpropiolic acid ($-C\equiv C-$; dibromide + alc. KOH). γ-Phenylbutyric acid by succinoylation of benzene and Clemmensen reduction. δ-Phenylvaleric acid from cinnamaldehyde and malonic ester, followed by decarboxylation and reduction. ϵ-Phenylcaproic acid: $C_6H_5MgBr +$ cyclohexanone $\longrightarrow$ carbinol; oxidation with CrO_3 in HOAc (anhydrous) to $C_6H_5CO(CH_2)_4CO_2H$; reduction.

Steric hindrance to Fischer esterification of o- and di-o-substituted benzoic acids (V. Meyer, 1894). Blocking effect noted with both op- and m-directing groups. Group volume important. Esters, available through Ag salts or with diazomethane, difficultly hydrolyzable. Esterification of hindered acids by pouring H_2SO_4 solution into methanol (Newman, 1941). Mechanistic interpretation.

PROBLEMS

1. Suggest methods for the preparation of 2,4- and 2,5-dimethylbenzoic acid, starting with coal-tar hydrocarbons.

2. Indicate all the steps in the preparation of anthranilic acid from naphthalene.

3. Outline the steps in the preparation of m-toluic acid, starting with toluene.

4. Explain why polycarboxy derivatives of benzene are identified in the form of certain derivatives and not in the free form.

5. Suggest a scheme for the synthesis of 4,4′-dibromodiphenic acid (4,4′-dibromodiphenyl-2,2′-dicarboxylic acid).

6. How could the following substances be synthesized:

(a) γ-p-Tolylbutyric acid
(b) 1,5-Diphenylpentane
(c) β-Tetralone from
o-$HO_2CCH_2C_6H_4CH_2CH_2CO_2H$:

AROMATIC ALDEHYDES AND KETONES

Aldehydes and ketones in which the carbonyl group is linked to an aromatic nucleus differ from aliphatic carbonyl compounds in relatively minor respects and are of particular value as intermediates in synthesis. Some of the many methods available for their preparation are cited below as applied to specific examples.

PREPARATION OF ALDEHYDES

25.1

Benzaldehyde (b.p. 179°) was long known as oil of bitter almonds because it was initially prepared from almond seeds, which contain the glycoside amygdalin, the β-gentiobioside of mandelonitrile, $C_6H_5CH(CN)O—C_{12}H_{21}O_{10}$. Enzymes liberated when the seeds are crushed hydrolyze amygdalin to benzaldehyde, hydrogen cyanide, and glucose. Benzaldehyde is now made from toluene, either by side-chain halogenation to benzal chloride and hydrolysis or by oxi-

$Ar\,CH_3 \longrightarrow Ar\,CHO$

$$C_6H_5CH_3 \longrightarrow C_6H_5CHCl_2 \xrightarrow[76\%]{} C_6H_5CHO$$

dation with manganese dioxide in 65% sulfuric acid at 40°, followed by steam distillation. The latter method is applicable to the preparation of o-nitrobenzaldehyde from o-nitrotoluene. The m-isomer is available in good yield by nitration of benzaldehyde.

25.2

$ArH \longrightarrow Ar\,CHO$

Formylation. — One Friedel-Crafts type method for direct introduction of the formyl group (—CHO) involves reaction of a hydrocarbon with carbon monoxide and hydrogen chloride in the presence of cuprous chloride and aluminum chloride (Gattermann-Koch, 1897). Formyl chloride may be formed as a transient intermediate, but has not been isolated as such; formyl fluoride however is known.

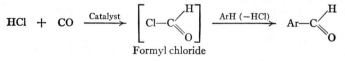

$$HCl \;+\; CO \xrightarrow{\text{Catalyst}} \left[\underset{\underset{O}{\big\|}}{Cl-C} \diagup^{H} \right] \xrightarrow{ArH\,(-HCl)} \underset{\underset{O}{\big\|}}{Ar-C}\diagup^{H}$$

Formyl chloride

Cuprous chloride probably functions as a catalyst because it can bind carbon monoxide in the form of a labile molecular complex. Another method utilizes hydrogen cyanide as source of the formyl group (Gattermann, 1907). A convenient procedure applicable to phenols (R. Adams, 1923) is to pass hydrogen chloride into a mixture of phenol and zinc cyanide in absolute ether; this combination liberates hydrogen cyanide required for the condensation and produces zinc chloride as catalyst. The method is illustrated for the reaction of thymol.

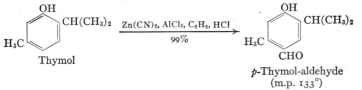

Thymol $\xrightarrow[99\%]{\text{Zn(CN)}_2,\ \text{AlCl}_3,\ \text{C}_6\text{H}_6,\ \text{HCl}}$ *p*-Thymol-aldehyde (m.p. 133°)

Salicylaldehyde by the Reimer-Tiemann Reaction. — The Reimer-Tiemann reaction (1876) was discovered in Hofmann's laboratory as the result of an experiment carried out to determine how a phenol would respond when substituted for an amine in the Hofmann isonitrile reaction, involving treatment with chloroform and alkali (21.18). A reaction occurs, but results in introduction of an aldehydic group *ortho* or *para* to the hydroxyl group:

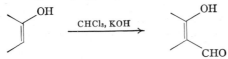

CHCl₃, KOH

The reaction succeeds with most phenols containing an available activated position, but is not applicable to hydrocarbons, phenol ethers, or even tertiary amines. The specific requirement of a free hydroxyl group and of an alkaline medium indicates that the reactive species undergoing the special substitution is the phenoxide ion. The superior reactivity of the phenoxide ion, noted also in diazo coupling (21.24), is explained by the opportunity for distribution of the negative charge on oxygen to *ortho* and *para* positions in the ring. In a free phenol or ether, contribution by resonance structures of comparable *o*-, *p*-electron density requires separation of charge in the nonionized molecule.

As applied to phenol, the reaction gives chiefly the *o*-derivative, salicylaldehyde (b.p. 197°), and although the yield is low the product

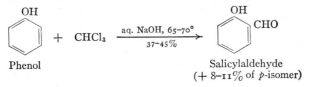

Phenol + CHCl₃ $\xrightarrow[37-45\%]{\text{aq. NaOH, 65-70°}}$ Salicylaldehyde (+ 8–11% of *p*-isomer)

is easily isolable in pure form. At the end of the reaction the mixture is acidified and steam distilled; salicylaldehyde (m.p. −7°, chelated) passes into the distillate along with a considerable amount of phenol, from which it can be separated through the bisulfite-addition product. From the residue not volatile with steam the solid isomer, *p*-hydroxy-benzaldehyde (m.p. 116°, unchelated), can be isolated by crystallization.

The first step in the Reimer-Tiemann reaction probably consists in introduction of the dichloromethyl group. The postulated intermediate benzal halide, II, may be converted by alkali directly into the aldehyde. Another possibility is indicated by the work of Armstrong and Richardson (1933), who sought the reason for the in-

Mechanism

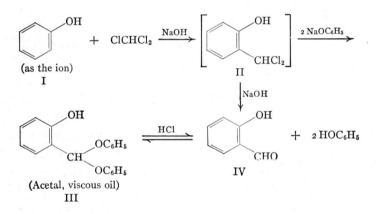

(as the ion)
I

II

III
(Acetal, viscous oil)

IV

evitable appearance in the reaction mixture of a considerable quantity of starting material. Evidence was obtained that the alkaline solution contains the diphenylacetal (III) of the ultimate reaction product, and that this is reasonably stable to alkali but is hydrolyzed readily when the mixture is acidified. The acetal may be produced as an intermediate by condensation of the benzal halide with two molecules of sodium phenoxide or it may be formed as a by-product by combination of salicylaldehyde with phenol; but in any case part of the salicylaldehyde produced is present in combined form along with phenol.

25.4 **Vanillin,** a partially methylated aldehyde of the catechol series, is the fragrant constituent of the extract of vanilla bean, and occurs also in the sugar beet and in balsams and resins; it is an important component of artificial flavors. One synthesis utilizes eugenol, available from essential oils. Under the influence of alcoholic alkali at 140° or of concentrated aqueous potassium hydroxide at 220°, the double bond of this allyl compound migrates to a position of conjugation with the ring and gives isoeugenol. This is acetylated to protect

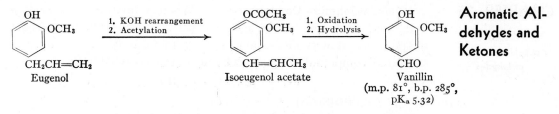

OH
OCH₃

CH₂CH=CH₂
Eugenol

1. KOH rearrangement
2. Acetylation

OCOCH₃
OCH₃

CH=CHCH₃
Isoeugenol acetate

1. Oxidation
2. Hydrolysis

OH
OCH₃

CHO
Vanillin
(m.p. 81°, b.p. 285°,
pKₐ 5.32)

the phenolic group and ozonized, when the double bond of the α-pro-
penyl group is severed and an aldehyde group produced. A second

OH
OCH₃

Guaiacol

CHCl₃, NaOH

OH
OCH₃

CHO
Vanillin

+

CHO
OH
OCH₃

2-Hydroxy-3-methoxybenzaldehyde
(m.p. 45°, b.p. 266°)

process is application of the Reimer-Tiemann reaction to guaiacol;
vanillin is the chief product but is accompanied by **2-hydroxy-3-
methoxybenzaldehyde,** which can be separated by virtue of its greater
volatility with steam (chelation). This by-product of the vanillin
preparation and its ether, **2,3-dimethoxybenzaldehyde** (m.p. 54°),
are cheap materials available for use in synthesis. Still more useful
in synthesis is **veratraldehyde,** or 3,4-dimethoxybenzaldehyde, obtainable in 92–95% yield by methylation of vanillin with dimethyl sulfate;
it can be synthesized by the Gattermann reaction from veratrole,
hydrogen cyanide, and aluminum chloride.

CHO
OCH₃
OCH₃
Veratraldehyde
(m.p. 44°, b.p. 285°)

The **Rosenmund reaction** (10.6) affords a means of preparing
aromatic aldehydes from the corresponding acids:

25.5

$$ArCOCl \xrightarrow{H_2, \ Pd—BaSO_4} ArCHO + HCl$$

An alternate method is reduction with lithium tri-*t*-butoxyalumino-
hydride, Li[(CH₃)₃CO]₃AlH (H. C. Brown, 1956).

REACTIONS OF ALDEHYDES

Aromatic aldehydes enter into reactions of reduction, oxidation,
addition, and condensation in much the same fashion as aliphatic
aldehydes, with the minor difference that the aryl residue depresses
somewhat the reactivity of the carbonyl group. Absence of hydrogen
atoms at the α-carbon atom adjacent to the carbonyl group prevents
self-condensation of the aldol type under the influence of acids or
bases, and hence other reactions promoted by these agents are realizable. The reactions are not specific to aromatic aldehydes, for most
of them are shown also by aliphatic aldehydes of the type R₃CCHO.
One is the **Cannizzaro reaction** (10.15), a disproportionation induced
by concentrated alkali, resulting in transformation of half of the aldehyde into the corresponding alcohol and of the other half into the acid.

Claisen-Schmidt Condensation. — When a mixture of benzaldehyde and acetaldehyde is agitated with aqueous alkali at room temperature, slow condensation occurs with formation of the α,β-unsaturated compound **cinnamaldehyde**, $C_6H_5CH=CHCHO$. The re-

$$C_6H_5CHO + CH_3CHO[NaOH] \underset{\displaystyle \left[\underset{OH}{\underset{|}{C_6H_5CHCH_2CHO}}\right] \xrightarrow{-H_2O}}{\overset{\displaystyle CH_3CHO \overset{\displaystyle CH_3CHCH_2CHO}{\underset{OH}{|}}}{\rightleftarrows}} \quad \underset{\substack{Cinnamaldehyde \\ (b.p.\ 127°/15\ mm.)}}{C_6H_5CH=CHCHO}$$

action probably involves a reversible aldol addition of acetaldehyde to the carbonyl group of benzaldehyde and an irreversible elimination of water from the addition product; the dehydration is favored by the circumstance that the intermediate has an activated hydrogen atom in an α-position to the carbonyl group and also, on the adjacent carbon atom, a hydroxyl group that is activated by the phenyl group. Acetaldehyde undergoes bimolecular condensation to form aldol, but this reaction is not followed by irreversible dehydration, and the other aldol intermediate thus is utilized for production of cinnamaldehyde. Cinnamaldehyde, a fragrant liquid, occurs as the chief constituent of oil of cinnamon and oil of cassia and is used in flavoring and in perfumery. It can be purified through the bisulfite-addition compound.

α,β-Unsaturated ketones

The Claisen-Schmidt condensation is applicable also to synthesis of α,β-unsaturated ketones, as illustrated by the following examples:

1. $C_6H_5CHO + \underset{(excess)}{CH_3COCH_3} \xrightarrow[65-78\%]{10\%\ aq.\ NaOH,\ 25-31°} \underset{\substack{Benzalacetone \\ (yellow,\ m.p.\ 42°,\ b.p.\ 262°)}}{C_6H_5CH=CHCOCH_3}$

2. $C_6H_5CHO + CH_3COC_6H_5 \xrightarrow[85\%]{aq.\text{-}alc.\ NaOH,\ 15-30°} \underset{\substack{Benzalacetophenone \\ (yellow,\ m.p.\ 62°)}}{C_6H_5CH=CHCOC_6H_5}$

One technical process for production of cinnamic acid is oxidation of benzalacetone with sodium hypochlorite.

25.7
α,β-Unsaturated acids

Perkin Reaction. — W. H. Perkin in 1868 discovered a reaction of aromatic aldehydes of value for synthesis of α,β-unsaturated acids. An aromatic aldehyde is heated with the anhydride of an aliphatic acid and the sodium or potassium salt of the same acid; for example a mixture of benzaldehyde, acetic anhydride, and potassium acetate is heated at 175–180° for five hours under reflux, the melt is poured into water, steam distilled to remove unchanged benzaldehyde, and the aqueous solution is clarified with decolorizing carbon and acidified. The reaction product, which crystallizes on cooling, is cinnamic acid.

$$C_6H_5CHO + (CH_3CO)_2O \xrightarrow[55-60\%]{CH_3COOK,\ 175-180°} \underset{Cinnamic\ acid}{C_6H_5CH=CHCOOH}$$

Perkin thought that the aldehyde probably condenses with acetic anhydride, rather than with the metal salt of the acid, and that the salt is a basic catalyst; extensive investigations of the mechanism have led to eventual acceptance of this early inference. The reaction is considered to proceed through the enolic form of the anhydride.

Condensation with Malonic Acid. — Aldehydes, both aliphatic and aromatic, condense with malonic acid and related substances having an activated methylene group under basic catalysis. (**Knoevenagel**[1] **reaction,** 1898.) The condensation of benzaldehyde with

$$ArCHO + CH_2(COOH)_2 \xrightarrow{\text{Base}} [ArCH=C(COOH)_2] \xrightarrow{-CO_2} ArCH=CHCOOH$$

malonic acid proceeds well under catalysis by pyridine, and the initially formed benzalmalonic acid undergoes decarboxylation during the condensation to give cinnamic acid.

The **Reformatsky reaction** (1887) depends on interaction between a carbonyl compound, an α-halo ester, and activated zinc in the presence of anhydrous ether or ether—benzene, followed by hydrolysis. The halogen component, for example ethyl bromoacetate, combines with zinc to form an organozinc bromide that adds to the carbonyl group of the second component to give a complex readily hydrolyzed by water to a carbinol:

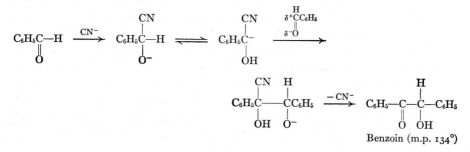

The organometal halide is sufficiently reactive to add to the carbonyl group of an aldehyde or ketone like a Grignard reagent, but not reactive enough to be incompatible with the ester group present. That the Reformatsky reaction is applicable to ketones as well as aldehydes makes it very useful in synthesis.

Benzoin Condensation. — Under the catalytic influence of an alkali cyanide in aqueous alcohol, benzaldehyde undergoes bimolecu-

$$C_6H_5C-H \ \underset{O}{\overset{\|}{}} \xrightarrow{CN^-} C_6H_5\overset{CN}{\underset{O^-}{\overset{|}{C}}}-H \rightleftharpoons C_6H_5\overset{CN}{\underset{OH}{\overset{|}{C^-}}} \xrightarrow{\overset{H}{\underset{\delta-O}{\overset{\delta+C C_6H_5}{\|}}}}$$

$$C_6H_5\overset{CN}{\underset{OH}{\overset{|}{C}}}-\overset{H}{\underset{O^-}{\overset{|}{C}}}C_6H_5 \xrightarrow{-CN^-} C_6H_5-\overset{}{\underset{O}{\overset{\|}{C}}}-\overset{H}{\underset{OH}{\overset{|}{C}}}-C_6H_5$$

Benzoin (m.p. 134°)

[1] Emil Knoevenagel, 1865–1921; b. Linden/Hannover, Germany; Ph.D. Göttingen; Heidelberg

lar condensation to the α-hydroxy ketone benzoin. Cyanide ion is an indispensable catalyst and probably participates as shown. Discovery of the benzoin condensation resulted from the fortuitous circumstance that early workers purified crude "oil of bitter almonds" by washing with aqueous alkali to extract acids; the crude material from amygdalin contained hydrogen cyanide, and the sodium cyanide produced in the alkali wash catalyzed formation of benzoin (Wöhler and Liebig, 1832).

25.11   **Autoxidation of Aldehydes.** — Oxidations induced by air at room temperature are known as autoxidations. Benzaldehyde readily undergoes oxidation to benzoic acid by air, particularly in the presence of traces of iron or on exposure to light, and the transformation is readily apparent because the aldehyde is a liquid and the acid a solid. If benzaldehyde is distilled through an air-cooled condenser and the hot liquid allowed to flow down the walls of a receiver in a thin film in contact with air, crystals of benzoic acid usually are visible in the film. Thus distillation should be conducted with exclusion of air and the material stored in a completely filled brown bottle.

Autoxidation of benzaldehyde has the characteristics of a free radical chain reaction, for it is photocatalytic, catalyzed by traces of metal derivatives, and suppressed by inhibitors. H. Bächström (1934) concluded from results of physicochemical studies that the reactive chain-propagating species is the benzoyl radical, produced

*Free radical
mechanism*

$$1. \ ArCH{=}O \ \xrightarrow{h\nu} \ ArCHO\cdot$$
$$2. \ ArCHO\cdot \ + \ ArCHO \ \longrightarrow \ Ar\dot{C}{=}O \ + \ Ar\dot{C}HOH$$
$$3. \ Ar\dot{C}{=}O \ + \ O_2 \ \longrightarrow \ ArC({=}O)O{-}O\cdot$$
$$4. \ ArC({=}O)O{-}O\cdot \ + \ ArCHO \ \longrightarrow \ ArCO_3H \ + \ Ar\dot{C}{=}O$$
$$5. \ ArCO_3H \ + \ ArCHO \ \longrightarrow \ 2\,ArCO_2H$$

photochemically (1 and 2), which is assumed to combine with oxygen to form a perbenzoyl radical (3). This reacts with benzaldehyde with regeneration of the benzoyl radical and formation of perbenzoic acid (4), which converts benzaldehyde into benzoic acid (5); perbenzoic acid indeed has been detected in autoxidized benzaldehyde. The essential feature of the process is that a free-radical intermediate promotes the ultimate transformation and is regenerated in each cycle. The chain mechanism explains the efficacy of antioxidants in inhibiting autoxidation at low concentration. Hydroquinone, which is easily oxidized, inhibits autoxidation of benzaldehyde at a concentration of only 0.001%, and it is commonly added to benzaldehyde for protection in storage; since the phenolic substance is relatively nonvolatile, the protective action applies only to the liquid phase and not to a vapor space over the liquid. The inhibitor molecules react with and destroy free-radical intermediates, each of which otherwise would initiate a chain process resulting in the conversion of hundreds of molecules of aldehyde into acid.

KETONES

Friedel-Crafts acylation (19.8) provides a convenient route to aromatic ketones, keto acids, and ketones of the α-tetralone type, the Fries reaction (22.19) makes available *o*- and *p*-acetophenols, and the Claisen-Schmidt reaction affords α,β-unsaturated ketones.

Acetophenone, $C_6H_5COCH_3$, m.p. 20°, typical of ketones of the aromatic-aliphatic type, enters into reactions that may involve substitution in the nucleus, attack of the activated hydrogen atoms in the methyl group, or addition to the carbonyl group. The additive power is somewhat less than that of typical aliphatic ketones, as indicated by the failure of acetophenone to form a bisulfite-addition product, but this ketone adds Grignard reagents in the normal fashion and can be reduced by specific reagents to the carbinol, the pinacol, or to ethylbenzene. One of the few deviations from normal behavior is that acetomesitylene, which has a highly hindered carbonyl group, does not add Grignard reagents but instead is converted into the magnesiohalide salt of the enolic form:

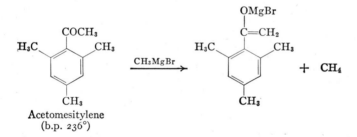

Acetomesitylene
(b.p. 236°)

Substitution in the nucleus is illustrated by the nitration of acetophenone with mixed acid at 0°; considerable substitution occurs in the *o*-position, but *m*-nitroacetophenone (m.p. 81°) can be isolated as the chief product in 55% yield.

ω-Substitutions. — Introduction of halogen into the methyl group of acetophenone proceeds readily and gives products with the halogen in a position designated as ω (terminal). **Phenacyl bromide,** or ω-bromoacetophenone, is prepared by bromination in ether in the presence of aluminum chloride, and although this reagent is a catalyst for nuclear bromination, the alternate reaction proceeds so readily and at so low a temperature as to predominate to the practical exclu-

$$C_6H_5COCH_3 \xrightarrow{\text{Br}_2(\text{AlCl}_3), \text{ ether, } 0°} C_6H_5COCH_2Br$$

Phenacyl bromide
(m.p. 51°)

sion of entrance of bromine into the ring. The product is a highly reactive, lachrymatory substance that reacts readily with liquid acids to give crystalline esters, and hence is used in identification of acids.

Condensation Reactions. — A sequence of **aldolization and dehydration** analogous to the formation of mesitylene from acetone (19.5) affords s-triphenylbenzene in fair yield.

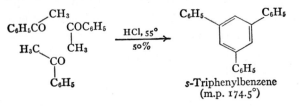

s-Triphenylbenzene
(m.p. 174.5°)

Ester condensation is exemplified by the reaction of acetophenone with ethyl benzoate to give a 1,3-diketone:

$$C_6H_5COOC_2H_5 \; + \; CH_3COC_6H_5 \quad \xrightarrow[\substack{\text{2. } H_2SO_4 \\ 62-71\%}]{\substack{\text{1. } NaOC_2H_5,\ 150-160°}} \quad C_6H_5COCH_2COC_6H_5$$

Dibenzoylmethane
(m.p. 78°)

One of many types of the **Michael reaction** (1887) is illustrated by the condensation of benzalacetophenone with malonic ester in presence of a base:

$$C_6H_5CH{=}CH{-}CC_6H_5 \quad \xrightarrow{-Na^+} \quad C_6H_5CHCH{=}CC_6H_5 \quad \xrightarrow{H^+} \quad C_6H_5CHCH_2CC_6H_5$$

$$[\bar{C}H(CO_2C_2H_5)_2]Na^+ \qquad\qquad \underset{CH(CO_2C_2H_5)_2}{|} \qquad\qquad \underset{CH(CO_2C_2H_5)_2}{|}$$

REARRANGEMENTS

Benzopinacol is formed in high yield on exposure of benzophenone to light in solution in isopropyl alcohol, which functions as hydrogen donor. When heated in acetic acid solution with a trace of iodine, benzo-

$$2\,(C_6H_5)_2C{=}O \; + \; (CH_3)_2CHOH \quad \xrightarrow[95\%]{\text{Sunlight}} \quad \underset{(C_6H_5)_2C{-}OH}{\overset{(C_6H_5)_2C{-}OH}{|}} \; + \; \underset{CH_3}{\overset{CH_3}{>}}C{=}O$$

Benzopinacol
(m.p. 189°)

pinacol rearranges in 95% yield to benzopinacolone, $(C_6H_5)_3CCOC_6H_5$. The reaction is considered to involve formation of a carbonium ion

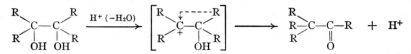

with an electron sextet, migration of a phenyl group, and expulsion of a proton.

Isomerism and Rearrangement of Oximes. — Acetophenone condenses in the usual way with aniline, phenylhydrazine, hydroxylamine, and other amine derivatives, though somewhat less readily than acetone; still more drastic conditions are required with benzophenone. The oxime derivatives are particularly interesting, for they exist in two geometrically isomeric forms. *Cis* and *trans* oximes of both aldehydes and ketones of aliphatic and aromatic types are known. Thus the product of the reaction of benzaldehyde with hydroxylamine in the presence of excess sodium hydroxide is a low-melting substance of *cis* configuration, which is stable to alkali but rapidly rearranged by acids to the higher-melting *trans* form.

$$
\begin{array}{ccc}
\underset{\|}{C_6H_5-C-H} & \xrightarrow[\text{2. Na}_2\text{CO}_3]{\text{1. dry HCl, ether}} & \underset{\|}{C_6H_5-C-H} \\
N-OH & & HO-N
\end{array}
$$

cis-Benzaldoxime   *trans*-Benzaldoxime
(m.p. 35°)   (m.p. 130°)

Oximes of ketones also have been isolated in two geometrical forms, and in this series the configuration determines the course of a characteristic rearrangement discovered by Beckmann[2] (1886). The **Beckmann rearrangement,** for example of benzophenone oxime, is brought about by treatment of the oxime with phosphorus pentachloride in ether solution, and results in conversion into benzanilide by a process involving exchange of place between the hydroxyl group and a phenyl group on the opposite side of the molecule, and ketonization of the enolic intermediate:

$$
\begin{array}{ccc}
\underset{\|}{C_6H_5-C-C_6H_5} & \xrightarrow{\text{PCl}_5,\text{ ether}} & \underset{\|}{C_6H_5-C-OH} \\
HO-N & & C_6H_5-N
\end{array}
\longrightarrow
\begin{array}{c}
C_6H_5C=O \\
| \\
NHC_6H_5
\end{array}
$$

Benzophenone oxime   Benzanilide
(m.p. 144)

Study of oximes of unsymmetrical ketones has established that the migrating hydrocarbon group is that *trans* to the migrating hydroxyl group.

Benzilic Acid Rearrangement. — Oxidation of benzoin (25.10) with nitric acid in acetic acid affords in high yield a yellow α-diketone known as benzil, $C_6H_5COCOC_6H_5$. Among a number of transformations which this substance is capable of undergoing is alkali-induced rearrangement to benzilic acid, $(C_6H_5)_2C(OH)CO_2H$. The rearrangement, effected in good yield by refluxing benzil with alcoholic potassium hydroxide, is probably initiated through nucleophilic attack by

---

[2] Ernst Beckmann, 1853–1923; b. Solingen, Germany, Ph.D. Leipzig (Kolbe); Giessen, Erlangen, Leipzig, KWI Berlin; *Ber.*, **61A**, 87 (1928)

$$C_6H_5\overset{O}{\overset{\|}{C}}-\overset{O}{\overset{\|}{C}}C_6H_5 \xrightarrow{\text{OH}^-} \left[C_6H_5\overset{\zeta O}{C}-\overset{\zeta O^-}{\underset{\underset{\overset{\|}{OH}}{}}{C}}\boxed{\vdots C_6H_5} \longrightarrow \underset{C_6H_5}{\overset{C_6H_5}{\diagdown}}\overset{O}{\overset{\|}{C}}-\overset{O}{\overset{\|}{\underset{OH}{C}}} \right]$$

Benzilic acid
rearrangement

$$\xrightarrow{\text{H}^+} (C_6H_5)_2C(OH)CO_2H$$

Benzilic acid

M. p. 151°, pK$_a$ 3.04

hydroxide ion on one of the carbonyl groups and follows the path shown in the formulation.

SUMMARY

Benzaldehyde (isolated from amygdalin) made from toluene through benzal chloride.

Direct formylation: ArH $\longrightarrow$ ArCHO. Gattermann-Koch synthesis: ArH + CO + HCl (AlCl$_3$-Cu$_2$Cl$_2$). Gattermann synthesis: ArH + HCN (AlCl$_3$ or ZnCl$_2$); applicable to phenols and phenol ethers; modification employing Zn(CN)$_2$ + HCl in ether (R. Adams), e.g. thymol $\longrightarrow$ p-aldehyde.

Reimer-Tiemann synthesis: phenol + CHCl$_3$ + NaOH $\longrightarrow$ phenol aldehyde (chiefly *ortho*). Example: phenol $\longrightarrow$ salicyaldehyde (40%) + p-isomer (10%). Mechanism: introduction of —CHCl$_2$, hydrolysis to —CHO, or conversion to alkali-stable acetal —CH(OC$_6$H$_5$)$_2$ and acid hydrolysis.

Aldehydic derivatives of polyhydric phenols. Vanillin (vanilla bean) = 3-methoxy-4-hydroxybenzaldehyde; preparation from eugenol (allyl derivative) by bond shift and oxidation; Reimer-Tiemann synthesis from guaiacol (catechol monomethyl ether). Veratraldehyde = 3,4-dimethoxybenzaldehyde; by methylation of vanillin; by Gattermann reaction from veratrole.

Rosenmund reaction: RCOCl $\longrightarrow$ RCHO + HCl; special catalyst to avoid overreduction.

Reactions

Cannizzaro reaction: 2 ArCHO $\longrightarrow$ ArCH$_2$OH + ArCO$_2$H (strong alkali). Shown also by (CH$_3$)$_3$CCHO and CH$_2$O.

Claisen-Schmidt condensation: C$_6$H$_5$CHO + CH$_3$CHO $\longrightarrow$ C$_6$H$_5$CH=CHCHO (cinnamaldehyde). Ready dehydration, due to activation of H and OH, explains irreversibility. Preparation of benzalacetone and benzalacetophenone.

Perkin reaction:

C$_6$H$_5$CHO + (CH$_3$CO)$_2$O(+ CH$_3$CO$_2$K) $\longrightarrow$
$\quad$ C$_6$H$_5$CH=CHCOOH
(cinnamic acid).

Knoevenagel-type reaction:

ArCHO + CH$_2$(CO$_2$H) in pyridine (+ trace piperidine) $\longrightarrow$ ArCH=CHCO$_2$H.

Reformatsky reaction:

R$_2$CO + BrCH$_2$CO$_2$C$_2$H$_5$ (+ Zn) $\longrightarrow$
$\quad$ R$_2$C(OH)CH$_2$CO$_2$C$_2$H$_5$.

Benzoin condensation:

2 C$_6$H$_5$CHO (+ KCN) $\longrightarrow$ C$_6$H$_5$COCH(OH)C$_6$H$_5$.

Mechanism: attack by CN$^-$ at positively polarized carbon atom, hydrogen shift in the ion, condensation, etc.

Autoxidation of benzaldehyde (liquid) to benzoic acid (solid). A photocatalytic chain reaction initiated by benzoyl radicals and involving perbenzoic acid. Inhibitor: hydroquinone (0.001%).

Ketones. By Friedel-Crafts, Claisen-Schmidt, and Fries reactions.

Reactions of ketones. ω-Substitution:

$\quad$ C$_6$H$_5$COCH$_3$ $\longrightarrow$ C$_6$H$_5$COCH$_2$Br

(ω-bromoacetophenone or phenacyl bromide; reacts with liquid acids to give crystalline esters).

Condensation reactions. Acetophenone $\longrightarrow$ s-triphenylbenzene. Ester condensation:

CH$_3$CO$_2$C$_2$H$_5$ + CH$_3$COC$_6$H$_5$ $\longrightarrow$
$\quad$ C$_6$H$_5$COCH$_2$COC$_6$H$_5$.

Michael condensation: C$_6$H$_5$CH=CHCOC$_6$H$_5$
$\quad$ + $\overset{-}{\text{C}}$H(CO$_2$C$_2$H$_5$)$_2$Na$^+$ (1,4-addition).

Pinacol rearrangement: $(C_6H_5)_2C(OH)C(OH)(C_6H_5)_2$ (benzopinacol, from benzophenone and isopropyl alcohol in sunlight) $\longrightarrow (C_6H_5)_3CCOC_6H_5$. Rearrangement promoted by an electrophilic agent (H^+), which eliminates one OH to give carbonium ion; charged carbon has electron sextet and attracts migrating group.

Oximes. Geometrical isomers, *cis* and *trans*. Beckmann rearrangement of ketoximes:

$$C_6H_5C(=NOH)C_6H_5 \longrightarrow C_6H_5C(=O)NHC_6H_5.$$

Benzil, $C_6H_5COCOC_6H_5$ (yellow). By oxidation of benzoin with HNO_3. Base-induced rearrangement to benzilic acid. $(C_6H_5)_2C(OH)CO_2H$.

PROBLEMS

1. Suggest methods for the synthesis of the following aldehydes:

   (*a*) *p*-Bromobenzaldehyde
   (*b*) 2,5-Dimethylbenzaldehyde
   (*c*) 2,4-Dimethoxybenzaldehyde
   (*d*) Terephthaldehyde

2. Prepare a chart summarizing the principal methods available for introduction into the aromatic nucleus of each of the following groups: CH_3, NO_2, NH_2, SO_3H, OH, Cl, I, CN, COOH, CHO, $COCH_3$.

3. How can each of the substituents mentioned in the preceding question be eliminated from the nucleus (replaced by hydrogen)?

4. Would you expect condensation to occur between the following pairs of components? If so, indicate the type of catalyst required and write the reactions:

   (*a*) $C_6H_5CHO + CH_3CH_2CH_2CHO$
   (*b*) $C_6H_5CH=CHCHO + C_6H_5COCH_3$
   (*c*) $C_6H_5CHO + CH_3CH=CHCHO$

5. Suggest a synthesis of *o*-bromocinnamic acid from *o*-bromotoluene.

6. Formulate a synthesis of the acid

   $$C_6H_5CH(CH_3)CH_2COOH$$

   from acetophenone by the Reformatsky reaction.

7. Summarize methods of preparing aromatic aldehydes and ketones that are applicable specifically to phenols and amines.

8. A substance A of the formula $C_{12}H_{10}O$ on reaction with hydroxylamine yields $C_{12}H_{11}ON$, which is converted by the action of phosphorus pentachloride into a new substance $C_{12}H_{11}ON$. The latter on alkaline hydrolysis affords β-naphthylamine. What is the structure of A?

READING REFERENCES

R. L. Shriner, "The Reformatsky Reaction," in R. Adams, *Organic Reactions*, I, 1–37, Wiley, New York (1942)

J. R. Johnson, "The Perkin Reaction and Related Reactions," *ibid.*, I, 210–265 (1942)

T. A. Geissman, "The Cannizzaro Reaction," *ibid.*, II, 94–113 (1944)

N. N. Crounse, "The Gattermann-Koch Reaction," *ibid.*, V, 290–300 (1949)

E. S. Wallis, "Molecular Rearrangements," in H. Gilman, *Organic Chemistry*, I, 2nd Ed., 965–1031, Wiley, New York (1943)

J. R. Johnson, "Modern Electronic Concepts of Valence," *ibid.*, II, 2nd Ed., 1821–1942 (1943)

chapter 26

QUINONES

The generic name quinone is derived from the fact that the first-known and commonest member of the series was discovered in Liebig's laboratory as an oxidation product of quinic acid with manganese dioxide and sulfuric acid (Woskresensky, 1838). Quinic acid, a constituent of cinchona bark and of the coffee bean, is a 1,3,4,5-tetra-hydroxyhexahydrobenzoic acid of the configuration shown, and its conversion into quinone involves dehydration, decarboxylation, and

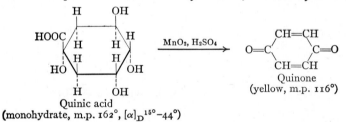

Quinic acid
(monohydrate, m.p. 162°, $[\alpha]_D^{15°} -44°$)

Quinone
(yellow, m.p. 116°)

oxidation. The yellow reaction product is called quinone, or *p*-benzo-quinone; the isomeric *o*-benzoquinone is known, but *meta* quinones do not exist.

One characteristic of quinones is color, and a usual differentiation between *para* and *ortho* quinones is that most of the former are yellow and the majority of the latter are orange or red. Particularly beautiful color phenomena often are observed on dusting a few crystals of a quinone on the surface of a dilute aqueous solution of alkali or on a drop or two of concentrated sulfuric acid. Hydroxyquinones form intensely colored alkali salts, and quinones of all types form vividly colored oxonium salts in concentrated sulfuric acid. The quinone ring contains only two double bonds and is nonaromatic; quinones are analogous to open-chain α,β-unsaturated ketones but considerably more reactive. They are reduced by mild reagents to colorless hydro-quinones.

ortho (red)

para (yellow)

Quinone. — Quinone is the end product of oxidation of aniline in sulfuric acid solution with potassium dichromate and then with lead peroxide. An initially formed free radical condenses with aniline to form a succession of intensely colored dyes, which afford quinone by oxidation and hydrolysis, illustrated as follows:

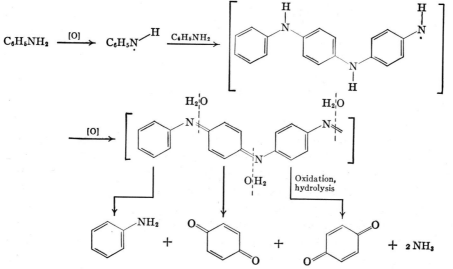

Quinone is steam-volatile and in the solid state has considerable vapor pressure; when heated gently it sublimes readily to form large yellow crystals. The substance has a characteristic pungent odor and causes sneezing, particularly in individuals subject to hay fever. It is attacked by aqueous alkali, with transient coloration, and is rapidly converted into a humuslike material. Quinone readily combines with proteins, probably by addition reactions involving free amino and sulfhydryl groups; it stains the skin and can be used for tanning leather.

When a yellow solution of quinone in alcohol is added to a colorless solution of hydroquinone in the same solvent, the color deepens immediately to brown-red, and dark green crystals having glistening metallic luster then separate. The substance, known as quinhydrone (m.p. 171°), is a molecular complex of equimolecular amounts of quinone and hydroquinone, and it yields the former substance on oxidation and the latter on reduction. The complex is much less soluble in water or organic solvents than either component, but dissociates to the components to a point of equilibrium.

OXIDATION–REDUCTION POTENTIALS

The reduction of quinone to hydroquinone in aqueous solution is a rapid, quantitative, and reversible process comparable to the reduction of ferric to ferrous ions, and can be formulated as an electro-chemical reaction:

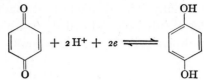

A platinum electrode introduced into a solution containing quinone and hydroquinone at a fixed hydrogen-ion concentration (buffered solution) acquires an electric potential that can be measured by making connection through a conducting liquid to a reference half-cell such as a hydrogen electrode. The electrode potential (E) of the organic half-cell is dependent on the concentrations of the species entering into the equilibrium, namely quinone, hydroquinone, and hydrogen ions, in accordance with the equation:

Half-cell potential

$$E^{25°} = E_0 + 0.05912 \log [H^+] + 0.02956 \log \frac{[Quinone]}{[Hydroquinone]}$$

The quantity E_0 is a normal potential characteristic of a specific quinone-hydroquinone system, and is defined as the potential of the half-cell when the hydrogen-ion concentration is unity and the concentration of the quinone, or oxidant, is equal to that of the hydro-quinone, or reductant. Thus the second term in the right-hand side of the equation is eliminated if $[H^+] = 1$, and the third term disappears if $[Quinone] = [Hydroquinone]$. A simple experimental method that ensures the latter condition is to employ quinhydrone, for the complex dissociates to equivalent amounts of the oxidant and reductant. The only variable then remaining is associated with the hydrogen-ion concentration, which can be determined. The normal potential is a constant specific to a given quinone-hydroquinone pair, and provides a

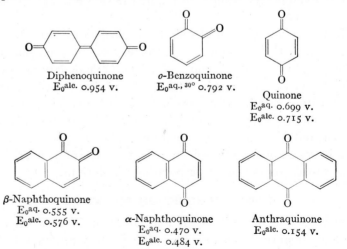

Diphenoquinone
$E_0^{alc.}$ 0.954 v.

o-Benzoquinone
$E_0^{aq., 30°}$ 0.792 v.

Quinone
$E_0^{aq.}$ 0.699 v.
$E_0^{alc.}$ 0.715 v.

Normal potentials
(E_0)

β-Naphthoquinone
$E_0^{aq.}$ 0.555 v.
$E_0^{alc.}$ 0.576 v.

α-Naphthoquinone
$E_0^{aq.}$ 0.470 v.
$E_0^{alc.}$ 0.484 v.

Anthraquinone
$E_0^{alc.}$ 0.154 v.

precise characterization of the oxidizing power of the quinone or, conversely, of the reducing intensity of the hydroquinone. The values for quinones derived from benzene and from some of the polynuclear hydrocarbons are shown in the chart (determinations at 25°). Diphenoquinone, with the unsaturated conjugated quinonoid system extending throughout two rings, has a very high potential and is a powerful oxidizing agent. Since *ortho* quinones of the benzene and naphthalene series have potentials higher by 85–95 mv. than the isomeric *para* quinones, the former structure has a higher energy content than the latter. Comparison of the *ortho* and *para* benzoquinones with the corresponding naphthoquinones indicates a regular difference in potential of 230–240 mv., which represents a markedly diminished energy content of the bicyclic compounds. Stabilization attending fusion of a benzene ring to a double bond of either *o-* or *p*-benzoquinone can be attributed to the fact that the double bond is then incorporated in the aromatic nucleus and hence is relatively inert. In anthraquinone both the otherwise reactive quinonoid double bonds participate in benzenoid ring systems; hence the quinone has a low potential. Conversely, its reduction product, anthrahydroquinone, is a powerful reducing agent.

Substituent groups often exert a marked influence on the oxidation-reduction potential in either a positive or negative sense, as illustrated in Table I for a series of α-naphthoquinone derivatives (Fieser[1] and Fieser,[2] 1935). *m*-Directing groups, such as NO$_2$, CN, SO$_2$Ar, COAr, COOH, and SO$_3$H, as well as halogens, raise the po-

26.4

TABLE

EFFECT OF 2-SUBSTITUENTS ON THE POTENTIAL
OF 1,4-NAPHTHOQUINONE

SUBSTITUENT	EFFECT, IN MV.	SUBSTITUENT	EFFECT, IN MV.
NHCH$_3$	−252	NHCOCH$_3$	−67
NH$_2$	−210	C$_6$H$_5$	−32
N(CH$_3$)$_2$	−181	OCOCH$_3$	−9
OH	−128	Cl	+24
OCH$_3$	−131	SO$_3$Na	+69
CH$_3$	−76	SO$_2$C$_6$H$_4$CH$_3$	+121

tential of the parent quinone, whereas a potential-lowering effect is exerted by the following groups, arranged approximately in order of decreasing effectiveness: NHR, NH$_2$, N(CH$_3$)$_2$, OH, OR, CH$_3$, NHCOCH$_3$, C$_6$H$_5$, OCOCH$_3$. In general, groups that lower the

[1] Louis F. Fieser, b. 1899 Columbus, Ohio; Ph.D. Harvard (Conant); postdoctoral work Frankfurt (von Braun), Oxford (Perkin, Jr.); Bryn Mawr, Harvard
[2] Mary Fieser, b. 1909 Atchison, Kansas; stud. Harvard (L. F. Fieser); Harvard

potential of a quinone facilitate substitution in the benzene ring (electron-releasing), whereas groups that increase the potential retard benzene substitutions.

Oxidation-reduction potential data are valuable in interpretation of the behavior of those hydroxy- and aminoquinones that can exist in tautomeric forms, for example 2-hydroxy-1,4-naphthoquinone:

α-Form the more stable tautomer

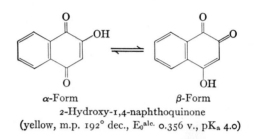

α-Form   β-Form
2-Hydroxy-1,4-naphthoquinone
(yellow, m.p. 192° dec., $E_0^{alc.}$ 0.356 v., pK_a 4.0)

The α-form is estimated to have a potential 80 mv. lower than the β-form, which means that it predominates in the equilibrium mixture to the extent of over 99%.

PREPARATION

26.5   The general procedure for preparing a quinone starts with a phenol or an amine, followed by introduction of either a hydroxyl or an amino group in an *ortho* or *para* position and oxidation of the intermediate in acid solution. The initial product of oxidation of *p*-aminophenol, *p*-quinonimine, is extremely sensitive and has been isolated and characterized potentiometrically only by special techniques; even in an oxidation conducted at 0° in dilute acid solution, it is only a transient intermediate and undergoes hydrolysis to quinone. *p*-Phenylenediamine similarly is converted into quinone through the easily hydrolyzed

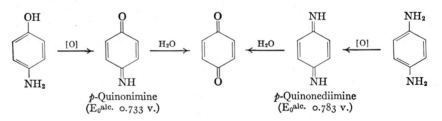

p-Quinonimine   *p*-Quinonediimine
($E_0^{alc.}$ 0.733 v.)   ($E_0^{alc.}$ 0.783 v.)

intermediate *p*-quinonediimine. One route to a bifunctional compound suitable for oxidation is illustrated by the preparation of β-naphthoquinone from β-naphthol. The naphthol is coupled in alkaline solution with diazotized sulfanilic acid, and the azo dye Orange II, without being isolated, is reduced directly with sodium hydrosulfite. The sulfanilic acid resulting from reductive fission remains in the

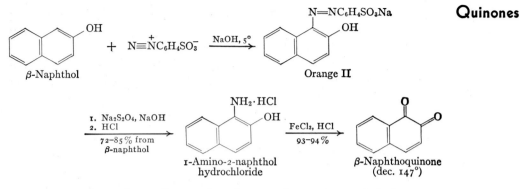

β-Naphthol   + N≡NC₆H₄SO₃⁻ →(NaOH, 5°)→ Orange II

1. Na₂S₂O₄, NaOH
2. HCl
72–85% from β-naphthol → 1-Amino-2-naphthol hydrochloride →(FeCl₃, HCl, 93–94%)→ β-Naphthoquinone (dec. 147°)

aqueous liquor as the sodium salt, whereas the aminonaphthol precipitates; this is purified as the hydrochloride, which is oxidized with ferric chloride to the quinone. α-Naphthoquinone can be made in the same way (58% overall yield from α-naphthol).

Some quinones, particularly those in the *ortho* series, are so reactive and sensitive that oxidation of a suitable bifunctional intermediate must be carried out under carefully controlled conditions. Investigators attempted without success to convert catechol into a quinone till Willstätter (1904), recognizing that *o*-benzoquinone is extremely sensitive to water, devised a preparation that consists in oxidation in absolute ether solution with carefully dehydrated silver oxide in the presence of fused sodium sulfate to absorb the water formed:

26.6

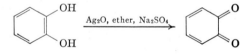

OH / OH →(Ag₂O, ether, Na₂SO₄)→ O / O

REACTIONS

Reactions of one type, exemplified by the reaction of quinone with dry hydrogen chloride, can be represented as 1,4-additions, followed by enolization, but the mechanism is not known. Additions conducted in aqueous or alcoholic solution are attended with oxidation-

26.7

1,4-Addition

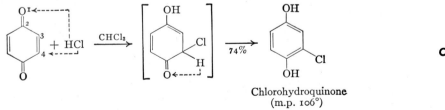

+ HCl →(CHCl₃)→ [intermediate] →(74%)→ Chlorohydroquinone (m.p. 106°)

Of HCl

reduction equilibration of product with starting material. Thus aniline reacts with α-naphthoquinone (I) in alcoholic solution with prompt separation of red needles of 2-anilino-1,4-naphthoquinone

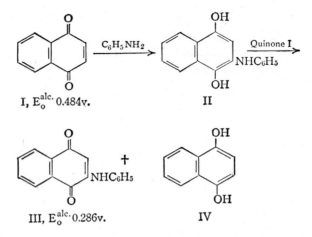

I, $E_0^{alc.}$ 0.484v. II

Of ArNH₂

III, $E_0^{alc.}$ 0.286v. IV

(III), formed by oxidation of the initial product II by I. The potential of the substituted quinone is so far below that of the starting material that the reaction is practically complete; hence two moles of I are required to produce one of III. In bisulfite addition, the group introduced raises the potential and oxidation of the substituted product does not occur. The reaction is applicable to nitrosophenols, in equilibrium with quinone oximes, as in the preparation of 1,2-naphthoquinone-4-sulfonate. On oxidation of the aminonaphtholsulfonic

Of NaHSO₃

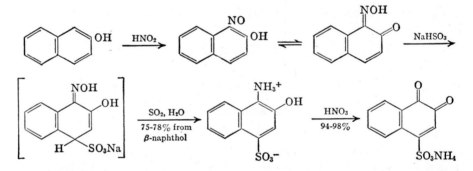

acid with nitric acid the ammonia liberated on cleavage of the imino group forms a salt with the sulfonic acid. Reactions of the quinone-sulfonate that probably proceed by 1,4-additions and illustrate the reactivity specific to quinones are as follows:

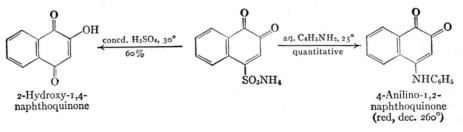

2-Hydroxy-1,4-naphthoquinone

4-Anilino-1,2-naphthoquinone
(red, dec. 260°)

The Thiele[3] reaction (1898), in which acetic anhydride is added to a quinone under catalysis by sulfuric acid or boron fluoride etherate with formation of the hydroxyhydroquinone triacetate, affords a

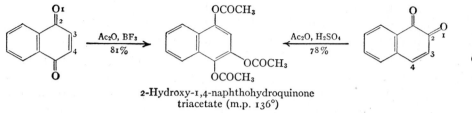

2-Hydroxy-1,4-naphthohydroquinone
triacetate (m.p. 136°)

means of obtaining hydroxyquinones. Thus the product from either α- or β-naphthoquinone on alkaline hydrolysis and air oxidation gives 2-hydroxy-1,4-naphthoquinone.

2-Methyl-1,4-naphthoquinone forms a dibromide from which hydrogen bromide is eliminated with production of a bromoquinone,

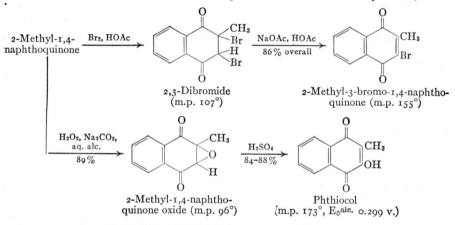

2,3-Dibromide
(m.p. 107°)

2-Methyl-3-bromo-1,4-naphtho-
quinone (m.p. 155°)

2-Methyl-1,4-naphtho-
quinone oxide (m.p. 96°)

Phthiocol
(m.p. 173°, E₀ᵃˡᶜ. 0.299 v.)

and it reacts with hydrogen peroxide under basic catalysis to give an oxide. The oxide ring is easily opened by sulfuric acid in the cold, and combination of the two reactions affords a convenient synthesis of phthiocol (26.13).

One example of the Diels-Alder reaction of quinones has been cited (13.11). p-Benzoquinone can be converted efficiently into either a mono or di adduct of butadiene; the former (1) is convertible by

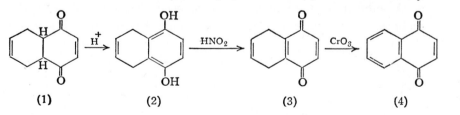

(1)   (2)   (3)   (4)

[3] Johannes Thiele, 1865–1918; b. Ratibor, Germany; Ph.D. Halle; Munich, Strasbourg; *Ber.*, **60A**, 75 (1927)

enolization (2) and oxidation (3, 4) into α-naphthoquinone (overall yield 76%).

Quinones are particularly prone to undergo substitutions involving attack by free radicals. One is alkylation of the quinone nucleus with either an acyl peroxide or a lead tetraacylate (Fieser *et al.*, 1942). When a solution of 2-methyl-1,4-naphthoquinone in acetic acid is warmed with slightly more than one equivalent of acetyl peroxide or with 3–4 equivalents of lead tetraacetate, a brisk reaction ensues with evolution of gas, and the starting material is converted into the 2,3-dimethyl compound:

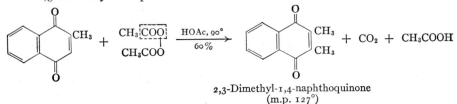

2,3-Dimethyl-1,4-naphthoquinone
(m.p. 127°)

In the warm solution acetyl peroxide probably decomposes with liberation of carbon dioxide and formation of methyl and acetate radicals; the latter radical functions as acceptor for the hydrogen atom of the quinonoid nucleus, while the methyl radical substitutes at the position vacated. Lead tetraacetate, an equally efficient alkylating agent, perhaps undergoes decomposition in large part to the same reactive species:

$$CH_3COO \quad OCOCH_3 \atop CH_3COO \quad OCOCH_3 \Big\rangle Pb \longrightarrow CH_3\cdot + CO_2 + CH_3COO\cdot + Pb(OCOCH_3)_2$$

NATURALLY OCCURRING QUINONES

26.12

A considerable number of pigments characterized as quinones have been isolated from high and lower plants, and a few members of the series have been found in animal organisms. Some are dyes (alizarin 19.14), some are growth factors (vitamins K 15.6), some are antibiotics, some catalyze respiratory processes, and some are respiration inhibitors.

A number of mold pigments have been characterized as benzoquinones or dibenzoquinones, for example **fumigatin** (*Aspergillus*

Benzoquinones

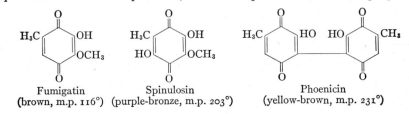

Fumigatin
(brown, m.p. 116°)

Spinulosin
(purple-bronze, m.p. 203°)

Phoenicin
(yellow-brown, m.p. 231°)

fumigatus Fresenius), **spinulosin,** and **phoenicin** (Raistrick,[4] Oxford, 1938). The secretion of the Uruguayan arachnid *Gonyleptide* contains an antibiotic pigment (C. Estable) characterized as a mixture of **2,3-dimethylquinone** (a), **2,5-dimethylquinone** (b), and **2,3,5-trimethylquinone** (c) (Fieser and Ardao, 1955). The mixture resulting from treatment of a 115-mg. sample with butadiene was reduced with hydrosulfite and the hydroquinones of (b) and (c) extracted with alkali from an ethereal solution retaining the adduct of (a); the mixture of (b) and (c) on Thiele reaction and steam distillation afforded (c) in the distillate and the Thiele product from (b) in the residue.

A yellow pigment **lawsone** extracted from leaves of the tropical shrub henna (*Lawsonia inermis*) is identical with synthetic 2-hydroxy-1,4-naphthoquinone. It dyes wool and silk an orange shade, and a paste made from powdered henna leaves and catechu has been used for tinting the hair red. The isomeric 8-hydroxy compound **juglone** is present in the shells of unripe walnuts, largely as α-hydrojuglone,

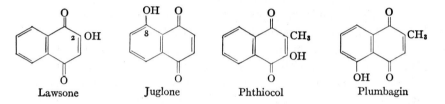

Lawsone   Juglone   Phthiocol   Plumbagin

a ketonic form of the normal reduction product, or hydroquinone. The colorless hydro compound undergoes rapid oxidation on exposure to air and the resulting quinone produces stains on the skin, probably in consequence of addition of active groups of the protein to the quinone.

Two monohydroxy derivatives of 2-methyl-1,4-naphthoquinone have been isolated from natural sources. **Plumbagin,** shown by synthesis to be the 5-hydroxy isomer, was known in a fairly pure form as early as 1828 and is the active principle of Chita, a drug of medicinal value obtained from Indian shrubs of various *Plumbago* species. **Phthiocol,** or 2-hydroxy-3-methyl-1,4-naphthoquinone (synthesis, 26.9), has been isolated from human tubercle bacilli (*Mycobacterium tuberculosis*), but probably is formed during the isolation process by degradation of a vitamin K factor during saponification with alcoholic potassium hydroxide.

Echinochrome A of sea urchin eggs (10 mg. per ovary) was characterized by Kuhn and Wallenfels (1939) as a pentahydroxyquinone derivative of β-ethyl- rather than β-methylnaphthalene, the parent hydrocarbon of the plant pigments cited above. Two tautomeric *para*

[4] Harold Raistrick, b. 1890 Pudsey, Yorkshire; School Hyg. Trop. Med., London

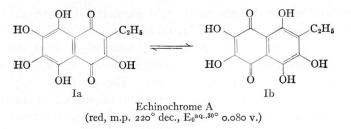

Echinochrome A
(red, m.p. 220° dec., $E_0^{aq.,30°}$ 0.080 v.)

quinone forms are possible, Ia and Ib, but form Ib, with two power-fully effective hydroxyl groups in the quinone nucleus, probably has a potential some 50 mv. lower than that of Ia and hence predominates to the extent of 99% of the equilibrium mixture in solution.

26.15   **Alkannin,** a dark red pigment occurring as an ester in the root of *Alkanna tinctoria*, has been characterized by Brockmann[5] (1935) as a derivative of naphthazarin (5,8-dihydroxy-1,4-naphthoquinone) having as a substituent in the quinonoid ring an unsaturated side chain containing a secondary alcoholic group. Another red pigment of the same composition and properties, **shikonin** (m.p. 147°), has been isolated from the root of the Japanese plant shikone. Brockmann discovered that the pigment is the dextrorotatory enantiomer of alkannin, for on reaction with methanol and hydrogen chloride it yields an optically inactive methyl ether identical with that obtained from the

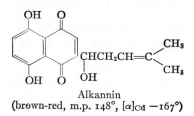

Alkannin
(brown-red, m.p. 148°, $[\alpha]_{Cd}$ −167°)

levorotatory pigment from *Alkanna tinctoria*. Instances of the occurrence in nature of both the *d*- and *l*-forms of an asymmetric compound are rare.

SUMMARY

Types: *ortho* (red), *para* (yellow); no *meta* quinones. Color reactions with concd. sulfuric acid and often with alkali. Highly reactive, nonaromatic.

p-Benzoquinone (quinone) by oxidation of aniline: condensation of the radical $C_6H_5NH\cdot$ to polymeric dye that is hydrolyzed and oxidized. Quinone sublimes easily (pungent odor), reacts with dilute alkali and with proteins, forms 1:1 complex with hydroquinone: quinhydrone (green).

Oxidation-reduction potentials. Reduction of quinone (yellow) to hydroquinone (colorless) rapid, quantitative, reversible. E (potential of half-cell) = E_0 (normal potential, a constant characteristic of a given system) $+ 0.06 \log [H^+] + 0.03 \log$ [Quinone]/[Hydroquinone]; E_0 is the potential measured when $[H^+] = 1$ and [Quinone] = [Hydroquinone]. Normal potentials of parent quinones: *ortho* > *para*; benzo- > naphtho- >

[5] Hans Brockmann, b. 1903 Altkloster, Germany; Ph.D. Halle (Abderhalden), D.Sc. Heidelberg (Kuhn); Göttingen

anthra-. Effect of substituents: *m*-directing groups and halogens raise E_0, *o*-, *p*-directing groups have potential-lowering effect.

Preparation. Oxidation of *p*-aminophenol to *p*-quinonimine, which suffers rapid hydrolysis. Similar oxidation of *p*-phenylenediamine. Synthesis of β-naphthoquinone from β-naphthol by diazo coupling, etc. Moisture-sensitive *o*-benzoquinone by oxidation of catechol with Ag_2O in dry ether + anhydrous Na_2SO_4.

Reactions

1,4-Additions. Quinone + dry HCl $\longrightarrow$ chlorohydroquinone. Naphthoquinone (2 moles) + aniline $\longrightarrow$ anilinonaphthoquinone + naphthohydroquinone (oxidation of primary reaction product by starting material because of relative potentials). Bisulfite addition to a nitrosonaphthol.

Thiele reaction: quinone + $(CH_3CO)_2O$ (H^+) $\longrightarrow$ hydroxyhydroquinone triacetate.

Ethylenic additions: bromine; oxide formation (hydrolysis of an oxide to a hydroxyquinone); Diels-Alder synthesis of α-naphthoquinone.

Naturally Occurring Quinones

Benzoquinones. From molds: methyl-, methoxy-, and hydroxy-substituted quinones and diquinones (fumigatin, spinulosin, phoenicin). Polymethylquinones from an arachnid.

Hydroxy- and alkyl-substituted 1,4-naphthoquinones: lawsone (2-OH, henna), juglone (8-OH, walnut shells), plumbagin (2-CH$_3$-5-OH, Indian shrub), phthiocol (2-OH-3-CH$_3$; tubercle bacilli, hydrolysis of vitamin K), echinochrome A (ethylpentahydroxy, sea urchin eggs). Alkannin and shikonin (enantiomers).

PROBLEM

1. Devise syntheses of the following quinones:

   (*a*) 2,5-Dimethyl-1,4-benzoquinone from *p*-xylene.

   (*b*) Lawsone from either α- or β-naphthol.

   (*c*) Hydrolapachol (2-hydroxy-3-isopentyl-1,4-naphthoquinone) from lawsone.

   (*d*) Spinulosin from fumigatin.

   (*e*) Embelin, 3-undecyl-2,5-dihydroxy-1,4-benzoquinone, from the dihydroxyquinone.

   (*f*) 2-Hydroxy-3-*n*-decyl-1,4-naphthoquinone from 2-*n*-decyl-1,4-naphthoquinone.

READING REFERENCES

The Constitution and Properties of Lapachol, Lomatiol, and Other Hydroxynaphthoquinone Derivatives, Memorial Volume to Samuel C. Hooker (1936)

F. Mayer, *The Chemistry of Natural Coloring Matters,* 96–161, Reinhold, New York (1943)

chapter 27

NAPHTHALENE

27.1

Uses

Naphthalene, the most abundant single constituent of coal tar, is important as a source of phthalic acid and anthranilic acid, which are intermediates to indigo, indanthrene, and triphenylmethane dyes, and of intermediates for azo dyes. Use of the hydrocarbon as a moth repellent and insecticide has fallen off with the introduction of *p*-dichlorobenzene. Liquid hydro derivatives of naphthalene (m.p. 80°) utilized in motor fuels and lubricants and as solvents are the 1,2,3,4-tetrahydride, tetralin, and the decahydride, decalin.

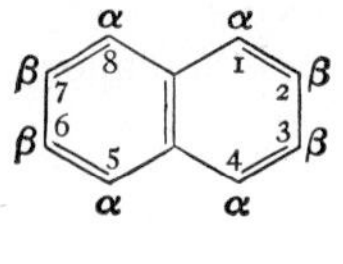

Monosubstituted naphthalenes usually are designated by the prefix α- or β-, while the positions of groups in polysubstituted derivatives are indicated by numbers. Ten isomeric disubstitution products are possible; all ten dihydroxy derivatives are known. 1,8-Derivatives are designated *peri*- (Gr. *peri*, near) and 2,6-derivatives are designated *amphi*- (Gr. *amph*-, on both sides). Structures of the simpler derivatives are established by oxidation to phthalic acid or a substituted phthalic acid. A nitro group stabilizes the ring to which it is attached, and hence the unsubstituted ring (A) of α-nitronaphthalene is degraded on oxidation and the product is 3-nitrophthalic acid. If the nitro compound is reduced, the substituted ring (B) becomes the more vulnerable center, and oxidation of α-naphthylamine yields phthalic acid. This sequence of reactions proves that naphthalene contains two fused benzene rings, for each ring is identified in a degradation product with carbon substituents in the *o*-positions. This structure was postulated by Erlenmeyer[1] in 1866 and proved by

Structure proof

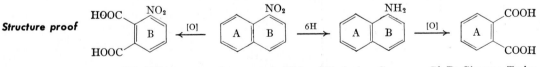

[1] Emil Erlenmeyer, 1825–1909; b. Wehen/Wiesbaden, Germany; Ph.D. Giessen; Techn. Hochsch. Munich; *Ber.*, **43**, 3645 (1910)

Graebe[2] (1868), who applied the above principle in a more elaborate sequence involving chlorinated quinones. Structures of substances such as β-naphthol or β-ethylnaphthalene, which yield phthalic acid on drastic oxidation, are established by correlation with other derivatives that undergo degradation in the alternate direction. β-Ethylnaphthalene results from Clemmensen reduction of an aceto compound established as a β-derivative by oxidation to trimellitic acid (benzene-1,2,4-tricarboxylic acid). β-Naphthol can be correlated through β-naphthylamine and β-naphthonitrile with β-naphthoic acid, which also yields the 1,2,4-acid.

BOND STRUCTURE

When the concept of the Kekulé ring system is extended to naphthalene, three resonance bond structures are possible, the symmetrical

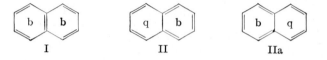

structure I and the two unsymmetrical, equivalent structures II and IIa. In formulations of the unsymmetrical structures, one of the two rings is indicated as being quinonoid in character (q) because the arrangement of double bonds corresponds to that of o-benzoquinone. Rings that correspond to the normal Kekulé benzene formula in containing three double bonds, in contrast with a quinonoid ring containing two, are described as normal benzenoid rings (b). Fries (1927), recognizing that quinonoid systems are more reactive, or less stable, than normal benzenoid systems, formulated a generalization known as the Fries rule, which states that the most stable form of a polynuclear hydrocarbon is that in which the maximum number of rings have the normal benzenoid arrangement of three double bonds. On this basis the symmetrical structure composed of two normal Kekulé rings would be expected to be more stable than the quinonoid structures.

Certain peculiarities in the reactions of β-naphthol and β-naphthylamine are interpretable only on the basis of the symmetrical formula. A striking difference in the two positions *ortho* to the functional group in these compounds was noted first by Marckwald (1893) and investigated extensively by Zincke,[3] Fries, and others. Whereas the

[2] Carl Graebe, 1841–1927; b. Frankfort, Germany; Ph.D. Heidelberg (Bunsen); Königsberg, Geneva; *Ber.*, **61A**, 9 (1928)

[3] Theodor Zincke, 1843–1928; b. Ülsen, Germany; Ph.D. Göttingen; Marburg; *Ber.*, **62A**, 17 (1929)

471

1-position exhibits functions normally associated with the *o*-position of an amine or a phenol, the 3-position does not. On reaction with a diazotized amine in alkaline solution, β-naphthol (III) couples exclusively at the 1-position in preference to the alternate position 3.

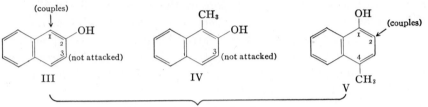

**Failure of IV
to couple**

Response to diazotized amines

The lack of reactivity at the 3-position is more apparent in the behavior of 1-methyl-2-naphthol (IV), for this naphthol fails to couple. The possibility that the resistance to attack is due to any lack of reactivity inherent in a β-position in the naphthalene nucleus can be dismissed, for 4-methyl-1-naphthol (V) couples at the β-position 2. The behavior of IV is therefore anomalous, and one of the two positions adjacent to the hydroxylated carbon atom does not have the characteristics of a normal *ortho* position. An interpretation of this deviating behavior can be developed from the consideration that aliphatic enols having the grouping —CH=C(OH)— couple with diazotized amines to give azo compounds, —C(N=NAr)=C(OH)—, whereas alcohols with the grouping —CH₂—CH(OH)— do not. The diazo group evidently can attack a position connected to a hydroxylated carbon by a double bond, but not one joined by a single linkage. This relationship would indicate that in β-naphthol the 1- and 2-carbon atoms are connected by a double bond and the 2- and 3-carbon atoms by a single bond. Position 1 is therefore described as a normal *ortho*

**Abnormal position 3
is nonenolic**

position because it is enolic, —$\overset{1}{C}$H=C(OH)—, whereas the 3-position, with the grouping =C(OH)—$\overset{3}{C}$H=, is nonenolic and hence abnormal. *p*-Coupling, as observed with α-naphthol, can be ascribed to attack at the end of a dienolic system: —CH=CHCH=C(OH)—.

The facts cited suggest that the bond structure of the naphthalene nucleus is not so mobile as that of benzene and that there is a relative

Bond fixation

fixation of bonds in at least that part of the molecule at which substitution occurs. Investigations of the properties of compounds

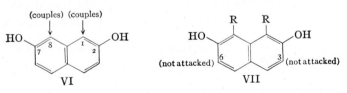

hydroxylated in both rings have shown that the two rings have the same character (Fieser and Lothrop, 1935). 2,7-Dihydroxynaphthalene (VI) couples at positions 1 and 8, but if these positions are blocked by alkyl groups (VII), no coupling occurs. The observation is consistent with the symmetrical, but not the unsymmetrical formulation for naphthalene.

Analogous phenomena are encountered in other reactions. β-Naphthol allyl ether (VIII) undergoes the Claisen rearrangement when heated and affords 1-allyl-2-naphthol (IX), but when the

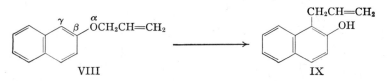

1-position is blocked by an alkyl group no rearrangement occurs. If the normal reaction is regarded as an α,γ-migration of the allyl group, the failure of the 1-substituted compounds to rearrange is an indication that the double bond normally present at the 1,2-position does not shift to the alternate 2,3-position to form a second α,γ-system, even at the elevated reaction temperature, in an extent sufficient to allow the allyl group to migrate.

Another manifestation of bond fixation is the course of the halogenation and nitration of β-naphthol and β-naphthylamine derivatives (Zincke, Fries), as illustrated in the following typical example. *p*-Cresol is easily chlorinated in both free *o*-positions, and the reaction sequence can be visualized as proceeding by substitution at an initial enolic position, progression of the double bonds to render the alternate *o*-position enolic, and further substitution at this site. Chlorination of β-naphthol follows a different course, for the initially formed 1-chloro derivative (X) can be converted by interaction with a second mole of chlorine (particularly in the presence of sodium acetate) into the keto dichloride XI (1,1-dichloro-2-keto-1,2-dihydronaphthalene). Ap-

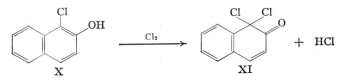

parently there is in this case no bond migration to produce an enolic center at the 3-position, $-C(OH)\overset{3}{=}CH-$, and chlorine attacks the less reactive system $-\overset{1}{C}Cl=C(OH)-$ with introduction of a second halogen at the 1-position. The comparable ketonic substances XII and XIII result from chlorination and nitration of 1-methyl-2-naph-

473

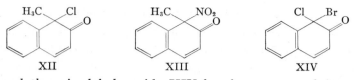

XII   XIII   XIV

thol, and the mixed halogenide XIV has been prepared from both the 1-bromo and 1-chloro derivatives of β-naphthol.

27.3

X-ray evidence

X-ray and electron-diffraction analysis (Robertson, 1951) has confirmed chemical evidence. Whereas in benzene the C—C bond distances are all 1.40Å, intermediate between aliphatic C—C (1.54Å) and C=C (1.33Å), the bond distances in naphthalene are not identical. The 1,2 bond distance is 1.36Å, shorter than any other bond, and the 2,3 distance is 1.39Å. That these distances do not quite correspond to aliphatic double and single bonds indicates some resonance stabilization, and the chemical evidence requires only bond fixation in the part of the molecule undergoing substitution and is not incompatible with resonance stabilization in another part. Attack of a 1,8-dialkyl-2,7-dihydroxynaphthalene (XV) by $C_6H_5N_2^+$, Cl^+, or other electrophilic agents requires a center of adequate electron density at an unsubstituted center, as in the *o*-quinonoid structure XVIII. However, four other resonance structures are possible in which the negative charge is located at a position at which substitution is blocked by an alkyl group. A separation of charge associated with the 2-hydroxyl group

Resonance stabilization in the ring not undergoing attack

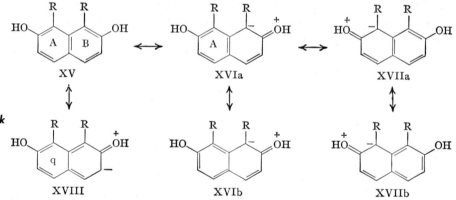

XV   XVIa   XVIIa

XVIII   XVIb   XVIIb

gives structure XVIa, with a negative charge at position 1 and a now isolated Kekulé ring (A) susceptible to usual resonance stabilization (structure XVIb). Charge separation at the alternate hydroxyl group gives a structure (XVIIa) that is likewise stabilized by resonance with an alternate Kekulé structure, XVIIb. That substitution does not occur at position 2 (or 7) means that structure XVIII (or its equivalent counterpart) is an excited structure that makes little contribution to the hybrid because of the high energy associated with the *o*-quinonoid arrangement of linkages.

In reactions of the normal type represented by nitration and halogenation the more reactive α-positions of naphthalene are attacked almost exclusively, whereas reversible reactions subject to steric hindrance result in substitution in the less hindered β-position to an extent that increases with increasing reaction temperature but varies with the reagent and perhaps with the bulkiness of specific group complexes. Nitration, bromination, or chlorination of naphthalene affords exclusively α-substituted derivatives; a possible analogy is the preferential α-bromination of an alkylbenzene. Thus one factor contribut-

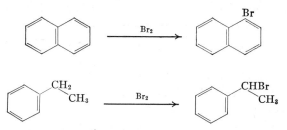

ing to the greater reactivity of the α-position of naphthalene is that this position is activated by the adjacent aromatic ring, whereas the β-position is too far removed to be affected. A further analogy can be drawn between the reduction of naphthalene with sodium amalgam to give 1,4-dihydronaphthalene and the reduction of diphenylbutadiene with aluminum amalgam in a reaction involving addition to the ends of a 1,4-system.

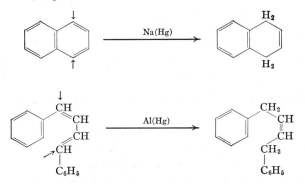

Sulfonation, notably subject to both steric and temperature effects, can be controlled to yield either the α- or β-sulfonic acid derivative. With concentrated acid at a low temperature, the hydrocarbon can be sulfonated largely in the α-position; the β-sulfonic acid can be produced in high yield by introducing sulfuric acid into molten naphthalene at 165° and stirring the mixture for a few minutes. Naphthalene-α-sulfonic acid when heated with sulfuric acid is transformed

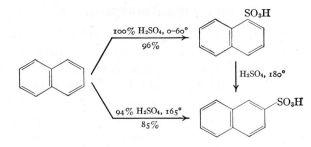

α-Position hindered

into the β-isomer, probably as the result of reversal of the substitution followed by resulfonation.

27.6   The course of Friedel-Crafts acylations of naphthalene varies more with the nature of the reagent and solvent than with the temperature. The hydrocarbon is converted by acetyl chloride or acetic anhydride

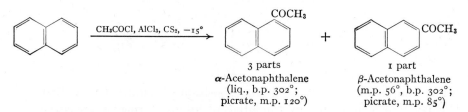

	3 parts	1 part
	α-Acetonaphthalene	β-Acetonaphthalene
	(liq., b.p. 302°;	(m.p. 56°, b.p. 302°;
	picrate, m.p. 120°)	picrate, m.p. 85°)

in carbon disulfide solution into a mixture of the α- and β-aceto derivatives in the ratio of about 3:1. The ketones boil at the same temperature and the solid β-isomer is not present in large enough amount to be separable from the liquid α-isomer by crystallization. However, the relationship in properties is reversed in the picrates, for the picrate of the liquid α-isomer is the higher melting and the less soluble; hence

α-Acetonaphthalene the more abundant liquid ketone can be isolated in pure form by one crystallization of the picrate mixture and regeneration by cleavage with ammonia. β-Acetonaphthalene is more readily available, for it is the chief product of acylation in nitrobenzene solution and, being

β-Isomer in high yield

$$\text{Naphthalene} \xrightarrow[\text{90\%}]{\text{CH}_3\text{COCl, AlCl}_3,\ \text{C}_6\text{H}_5\text{NO}_2} \text{β-Acetonaphthalene}$$

a solid, can be freed easily from a small amount of the accompanying liquid isomer by crystallization. Since nitrobenzene is known to form molecular complexes with aluminum chloride and acid chlorides, the preferential β-substitution may be attributable to an avoidance of the hindered α-position by a bulky intermediate complex. Friedel-

Succinoylation

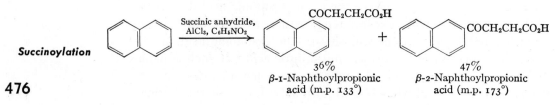

	36%	47%
	β-1-Naphthoylpropionic	β-2-Naphthoylpropionic
	acid (m.p. 133°)	acid (m.p. 173°)

Crafts succinoylation of naphthalene proceeds most satisfactorily in nitrobenzene solution and affords a mixture of isomeric keto acids that can be separated by special procedures.

Friedel-Crafts substitution of an acyl group derived from an aromatic acid gives predominantly the α-isomer, and the course of the reaction is not greatly influenced by the solvent or temperature. Benzoylation is best accomplished by the Perrier procedure (1904).

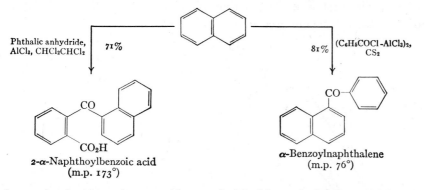

Phthalic anhydride, AlCl₃, CHCl₂CHCl₂   71%   81%   (C₆H₅COCl -AlCl₃)₂, CS₂

2-α-Naphthoylbenzoic acid (m.p. 173°)

α-Benzoylnaphthalene (m.p. 76°)

An equimolecular mixture of benzoyl chloride and aluminum chloride is heated over a free flame until the solid has dissolved and is then cooled; the resulting crystalline molecular complex is dissolved in carbon disulfide and the hydrocarbon component added. A rapid reaction ensues, with separation of a crystalline aluminum chloride complex of α-benzoylnaphthalene, from which the pure ketone is liberated on decomposition with water. Some β-benzoylnaphthalene (m.p. 82°) is produced but remains in the carbon disulfide mother liquor as a much more soluble complex.

MONOSUBSTITUTION PRODUCTS

The chief substitution reactions of naphthalene of practical value are summarized in Chart 1, which also shows key transformation products of the resulting substances. Nitration must be conducted under controlled conditions to avoid formation of dinitro compounds, for the nitro group initially introduced into one ring has only a weak deactivating influence on the other nucleus. Naphthalene reacts much more readily than benzene, and best results are obtained with diluted mixed acid.

Naphthalene is easily halogenated, for example by bromine in carbon tetrachloride solution at the reflux temperature (72–75% yield). Some dihalogenation invariably occurs, but dihalides can be eliminated by fractionation after the crude product has been warmed with powdered sodium hydroxide or steam distilled from an alkaline medium to destroy material containing labile halogen. α-Bromo-naphthalene readily forms a Grignard reagent, and carbonation of this derivative is the preferred method for preparation of α-naphthoic acid. A convenient preparation of α-naphthonitrile by heating α-bromonaphthalene with pyridine and cuprous cyanide under reflux has been described (23.8); the less expensive but higher boiling α-chloro compound can be employed with the use of pressure equipment. The best route to β-naphthoic acid is hypochlorite oxidation of β-acetonaphthalene (24.2).

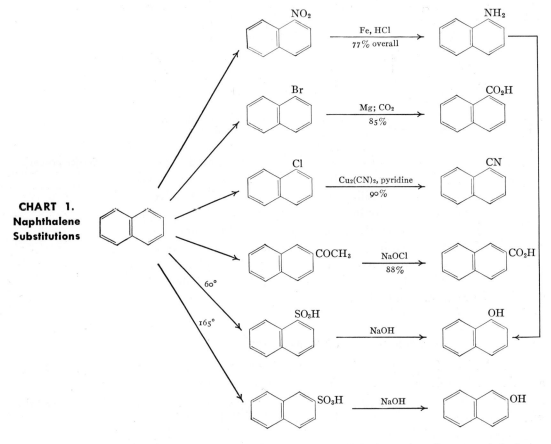

**CHART 1.
Naphthalene
Substitutions**

β-Naphthol

α-Naphthol

β-Naphthol is produced by alkali fusion of sodium naphthalene-β-sulfonate. The reaction can be conducted with 1 part of sodium hydroxide, mixed with 23% of water to lower the melting point, and 1.5 parts of the sulfonate. The sulfonate is added to the melt at 270–290°, and the temperature eventually is brought to 318°. The cooled melt is extracted with water, and the solution is acidified; the yield is 84%. α-Naphthol can be prepared similarly, but the product is not pure. A better process consists in hydrolysis of α-naphthylamine with 9.2% aqueous sulfuric acid at 200° and 14 atmospheres pressure; the product is pure and the yield 94–95%. The ready hydrolysis of the amine to the naphthol is a reaction seldom encountered in the benzene series but often applicable to amines of the more reactive naphthalene.

Bucherer Reaction. — β-Naphthylamine is prepared by a procedure developed by Bucherer[4] (1904), consisting in heating β-naphthol with aqueous ammonium sulfite or bisulfite. A sulfite solution is prepared by saturating concentrated ammonia solution with sulfur dioxide and adding an equal volume of concentrated ammonia solution; β-naphthol is added, and the charge is heated in an autoclave provided with a stirrer or a shaking mechanism. The correspond-

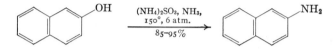

ing amine is obtained in excellent purity and yield. Several comparable aminations have been realized in the naphthalene series, but the reaction requires a reactive aromatic nucleus and is not practicable for benzene derivatives. The amination is reversible; for example, β-naphthylamine can be reconverted into β-naphthol by heating with aqueous sodium bisulfite solution and then adding alkali and boiling the solution until the ammonia is expelled. Intermediate bisulfite products have been isolated and are currently regarded as resulting from tautomerization of the naphthol or naphthylamine followed by addition of bisulfite to the carbonyl or ketimine group. The addition product is produced by heating the naphthol with sodium bisulfite; it is stable in the presence of excess bisulfite or dilute mineral acid, but is hydrolyzed by alkali and is converted into the amine on reaction with ammonia. The same intermediate is produced by the action of sodium bisulfite on the naphthylamine and can be subsequently hydrolyzed by alkali.

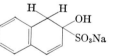

Other Derivatives. — The ready preparation of β-naphthylamine by the Bucherer reaction makes available substances otherwise difficultly accessible. Thus β-bromonaphthalene can be prepared in moderate yield by the Sandmeyer reaction, which likewise is employed

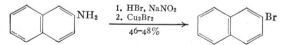

for the preparation of β-naphthonitrile. β-Nitronaphthalene is produced to a certain extent by the action of sodium nitrite on diazotized

[4] Hans Th. Bucherer, 1869–1949; b. Cologne, Germany; Ph.D. Leipzig (Wislicenus); Techn. Hochsch. Munich

27.11

OH

I

OH
NO₂

NO₂

II

CH₃

III

β-naphthylamine in the presence of cuprous hydroxide, but the process involves a time-consuming steam distillation of the difficultly volatile product, and the yield is only 10%.

The course of substitution reactions of naphthalene derivatives is determined by a combination of factors. The group initially present exerts a directive influence, and either activates or deactivates the ring to which it is attached. α-Positions are, *per se*, more reactive than β-positions to normal substitutions or to sulfonations and Friedel-Crafts reactions conducted at low temperatures. In α-naphthol (I), the 4-position is particularly favored because it is a reactive α-position *para* to the powerfully activating hydroxyl group, and consequently it is the first point of attack. Dinitration of α-naphthol is conducted, as in the preparation of picric acid, by conversion into the disulfonic acid and treatment of this derivative with nitric acid; the product is 2,4-dinitro-1-naphthol (II), or Martius Yellow (a dye). After introduction of one sulfonic acid or nitro group, the ring carrying the substituents is activated by the hydroxyl group and deactivated by the unsaturated, *meta* directing group, but the outcome of the reaction shows that the activating influence predominates. In α-methylnaphthalene (III) the 4-position is also the preferential point of attack, for example in nitration or in low-temperature sulfonation (conducted with chlorosulfonic acid in carbon tetrachloride solution at 0°; 88% yield). α-Methylnaphthalene is substituted at the 4-position also in Friedel-Crafts acylations, even in nitrobenzene solution, which indicates that the *p*-directing effect of the methyl group overcomes the hindrance effect noted with naphthalene itself.

If one ring of the naphthalene nucleus carries a *m*-directing, deactivating group, a substituent tends to enter the other ring, preferentially at the more reactive α-position. Thus α-nitronaphthalene gives on nitration a mixture of the 1,5- and 1,8-dinitro compounds in which the latter predominates. The higher-melting 1,5-dinitro-naphthalene is much less soluble than the isomer, and separation can be accomplished by crystallization from pyridine or by warming the nitration mixture till the solid is dissolved and then allowing the 1,5-compound to crystallize.

Dinitration

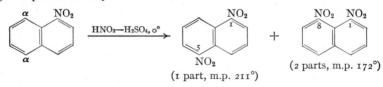

α NO₂ $\xrightarrow{\text{HNO}_3-\text{H}_2\text{SO}_4,\ 0°}$ NO₂ $\overset{1}{}$ +   NO₂ NO₂ $\overset{8\ \ 1}{}$

α $\overset{5}{}$ NO₂   (2 parts, m.p. 172°)

(1 part, m.p. 211°)

27.12

In β-naphthol, β-methoxynaphthalene, and β-methylnaphthalene, the point of first attack is the activated 1-position, which is the only available normal position *ortho* or *para* to the directing group. Thus β-naphthol couples exclusively at this position and β-methylnaphthalene undergoes bromination and nitration at the 1-position. This position, however, though particularly reactive by virtue of both the α- and the o-relationships, is flanked by a substituent on one side and by the adjacent ring on the other, and it is consequently hindered. In reactions subject to hindrance and to temperature effects, a 1-

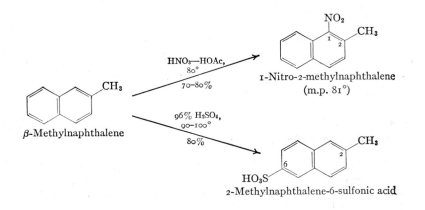

1-Nitro-2-methylnaphthalene
(m.p. 81°)

2-Methylnaphthalene-6-sulfonic acid

*Substitutions free from
and subject to
hindrance effect*

derivative is produced only as a transient phase, for under the usual operating conditions the substituent assumes a position in the second ring. Nitration of β-methylnaphthalene, which proceeds normally, may be contrasted to the sulfonation at only slightly elevated temperature, which affords the pure 6-sulfonic acid in high yield. Unhindered β-positions are available in the second ring at 6 and 7, and the fact that the 6-derivative is produced in high yield shows that the methyl group across the molecule in the *amphi* position controls the course of the heteronuclear substitution. β-Naphthol is similarly sulfonated at the *amphi*-position 6.

In Friedel-Crafts acylations, which also are subject to hindrance, β-methylnaphthalene is substituted in the 1-position in large part, though not exclusively, when the reaction is conducted with carbon disulfide or tetrachloroethane as solvent. In nitrobenzene solution β-methylnaphthalene is substituted principally in the 6-position (R. D. Haworth, 1932), as illustrated for the succinoylation reaction:

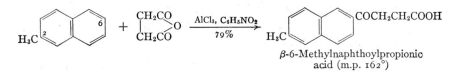

β-6-Methylnaphthoylpropionic
acid (m.p. 162°)

The effect of hindrance in the Friedel-Crafts reaction is illustrated further by the acetylation of β-methoxynaphthalene under different conditions. In carbon disulfide solution the chief product is the

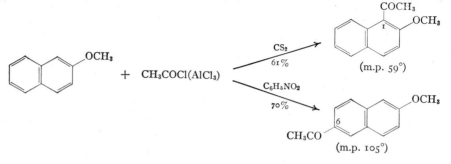

i-aceto derivative; but when the reaction is conducted in solution in nitrobenzene the 6-aceto derivative is produced in good yield.

RELATIVE REACTIVITY OF NAPHTHALENE AND BENZENE

27.13
Substitutions generally proceed under milder conditions with naphthalene than with benzene. A striking demonstration of the greater susceptibility of the bicyclic hydrocarbon to substitution is that benzene can be used as solvent in the Friedel-Crafts reaction of naphthalene with phthalic anhydride to form 2-α-naphthoylbenzoic acid (27.7), for even though benzene is employed in large excess of naphthalene, very little o-benzoylbenzoic acid is formed. Naphthalene also shows greater reactivity in additions. It is reduced by sodium amalgam to the 1,4-dihydride (27.4), whereas benzene under the same conditions is unattacked. Naphthalene also is reducible to the tetrahydro stage (tetralin) with sodium and amyl alcohol, and the reaction stops abruptly at this stage because the benzenoid ring in the reaction product is resistant to addition, even though the saturated side ring affixed at adjacent positions must have an activating influence. Tetralin, a useful intermediate for syntheses, is prepared technically by partial catalytic hydrogenation.

Tetralin

A similar difference in reactivity is observable in oxidation reactions. Naphthalene is oxidized more readily than benzene, but a better criterion is the course of oxidation of the methyl derivatives of the two hydrocarbons. In toluene the methyl group is more susceptible to oxidation than the aromatic nucleus, for oxidation of the hydrocarbon affords benzoic acid in high yield. In the case of β-methylnaphthalene, the reactive α-positions in the nucleus appear more susceptible than the methyl group, for oxidation with chromic acid under mild conditions affords chiefly 2-methyl-1,4-naphthoquinone. Naphthalene itself has been converted by oxidation with chromic acid in acetic acid at a moderate temperature into α-naphthoquinone in 16% yield; the higher yield obtained with the β-methyl

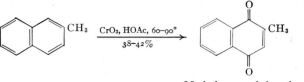

2-Methyl-1,4-naphthoquinone

derivative can be attributed to the activating influence of the alkyl substituent on the adjacent α-position of the nucleus.

SUMMARY

Naphthalene, most abundant constituent of coal tar; intermediate for dyes; formerly used for moth balls; tetralin and decalin used as fuels, solvents.

Positions (1-8): α-, β-, peri- (1,8-), amphi- (2,6-). Proof of presence of two o-fused rings: nitronaphthalene ——→ nitrophthalic acid; naphthylamine ——→ phthalic acid. Structures of substitution products established by oxidations and interconversions.

Bond structure. Fries rule of stability of benzenoid vs. quinonoid rings. Evidence for the symmetrical structure. (a) β-Naphthol couples at C₁ if available, does not couple at C₃ even if C₁ is blocked; comparison with aliphatic enols indicates that C₁ is enolic, C₃ nonenolic. (b) 2,7-Dihydroxynaphthalene does not couple if C₁ and C₈ are blocked. (c) Normal rearrangement of β-naphthol allyl ether is blocked by alkyl group at C₁ (no rearrangement to C₃, even at a high temperature). (d) Chlorination of 1-chloro-2-naphthol gives a 1,1-dichloro-2-ketone.

Conclusion: bond fixation (α,β-double bond, β,β-single bond) at site of substitution. X-ray evidence shows 1,2 bond to be shorter than 2,3 bond. Charge separation in one ring permits resonance stabilization between alternate Kekulé structures of second ring. Contribution of excited o-quinonoid structure negligible because of high energy content.

Substitution Reactions

Normal-type substitutions (nitration, halogenation, oxidation) give α-substituted naphthalenes. Analogies: α-bromination of alkylbenzenes (activation by phenyl group); 1,4-reduction of diphenylbutadiene and of naphthalene.

Abnormal-type substitutions give β-products at high temperatures or as result of hindrance factors. Naphthalene-α-sulfonic acid produced at 0-60°; β-acid at 165°. Friedel-Crafts reaction: CH_3COCl in CS_2 ——→ α-acetonaphthalene (3 parts) + β-acetonaphthalene (1 part); CH_3COCl in $C_6H_5NO_2$ (complex) ——→ 90% β-acetonaphthalene; succinic anhydride in $C_6H_5NO_2$ ——→ about equal parts of α- and β-succinoyl derivatives; phthalic anhydride or C_6H_5COCl (Perrier procedure) ——→ chiefly α-derivatives.

Monosubstituted Naphthalenes

By direct substitution: α-NO₂, α-Br, α-SO₃H (0-60°); β-SO₃H (165°), β-COCH₃ (Friedel-Crafts in $C_6H_5NO_2$). By transformations: α-NO₂ ——→ α-NH₂ ——→ α-OH; α-Br ——→ α-MgBr ——→ α-CO₂H; α-Cl ——→ α-CN ——→ α-CO₂H; β-COCH₃ ——→ β-CO₂H; β-SO₃H ——→ β-OH; β-OH ——→ β-NH₂ [Bucherer reaction; use of $(NH_4)_2SO_3$ under pressure; intermediate addition product; reversibility]; β-NH₂ ——→ β-Br; β-NH₂ ——→ β-NO₂ (10%).

Substitutions of Naphthalene Derivatives

Monosubstitution of α-naphthol ——→ 4-derivative; dinitration (through disulfonate) ——→ 2,4-dinitro-1-naphthol (Martius Yellow). α-Methylnaphthalene ——→ 4-NO₂, 4-SO₃H, 4-COR derivatives. 1-Nitronaphthalene ——→ 1,5- and 1,8-dinitronaphthalene.

amphi-Substitution. β-Methylnaphthalene is nitrated and brominated at C₁ but, because of hindrance, is sulfonated at C₆ (amphi); Friedel-Crafts succinoylation in $C_6H_5NO_2$ also gives 6-acyl derivatives.

Relative Reactivity of Naphthalene and Benzene

Naphthalene > benzene; (a) competition of naphthalene with benzene in large excess for Friedel-Crafts condensation with phthalic anhydride; (b) reduction of naphthalene with Na + $C_5H_{11}OH$ stops at the tetralin stage; (c) whereas toluene ⟶ benzoic acid, β-methylnaphthalene ⟶ 2-methyl-1,4-naphthoquinone.

PROBLEMS

1. Suggest methods for the preparation of each of the following compounds from an available monosubstitution product of naphthalene:
   (*a*) β-Benzoylnaphthalene
   (*b*) α-Naphthaldehyde
   (*c*) β-Iodonaphthalene
   (*d*) β-Isopropylnaphthalene
2. Indicate methods by which each of the following compounds can be prepared from β-naphthol:
   (*a*) 2,6-Dihydroxynaphthalene
   (*b*) 1-Amino-2-naphthol
   (*c*) 1-Nitroso-2-naphthol
   (*d*) 6-Ethyl-2-hydroxynaphthalene
   (*e*) 1-*n*-Propyl-2-naphthol
3. Give methods for the preparation of each of the following compounds from β-methylnaphthalene:
   (*a*) 1-Amino-2-methylnaphthalene
   (*b*) 2-Methylnaphthalene-6-carboxylic acid
   (*c*) 6-Methyl-2-naphthylamine
   (*d*) 2-Hydroxy-3-methyl-1,4-naphthoquinone
4. How could the following compounds be obtained starting with α-nitronaphthalene or its reduction product?
   (*a*) 1,5-Diaminonaphthalene
   (*b*) 1,3-Dibromonaphthalene
   (*c*) 2,4-Diamino-1-naphthol
5. Acenaphthene (24.10) on Friedel-Crafts reaction with succinic anhydride (succinoylation) in nitrobenzene solution gives a mixture of two acids, both of which on permanganate oxidation yield prehnitic acid (1,2,3,4-acid; this is a good preparative method). What are the structures of the two products?
6. Outline a synthesis of phenanthrene from naphthalene.

POLYNUCLEAR HYDROCARBONS

PHENANTHRENE

Phenanthrene is made up of three benzene rings fused at the *o*-positions in the angular arrangement, and the name is derived from the fact that the structure includes a diphenyl unit and is isomeric with that of anthracene. On the basis of the Fries rule (27.2), the bond structure I, which contains three normal Kekulé rings, would be expected to represent the most stable state; the ring systems AB and BC correspond to normal naphthalenoid units. Evidence of the same nature as that adduced for naphthalene indicates that a comparable condition of bond fixation exists. Thus the allyl ether of 2-phenanthrol (II) undergoes Claisen rearrangement to the 1-allyl-2-hydroxy compound III, but the allyl ether of III fails to undergo further rearrangement; the normal diazo coupling of 2-phenanthrol in the 1-position is blocked by an alkyl substituent at position 1.

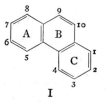

I

Bond fixation

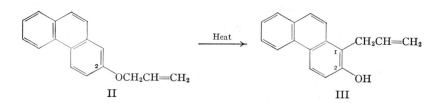

The positions 1, 2, 3, 4, and 9 are all different, and hence five monosubstitution products are possible. The number of possible disubstitution products is twenty-five. All the monomethylphenanthrenes and the phenanthrols are known.

The majority of substitution reactions proceed poorly with phenanthrene, for the reaction mixture usually contains not only several monosubstitution products but appreciable amounts of di derivatives and unchanged hydrocarbon. The one exception is bromination,

485

which affords 9-bromophenanthrene in good yield (18.6). This compound is a useful intermediate for preparation of the 9-nitrile and 9-carboxylic acid:

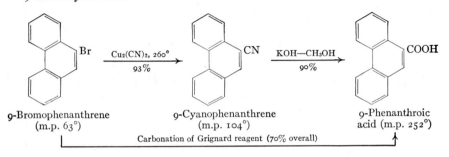

9-Bromophenanthrene
(m.p. 63°)

9-Cyanophenanthrene
(m.p. 104°)

9-Phenanthroic
acid (m.p. 252°)

Carbonation of Grignard reagent (70% overall)

In the absence of catalyst, bromine adds to the 9,10-double bond. Another useful addition illustrating the olefinic character of the 9,10-double bond is hydrogenation of phenanthrene to the 9,10-dihydride, accomplished in nearly quantitative yield by the use of copper—chromium oxide at a moderate temperature.

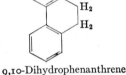

9,10-Dihydrophenanthrene
(m.p. 35°)

The course of sulfonation and of Friedel-Crafts reactions is influenced by hindrance at positions corresponding to α-positions in the naphthalene rings. The β-positions 2, 3, 6, and 7 are favored sites of attack, but α-derivatives have been isolated in small amounts even in low-temperature reactions. Results of sulfonations at two temperatures are indicated in Chart 1. The mixture resulting from sulfonation at 60° contains, in addition to the four monosulfonic acids indicated, the 2,6-, 2,7-, 2,8-, 3,6-, and 3,8-disulfonic acids.

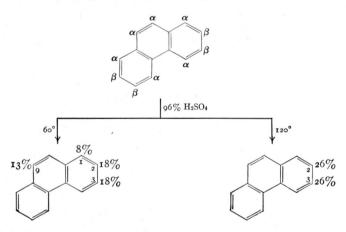

**CHART 1.
Monosulfonation
of Phenanthrene**

Oxidation of phenanthrene takes the normal course of attack at the reactive central position and affords the 9,10-quinone; the yield is much higher than that obtained in the oxidation of naphthalene. The orange o-quinone is readily purified by extraction from the reaction mixture as the colorless water-soluble bisulfite compound, which is subsequently decomposed by neutralization with soda of the sodium

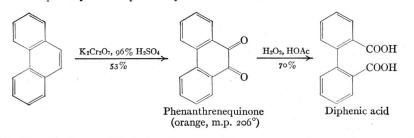

Phenanthrenequinone   Diphenic acid
(orange, m.p. 206°)

bisulfite in the equilibrium mixture. The quinone ring can be opened by further oxidation, preferably with hydrogen peroxide in acetic acid solution, with the production of diphenic acid. Alkylphenanthrenes having no substituents at 9 and 10 are converted into the corresponding alkyl-9,10-phenanthrenequinones on oxidation with chromic acid, as illustrated by the example of retene, a hydrocarbon of pine wood oil which on oxidation affords retenequinone.

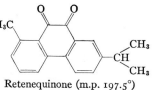

Retenequinone (m.p. 197.5°)

ANTHRACENE

The linear tricyclic hydrocarbon anthracene (Gr. *anthrax*, coal) is an important dye intermediate produced in quantity from coal tar. X-ray measurements indicate that all fourteen carbon atoms lie in the same plane. Since the hydrocarbon is easily converted into and obtained from anthraquinone, the numbering system conforms to that obviously applicable to the quinone. The middle or *meso* posi-

28.2

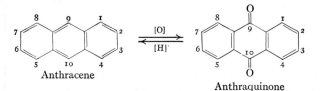

Anthracene   Anthraquinone

tions in the hydrocarbon thus acquire the numbers 9 and 10. Three mono- and fifteen disubstitution products are possible. No formulation of anthracene is possible in which all three rings have the normal bond arrangement of an isolated benzene ring. Structure I at least contains only one *o*-quinonoid ring, whereas the alternate structure II has two, and hence on the basis of the Fries rule, I would be the more stable. Chemical evidence indicates that the diquinonoid form II does not participate in the reactions of derivatives of the hydrocarbon. A differentiation can be made from the fact that in I the α- and β-positions in each terminal ring are connected by double bonds, whereas in II the connecting link is a single bond in one case.

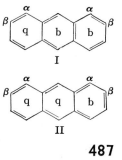

487

The course of bromination of 2,6-dihydroxyanthracene should provide an index of the preferred locations of the enolic *ortho* positions, and since the exclusive product of dibromination is the 1,5-isomer, the product can be formulated in accordance with formula I for the hydrocarbon, as shown in III. A more rigorous test is the behavior of 1,5-dimethyl-2,6-dihydroxyanthracene (IV) toward diazo coupling components; with the positions of normal substitution blocked by alkyl groups, no coupling occurs; evidently the bond structure IV, with double bonds located at all α,β-positions, is relatively immobile.

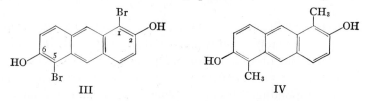

III   IV

In anthracene, or any symmetrically substituted derivatives, the structures Ia and Ib are equivalent and contribute equally to the resonance; change from one to the other requires merely a progression of the bonds in the central nucleus. In an unsymmetrical derivative such as 1,2-benzanthracene, however, the corresponding forms are not identical. Whereas form Va contains an *o*-benzoquinonoid ring,

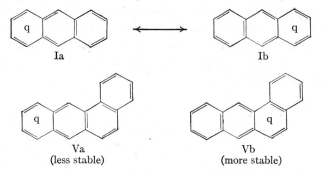

Ia   Ib

Va   Vb
(less stable)   (more stable)

the nonbenzenoid nucleus in Vb forms a β-naphthoquinonoid system with the attached 1,2-benz ring. Since β-naphthoquinone has a much lower reduction potential than *o*-benzoquinone, Vb must have the lower energy content and the greater stability.

Reactive 9,10-positions

Particularly high reactivity is manifested at the *meso* or 9,10-positions in anthracene, a property probably attributable in part to the quinonoid system of linkages terminating at these positions and in part to the fact that the 9- and 10-positions are adjacent to and activated by both terminal rings.

Oxidation to anthraquinone can be accomplished in substantially quantitative yield with either chromic acid in acetic acid or sodium dichromate and aqueous sulfuric acid, and the reaction proceeds more readily than oxidation of phenanthrene. Thus crude phenanthrene from coal tar can be freed from anthracene, which has the unusual effect of raising the melting point, by preferential oxidation of the latter to the quinone. Another indication that anthracene surpasses the angular isomer in energy content is that the heat of combustion is higher by 7.0 kg.-cal. The special reactivity is evident further in additions. Hydrogen and bromine add to give the 9,10-dihydride and the 9,10-dibromide, respectively, but a more distinctive property is the ability of anthracene to function as a diene component in the Diels-Alder reaction. When heated with the hydrocarbon in boiling xylene solution, maleic anhydride adds to the diene system of the central nucleus to give a crystalline product having a carbon bridge spanning the *meso* positions and forming a part of two new six-membered rings. The reaction is reversible and is favored by excess maleic anhydride.

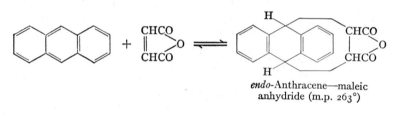

endo-Anthracene—maleic
anhydride (m.p. 263°)

ANTHRAQUINONES

Preparation and Synthesis. — Alkyl and acetoxyl derivatives of anthracene, like the parent hydrocarbon, are convertible into anthraquinones in high yield by direct oxidation. The success and high yield of the reactions can be attributed to both the special reactivity of the *meso* positions and the great stability of anthraquinone. The double bonds associated with the central ring are rendered inert by incorporation in the terminal benzene rings, and these rings are subject to the deactivating influence of the quinonoid carbonyl groups. The system thus is resistant to oxidizing agents not only under conditions suitable for effecting oxidation at the *meso* centers but under the drastic conditions often required for production of carboxylic acids. Anthraquinone-β-carboxylic acid is made by oxidation of the β-methyl compound with chromic acid in boiling acetic acid solution, extraction

28.3

Stability of the
quinone

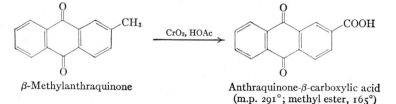

β-Methylanthraquinone

Anthraquinone-β-carboxylic acid
(m.p. 291°; methyl ester, 165°)

with dilute ammonia, and reoxidation of the residue; there is no attack of the nucleus.

Anthraquinones of wide variety can be made in high yield by the phthalic anhydride synthesis. Phthalic anhydride is condensed with benzene in the presence of aluminum chloride to *o*-benzoylbenzoic acid (19.8), and the keto acid is heated with concentrated sulfuric acid on the steam bath, when cyclization occurs with formation of anthraquinone. Water is eliminated between the carboxyl group

Phthalic anhydride synthesis

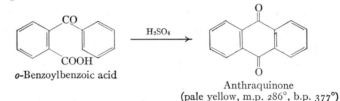

O-Benzoylbenzoic acid

Anthraquinone
(pale yellow, m.p. 286°, b.p. 377°)

and the nuclear position of the second aryl ring *ortho* to the carbonyl group. The process rivals that of the oxidation of coal-tar anthracene as a source of the large supplies of anthraquinone required as a dye intermediate. The keto acids resulting from the Friedel-Crafts condensation of phthalic anhydride with toluene, *p*-xylene, and naphthalene afford the following anthraquinones:

β-Methylanthraquinone
(m.p. 173°) 1,4-Dimethylanthraquinone
(m.p. 119°) 1,2-Benzanthraquinone
(m.p. 168°)

28.4   The ready cyclization of *o*-benzoylbenzoic acid is remarkable because it involves intramolecular acylation *ortho* to a ketonic function;

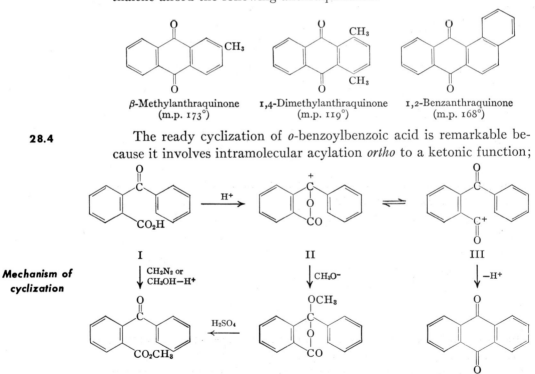

I

II

III

Mechanism of cyclization

IV (m.p. 52°)   V (m.p. 82°)   VI

ordinarily ketones are not amenable to Friedel-Crafts acylation. Newman (1942) suggested that the reaction proceeds through the carbonium ions II and III, and showed that if a cold solution of *o*-benzoylbenzoic acid in 98% sulfuric acid is poured into methanol the chief product is the pseudo ester V; this is rearranged by sulfuric acid into the lower-melting normal ester IV.

Substitution Reactions. — The resistance of anthraquinone to oxidation is paralleled by its behavior in substitutions. Halogenation is achieved with such difficulty as to be impracticable. Concentrated sulfuric acid has little action except at excessive temperatures, and oleum is required for efficient sulfonation. Anthraquinone is not subject to Friedel-Crafts acylation or alkylation under any known conditions. The resistance to substitution in a benzenoid ring can be ascribed to the deactivating influence of the two *m*-directing carbonyl groups; the α-position is *ortho* to and protected by one of these groups, and the β-position is *para* to the other. Nitration, accomplished with

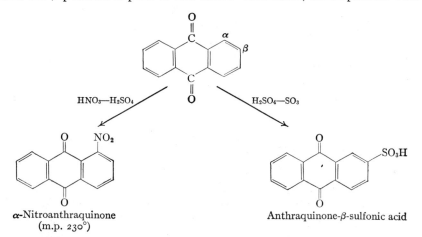

α-Nitroanthraquinone
(m.p. 230°)

Anthraquinone-β-sulfonic acid

mixed acid under forcing conditions, affords chiefly the α-nitro derivative as the initial product, but the group first introduced has little influence on the reactivity of the other terminal ring and hence some α-substitution in this ring is inevitable, with the result that the α-nitro compound is contaminated with appreciable amounts of the 1,5- and 1,8-dinitro derivatives.

Sulfonation with fuming sulfuric acid results in attack of the less hindered β-position. Since a second sulfonic acid group enters the other terminal ring nearly as easily as the first, the most satisfactory results are obtained by conducting the reaction under such conditions that about half of the anthraquinone is sulfonated and the rest left in a recoverable condition. A remarkable alteration in the direction of substitution brought about by addition of a trace of a mercury salt to the sulfonation mixture was discovered independently by R. E. Schmidt in Germany and by Iljinsky in Russia (1903–04); in the presence of this catalyst the sulfonic acid group enters the α-position almost exclusively. The α-sulfonic acid, isolated as the potassium salt, can be prepared in good yield (based on material utilized) by stirring an intimate mixture of anthraquinone with 2% of mercuric sulfate into 20% oleum at 135° and adding 60% oleum to the solution.

28.6   **Replacement Reactions.** — β-Aminoanthraquinone is made by a reaction specific to the anthraquinone series that consists in replacement of the β-sulfonic acid group by an amino group. The sulfonate group is rendered labile to nucleophilic displacement by the quinonoid carbonyl group in the *para* position, just as a halogen or nitro sub-

Nucleophilic
displacement

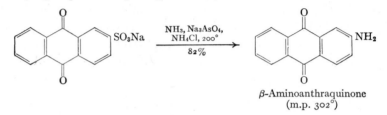

NH₃, Na₃AsO₄,
NH₄Cl, 200°
$\xrightarrow{\hspace{2cm}}$
82%

β-Aminoanthraquinone
(m.p. 302°)

stituent in the benzene ring is activated by *ortho* or *para* unsaturated groups. An even better yield of β-aminoanthraquinone is obtained by amination of β-chloroanthraquinone, prepared from phthalic anhydride and chlorobenzene.

28.7   **Reduction Products.** — When a suspension of anthraquinone in aqueous alkali is treated with a reducing agent of suitable potential, notably sodium hydrosulfite or zinc dust, the material dissolves to give a rich blood-red solution of the sodium salt of anthrahydroquinone. On shaking with air the red color is discharged and anthraquinone is reprecipitated. The conversion of a phenolic alkali-soluble hydroquinone into a water-insoluble quinone by air oxidation is the basis of vat dyeing, and hence the red liquor resulting on alkaline reduction of anthraquinone is known as a vat. The color is associated with salt

Alkaline reduction
to vat

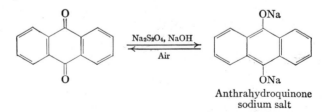

Na₂S₂O₄, NaOH
$\underset{\text{Air}}{\rightleftarrows}$

Anthrahydroquinone
sodium salt

formation, for anthrahydroquinone itself, isolated with difficulty because of its extreme sensitivity to air, is yellow. All but very few anthraquinones give characteristic red vats and are hence distinguishable from quinones of other series, for example phenanthrenequinones, which give yellow vats. Purification is often accomplished by vatting a crude anthraquinone with excess hydrosulfite and alkali, filtering the red solution to remove hydrocarbon or other inert material, and blowing air through the solution. A reagent useful as an absorbent for oxygen in gas analysis or as a wash liquor for removing traces of oxygen from nitrogen or hydrogen is made by dissolving sodium hydrosulfite in alkali and adding a small amount of sodium anthraquinone-β-sulfonate. The water-soluble quinone is reduced to a blood-red vat having strong affinity for oxygen (Fieser's solution, 1924).

If the red vat from anthraquinone is boiled in the presence of excess hydrosulfite or zinc dust, the color fades to yellow as the result of

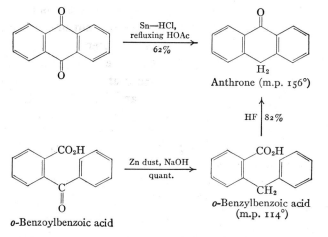

Anthrone (m.p. 156°)

o-Benzoylbenzoic acid

o-Benzylbenzoic acid (m.p. 114°)

CHART 2.
Preparation of
Anthrone

further reduction involving elimination of one oxygen atom and formation of anthrone. Reduction to this stage is accomplished more satisfactorily by the action of tin and hydrochloric acid on anthraquinone, as indicated in Chart 2, which also shows an efficient synthesis of anthrone from the product of the Friedel-Crafts reaction of phthalic anhydride and benzene. Anthrone is the keto form of a tautomeric pair of which the enol form is anthranol:

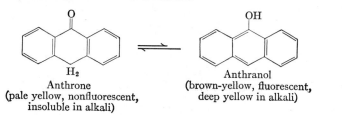

Anthrone
(pale yellow, nonfluorescent,
insoluble in alkali)

Anthranol
(brown-yellow, fluorescent,
deep yellow in alkali)

Tautomerism

As noted above, the red vat from anthraquinone fades to yellow on further reduction in alkaline solution as result of conversion to the sodium salt of anthranol. Elimination of a *meso* hydroxyl group on

28.8

reduction with zinc dust or hydrosulfite and alkali or ammonia is a special reaction evidently dependent on the activated character of the *meso* position. The second *meso* hydroxyl group can be eliminated

Reduction to the hydrocarbon

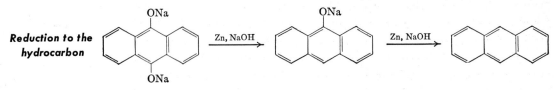

as well, merely by continued reaction under the same conditions. Thus if anthraquinone or a substitution product is submitted to exhaustive reduction with zinc dust and sodium or ammonium hydroxide, the final reaction product is anthracene or a corresponding derivative. Since hydroxyl groups in the terminal benzene rings are not attacked, hydroxyanthraquinones are convertible by this method into hydroxyanthracenes. The α- and β-sulfonic acid derivatives of anthraquinone can be reduced with zinc dust and ammonia to the anthracene-α- and -β- sulfonates, which on fusion with alkali afford α- and β-anthrol. The anthramines are similarly obtainable by reduction of the aminoanthraquinones. Anthraquinone itself is reduced preferably in two stages; anthrone is prepared by the method described above and is refluxed with copper sulfate activated zinc dust, sodium hydroxide solution, and toluene. The hydrocarbon is obtained in a pure and spectacularly fluorescent form in 93% yield.

VAT DYES

28.9   Indigo, a blue dye known since early antiquity and long prized for its brilliant color and fastness, is obtained from species of the Indian plant *Indigofera*. However the dye does not occur as such in the indigo plant but is derived from the colorless glucoside indican.

Indigo from a natural glycoside

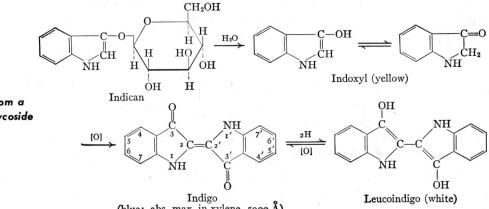

On extraction of the crushed plant with water the glucoside is hydrolyzed by enzymes to glucose and indoxyl, and the latter is oxidized by air to the blue dye. If the mixture is made alkaline, indigo is reduced by fermentation of the glucose liberated to colorless leucoindigo which, being enolic, is soluble in the alkaline solution. When cotton fiber is immersed in the alkaline solution of the reduced dye, or vat, leucoindigo is adsorbed on the fiber by hydrogen bonding and is not removed when the fiber is washed free of excess reducing agent. On exposure of the fiber to air, leucoindigo is oxidized to indigo and a very stable dyeing is obtained. The structure of indigo was established by Baeyer in 1883 as the result of researches extending over a period of eighteen years. A synthesis developed by Heumann[1] in 1890 and consisting in fusion of phenylglycine with alkali at 300° was vastly improved (1901) by the finding that the cyclization can be

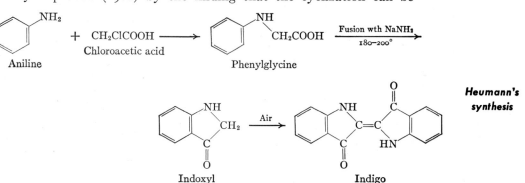

Aniline   + CH₂ClCOOH → Phenylglycine   Fusion with NaNH₂ 180–200°

$$\text{Aniline} + CH_2ClCOOH \longrightarrow \text{Phenylglycine} \xrightarrow[180-200°]{\text{Fusion wth NaNH}_2}$$

Chloroacetic acid

Indoxyl → (Air) → Indigo

*Heumann's
synthesis*

effected by the action of sodamide at a lower temperature, with considerable improvement in yield. Synthetic indigo, readily available and of standard quality, soon displaced the natural dye. The early process of vatting indigo with alkaline glucose gave way to reduction with alkaline sodium hydrosulfite.

In subsequent years a number of compounds of indigoid structure were synthesized and some proved satisfactory for introduction as new vat dyes. Actually, the indigo molecule contains an enedione system identical with that present in a quinone, and the system indigo-leucoindigo is analogous to a quinone-hydroquinone oxidation-reduction system. Hence any water-insoluble quinone or quinonoid compound of high tinctorial quality and stability is a potential vat dye, since it can be reduced in an alkaline medium to the alkali-soluble hydroquinone or leuco form and regenerated on the fiber by air oxidation. However, the quinonelike character of indigo was not apparent to early dye chemists, and the

28.10

*Indigo analogous
to a quinone*

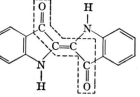

[1] Karl Heumann, 1850–93; b. Darmstadt, Germany; Ph.D. Heidelberg; Zurich ETH; *Ber.*, **27**, 2653 (1894)

first trial of a nonindigoid quinonoid compound as a vat dye was the result of an accidental discovery made in 1901 by René Bohn[2] of the Badische Anilin- und Soda-Fabrik. Bohn, who had done his research for the doctorate under Heumann, in seeking to synthesize an anthraquinone derivative of indigo, condensed β-aminoanthraquinone with chloroacetic acid and attempted to close the ring by treatment with caustic alkali. Anthraquinone is substituted only with difficulty and at high temperatures, but under conditions sufficiently drastic to promote reaction Bohn obtained a blue compound having properties expected of a vat dye, and he consequently named it indanthrene (<u>ind</u>igo of <u>anthracene</u>). The

Indanthrene (in U.S., "indanthrone")

analytical results, however, did not correspond to the expected formula, and Bohn soon found that the dye is obtained by alkali fusion of β-aminoanthraquinone itself. Yields of 48–50% are obtainable by fusion with potassium hydroxide and potassium nitrate (oxidizing agent) at temperatures of 150–200°. Bohn (1903) also obtained the blue dye by heating 1-amino-2-bromoanthraquinone in nitrobenzene solution (190°) with condensing agents, and recognized the substance as having a condensed-ring system. The synthesis from the bromoamine established the structure. Indanthrene, which

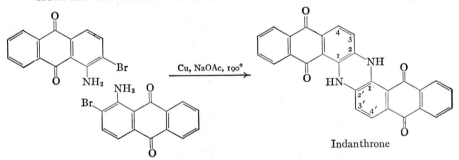

Indanthrone

proved to be a vat dye of superior fastness, is thus an anthraquinone derivative insoluble in water and applicable as a vat dye by conversion to the alkali-soluble hydroquinone. Many other anthraquinonoid vat dyes of superior quality are now available.

SUMMARY

Phenanthrene

Most stable bond structure that with three benzenoid rings. Evidence of bond fixation from diazo coupling and Claisen rearrangement reaction. Method of numbering.

Reactions. 9-Bromophenanthrene available in good yield; conversion through the nitrile into 9-phenanthroic acid. Phenanthrene easily hydrogenated to 9,10-dihydride. Substitutions other than bromination give mixtures; sulfonation attacks β-positions to give chiefly 2- and 3-mono and five di derivatives. Ready oxidation to 9,10-phenanthrenequinone (soluble bisulfite-addition compound); further oxidation with H_2O_2 gives diphenic acid.

[2] René Bohn; 1862–1922; b. Dornach/Mühlhausen, Alsace; Ph.D. Zurich (Heumann); BASF Ludwigshafen

Anthracene

Numbering system corresponds to that of anthra-quinone; central positions designated *meso*.

Carbon atoms are coplanar. Most stable bond structure contains one quinonoid ring. Evidence of bond fixation: 1,5-dimethyl-2,6-dihydroxyanthra-cene does not couple. Resonance in central ring. In 1,2-benzanthracene the structure with a 1,2-naphthoquinonoid system is more stable than that with an *o*-benzoquinonoid system.

High reactivity at *meso* positions attributed to quinonoid system and to activation by flanking rings. Manifestation of special reactivity: ease of oxidation to anthraquinone (method of purifying phenanthrene); heat of combustion 7 kg.-cal. greater than that of phenanthrene; formation of 9,10-dibromide and 9,10-dihydride; Diels-Alder addition of maleic anhydride.

Anthraquinones

High yield in oxidation of anthracene and purifica-tion of product with H_2SO_4 attributable to stability of anthraquinone: quinone double bonds are incorporated in benzenoid rings and these are deactivated by the two carbonyl substituents (*m*-directors). Anthraquinone-β-carboxylic acid available by drastic oxidation of β-methyl compound.

Phthalic anhydride synthesis through *o*-benzoyl-benzoic acid and cyclization with H_2SO_4. Syntheses from toluene, *p*-xylene, naphthalene. Ring closure involves intramolecular acylation *ortho* to a keto group. Newman's postulate of intermediate acyl carbonium ion; evidence from conversion of *o*-benzoylbenzoic acid into a pseudo ester.

Substitutions occur only with difficulty owing to deactivation by carbonyl groups. Nitration $\longrightarrow$ chiefly α-NO_2. Sulfonation (strong oleum at 135°) $\longrightarrow$ β-SO_3H ($+$ β,β'-disulfonates). Sulfo-nation in presence of $HgSO_4$ $\longrightarrow$ α-SO_3H.

Replacements. β-Sulfonic acid $\longrightarrow$ β-amino-anthraquinone (labilization of —SO_3H by *p*-keto group). β-Chloroanthraquinone $\longrightarrow$ β-amino-anthraquinone.

Reduction. Hydrosulfite $+$ alkali $\longrightarrow$ red solution of anthrahydroquinone sodium salt (vat). Purification by vatting and air oxidation. Oxygen absorbent utilizing sodium anthraquinone-β-sulfonate. Further reduction with Sn–HCl to anthrone (elimination of activated *meso* hydroxyl); synthesis from *o*-benzoylbenzoic acid through *o*-benzylbenzoic acid and ring closure. Anthrone $\rightleftharpoons$ anthranol. Reduction of anthraquinone with zinc and ammonia to anthracene. Applicable to anthraquinones carrying R, OH, NH_2 groups.

Vat Dyes

Glycoside indican of indigo plant hydrolyzed to indoxyl, which on air oxidation gives indigo. Vatting of indigo and air oxidation on the fiber (cellulosic). Heumann's synthesis.

Bohn's discovery of indanthrene in an attempt to make an indigo of anthraquinone.

PROBLEMS

1. Formulate the synthesis of:
   (a) 9-Methylphenanthrene from phenanthrene
   (b) 4-Methylphenanthrene from γ-(2-naphthyl)-butyric acid

2. Sulfonation of retene (28.1) gives two mono-sulfonic acids that on alkali fusion afford two isomeric retenols, m.p. 162° and 202°. The structure of the higher-melting isomer was inferred from the observation that it fails to couple with diazonium salts. What is the structure?

3. The structure of one of the disulfonic acids resulting from sulfonation of phenanthrene was established by alkali fusion, methylation of the dihydroxyphenanthrene, oxidation to a di-methoxy-9,10-phenanthrenequinone, and oxida-tion of the quinone with hydrogen peroxide to a dibasic acid that proved identical with an acid synthesized by the action of cuprous ammonium hydroxide on the diazonium salt derived from 4-methoxy-2-aminobenzoic acid.

   (a) What is the structure of the disulfonic acid?

(b) The 4-methoxy-2-aminobenzoic acid was prepared by a five-step synthesis starting with the nitration of *p*-toluidine in sulfuric acid solution; formulate the process.

4. Formulate a synthesis of β-aminoanthraquinone starting with phthalic anhydride and chlorobenzene.

5. Formulate a synthesis of 3-methyl-1,2-benzanthracene starting with α-methylnaphthalene.
6. How can 1-anthranol be prepared starting with anthraquinone?
7. Suggest a synthesis of 9-methylanthracene (see Chart 2).

READING REFERENCES

J. Houben, *Das Anthracen und die Anthrachinone*, G. Thieme, Leipzig (1929)

E. de B. Barnett, *Anthracene and Anthraquinone*, Van Nostrand, New York (1921)

A. E. Everest, *The Higher Coal-Tar Hydrocarbons*, Longmans, Green, New York (1927)

L. F. Fieser, "The Elbs Reaction," in R. Adams, *Organic Reactions*, I, 129–154, Wiley, New York (1942)

G. M. Badger, "The Carcinogenic Hydrocarbons: Chemical Constitution and Carcinogenic Activity," *British Journal of Cancer*, **2**, 309 (1948)

W. Baker, "Non-Benzenoid Aromatic Hydrocarbons," *J. Chem. Soc.*, 258 (1945)

PART II

One purpose of this part of the book is to illustrate some of the ways in which the reactions and principles of organic chemistry have been employed in specific research projects. Each section is independent and should be understandable after study of the chapter indicated. The researches were selected on the basis of interest and appropriateness as illustrative examples, and not for their estimated relative importance. They represent investigations in a variety of fields, and some of them afford an introduction to types of compounds not discussed in Part I. The majority include at least some work of recent date, but a few are historical. One records the extensive experimentation by which a now commonplace relationship was established.

Where a large team of investigators is involved and citation of all names is not feasible, the name of either a principal contributor or of the laboratory is given to show where the work was done and for guidance to the literature. Papers reporting a given research can be found from the date, name of a participant, and country. Those by American investigators are for the most part published in *J. Am. Chem. Soc.* or *J. Org. Chem.* and those by British chemists in *J. Chem. Soc.* Swiss chemists publish in *Helvetica Chimica Acta* in either German (Zurich, Basel) or French (Geneva), German papers appear in either *Berichte der Deutschen Chemischen Gesellschaft* (*Ber.*) or in *Annalen der Chemie* (*Ann.*), and Austrian papers in *Monatshefte für Chemie*. Papers from Scandinavian countries are published in English in *Acta Chemica Scandinavia;* French papers appear in *Bulletin de la Société Chimique de France* or *Annales de Chimie*. Chemists of Belgium and the Netherlands publish in *Recueil des Travaux Chimique des Pays-Bas*, usually in English, sometimes in French. Local journals are operative in India (in English), Japan (some papers in English), and Italy.

II. 1

COSMENE (*After Chapter 7*)

On spectroscopic examination of the essential oils of plants belonging to the family Compositae cultivated in Norway, Jörgine S. Sörensen and Nils A. Sörensen[1] (1954) noted the presence of a very volatile substance characterized by a four-banded ultraviolet absorption spectrum, by which the substance is easily recognized. The intensity of absorption provides a means of determining the relative amounts present in different preparations. Nine species were found to contain the chromophoric substance, and of these *Cosmos bipinnatus* was selected as the best source for isolation; the content of essential oil is about 0.5%. The volatility and light absorption suggested that the substance is a hydrocarbon polyene, and it was named cosmene. Cosmene is "utterly unstable" in air and in light,

and rapidly polymerizes to a white, insoluble solid. Hence steam distillation of the plant for separation of the essential oil was done in a slow stream of pure nitrogen with exclusion of light. Purification of cosmene, followed throughout by spectrographic analysis, was accomplished by vacuum distillation and by crystallization from petroleum ether at $-70°$.

The constants found for pure cosmene are: m.p. $-2°$ to $-1°$, b.p. $30°/0.3$ mm., n_D^{20} (refractive index at $20°$) 1.5850. The hydrocarbon is altered so rapidly on contact with air that elementary analyses were only in approximate accord with the formula $C_{10}H_{14}$, inferred intuitively from the low boiling point and from ultraviolet and infrared spectrographic characterization. The Norwegian investigators noted particularly that the four-banded

[1] Nils Andreas Sörensen, b. 1909 Oslo; Dr. Techn. Norway Inst. Techn. (C. N. Rüber); postdoctoral work KWI Heidelberg (Kuhn); Norway Inst. Techn., Trondheim

spectrum of cosmene resembles closely the spectrum reported for octatetraene-1,3,5,7:

	λ max, mμ			
Cosmene	272	278	296	309.7
CH₂=CH(CH=CH)₂CH=CH₂	268	283	290.5	304

$$\text{Cosmene} \quad 272 \quad 278 \quad 296 \quad 309.7$$
$$CH_2{=}CH(CH{=}CH)_2CH{=}CH_2 \quad 268 \quad 283 \quad 290.5 \quad 304$$

A synthetic route to this tetraene had been discovered by G. F. Woods[2] (1946–49) in exploring the chemistry of dihydropyran (II), a reagent useful for protection of alcoholic hydroxyl functions (7.32), for which a practical method of preparation from I had been developed (R. Paul, 1933). Woods

lenic, or benzenoid centers. The tetraene (m.p. 50°) was analyzed without difficulty, but a sample left to dry in a Büchner funnel decomposed with near-explosive force.

The four-banded spectrum of cosmene ($C_{10}H_{14}$) matches that of octatetraene-1,3,5,7 (C_8H_{10}) except for a general displacement of the bands to longer wave length. Sörensen and Sörensen attributed the bathochromic displacement to the presence in cosmene of two methyl groups, since the infrared spectrum shows a strong band at 1372 cm.$^{-1}$ characteristic of the methyl group, which is lacking in

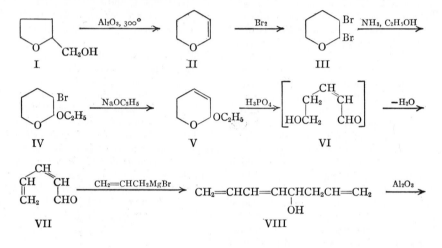

investigated the dibromide III, and found that one bromine atom is more reactive than the other and can be replaced by an ethoxyl group to give IV. The latter on dehydrohalogenation affords V, which on hydrolysis with phosphoric acid gives a transient product VI, which suffers dehydration and affords the doubly unsaturated aldehyde VII. Condensation of this dienal with allylmagnesium bromide gave the carbinol VIII, and this on dehydration gave octatetraene-1,3,5,7 (IX). That no rearrangement occurs in the formation of the triply unsaturated alcohol VIII was established by saturation of the three double bonds by hydrogenation, and oxidation to a known ketone, identified as the semicarbazone. The structure inferred for the tetraene IX was confirmed by hydrogenation to *n*-octane and by observation that the infrared spectrum establishes the absence of allenic, acety-

the spectrum of octatetraene-1,3,5,7, and shows no band at 770 cm.$^{-1}$ characteristic of an ethyl group. They suggested the isoprenoid formula X, since

$$CH_2{=}\underset{\underset{X}{}}{\overset{\overset{CH_3}{|}}{C}}{-}CH{=}CH{-}CH{=}\overset{\overset{CH_3}{|}}{C}{-}CH{=}CH_2$$

isoprenoids (4.32) are common constituents of essential oils.

In work which at the time was unpublished, Whiting[3] had developed the following novel reduction reaction:

$$\underset{\underset{OH}{|}}{C_6H_5CH}C{\equiv}C\underset{\underset{OH}{|}}{CHC_6H_5} \xrightarrow{\text{LiAlH}_4}$$

$$C_6H_5CH{=}CHCH{=}CHC_6H_5$$

[2] G. Forrest Woods, b. 1913 Chicago; Ph.D. Harvard (Kohler, Bartlett); Univ. Maryland
[3] Mark C. Whiting, b. 1925 Jarrow, England; Ph.D. London (E. R. H. Jones); postdoctoral work Harvard (Woodward); Manchester, Oxford

Since the reaction seemed ideal for the purpose, he undertook the synthesis of the polyene of the structure proposed for cosmene. The starting material, 3-methylpentene-1-yne-4-ol-3 (XIII) was prepared by a procedure of Oroshnik [4] involving addition of methyl vinyl ketone (XI, commercially available) to a stirred suspension of lithium acetylide in liquid ammonia; the addition product XII separates as a gummy mass and is left as a residue when the mixture stands at room temperature until the ammonia has evaporated. Acidification gives the carbinol XIII, which Whiting converted into the dimagnesio halide derivative XIV by reaction with two moles of Grignard reagent. The solvent ether was displaced by benzene until the boiling point of the distillate had reached 70°, and the mixture was cooled during addition of a benzene solution of α-methacraldehyde (XV). At the end of the reaction ammonium chloride solution was added to decompose the dimagnesio halide complex (a mineral acid would be liable to effect rearrangement) and the diol XVI was recovered (b.p. 77°/10⁻³ mm.). The last step, reduction of the diol with lithium aluminum hydride, gave 2,6-dimethyloctatetraene-1,3,5,7, identical with cosmene (X).

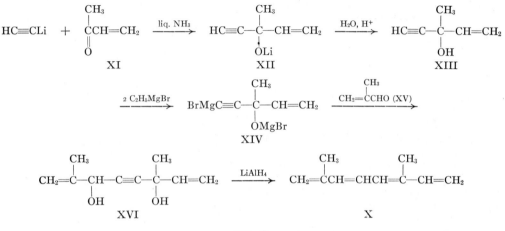

II. 2

CUMULENES (*After Chapter 8*)

Substances containing unsaturation of the type $R_2C=(C=C)_n=CR_2$ are known as cumulenes; and those of the formula $R_2C=C=CR_2$ are allenes. The ready isomerization of allene itself to methylacetylene has been noted:

$$CH_2C=CH_2 \longrightarrow CH_3C\equiv CH \quad (5.2).$$

The reverse isomerization was postulated by Favorsky [1] (1888) to explain the rearrangement of 1-alkynes to 2-alkynes observed to occur at a high temperature in an alkaline medium (1). An electron-attracting group on the carbon adjacent to the triple bond greatly facilitates acetylene–allene isomerization, as shown by the conversion of propargyl bromide (2) into bromoallene under catalysis by cuprous salts (T. L. Jacobs,[2] 1953). The reaction made available for study halides that had been difficultly accessible. Rate constants for the reaction of RBr with NaI in acetone at 25° show that bromoallene is comparable to vinyl halides in lack of reactivity. Propargyl bromide surpasses allyl

1. $RCH_2C\equiv CH \xrightarrow{\text{KOH, } 170°}$

$[RCH=C=CH_2] \longrightarrow RC\equiv CCH_3$

2. $CH\equiv CCH_2Br \xrightarrow{Cu_2Br_2,\ 70°} CH_2=C=CHBr$

Halide	K(mole⁻¹, hr.⁻¹)
$CH_2=C=CHBr$	0.0112
$CH_3CH=CHBr$	0.0005
$CH_2=CHBr$	0.014
$CH\equiv CCH_2Br$	612
$CH_2=CHCH_2Br$	438

[4] William Oroshnik, b. 1914 New York; Ph.D. Polytechn. Inst. Brooklyn (Spoerri); Ortho Pharmaceut. Corp.
[1] Alexei J. Favorsky, b. 1860 Russia; Ph.D. St. Petersburg; Leningrad
[2] Thomas L. Jacobs, b. 1908 Forest City, Iowa; Ph.D. Cornell (J. R. Johnson); Harvard, U. Calif. Los Angeles

bromide in reactivity, and its ready isomerization to bromoallene (2) presumably involves a hybrid ion:

$$CH \equiv CCH_2Br \xrightarrow{-Br^-} CH \equiv C\overset{+}{C}H_2 \longleftrightarrow$$

$$\overset{+}{C}H = C = CH_2 \xrightarrow{Br^-} BrCH = C = CH_2$$

The electron-attracting carboxyl group also promotes isomerization, and here no migration of a large atom or group is involved. In a study of β,γ-acetylenic acids such as the butynoic acid I, Whiting (1954) found that the substance is isomerized to allenecarboxylic acid (II) in 92% yield

ethylene glycol (W. M. Schubert, *et al.*, Univ. Wash-

$$BrCH_2C \equiv CCH_2Br \xrightarrow[85\%]{Zn} CH_2 = C = C = CH_2$$
$$\text{Butatriene}$$

ington). The most striking property is the tendency to polymerize, even at 0°.

Kuhn, *et al.*, prepared a series of diphenylcumulenes of the type $(C_6H_5)_2C = (C = C)_n = C(C_6H_5)_2$ (1938–54), mainly to study the ultraviolet absorption characteristics of cumulated systems in comparison with those of conjugated polyene systems. However, the terminal aromatic rings in conjugation with the first of the cumulated double bonds

$$CH \equiv CCH_2CO_2H \xrightarrow{K_2CO_3} CH_2 = C = CHCO_2H \rightleftharpoons CH_3C \equiv CCO_2H$$
$$\qquad\qquad I \qquad\qquad\qquad\qquad\qquad II \qquad\qquad\qquad\qquad III$$

$$K_2CO_3 \text{ (as ester)} \Big| \qquad\qquad\qquad \Big| NaOC_2H_5 \text{ (as ester)}$$

$$\longrightarrow CH_3C = CHCO_2CH_3 \longleftarrow$$
$$\qquad\qquad |$$
$$\qquad\quad OC_2H_5$$
$$\qquad\qquad IV$$

on standing in potassium carbonate solution at 40° for three hours. At a temperature of 90° the allene II is isomerized to tetrolic acid (III) in 60% yield. That the allenic system is more susceptible than the acetylenic system to nucleophilic attack is shown by the fact that the ester of II adds ethanol to give IV under catalysis by potassium carbonate; formation of the same compound from the ester of the α,β-acetylenic acid III is accomplished only with a more basic catalyst. Further evidence is that the allenic acid II on reaction with a limited amount of lithium aluminum hydride is reduced to vinylacetic acid, $CH_2 = CHCH_2CO_2H$, whereas tetrolic acid (III) is reduced to the acetylenic alcohol $CH_3C \equiv CCH_2OH$.

The examples cited in illustration of the rearrangement of allenes to acetylenes and of the reverse rearrangements all involve three-carbon systems in which formation of a conjugated diene is not possible. It is important to note that, when the structure permits, allenes isomerize to resonance-stabilized dienes rather than to acetylenes (Whiting):

$$CH_2 = C = CHCH_2CO_2H \xrightarrow{80\%}$$
$$\qquad\qquad\qquad CH_2 = CHCH = CHCO_2H$$

The simplest cumulene, butatriene, was not known until 1954, when it was prepared by reaction of 1,4-dibromobutyne-2 with zinc dust in di-

introduce complications. Bohlmann[3] (1954) synthesized a series better adapted to spectroscopic analysis in which all positions α to the unsaturated system are blocked by methyl groups, so that isom-

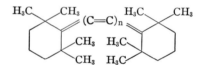

erization to acetylenes or conjugated dienes is not possible. The products are all solids, of m.p. above 100°. Selective light absorption occurs at much lower wave length than in resonance-stabilized conjugated polyenes. Whereas butadiene,

$$CH_2 = CHCH = CH_2,$$

has an absorption maximum (λ_{max}) at 217 mμ, and the conjugated triene system

$$-CH = CHCH = CHCH = CH-$$

absorbs selectively at 265 mμ, the aliphatic cumulene system $>C = C = C = C<$ shows only a subsidiary maximum; $>C = C = C = C = C<$ absorbs at 238 mμ, and

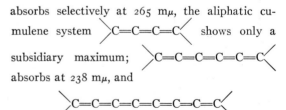

[3] Ferdinand Bohlmann, b. 1921 Oldenburg, Germany; Ph.D. Göttingen (K. Dimroth); postdoctoral work Marburg, Braunschweig (Inhoffen); Braunschweig

has an absorption band at 284 mμ. The hydrocarbons were all synthesized from 2,2,6,6-tetramethylcyclohexanone (V), prepared by methylating 2-methylcyclohexanone three times by alternate treatment with sodamide, to form the sodio enolate, and methyl iodide. The triene (VII) was obtained by condensation of two moles of V with acetylenedimagnesium bromide to give the diol VI, which on reaction with phosphorus diiodide gave the cumulene VII. Kuhn interpreted the synthesis of diphenylcumulenes by this reaction as involving replacement of the two alcoholic hydroxyls by iodine and spontaneous elimination of iodine. The unsaturated system of VII is so highly shielded by the eight methyl groups that it does not add bromine. The next member of the series, having the system XI, was obtained by the reactions formulated. Reaction of the diol VIII with phosphorus diiodide was not satisfactory, but on reaction with phosphorus tribromide the initial product IX underwent double propargyl rearrangement to give

X. The cumulene XI adds only one mole of bromine and the product is X.

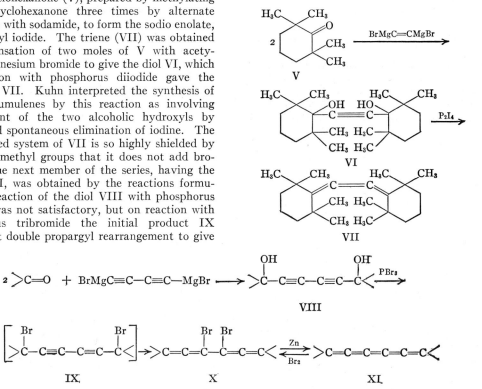

II. 3

URIC ACID (*After Chapter 11*)

Uric acid, a white crystalline solid very sparingly soluble in water and decomposing above 400° without melting, was discovered by Scheele in 1776 as a constituent of human urinary calculi (pebbles). It was later found to be the chief end product of nitrogenous metabolism in snakes and birds. Thus uric acid constitutes 90% of the excrement of the boa constrictor and is a major component of guano deposits. It occurs normally in human urine in only very small amounts, but excessive amounts are present in the urine of patients suffering from gout, a disease which is thus recognizable from the results of urine analysis.

Wöhler (1829) extended Scheele's study of the pyrolysis of uric acid and identified one of the products as urea, and Liebig (1834) established the empirical formula of uric acid: $C_5H_4O_3N_4$. These two chemists then undertook a joint investigation which resulted in the publication, in 1838, of a 102-page paper reporting characterization of no less than twelve new compounds obtained by various degradations of uric acid. The opening sentence of the paper reads: "There is in all organic chemistry no substance that claims the interest of the physiologist and the chemist to such a high degree as uric acid." Each of the new compounds was analyzed accurately and fully characterized, but interpretation of the results obtained by these two experimenters only became possible two decades later when Kekulé (1859) laid the foundation for structural organic chemistry. Very little further work on uric acid was done in this period. Then Adolf von Baeyer undertook research on the problem at the Berlin laboratory 1863–64 and, published four papers reporting results obtained in a reinvestigation and extension of the work of Liebig and Wöhler. Baeyer's work clarified empirical correlations between many known degradation products and some new ones, particularly a key compound in the series which he discovered and named barbituric acid in honor of a friend, Barbara. Although the work was published a few years after Kekulé's proposal of his structural theory, Baeyer interpreted the extensive results from his own experimentation as well as from that of Liebig and Wöhler only in empirical formulations. Baeyer

dation to urea. A synthesis of barbituric acid had been achieved (Grimaux, 1879), and two reasonable structural formulas for uric acid had been proposed. Fischer's work, extending over a period of 18 years and summarized in a review paper published in 1899, established a structure suggested in 1875 by Medicus and clarified the host of interrelated degradation products characterized by the earlier investigators.

The structure finally established is represented in the classical literature by formula (a), in which one ureide grouping occupies the 1,2,3-position in a

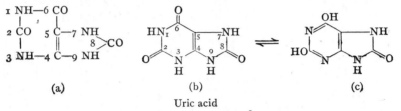

Uric acid
(pK$_a$ 5.7; solubility in water at 18°, 1:39,480)

turned his efforts to research on the structure of indigo, and work on uric acid again lapsed until, about two decades later, the problem attracted the interest of another gifted experimentalist, Emil Fischer. In the meantime, Strecker (1868) had reported that uric acid is hydrolyzed by treatment with hydrochloric acid at 160° and affords ammonia, carbon dioxide, and glycine, H$_2$NCH$_2$CO$_2$H. The observation, of particular interest because glycine had been identified as a product of the acid hydrolysis of gelatin, a protein, established the presence in uric acid of an N—C—C grouping, as well as the N—C—N grouping evident from degra-

six-membered ring and a second the 7,8,9-position in a five-membered ring. The equivalent triketo formula (b) provides a convenient expression of the possibility, considered by Fischer, of tautomerism to the dienolic (phenolic) form (c). Formula (b) agrees better with spectrographic data, and it affords a better insight into the degradations. The major degradations involve opening of one or the other of the two rings. Oxidation with nitric acid cleaves the smaller ring with formation of urea and alloxan. Scheele had observed the formation of alloxan, later characterized by Liebig and Wöhler, and had devised a useful test for uric acid based

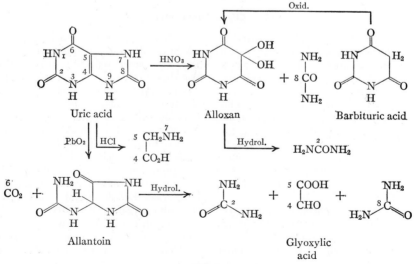

504

upon specific color reactions characteristic of alloxan. Alloxan is a stable hydrate of a 1,2,3-triketone, the central carbonyl group of which has unusual additive power because of the inductive effect of the two flanking electron-attracting groups. Fischer converted alloxan into a derivative of barbituric acid in a series of steps, but the correlation of the two substances is established most simply by the fact that barbituric acid yields alloxan on oxidation. Proof of the structure of barbituric acid by synthesis from urea thus established the structure of one ring of uric acid. The nature of the second ring follows from the results of another degradation in which the six-membered ring is cleaved. Liebig and Wöhler found that uric acid on mild oxidation loses one carbon atom as carbon dioxide and affords a product named allantoin because it proved identical with a substance isolated in 1799 from the allantoic liquid of cows. In the classical investigations allantoin was degraded further in a variety of ways, but the simplest reaction revealing the structure is hydrolysis to two moles of urea and one of glyoxylic acid.

A half century after Fischer's experiments had brought the classical investigations of structure to a successful conclusion, some of the degradative reactions on which the structure is based were put to new use for mapping out the pathway of biosynthesis of uric acid. The degradations formulated above involve conversion into the small fragments urea, glycine, carbon dioxide, and glyoxylic acid, and hence these substances would appear to be possible precursors, in the sense of supplying some parts of the uric acid molecule. That a suspected substance is in fact a biogenetic precursor can be determined by preparation of an isotopically labeled form and administration to an animal; in the present case, pigeons and man were used. Biosynthetic uric acid is then isolated from the urine and put through degradations revealing the positions of any labeled atoms incorporated. When isotopically labeled carbonate was administered and the biosynthetic uric acid was oxidized to allantoin, the carbon dioxide formed contained the isotope, and hence this is indeed the precursor of C_6. In contrast, isotopic formic acid gives material which on oxidation with lead dioxide affords non-isotopic carbon dioxide. However, nitric acid oxidation of the same uric acid reveals that the labeled carbon of formic acid enters the molecule at other sites. Both the urea formed in the oxidation and that resulting from hydrolysis of alloxan, when treated with the enzyme urease to effect conversion to carbon dioxide and ammonia, gave isotopic carbon dioxide, which shows that formic acid supplies C_2 and C_8. Experiments with donors of labeled

ammonia established that this precursor supplies N_1, N_3, and N_9, but not N_7. Acid hydrolysis of uric acid derived from N^{15}-labeled glycine gave glycine bearing isotopic nitrogen, and hence N_7 is supplied by the amino group of glycine. That C_4 and C_5 are supplied, respectively, by the carboxyl and methylene groups of glycine was established in parallel experiments with glycine labeled in each of these positions. The resulting uric acid was oxidized to allantoin, which was hydrolyzed to glyoxylic acid, isolated as the semicarbazone, $HO_2CCH=NNHCONH_2$. On permanganate oxidation of this derivative, carbon dioxide derived from the carboxyl group of glyoxylic acid appears rapidly (7 min.) and that from the aldehydic group is formed slowly (several hrs.), and hence the two positions are distinguishable. The results established that the carboxyl group of glycine is the precursor of C_4 and that the methylene group supplies C_5. Hence all the atoms in the bicyclic ring system are accounted for. The enzymatic synthesis of uric acid from the precursors indicated has been realized.

The classical uric acid work also resulted in a practical application to medicine. The first synthesis of barbituric acid was accomplished by condensing urea with malonic acid under the influence of phosphorus trichloride, but the procedure is improved by use of diethyl malonate in place of the acid and sodium ethoxide as the condensing agent. In 1903 E. Fischer and J. von Mering applied this procedure to the synthesis of a number of derivatives of barbituric acid, some of which were found valuable as soporifics. 5,5-Diethylbarbituric acid has been widely used under the

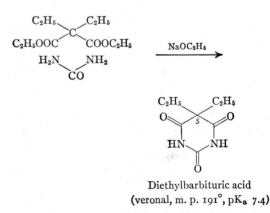

Diethylbarbituric acid
(veronal, m. p. 191°, pK_a 7.4)

name veronal or barbital to induce sleep and to some extent as a sedative and in anesthesia.

It is curious that the alkaloids caffeine, theophylline, and theobromine bear a certain structural analogy to the barbiturates but have physiological activity of directly opposite type: they are stimulants. The coffee bean contains caffeine (1.5%);

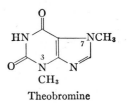

Theobromine

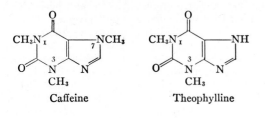

Caffeine   Theophylline

tea leaves contain caffeine (5%) and theophylline (trace); cocoa beans (*Theobroma cacao*) contain theobromine (1.8%).

II. 4

THE PELLETIERINES (*After Chapter 12*)

In an investigation of the bark of the pomegranate tree (*Punica granatum* L.), C. Tanret in 1878 isolated four alkaloids, which he named pelletierine, isopelletierine, pseudopelletierine, and methylpelletierine, in honor of the early French chemist P. Joseph Pelletier (1788–1842). Of the four natural bases, only pseudopelletierine was a crystalline solid, and it was the first to be characterized. Studies initiated in Italy by G. Ciamacian and P. Silber (1893) and by A. Piccinini (1899) and extended by R. Willstätter in Germany (1905)

CO and NCH₃). Hofmann degradation by conversion of the diester of II into the quaternary ammonium hydroxide III and pyrolysis gave IV. A second Hofmann degradation, followed by hydrogenation of the doubly unsaturated ester V and hydrolysis, afforded suberic acid, VI. Willstätter later (1911–13), with E. Waser and M. Heidelberger, used pseudopelletierine as starting material for the first synthesis of cyclooctatetraene. The alkaloid (I) was reduced to the alcohol VII, this was dehydrated, and VIII was exhaustively meth-

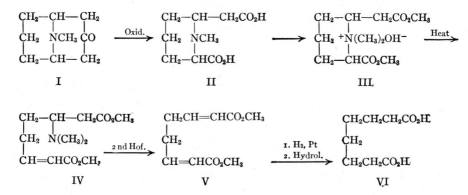

showed that the alkaloid is a tertiary amine containing a carbonyl group flanked by two methylene groups, since it reacts with benzaldehyde to form a dibenzylidene derivative,

—(C₆H₅CH=)CCOC(=CHC₆H₅)—.

On oxidation the alkaloid is converted into a dibasic acid containing all the original carbon atoms, and hence the carbonyl group must be present in a ring system. The structure I accounts for the observations noted, as well as for the lack of optical activity, since I has a plane of symmetry (extending through

ylated and the methohydroxide IX was distilled in vacuum. The unsaturated base X was put through a second Hofmann degradation to give cyclooctatriene, XI, which underwent 1,6-addition of bromine to give the dibromide XII. This on reaction with two equivalents of trimethylamine, followed by treatment of the quaternary bromide with silver oxide, gave the methohydroxide XIII, which on pyrolysis afforded cyclooctatetraene (XIV).

Isopelletierine was soon inferred to have the structure XVII, which was confirmed by independ-

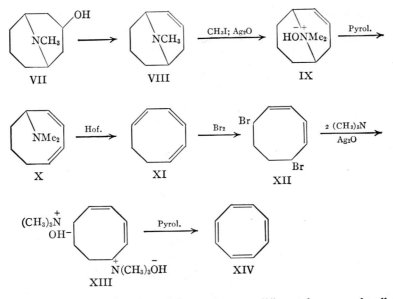

ent syntheses by Meisenheimer[1] (1928) and by Wibaut (1944). The latter involved a reaction of a type different from pseudopelletierine (I), but rearrangement of the formula as in XVIIIa reveals

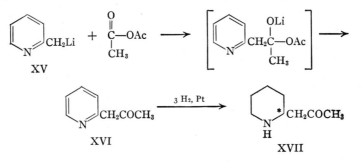

akin to the synthesis of a ketone from a Grignard reagent and an acid chloride. Thus the lithium derivative XV adds to the carbonyl group of acetic anhydride with formation of the ketone XVI. Saturation of the pyridine ring of XVI gave the piperidino ketone XVII, identical with natural isopelletierine. Tanret's methylpelletierine proved to be N-methylisopelletierine, XVIII. As this formula is written the alkaloid would appear to be

a close structural relationship and suggests a biogenetic one.

Pelletierine, the fourth alkaloid of the group, presented a problem which, though eventually found to be simple, was solved only seventy-six years after the initial isolation. Tanret had described pelletierine as an optically active liquid base isomeric with an optically inactive base which he therefore named isopelletierine and regarded as probably the *dl*-form of pelletierine. This early report was discounted, however, when K. Hess at Freiburg in 1917 in an extensive reinvestigation of the isolation confirmed the optical inactivity of isopelletierine but reported pelletierine likewise to be optically inactive. He concluded that the alkaloids are structural isomers and, in an investigation conducted with Annaliese Eichel, presented the

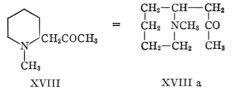

$$\begin{array}{ccc} CH_2 & CH & CH_2 \\ | & | & | \\ CH_2 & NCH_3 & CO \\ | & | & | \\ CH_2 & CH_2 & CH_3 \end{array}$$

XVIII   XVIII a

[1] Jacob Meisenheimer, 1876–1934; b. Greisheim, Germany; Ph.D. Munich; Berlin, Greiswald, Tübingen

following evidence purporting to establish the structure XIX. The substance was converted to the oxime and this was dehydrated with phosphorus pentachloride to a liquid which was isolated

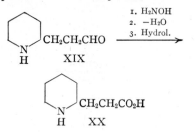

as the crystalline picrate and characterized as a nitrile by C, H, and N analyses on material regenerated from the purified derivative. Hydrolysis with ethanol and hydrogen chloride gave a substance melting at 122° and for which one analysis for C and H gave results agreeing with those required for the ethyl ester hydrochloride of XX. A gold salt melted at 128°, but was not analyzed. The acid XX was a known compound, made synthetically at Breslau in 1909, and its ethyl ester hydrochloride and gold salt were reported as melting at 122° and 128°, respectively. Hess did not secure or prepare a comparison sample; attempts were made to oxidize the alkaloid to the acid with various reagents, but without success. Nevertheless, Hess regarded the evidence as sufficient for assigning to pelletierine the amino aldehyde structure XIX.

derivatives of natural pelletierine (Hess) and of synthetic isopelletierine. Both derivatives melted at 72–74°, and a mixture showed no depression in melting point.

The next point for consideration was the discrepancy between Tanret's report that pelletierine is optically active and Hess's report that it is not. Galinovsky had initially processed pomegranate extract by benzoylation and fractional distillation in vacuum, whereby the unreacted tertiary amines (pseudo, methyl) are easily separated from the less volatile benzoyl derivatives of the secondary amines (higher mol. wt.). Since both heat treatment and subsequent hydrolysis might effect racemization of an initially optically active component, partition chromatography was used in a later study (1954). After adsorption of the alkaloid mixture on a buffered kieselguhr column, ether eluted pseudopelletierine and then chloroform eluted methylpelletierine. The residual secondary bases were removed by stripping the column with hydrochloric acid and adsorbed on a column of powdered glass saturated with an aqueous buffer. Elution, and recovery under sparing conditions, gave a base which afforded a crystalline levorotatory picrate, m.p. 132°, which is easily separated from the much less soluble dl-picrate, m.p. 148°, identical with isopelletierine picrate. The alkaloid occurs in the plant in the optically active form, but suffers partial or complete racemization, depending upon the severity of the conditions of processing. Tanret's

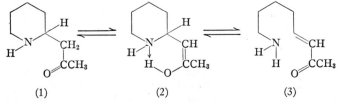

(1)　　　　　　(2)　　　　　　(3)

In retrospect it seems surprising that several subsequent investigators were sufficiently satisfied with Hess's conclusion to undertake the synthesis of XIX. The amino aldehyde proved elusive, and initial attempts in 1940–42 all failed. The diethyl acetal of XIX was secured in two laboratories, but attempted hydrolysis led to resinification. Eventually in 1952 Galinovsky[2] succeeded in liberating the free aldehyde in solution and in characterizing it through derivatives as XIX. This highly reactive substance is wholly unlike pelletierine, a stable, distillable substance. He then noticed that the physical constants reported for Hess's pelletierine and derivatives were close to those reported for isopelletierine, and hence prepared the N-benzoyl

experimentation had been skillful and the inference he had drawn correct. Galinovsky suggests that the ready racemization of (−)-isopelletierine (1) involves equilibration with the enol (2) and the unsaturated amino ketone (3), analogous to the equilibrium of a Mannich base with an amine and

$$CH_3CCH_2CH_2\overset{+}{N}H(C_2H_5)_2I^- \rightleftarrows CH_3CCH=CH_2$$
(4)　　　　　　　　　　　　(5)

$$+ (C_2H_5)_2\overset{+}{N}H_2\overset{-}{I}$$

a vinyl ketone. Thus (4) is a Mannich base (salt) often used in synthesis as the equivalent of methyl vinyl ketone (5).

² Friederich Galinovsky, b. 1908 Vienna; Ph.D. Vienna (Späth); Univ. Vienna

THIOCTIC ACID (α-Lipoic acid) (*After Chapter 12*)

In a study of the nutritional requirements of the protozoan *Tetrahymena geleii*, G. W. Kidder (Amherst College) found liver extracts to contain a factor required for normal growth (1944–45). In view of its essentiality for protozoa, the unknown factor was named protogen. Later protogen was shown to possess biological activity corresponding to that of a factor named lipoic acid, which is required by various lactic acid-producing bacteria and shown also (1946–49) to be a cofactor in the oxidative decarboxylation of pyruvic acid:

$$CH_3COCO_2H + \tfrac{1}{2}O_2 \longrightarrow CH_3CO_2H + CO_2.$$

α-Lipoic acid, now called thioctic acid, is released on hydrolysis of various tissues, but liver is the best source. The active principle was isolated from liver in 1951 in several laboratories. In one project, conducted jointly by groups at the University of Texas (chemical; L. J. Reed[1] *et al.*), the University of Illinois (bacteriological; I. C. Gunsalus[2] *et al.*), and the Eli Lilly research laboratory, ten tons of the water-insoluble residue of beef liver was processed. The assay procedure involved manometric determination of the carbon dioxide liberated on activation of pyruvate oxidation by resting *Streptococcus faecalis* cells. A 250-lb. batch of liver residue was hydrolyzed with 6 N sulfuric acid and the filtered hydrolyzate extracted with benzene, which afforded material of average activity of 150 units/ mg. The active material was then extracted into aqueous bicarbonate, and the extract acidified and extracted with benzene. The crude acidic material thus obtained was processed further in various ways. For example, a 12-g. sample having an activity of 1265 units/mg. was distributed between 2 liters each of benzene and 50% aqueous acetic acid in 10 separatory funnels (Craig countercurrent method). The benzene layers of funnels 7–9 yielded 5.0 g. of material having a potency of 2550 units/mg. This was esterified with diazomethane and the ester mixture chromatographed on alumina (benzene–*n*-heptane). Fractions 9–22 afforded a total of 196 mg. of material of activity in the range 18,000–40,000 units/mg., and when 136 mg. of this material was chromatographed further on Florisil 88% of the activity was concentrated into a series of fractions (18–28) affording 18.8 mg. of methyl

thioctate of a potency of 172,000 units/mg. This ester mixture was shaken with 0.1 N potassium hydroxide under nitrogen for six hours and the acidic fraction on crystallization from ligroin afforded 10 mg. of pale yellow platelets of pure thioctic acid, m.p. 47.5°, αD + 96.7° (2% in benzene), potency 250,000 units/mg. A second, less potent factor, β-lipoic acid, separates as ester in late fractions of the alumina chromatogram. Since much of the liver residue was expended in the course of developing the eventually successful procedures, the recovery of the original activity in the form of a total of 30 mg. of crystalline thioctic acid was only 2.5%. However, this amount of material sufficed for determination of structure.

Analyses and molecular weight determinations of thioctic acid established the formula $C_8H_{14}O_2S_2$. A band in the infrared spectrum at 5.8μ is indicative of an aliphatic carboxyl group, and the pK_a value of 4.76 (cf. *n*-butyric acid, 4.82) indicates that polar or unsaturated groups are not α or β to the carboxyl group. Thioctic acid does not give a positive nitroprusside test for the thiol group (—SH), but a polarographic study established that the sulfur is reducible at the dropping mercury electrode and therefore is present as a disulfide group. Desulfurization with Raney nickel converts thioctic acid into *n*-caprylic acid, $CH_3(CH_2)_6CO_2H$. Since thioctic acid does not contain a methyl group (Kuhn-Roth determination, absence of a striking infrared band at 3.37μ), one sulfur atom must be linked to the terminal carbon atom of the skeleton. These data suggest for the factor the three possible structures formulated. That the correct structure is the first was shown by synthesis in five laboratories

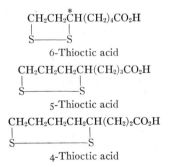

CH₂CH₂ĊH(CH₂)₄CO₂H
6-Thioctic acid

CH₂CH₂CH₂CH(CH₂)₃CO₂H
5-Thioctic acid

CH₂CH₂CH₂CH₂CH(CH₂)₂CO₂H
4-Thioctic acid

[1] Lester J. Reed, b. 1925 New Orleans; Ph.D. Illinois (Fuson); postdoctoral work Cornell Med. Coll. (du Vigneaud); Univ. Texas

[2] I. C. Gunsalus, b. 1912 Sully County, So. Dakota; Ph.D. Cornell (Sherman); postdoctoral work Wisconsin, Hopkins Marine Station (Van Niel), N. Y. Univ. (Ochoa); Cornell, Indiana, Illinois

(1952–55). The first syntheses gave *dl*-material, but identity could be inferred from characteristic physical and optical properties and from biological activity.

One synthesis (L. J. Reed, 1955) starts with addition of adipic acid half-ester acid chloride (1) to ethylene in the presence of aluminum chloride, and reduction of the keto ester (2) with sodium borohydride in ethanol to (3). The hydroxyl group was replaced by chlorine (4), and the two chlorines were converted into thiol groups through the dibenzylmercaptide (5). The C—S bonds in this derivative are activated by the benzyl groups and hence easily severed on reduction with sodium in liquid ammonia

α,β-unsaturated acid group of I probably involves 1,4-addition to the system —CH=CH—C(=O)OH and ketonization: —(CH$_3$COS)CH—CH=C(OH)$_2$ ——→ —(CH$_3$COS)CHCH$_2$COOH. The resulting *dl*-acid II was resolved with use of *d*- and *l*-ephedrine, C$_6$H$_5$CH(OH)CH(CH$_3$)NHCH$_3$. Treatment of an ethereal solution of *dl*-II with *l*-ephedrine gave a crystalline salt of the (−)-form. Alternatively, addition of *d*-ephedrine to an ethereal solution of the *dl*-acid precipitated the crystalline salt of the (+)-form, corresponding, as was found, to natural thioctic acid. Each optically pure form of II was converted into the thioctic acid by the following steps. The carboxyl group was reduced

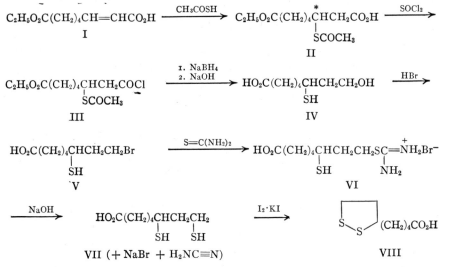

to give the 6,8-dithiol (6), which on oxidation with oxygen in the presence of a trace of ferric chloride afforded *dl*-thioctic acid in 35% overall yield.

A synthesis developed by the Folkers[3] group at Merck introduced a resolution of the first intermediate and permitted preparation of the (+) and (−) forms. Addition of thiolacetic acid to the

via the acid chloride III, and hydrolysis gave IV. The alcoholic hydroxyl group was replaced by bromine, and V was condensed with thiourea to give the isothiuronium salt VI, which on hydrolysis eliminated cyanamide and afforded the dithiol derivative VII. Oxidation, conducted as described above or with iodine in potassium iodide, completed

[3] Karl Folkers, b. 1906 Decatur, Ill.; Ph.D. Wisconsin (Adkins); postdoctoral work Yale (T. B. Johnson); Merck and Co.

510

the synthesis. Of the two enantiomers, only the natural (+)-form has biological activity. *dl-α*-Lipoic acid has half the activity of the natural form.

β-Lipoic acid (yellow oil, $\alpha D + 105°$) has the formula $C_8H_{14}O_3S_2$; it differs from *α*-lipoic acid only in containing one additional oxygen atom. Indeed, it can be obtained by mild oxidation of *α*-lipoic acid with hydroperoxides or with air and is converted into *α*-lipoic acid by reduction with sodium borohydride. The *β*-acid is thus identified as a sulfoxide, $\overset{+}{S}$—$\overset{-}{O}$; it is not known which sulfur atom is in the oxidized state.

II. 6

NATURAL ACETYLENIC ACIDS (*After Chapter 13*)

In 1892 Arnaud[1] investigated the seed fat of a species of *Picramnia tariri* from Guatemala and found it to consist essentially of the glyceride of a single fatty acid, which he named tariric acid. Unlike most glycerides, including synthetic tristearin and tripalmitin, tritaririn separates from a chilled ether solution in "magnificent crystals" (m.p. 47°). Arnaud established the formula $C_{18}H_{32}O_2$ for the acid (m.p. 50.5°), reported the preparation of a dibromide (m.p. 32°) and a tetrabromide (m.p. 125°), and then leisurely continued investigation of the structure. Since the technique of catalytic hydrogenation had not yet been developed, he tried various chemical reductions and in 1896 effected reduction by heating tariric acid with hydriodic acid and red phosphorus in a sealed tube at 210° for 10 hours. The product was stearic acid. Tariric acid is considerably higher melting than any known C_{18}-dienic acids, but the melting point is close to that of synthetic stearolic acid (m.p. 48°), obtainable by dehydrobromination of methyl oleate dibromide with sod-

$$CH_3(CH_2)_7CH{=}CH(CH_2)_7CO_2CH_3 \xrightarrow[\substack{68\%}]{\substack{1.\ Br_2 \\ 2.\ NaNH_2}}$$
$$CH_3(CH_2)_7C{\equiv}C(CH_2)_7CO_2H$$
$$\text{Stearolic acid}$$

amide in liquid ammonia (N. A. Khan, 1951). Since in this series absence of a depression in the melting point of a mixture is not conclusive evidence of identity, Arnaud compared the solubilities of a series of salts of the two acids and satisfied himself that they are different. In 1902 he reported that tariric acid on oxidation with either alkaline permanganate or nitric acid affords adipic and lauric acids and therefore is the 6,7-acetylenic derivative of stearic acid.

$$CH_3(CH_2)_{10}C{\equiv}C(CH_2)_4CO_2H \longrightarrow$$
$$\text{Tariric acid}$$
$$CH_3(CH_2)_{10}CO_2H \quad + \quad HO_2C(CH_2)_4CO_2H$$
$$\text{Lauric acid} \qquad\qquad \text{Adipic acid}$$

The synthesis of tariric acid was accomplished by P. B. Lumb and J. C. Smith[2] (1952) as follows. The ester $CH_2{=}CH(CH_2)_8CO_2C_2H_5$ (pyrolysis of castor oil, 7.7) was hydrogenated (Raney Ni) and the saturated ester reduced by the Bouveault-Blanc method (Na, C_2H_5OH) to the alcohol, which afforded the corresponding bromide. This was condensed with sodium acetylide to produce undecylacetylene. Attempts to convert this into a lithium derivative by a direct method were unsuccessful, but the derivative was obtained via the mercury derivative and condensed with 1-chloro-3-iodopropane (from $ClCH_2CH_2CH_2Cl$ and NaI in acetone). The resulting chloride was condensed with sodiomalonic ester, and saponification and decarboxylation gave material identical with natural tariric acid. Selective hydrogenation in a neutral aqueous solution of the sodium salt gave the corresponding *cis* ethylenic acid, identical with another natural product, petroselinic acid.

$$CH_3(CH_2)_{10}Br \xrightarrow{NaC{\equiv}CH} CH_3(CH_2)_{10}C{\equiv}CH \longrightarrow [CH_3(CH_2)_{10}C{\equiv}C]_2Hg$$

$$\xrightarrow{Li} CH_3(CH_2)_{10}C{\equiv}CLi \xrightarrow{ICH_2CH_2CH_2Cl} CH_3(CH_2)_{10}C{\equiv}CCH_2CH_2CH_2Cl$$

$$\xrightarrow{Na\overset{+}{C}H(CO_2C_2H_5)_2} CH_3(CH_2)_{10}C{\equiv}CCH_2CH_2CH_2CH(CO_2C_2H_5)_2 \xrightarrow[\substack{2.\ Heat}]{\substack{1.\ KOH}}$$

$$CH_3(CH_2)_{10}C{\equiv}C(CH_2)_4CO_2H \xrightarrow{H_2,\ Ni} CH_3(CH_2)_{10}\overset{H}{C}{=}\overset{H}{C}(CH_2)_4CO_2H$$
$$\text{Tariric acid} \qquad\qquad\qquad \text{Petroselinic acid}$$

[1] Albert Arnaud, 1853–1915; b. Paris; Ph.D. Paris (Chevreul); Muséum National d'Histoire Naturelle

[2] John Charles Smith, b. 1900 Wellington, New Zealand; Ph.D. Manchester (R. Robinson), D.Sc. Oxford; postdoctoral work Manchester, Graz, McGill, Pretoria, Melbourne; Oxford

Another natural acid characterized as acetylenic occurs in the seeds of an African tree and was called erythrogenic acid because on exposure to light it is converted into a vivid red polymer. Analytical characterization and hydrogenation experiments established that the substance is a stearic acid derivative having the equivalent of five double bonds. In 1940 both A. Castille in Belgium and Alph. Steger and J. van Loon in the Netherlands reported the degradation by ozonization to formaldehyde (a), adipic acid (b), oxalic acid (c), and

$$CH_2O \qquad HO_2C(CH_2)_4CO_2H$$
$$\text{(a)} \qquad\qquad \text{(b)}$$

$$HO_2CCO_2H \qquad HO_2C(CH_2)_7CO_2H$$
$$\text{(c)} \qquad\qquad\qquad \text{(d)}$$

azelaic acid (d). The formaldehyde could come only from a terminal double bond, and since only two other unsaturated centers are cleaved these have to be acetylenic linkages to account for the total unsaturation. Two formulas account equally well for the observed fragments, I, corresponding to the arrangement abcd, and II, corresponding to acbd. Castille published a preliminary communication in 1941 favoring I, but the experiments were not subsequently recorded. However, the group of E. R. H. Jones, then at Manchester, later investigated the ultraviolet absorption character-

$$CH_2=CH(CH_2)_4C\equiv CC\equiv C(CH_2)_7CO_2H$$
I

$$CH_2=CHC\equiv C(CH_2)_4C\equiv C(CH_2)_7CO_2H$$
II

istics of synthetic compounds containing double and triple bonds and could deduce from the spectrum reported for erythrogenic acid by Castille (1940) that the substance cannot be the vinylacetylene II and must, therefore, be I, which has conjugated acetylenic bonds and an isolated double bond. H. K. Black and B. C. L. Weedon[3] (1953) of the group therefore undertook the synthesis of I by shaking a mixture of octene-1-yne-7 and Δ^9-decynoic acid with oxygen in the presence of cuprous

$$CH_2=CH(CH_2)_4C\equiv CH \; + \; HC\equiv C(CH_2)_7CO_2H$$
$$\xrightarrow{\text{[O]}} \quad CH_2=CH(CH_2)_4C\equiv CC\equiv C(CH_2)_7CO_2H$$
Erythrogenic acid
M.p. 39°, λ_{max} 227, 237, 254 mμ

ammonium chloride. The oxidative cross-coupling gave the expected mixture of three products, but the two acidic components differ considerably in molecular weight and were easily separated. The C_{18}-acid proved identical with erythrogenic acid.

Spectroscopic characterization also aided investigation of matricaria methyl ester, assigned by Sörensen (1940) the structure and *cis, cis* configuration shown.

$$\begin{array}{ccccc} H\;H & & H\;H \\ CH_3C=CC\equiv CC\equiv CC=CCO_2CH_3 \end{array}$$
Matricaria methyl ester

A most unusual unsaturated acid is mycomycin, an optically active antibiotic elaborated by the fungus *Norcardia acidophilis*. The substance was discovered in 1947 by E. A. Johnson and K. L. Burdon of the department of bacteriology, Baylor Medical School, who extracted filtered and acidified broth with hexane, and then found that extraction of the hexane solution with sodium phosphate buffer removed an acidic substance exhibiting absorption maxima at 267 and 281 mμ, which could be correlated with the microbiological activity. Extreme sensitivity to heat was evidenced by rapid loss of both ultraviolet absorption and antibiotic activity unless the concentrates were stored at dry ice temperature. Isolation of the pure substance and elucidation of its structure was accomplished in 1952–53 by W. D. Celmer[4] and I. A. Solomons of Pfizer and Co. Concentration was effected by an eight-plate countercurrent distribution of a dilute solution of the antibiotic between chloroform and cold 2% pH 7.0 phosphate buffer, conducted in a nitrogen atmosphere. The antibiotic was finally obtained as white needles which exploded at about 75° in a capillary tube sealed with nitrogen. Repeated low-temperature recrystallization did not alter the ultraviolet spectrum or improve the stability.

Mycomycin is strongly levorotatory (αD − 130°) and has the formula $C_{13}H_{10}O_2$. The two oxygen atoms are present in a carboxyl group, since the neutralization equivalent found (200) agreed with that calculated (198). On catalytic hydrogenation, 1.01 millimole of substance (200 mg.) consumed 7.8 millimoles of hydrogen and afforded *n*-tridecanoic acid, $CH_3(CH_2)_{11}CO_2H$. In view of the extreme sensitivity of mycomycin, Celmer and Solomons undertook to isolate and characterize a transformation product, and found that when excess sodium hydroxide is added to mycomycin, the crystalline salt of an isomeric acid, isomycomycin, separates within a few minutes. This isomer also absorbs eight moles of hydrogen and yields *n*-tridecanoic acid and hence has the original straight chain of thirteen carbon atoms. However, it is optically inactive. Kuhn-Roth determination (9.8)

[3] Basil C. L. Weedon, b. 1923 London; Ph.D. and D.Sc. London (Heilbron, E. R. H. Jones); postdoctoral work Imperial Coll. (Heilbron, Linstead); London, ICI
[4] Walter D. Celmer, b. 1925 Plymouth, Penna.; Ph.D. Illinois (Carter); Pfizer and Co.

established that whereas mycomycin contains no C-methyl groups, one such group is present in isomycomycin. This can only be a terminal methyl group (C_{13}). The terminal part of the hydrocarbon chain in mycomycin was recognized as $HC\equiv C-$ from the observation that the methyl ester forms a silver derivative on treatment with alcoholic silver nitrate. Both acids show an infrared absorption band at 1730 cm.$^{-1}$ (wave numbers) characteristic of nonconjugated acids and superposable with the carboxyl band of n-tridecanoic acid, and therefore contain the grouping $-CH_2CO_2H$. Isomycomycin, in contrast to mycomycin, reacts very readily with maleic anhydride to form a Diels-Alder adduct. This reaction provided evidence of the presence of a conjugated diene system, $C=C-C=C$, since addition to an eneyne system, $C=C-C\equiv C$, could afford only an excessively strained allene-containing ring.

Analysis of the infrared spectra and comparison with the spectra of matricaria methyl ester and

absorption bands showed that the mono and disubstituted acetylenic bonds are conjugated (C_{10}-C_{13}). A 3,5-diene system was recognized in both isomers; the configurations, deducible from the infrared spectra, are: mycomycin, 3 (*trans*), 5 (*cis*); isomycomycin, 3 (*trans*), 5 (*trans*). *Trans, trans* dienes are known to undergo Diels-Alder addition much more readily than *trans, cis* dienes, but the failure of mycomycin to react with maleic anhydride could not be taken as evidence of its configuration because of the instability of the antibiotic.

The optical activity of mycomycin is accounted for by the presence of an unsymmetrically substituted allene grouping (Chapter 12, problem 12). The asymmetry is destroyed on isomerization with alkali to isomycomycin. This remarkable reaction involves an allene→acetylene isomerization, an acetylene migration, and a *trans, cis* to *trans, trans* isomerization.

Two similar highly unsaturated antibiotics isolated from fungus cultures, nemotinic acid and

$$HC\equiv C-C\equiv C-CH=C-CH-\underset{\underset{6}{|}}{\overset{\overset{H}{|}}{C}}=\underset{5}{\overset{\overset{H}{|}}{C}}-\underset{\underset{H}{|}}{\overset{\overset{H}{|}}{\underset{4}{C}}}=\underset{3}{C}-CH_2CO_2H \xrightarrow{\ OH^-\ }$$

Mycomycin

$$CH_3-C\equiv C-C\equiv C-C\equiv C-\underset{\underset{H}{|}}{\overset{\overset{H}{|}}{\underset{6}{C}}}=\underset{5}{\overset{\overset{H}{|}}{\underset{}{C}}}\cdot\underset{4}{\overset{\overset{H}{|}}{C}}=\underset{3}{C}-CH_2CO_2H$$

Isomycomycin

other related or model compounds led to complete elucidation of the complicated unsaturated systems of the two acids and of the stereochemistry. Thus the spectrum of mycomycin has characteristic bands at 3180, 2200, 1930 cm.$^{-1}$ attributable to $RC\equiv C-H$ (monosubstituted acetylene), to $RC\equiv CR$, and to the allene system (C_7-C_9), respectively. Fine structure spacing in the characteristic ultraviolet

nemotin, have been characterized (E. R. H. Jones, 1955). The acid has a pair of conjugated acetylenic

$$CH\equiv CC\equiv CCH=C=CHCH(OH)CH_2CH_2CO_2H$$
Nemotinic acid

linkages and an asymmetrically substituted allene group and is optically active. Nemotin is the corresponding γ-lactone.

II. 7

NEPETALACTONE (*After Chapter 13*)

An investigation of the active principle of catnip responsible for the attractiveness of the plant to certain species of the cat family was commenced in the department of pharmaceutical chemistry at Wisconsin by E. Kremers and Minnie Meyer and continued, on Professor Kremers' retirement, by a group in the chemistry department headed by S. M. McElvain (1941–42). Steam distillation of the plant (*Nepeta cataria*) gives about 0.3% of a volatile, odoriferous oil, about 80% of which dissolves

in alkali. On careful acidification of the alkaline solution a solid separates and can be purified by crystallization. This substance, named nepetalic acid, was characterized as follows: $C_{10}H_{16}O_3$, m.p. 76°, $\alpha D + 48°$. Solubility in bicarbonate and formation of a methyl ester (CH_2N_2) showed that two oxygens are present as a carboxyl group. Formation of a bisulfite addition product, an oxime, and a semicarbazone characterized the remaining oxygen as being present as a carbonyl group. That this group is aldehydic was inferred from a positive test with the Tollens reagent. The Fehling's test is negative if conducted in the ordinary way but positive if the test solution is diluted with two volumes of water and heated at 60°.

Nepetalic acid is odorless, but it is easily dehydrated to a volatile, physiologically active substance, nepetalactone: $C_{10}H_{14}O_2$, $\alpha_D - 13°$, liquid. The lactone does not form carbonyl derivatives and, unlike the acid, adds one equivalent of bromine. These facts are consistent with formula I for nepetalactone and with formulas IIa–c for tautomeric forms of nepetalic acid. Presumably lactonization to I involves the enol form IIa, and reduction of Tollens reagent involves the aldehyde form IIc. The presence of the lactol form IIb is indicated by infrared absorption bands characteristic of a saturated carbonyl group (5.85μ) and a hydroxyl

talactone, nepetalic anhydride, a product derived from dehydrative coupling of two molecules of hydrated nepetalactone, and the known terpene caryophyllene, $C_{15}H_{24}$ (see II.9), which has an odor midway between that of cloves and that of turpentine. Tests for physiological activity were carried out at the Madison zoo with ten African lions, including lions of both sexes, three cubs, and a partially blind female 25–30 years old. All but the cubs responded to nepetalactone as they had to the fresh plant, regularly given to them in the summer. They showed no interest in caryophyllene or in nepetalic acid or other odorless members of the series. The playful reaction of the adult lions to nepetalactone, the evident active principle, was similar to that of an ordinary house cat.

J. Meinwald at Cornell (1954) noted that of the three structures indicated by the Wisconsin work

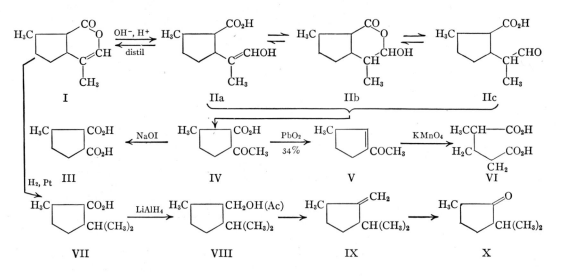

group (3.04μ). Oxidation of nepetalic acid with alkaline hydrogen peroxide probably proceeds through the enol IIa and gives formic acid and nepetonic acid (IV), recognized as having a methyl ketone group by hypoiodite oxidation to iodoform and the dibasic acid III, nepetic acid, $\alpha_D - 35°$. The latter acid was found on Kuhn-Roth determination (9.8) to contain one C-methyl group, and McElvain regarded the hydrocarbon part of the molecule as a methylcyclopentane unit. The ring methyl group of nepetalactone, then, must be at the position shown in I or at one of the other two possible positions.

The alkali-insoluble fraction of the steam-volatile oil from catnip was found to be a mixture of nepe-

as likely for nepetalactone only one (I) conforms to the isoprene rule (two head-to-tail units), and he established this structure as correct by the following degradation. In analogy with known cases, catalytic hydrogenation of the unsaturated lactone proceeded largely with hydrogenolysis of the activated C—O bond to give the acid VII, which on lithium aluminum hydride reduction and pyrolysis of the acetate of VIII gave the unsaturated hydrocarbon IX. Ozonization gave formaldehyde, identified as the dimedon derivative, and the known 2-methyl-5-isopropylcyclopentanone, X.

McElvain later (1955) effected another degradation of particular significance because it helped elucidation of the stereochemistry. Doering[1] (1952)

[1] William von E. Doering, b. 1917 Ft. Worth, Texas; Ph.D. Harvard (Linstead); Yale

had found that 1,2-dicarboxylic acids, for example (1), are oxidized by lead dioxide to the corresponding 1,2-olefins (2):

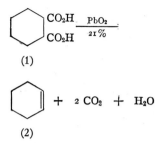

(1)

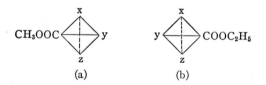

(2)

Nepetonic acid (IV) is a 1-aceto-2-carboxylic acid, and McElvain found it to be similarly oxidized by the specific reagent to the 1-aceto-1-olefin V. The substance was characterized as an α,β-unsaturated ketone by ultraviolet absorption at 237 mμ and by one infrared absorption band at 6.03μ attributable to the conjugated carbonyl group (compare 5.85μ for the saturated carbonyl group of IIb) and another at 6.2μ due to the conjugated olefinic group. Permanganate oxidation of V then gave a dibasic acid identified as $(+)$-α-methylglutaric acid (VI). The configuration of this acid relative to that of D-glyceraldehyde had been established by A. Fredga at Uppsala (1947) by a method of correlation based upon the fact that two optically active compounds of very similar structure but of opposite configuration, such as (a) and (b), form quasi-racemic molecular compounds. The quasi-racemates usually have some optical activity, except

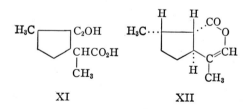

(a)   (b)

in the rare case when the two components by coincidence have identical but opposite molecular rotations, but in any case they are recognizable as quasi-racemates from melting point-composition diagrams (see 12.14). Whereas with a true racemate the first half of the diagram giving melting points of mixtures of from 0% A and 100% B to the 50:50 mixture is exactly matched by the second half extending to 100% A and 0% B, with a quasi-racemate the two halves of the curve are similar but not identical. The $(+)$-α-methylglutaric acid derived by degradation of nepetalactone had been found

by Fredga to form quasi-racemates with related substances known to belong to the D-series, and was thus characterized as being in the L-series, of

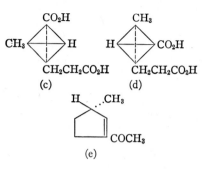

the configuration (c). Rotation of the tetrahedron (c) about the single bond connecting the asymmetric carbon atom to the —CH$_2$CH$_2$CO$_2$H group gives (d), and the corresponding configuration thus established for the unsaturated ketone V is (e). In nepetalactone, then, the methyl group in the cyclopentane ring extends to the rear of the ring (α, dotted bond), and the hydrogen at this asymmetric center extends to the front.

Since the *vic*-dicarboxylic acid nepetic acid (III) readily forms an anhydride, it was initially thought to be the *cis* diacid. Later observation that gentle hydrolysis of the anhydride affords an isomeric diacid, isonepetic acid, showed that the latter is *cis* and that the orientation of carboxyl groups in nepetic acid, and hence the ring juncture in nepetalactone, is *trans*. Evidence relating the configurations at the two ring junctions to that of the methyl-substituted carbon in the cyclopentane ring was found in the behavior of four isomeric nepetalinic acids of the structure XI. The isomer corresponding to nepetalactone in the configurations of the three asymmetric centers in the cyclopentane ring proved subject to epimerization and was thus shown not to have the most stable all-*trans* configuration. From this and other evidence, McElvain deduced for nepetalactone the absolute stereochemistry shown in formula XII.

CANTHARIDIN (*After Chapter 13*)

Cantharides, a preparation of dried beetles (*cantharis vesicatoria*), attracted early attention because of its vesicant and rubefacient activity. The active principle cantharidin, present to the extent of 0.6–1% along with fat, resin, and uric acid, was isolated by the French pharmacist Robiquet in 1810. The white, water-insoluble solid, m.p. 218°, was later investigated in several laboratories. The initially accepted formula $C_5H_6O_2$ was revised by J. Piccard (Basel) in 1877 to the correct one, $C_{10}H_{12}O_4$, as the result of vapor density determination of molecular weight by the Victor Meyer method. Piccard distilled cantharidin with phosphorus pentasulfide and identified the product as *o*-xylene, which accounts for all but two of the carbon atoms and suggests that cantharidin, since it contains too many hydrogen atoms to be aromatic, is a derivative of 1,2-dimethylcyclohexane. Piccard also found that cantharidin is converted by hydriodic acid to cantharic acid, a monobasic acid isomeric with cantharidin. That cantharidin dissolves slowly in alkali was well known but not correctly

elements of water, and hence cantharidin could be either a lactone acid or the anhydride of a dibasic acid. The latter alternative was established by titration experiments conducted in 1914 by P. W. Dankwortt, Privatdozent in the laboratory of J. Gadamer[1] at Breslau. The grouping —C(=O)OC(=O)— fused to a 1,2-dimethylcyclohexane unit would account for all carbon atoms and for all but one oxygen. Since tests for hydroxyl and carbonyl were negative, the fourth oxygen must constitute an oxide bridge.

Gadamer, interpreting the observations cited and new evidence from his own investigations (1914–16), deduced for cantharidin the structure shown in formula I. It will be noted that the skeletal structure contains two isoprene units in the rare head-to-head arrangement. *o*-Xylene (VI) results from elimination of the oxide bridge and anhydride group. Cantharidinic acid is the dibasic acid IV. Cantharic acid is the unsaturated γ-lactone monoacid II, related to the bromolactone acid III. Gadamer proved that cantharidin possesses a plane

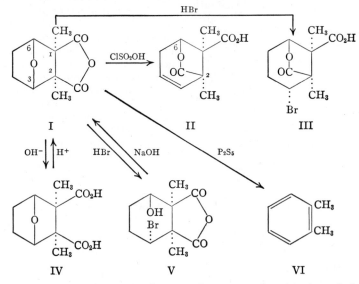

interpreted for some time. Benno Homolka (Munich, 1888) found that if the alkaline solution is acidified while hot, cantharidin precipitates, but that acidification in the cold gives a solution of dibasic cantharidinic acid, which was converted through the disilver salt to the dimethyl ester. Cantharidinic acid differs from cantharidin by the

of symmetry (passing through the two ring-oxygens) as follows. The substance itself is optically inactive, but gentle reaction with hydrobromic acid opens the oxide ring (with inversion at the linkage severed) to give a bromohydrin resolvable into optically active enantiomers, one of which is represented by formula V. When either optically active

[1] Johannes Georg Gadamer, 1867–1928; Ph.D. Marburg; Breslau, Marburg

form is reconverted into the oxide, the product is optically inactive cantharidin. Symmetry is possible only if the anhydride ring is *cis* fused, as represented in the formula by β (front) bonds extending to the carbonyl groups and α (rear) bonds extending to the methyls. There remained the question of whether the oxide bridge is *exo*, that is β and *cis* to the anhydride ring, or *endo* (α, *trans*). Woodward[2] (1941) and Ziegler (1942) noted that formation of the lactones II and III finds a satisfactory

bromo lactone IIIa, reconvertible into cantharidin by elimination of hydrogen bromide.

F. von Bruchhausen and H. W. Bersch at Münster (1928) had just commenced work on the synthesis of cantharidin when Diels and Alder published their first paper on their new diene addition reaction (Dec., 1927). This elegant reaction seemed to offer promise of a simple synthesis of cantharidin, and trial on a model compound was encouraging. Furan (1) was found to function satisfactorily as a diene

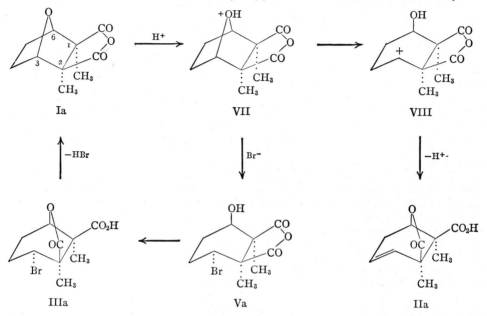

explanation only if the arrangement is *exo*, since in the γ-lactone ring the C_2 carbonyl and C_6 oxide link necessarily have the same orientation (β). Both reactions may involve initial protonation of cantharidin, represented by the projection formulas Ia ⟶ VII. Isomerization to the carbonium ion VIII and expulsion of a proton with lactonization gives cantharic acid, IIa. The second reaction

and reacted with maleic anhydride to give a crystalline product. This had the composition of the expected adduct (3), but it melted with decomposition at 118° with gas evolution. Hence the solidified melt was examined and found to melt at 51° and to give no depression when mixed with maleic anhydride. The substance thus could be merely a molecular complex. However, on hydrogenation

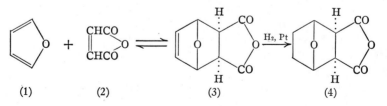

may involve back side attack of the oxonium ion VII by bromide ion, with fission of the oxide ring and inversion at C_3 to give the resolvable bromohydrin Va. The latter can be isomerized to the

it afforded the fully stable, distillable oxido anhydride (4) and therefore is indeed the adduct (3). The decomposition at the melting point is a reverse Diels-Alder reaction. von Bruchhausen and Bersch

[2] Robert B. Woodward, b. 1917 Boston; Ph.D. Mass. Inst. Techn.; Harvard Univ.

were disappointed in the hope of effecting addition of furan to dimethylmaleic anhydride to produce a dehydrocantharidin; it is possible that the reaction if realized would have given the natural *exo* product. They concluded that in this case the equilibrium favors reverse Diels-Alder reaction and saw the possibility of confirming the Gadamer formula by reversal of synthesis. Like the saturated model

out success in his work for the doctorate with Ziegler in 1939. The key intermediate X was readily available by addition of butadiene to dimethylmaleic anhydride and introduction of an additional double bond into the adduct IX to produce the diene X. After considerable work with model compounds had led to development of appropriate conditions, Schenck effected photochemical peroxidation of X

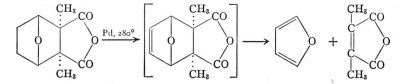

substance (4), cantharidin is very stable to heat; indeed in Piccard's vapor density determination the substance had withstood a temperature of 400°. An unsaturated derivative comparable to (3) should be more easily cleaved to diene and dienophile, and hence cantharidin was heated with palladium-charcoal to 280° in the hope of effecting dehydrogenation and reverse Diels-Alder reaction. Indeed dimethylmaleic anhydride was isolated and fully identified; the formation of furan was inferred from the odor and from a characteristic pine-splint test.

K. Ziegler, G. O. Schenck, and E. W. Krockow achieved the first synthesis of cantharidin (1942), but by a lengthy, low-yield (2%) process involving two remarkable pyrolyses and furnishing no evidence of the stereochemistry. Fully stereospecific

to the transannular peroxide XI; the reaction is comparable to a Diels-Alder addition. Hydrogenation opened the peroxide to a diol, which spontaneously lactonized to XII, and this on reaction with hydrogen bromide yielded the bromo lactone IIIa, which Gadamer had transformed into cantharidin, Ia.

Stork's synthesis likewise utilizes two Diels-Alder additions, one the reaction of furan with dimethyl acetylenedicarboxylate to form XIII. The less hindered double bond of the adduct XIII was selectively hydrogenated and the product XIV condensed with butadiene. The product could be inferred to have the stereochemistry shown in XV from the known behavior of the analog of XIV having a bridging methylene group; a methylene

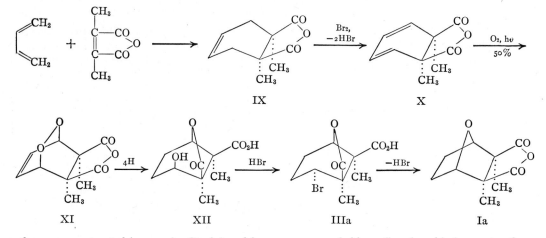

syntheses were reported in 1953 by Stork [3] and by G. O. Schenck. [4] The latter represented completion of a plan initially explored by Schenck with-

or oxygen bridge offers less hindrance to the approach of the diene than the —CH₂CH₂— bridge. The next problem, conversion of the carbomethoxy

[3] Gilbert Stork, b. 1921 Brussels, Belgium; Ph.D. Wisconsin (McElvain); Harvard, Columbia Univ.
[4] Günther O. Schenck, b. 1913 Lörrach/Baden, Germany; Ph.D. Halle (Ziegler); Göttingen

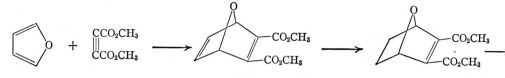

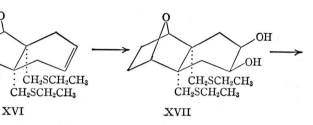

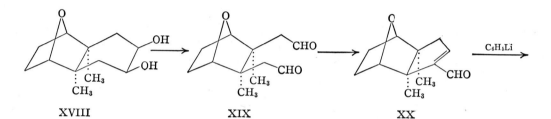

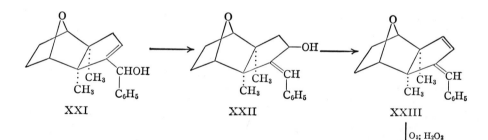

$$\downarrow O_3;\ H_2O_2$$

Cantharidin

groups into methyl groups, was accomplished by the sequence:

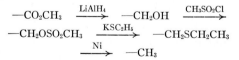

However, the last step of reductive desulfurization was accompanied by reduction of the double bond required for later degradation to an anhydride group. Hence, prior to desulfurization, the double bond of the dithioethyl derivative was hydroxylated.

Since the reagent used was osmium tetroxide and the attack must be on the less hindered side, the product is the β,β-cis-glycol XVII. Desulfurization (XVIII) and glycol cleavage with periodic acid gave the dialdehyde XIX, which was cyclized by intramolecular aldolization to the cyclopentene aldehyde XX (catalyst: piperidine acetate). Conversion of this substance to a derivative suitable for oxidation to a dicarboxylic acid anhydride was accomplished by addition of phenyllithium to give the carbinol XXI, allylic rearrangement to XXII, and dehydration to XXIII, but the last two reac-

519

tions required special conditions. A bimolecular 1,4-elimination reaction of XXI under strongly acid conditions such that the oxide bridge would be protonated would invite molecular rearrangement of one of the adjacent methyl groups. However, Braude [5] had developed a technique for effecting allylic rearrangement under mildly protonating conditions (e.g. anionotropic rearrangement) by use of a solution of 0.01 M hydrochloric acid in 60% dioxane (Lewis base), and had shown that the reaction is strictly unimolecular and proceeds without alteration of the carbon skeleton. Stork used this method for preparing XXII and effected nonionic dehydration to XXIII by pyrolysis of the stearate. Ozonolysis of the diene followed by oxidation with hydrogen peroxide gave directly crystalline cantharidin.

II. 9

MEDIUM SIZE RINGS (C_8-C_{12}) (*After Chapter 13*)

Mention has been made (13.14) of Ruzicka's striking observation (1928) that in cyclization of dibasic acids to ketones the C_5 and C_6 ring ketones are obtained in high yield, whereas the yield drops progressively in production of the C_7 and C_8 ketones, C_{13} the yields were practically negligible with the C_9-C_{11} ketones and were 8% and 15% with the next two members. A yield minimum thus exists in this refined method of cyclization, as in the pyrolytic process.

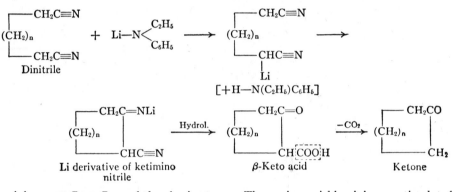

reaches a minimum at C_9 or C_{10}, and then begins to increase. In applying the high-dilution principle to inhibit bimolecular condensation, Ziegler (13.14) utilized the reaction of a dinitrile with ether-soluble lithium ethylanilide to produce a cyclic derivative which readily affords the cyclic ketone through the steps formulated. High dilution is achieved without use of a large volume of solvent by adding an ether solution of the dinitrile at a very slow rate to a vigorously stirred and refluxing solution of the condensing agent in ether. Yields of cycloheptanone and cyclooctanone were 95% and 88%, respectively, and, in contrast with the results of the pyrolytic method, cyclopentadecanone (Exaltone) and cycloheptadecanone (dihydrocivetone) were obtained in yields of 60% and 70%. Oddly enough, although all the ketones in the series C_{14} to C_{25} as well as the C_5-C_8 ketones could be obtained in yields of 60% and higher, in the series from C_9 to

The curious yield minimum stimulated interest in investigation of compounds of medium size rings, but the most interesting ones were too difficultly accessible for study until 1947, when a vastly improved method of cyclization was developed independently by M. Stoll and by Prelog.[1] The key step is an acyloin condensation, in which a solution of the diester of an α,ω-dicarboxylic acid in hot xylene is stirred vigorously with molten sodium. The first step is analogous to the reduction of a ketone to a pinacol, and the next reduction is a 1,4-addition of sodium. The enediol liberated on acidification ketonizes to the acyloin, which can be reduced to the ketone with zinc and hydrochloric acid or by dehydration and hydrogenation of the α,β-unsaturated ketone. The acyloin condensation is conducted under nitrogen, since the enediol is very sensitive to air oxidation, but high dilution is not required and the yields are spectacular (C_{21}-

[5] Ernest Alexander Braude, 1922–56; b. Berlin; Ph.D. and D.Sc. London (Heilbron, E. R. H. Jones); Imperial Coll., London

[1] Vladimir Prelog, b. 1906 Sarajevo, Yugoslavia; Dr. Ing. Prague (Votoček); ETH Zurich

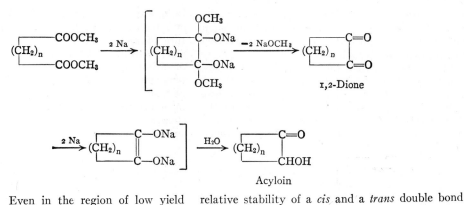

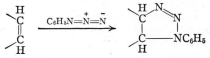

Acyloin

acyloin, 96%). Even in the region of low yield (C₉–C₁₂), yields of 40% are realized.*

The properties of medium-size ring compounds are indeed abnormal. Whereas in the series of homologous *n*-alkanes density increases steadily with increasing molecular weight and molecular refraction decreases, in the cycloalkanes from C_6 on density increases more rapidly and passes through a maximum and then falls off to the level of the higher *n*-alkanes, and the molecular refraction curve exhibits a minimum inflection. R. W. Fawcett and J. O. Harris (King's Coll., Univ. Durham, 1954) completed a series of conjugated cyclo-1,3-dienes, prepared for the most part by allylic bromination of the enes (NBS) and dehydrohalogenation (quinoline), and found that ultraviolet light absorption varies markedly with ring size, as can be seen from figures given for the positions of

Ring	C_5	C_6	C_7	C_8
λ_{max}, mμ	265	256	248	228

Ring	C_9	C_{10}	C_{11}	C_{12}
λ_{max}, mμ	219.5	224	227.5	230

the absorption bands. In this series, λ_{max} decreases to a minimum in the C₉-diene and then rises to a level comparable with that characteristic of openchain dienes of the type RCH=CHCH=CHR (227 mμ).

Ring size influences in an interesting way the relative stability of a *cis* and a *trans* double bond incorporated in the ring system. The first demonstration that two forms are possible was by Ziegler (1950). One form of cyclooctene had been made by dehydration of cyclooctanol, by partial hydrogenation of cyclooctatetraene (Reppe, 1948), and by reduction of cyclooctadiene-1,3 with lithium and methylaniline (only conjugated dienes are reducible, isolated double bonds are not affected). The liquid hydrocarbon can be characterized by reaction with phenyl azide to form a crystalline addition product, m.p. 87°. Ziegler prepared a cyclooctene by Hof-

mann degradation, that is, pyrolysis of cyclooctyltrimethylammonium hydroxide, and found it to be different, since the phenyl azide addition product melts at 111°. The new octene was found to be isomerized readily by acids to the previously known isomer. Actually Ziegler's product was later shown by Cope (1953) to be a mixture of the less and more stable isomers in the ratio of about 65:35. From analysis of models, Ziegler concluded that the more stable cyclooctene has the *cis* configuration. He also regarded a *trans*-cycloheptene as improbable. Cyclooctyne has been prepared (Blomquist,[2] 1953)

---

* Whether a given diester undergoes acyloin or Dieckmann condensation (10.21) may depend on both the structure of the diester and the conditions. Dieckmann and other ester condensations (10.20) are usually done with sodium ethoxide as condensing agent and involve

formation of an anion, $RO_2C(CH_2)_nCH_2CO_2R \xrightarrow{\bar{O}C_2H_5} RO_2C(CH_2)_n\bar{C}HCO_2R + C_2H_5OH$, and its addition to the second ester carbonyl group. However, diethyl adipate, which yields a Dieckmann keto ester on reaction with sodium ethoxide, reacts with one equivalent of sodium in xylene to give the same product in 78% yield; since alcohol is a product of ester condensation, a catalytic amount would suffice to initiate the reaction. On the other hand, diethyl adipate has been converted into the acyloin in 55% yield by reaction in toluene with 4 g. atoms of sodium per mole of ester in a nitrogen atmosphere and a stirring speed of 2500 r.p.m. (Sheehan, 1950). The difference appears attributable chiefly to the fact that the Dieckmann reaction is reversible and acyloin condensation irreversible. The relatively high yield of C₉–C₁₂ acyloins without high dilution may be because the condensation is a surface reaction, promoted by large surface areas.

[2] Alfred T. Blomquist, b. 1906 Chicago; Ph.D. Illinois (Marvel); Cornell

521

and, as predicted by Ziegler, is highly unstable. It reacts explosively with phenyl azide and has a marked tendency to rearrange to a less saturated hydrocarbon, probably bicyclic.

Blomquist prepared the *cis* and *trans* cyclononenes and cyclodecenes (1952) starting with the acyloins available by the Stoll-Prelog procedure. Oxidation gives an α-diketone convertible to the acetylene by the method of Curtius: formation of the dihydrazone and oxidation to the diazide, which

for preparation of *trans* diols (through formation and diaxial opening of the oxide, 13.8), gave a mixture of approximately equal parts of two diols. One, shown to be *trans*-cyclooctane-1,2-diol by quantitative reaction with periodic acid at room temperature (titration) and by oxidation with permanganate to suberic acid, was isolated by treatment of the mixture with acetone and anhydrous copper sulfate and distillation of the *trans*-diol acetonide from the less volatile residual diol. The

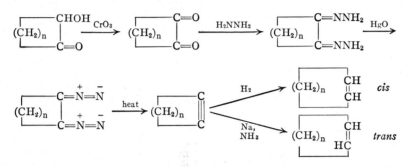

when heated loses nitrogen with production of a triple bond. As usual, selective hydrogenation of the acetylene gave the *cis* olefin and reduction with sodium and liquid ammonia the *trans* isomer. In the cyclononene and cyclodecene series, as in the cyclooctene series, the *cis* isomer is the more stable. In the C_{11} series, however, the stability relation is reversed to *trans* > *cis*, as in open-chain alkenes.

Ring size also affects reaction rates. Thus Ziegler (1954) found the rates of reaction of *trans*-cycloalkenes with phenyl azide to correspond approximately to the following ratios: C_8, 20,000; C_9, 2000; C_{10}, 20; C_{11}, 1. Cyclodecanone does not add hydrogen cyanide, and hence the carbonyl group is highly hindered.

That reactions of C_8–C_{11} cyclic compounds often proceed abnormally was observed in 1952 by Cope and by Prelog. Cope, investigating the preparation of the *cis*- and *trans*-cyclooctane-1,2-diols, obtained the former, as expected, by oxidation of *cis*-cyclooctene with osmium tetroxide in combination with hydrogen peroxide or sodium chlorate. The reaction of *cis*-cyclooctene with performic acid (30% H_2O_2 in formic acid), the standard reagent

latter, which crystallizes from ethyl acetate in needles, m.p. 86°, was also obtained along with the

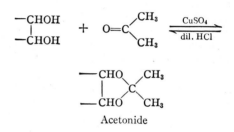

Acetonide

trans-1,2-diol by the action of formic acid on the preformed oxide I, followed by saponification of the initially formed formate. The abnormal diol forms a diacetate and on Oppenauer oxidation yields a diketone, and therefore it is a disecondary alcohol. Failure to react with periodic acid and with acetone showed that it is not a *vic*-glycol. Oxidation with permanganate and identification of the products as oxalic and adipic acid established the presence of the chains CCCCC and CC, consistent with formula III. That the carbon skeleton is still intact

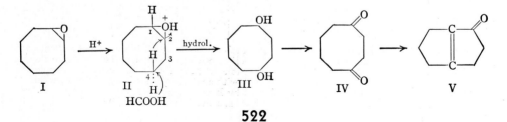

was shown by pyrolysis to a mixture of dienes, which on hydrogenation afforded cyclooctane. That the abnormal product is actually cyclooctane-1,4-diol (III) was proved by treatment of the diketone IV with sulfuric acid, which induced intramolecular aldolization to give the known bicyclo ketone V (liquid), isolated by steam distillation and characterized as the semicarbazone (m.p. 238°).

The explanation of the abnormal reaction advanced by Cope is that a hydrogen atom at C_4, which in the eight-membered ring is sterically adjacent to the 1,2-oxide ring, participates in the displacement reaction resulting in ring fission. The reaction can be interpreted as a hydride ion shift from C_4 to C_2 in the protonated oxide (II) with synchronous attack by the solvent at the resulting C_4-carbonium ion. This proximity, or transannular, effect is evidently due to the special conformation of the medium size ring.

Whereas *cis*-cycloheptene and *cis*- and *trans*-cyclododecene react normally on performic acid oxidation, the C_9, C_{10}, and C_{11} cycloalkenes give chiefly abnormal products. Thus *trans*-cyclodecene (I) gave a complicated mixture from which five products were separated by chromatography. Three were

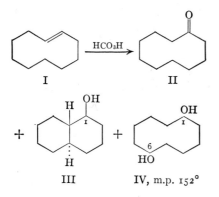

I   II   III   IV, m.p. 152°

identified as cyclodecanone (II), a *trans-α*-decalol (III), and cyclodecane-1,6-diol (IV); the latter product evidently arises through a transannular displacement similar to that discussed above. The other two products, m.p. 98° and 63°, have the composition of bicyclic diols, $C_{10}H_{18}O_2$. *cis*-Cyclodecene (V) on oxidation gave the allylic alcohol VI, a 1,6-diol (VII) stereoisomeric with IV, and two isomers of the formula $C_{10}H_{18}O_2$, one (m.p. 98°) identical with that in the other series. A proximity effect is operative also in peracid oxidation of cyclononene, for two stereoisomeric 1,5-diols were isolated.

Comparison of the rates of reaction of the cyclononenes and cyclooctenes with peracids established

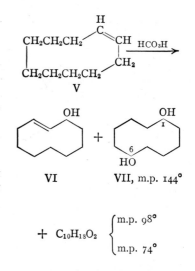

VI   VII, m.p. 144°

$+ \ C_{10}H_{18}O_2 \begin{cases} \text{m.p. } 98° \\ \\ \text{m.p. } 74° \end{cases}$

that the *trans* double bond is more reactive than the *cis* and therefore more strained. This observation was useful in elucidation of the configuration of caryophyllene, a hydrocarbon constituent of oil of cloves. Early work (1834–88) established the formula $C_{15}H_{24}$ and the presence of two double bonds, and therefore of two rings (4.28). Oxidative degradations in several laboratories eventually established the presence of a four-membered ring fused to a nine-membered ring in a carbon skeleton made up of three isoprene units linked head-to-tail. The larger ring contains one exocyclic double bond

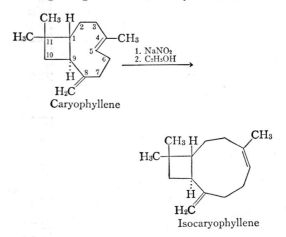

Caryophyllene

Isocaryophyllene

(=CH$_2$) and one endocyclic double bond, the configuration of which remained to be elucidated. Caryophyllene very readily undergoes isomerization and cyclization and thus appears strained. It reacts with nitrous acid to form a beautiful blue addition compound, which is decomposed by the action of

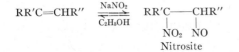

Nitrosite

ethanol with regeneration of a hydrocarbon which, however, is the isomeric substance isocaryophyllene. Barton (1953) found that caryophyllene reacts more rapidly than isocaryophyllene with peracids and deduced the *trans* configuration for the former and the *cis* for the latter.

An abnormal reaction of a different type was observed by Blomquist (1955) on pyrolysis of cyclononyl acetate. Cyclononene was a minor product (25%), and the main product (70%) is the open-chain diene, 1,8-nonadiene. Blomquist inter-

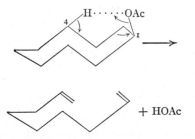

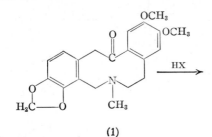

+ HOAc

prets the formation of the diene as a transannular 1,4-elimination of acetic acid involving an intermediate six-membered ring transition state.

R. Robinson postulated a transannular interaction to account for the fact that certain salts of the alkaloid protopine (1) do not show infrared absorption characteristic of the carbonyl group. He suggested that these salts are neutralized in-

Cope (1955) encountered a proximity effect of a further type in investigating the reduction of cyclodecane-1-ol-6-one oxime (I). The amino alcohol

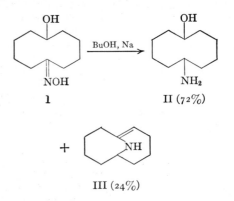

II (72%)

+ III (24%)

was produced in both *cis* and *trans* forms, but was not the exclusive product of either hydrogenation or chemical reduction (sodium–butanol). In the latter case the amine III was obtained in appreciable amounts. Hydrogenation of III established the presence of one double bond and its position was deduced from the appearance in the ultraviolet spectrum of an absorption band at 226 mμ characteristic of a vinylamine (confirmed by infrared absorption). Formation of an alkali-insoluble benzenesulfonamide confirmed the secondary amine character, and Hofmann degradation established the cyclic structure. Formation of III is considered due to the spatial proximity of the two functional groups in I.

Strain Energy. — The strain energy evident in

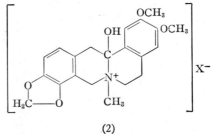

(1)   (2)

ternally and have the structure (2). This proximity effect has been investigated extensively with simpler related bases by Leonard[3] (1954–55). Internal bonding is appreciable only in C_9 and C_{10} rings and disappears from C_{11} on; it decreases with increasing size of the N-alkyl group, and is dependent upon the relative positions of the tertiary nitrogen and the carbonyl group.

rings of medium size is attributable to repulsions between proximate hydrogen atoms. Since the repulsive force and consequent strain increases with increasing proximity, some indication of the relative strain energies of the cycloalkanes is afforded by the distances between hydrogen centers, as recorded in the table (measurements made with Barton models, 13.7). In cyclopentane the eclipsed hydrogens

[3] Nelson J. Leonard, b. 1916, Newark, N. J.; Ph.D. Columbia (Elderfield), postdoctoral work Illinois (R. Adams); Illinois

of each ethane or 1,2-unit are separated by only 2.33 Å, as compared with a distance of 2.50 Å for the skew hydrogens of cyclohexane, and the heats of combustion per methylene group of cyclopentane and cyclohexane show that the C_5 hydrocarbon is indeed the more strained. Cyclohexane hydrogens in the 1,3-relationship are too far separated (2.65 Å) to exert appreciable repulsive force, and in the higher hydrocarbons both 1,3- and bow-stern interactions,

stable conformation possible, shown for C_7 and C_8 in the photographs. The increase in strain energy from C_6 to C_7 to C_8 to C_9 evident from heats of combustion is paralleled in decreasing H—H distances in the 1,2-units. The heat of combustion of cyclodecane is not available, but the yield minimum at C_9–C_{10} in cyclization reactions shows that C_9 and C_{10} rings are both under severe strain. The proximity distances suggest strains greater than

Strain Energy and H—H Distances of Cycloalkanes

	Heat of combustion kg.-cal./CH$_2$	1,2-units		1,3-units		Bow-stern	
		No.	Å	No.	Å	No.	Å
C_5	158.7	5	2.33				
C_6	157.4	6	2.50	3	(2.65)		
C_7	158.3	7	2.40	3	(2.40)		
C_8	158.6	8	2.33	4	(2.10)	1	1.85
C_9	158.8	9	2.38			4	2.00
C_{10}		10	2.43	3	1.90		

since these units are not as rigid as 1,2-units, appear to contribute to strain energy only if the hydrogen centers are closer than 2.1 Å. The measurements for the higher hydrocarbons apply to the most

those in the C_7 and C_8 rings, since 1,2-interactions of comparable magnitude are, in the C_9–C_{10} rings, reinforced by three or four strong 1,3 or bow-stern interactions.

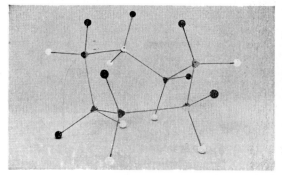 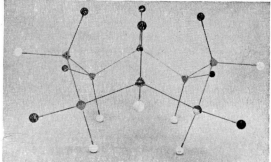

II. 10

SYNTHESIS OF SUCROSE (*After Chapter 14*)

Enzymatic synthesis of sucrose was achieved before chemical synthesis. Since the widely distributed enzyme invertase hydrolyzes the disaccharide to glucose and fructose, and since enzymatic reactions are often reversible, several attempts were made to synthesize sucrose from the two hexoses in the presence of invertase, but without success. The presence in sucrose-producing plants of con-

siderable amounts of hexose phosphates suggested that phosphorylation may be an essential step, and indeed Cori[1] and Cori[2] demonstrated (1937–41) that the synthesis of glycogen in animals involves condensation of units of glucose-1-phosphate (1), formed from glucose by reactions (2) and (3). C. S. Hanes (1940) proved that the synthesis and degradation of starch in plants similarly involves glucose-

[1] Carl Cori, b. 1896 Prague; M.D. Prague; Washington Univ. School Med., St. Louis; Nobel Prize 1947
[2] Gerty Cori, b. 1896 Prague; M.D. Prague; Washington Univ. School Med., St. Louis; Nobel Prize 1947

I-phosphate. M. Doudoroff and W. Z. Hassid[3] (1943) isolated from *Pseudomonas saccharophila* bacilli a partially purified enzyme which, in the presence of phosphate, catalyzes phosphorolysis of

W. W. Pigman and R. M. Goepp, Jr. in *Chemistry of the Carbohydrates* (1948) comment that "the chemical synthesis of sucrose remains one of the outstanding unsolved problems of sugar chemistry."

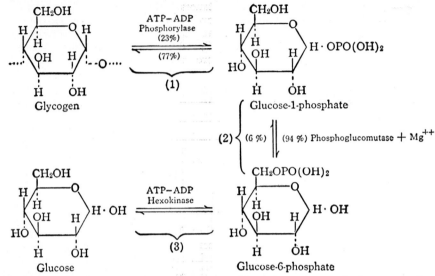

sucrose to glucose-1-phosphate and fructose. With H. A. Barker (1944) they proved the reaction to be reversible and isolated crystalline sucrose from a buffered solution of the two hydrolytic products and the enzyme, named sucrose phosphorylase. The enzyme is specific with regard to the glucose portion, but fructose can be replaced by a number of ketohexoses and aldohexoses. The requirement of glucose is due to the fact that the enzymatic reaction involves formation of a glucose—enzyme complex:

Glucose-1-phosphate + Enzyme ⇌
Glucose—Enzyme + Phosphate

The equilibrium was established by observation that if glucose-1-phosphate is incubated with the enzyme in the presence of radioactive phosphate, a rapid redistribution of the isotope between organic and inorganic phosphate occurs.

Completion or confirmation of the evidence of structure is often one objective prompting attempted chemical synthesis, but synthesis of natural products has always been an attractive goal even though the evidence of structure is secure and the product as abundantly available as sucrose. Although the structure, α-D-glucopyranosyl-β-D-fructofuranoside (14.17), was firmly established by 1930, efforts to effect synthesis continued without abate. Thus

Several investigators had attempted synthesis by condensation of the tetraacetyl derivatives of glucose and fructose. Acetylation of glucose gives the 1β-pentaacetyl derivative I, which reacts with hydrobromic acid with Walden inversion to give tetraacetyl α-bromoglucose, II. The bromine atom in II is very reactive and easily replaced by hydroxyl to give a mixture of 2,3,4,6-tetraacetyl anomers, III. A similar tetraacetyl fructose derivative having a free anomeric hydroxyl group, IV, is available by acetolysis of the triacetate of the fructoside inulin and hydrolysis of the intermediate bromide. Many attempts were made to condense these tetraacetates of glucose and fructose in the presence of a dehydrating agent in the hope of obtaining octaacetylsucrose. Such a condensation might afford the desired α-glucosido-β-fructoside, but could equally well give the alternate α-α, β-β, or β-α disaccharides. The only pure product isolated was the octaacetate of the β-α isomer (isosucrose, J. C. Irvine, Univ. St. Andrews, 1929). A claim that sucrose octaacetate is formed on heating the tetraacetates with zinc chloride (A. Pictet and H. Vogel, 1929) could not be substantiated and was later withdrawn (Pictet, 1933).

The synthetic objective was finally achieved by R. U. Lemieux[4] and G. Huber (1953) from consideration of the mechanism of replacement reactions.

[3] William Zev Hassid; b. 1897 Jaffa, Palestine; Ph.D. California; Univ. California
[4] Raymond U. Lemieux, b. 1920 Lac la Biche, Alberta, Canada; Ph.D. McGill (Purves), postdoctoral work Ohio State (Wolfrom); Saskatoon, Univ. Ottawa

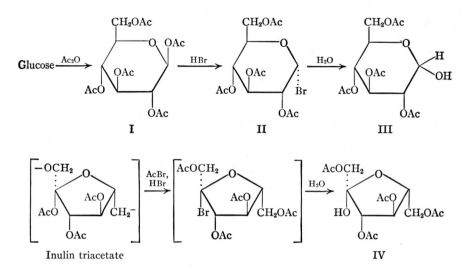

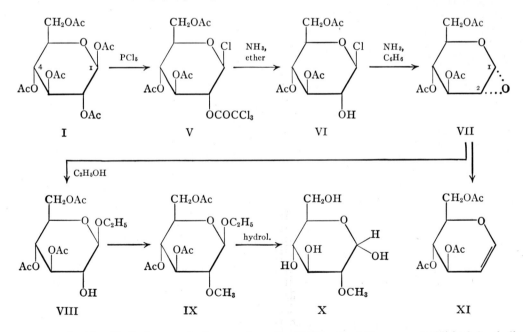

The background for the work was a discovery by Percy Brigl (Tübingen, 1922) that β-glucose penta-acetate, I, reacts with phosphorus pentachloride to give a product, V, with chlorine at the anomeric position 1 and a trichloroacetoxy group at 2 derived from chlorination of the acetoxy group. By careful

passing ammonia into a suspension of VI in benzene for several days, Brigl observed gradual replacement of the original solid by ammonium chloride and from the solution isolated the crystalline oxide VII, resulting from *trans* elimination of HCl with inversion at C_1. The structure of this substance, later called

treatment at 0° with a limited amount of ammonia in dry ether, the trichloroacetyl group could be selectively eliminated as CCl_3CONH_2 to give the triacetate VI, having chlorine in the anomeric position, *trans* to a free hydroxyl group at C_2. On

the Brigl anhydride, was established by indirect conversion to a dichloride which was recognized as the *trans* 1,2-dichloride by its ready reaction with zinc dust to give crystalline glucal triacetate, XI, which Fischer had obtained in high yield (1914) by shaking an acetic acid solution of tetraacetyl α-bromoglucose with zinc dust:

$$\overset{\text{O}}{\overbrace{\text{AcOCH}_2\text{CHCH(OAc)CH(OAc)CH(OAc)CHBr}}}$$

$$+ \ 2\,\text{H} \longrightarrow \overset{\text{O}}{\overbrace{\text{AcOCH}_2\text{CHCH(OAc)CH(OAc)CH}}}\text{=CH}$$

$$+ \ \text{HBr} \ + \ \text{AcOH}$$

Brigl found that the oxide ring of VII opens with unusual ease; for example, the substance reacts with ethanol at room temperature with usual diaxial opening of the ring to give the β-glycosidic ether VIII. The direction of ring opening is understandable on the assumption that the reaction involves attack by $C_2H_5O^-$ at one of the two oxidic carbons; since C_1 is linked to the electronegative pyranoside oxygen, it is polarized more than C_2 in a sense that makes it the more inviting center. Confirmatory evidence of the structure assigned was adduced by W. J. Hickinbottom (Birmingham, 1928) by methylation of VIII (CH_3I, Ag_2O) to IX and hydrolysis to X, the structure of which follows from observation that it forms a phenylhydrazone but not an osazone.

In 1950 both M. P. Bardolph and G. H. Coleman (State Univ. Iowa) and A. Dyverman and B. Lindberg (Roy. Techn. Inst., Stockholm) found that

siders prone to react in the specific conformation VIIa. In the half-chair ring the pyranoside oxygen

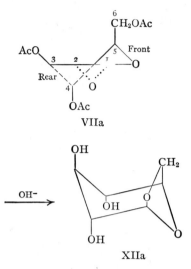

atom is coplanar with C_1, C_2, and C_3; C_5 projects above this plane to the front and C_4 projects below it to the rear. The six-ring arrangement appears from models to be attended with more strain than expected for levoglucosan, as represented in XIIa, and this factor may accentuate reactivity derived

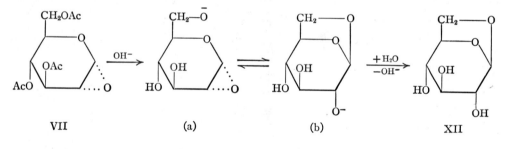

the Brigl anhydride VII is converted very rapidly into levoglucosan, XII, a levorotatory anhydro sugar first prepared by Tanret (1894) by mild heat treatment of glucose. Lemieux interpreted the alkaline rearrangement in terms of participation of the neighboring hydroxyl group at C_6: the anion (a) is formed to some extent in the alkaline medium and rearranges into the more stable anion (b), which affords levoglucosan (XII) with regeneration of hydroxide ion. B. Ottar, working in Hassel's laboratory (1947) established by an electron-diffraction investigation that in cyclohexene oxide the six-carbon ring has what may be described as a half-chair conformation. Lemieux assumes the same arrangement for the Brigl anhydride, which he con-

from the strained epoxide ring. P. Karrer and W. Fioroni (1923) found the following heats of combustion: Brigl's anhydride, 4594.8 cal./g.; triacetyllevoglucosan, 4530.5 cal./g.

Brigl had found his anhydride to react with methanol to give β-methylglucoside triacetate as the sole product, as shown by conversion to the known tetraacetate, whereas for coupling to fructose to produce sucrose, formation of an α-glucoside link is required. However, Brigl obtained αβ-mixtures in some cases and found that phenol reacts chiefly to give the α-glucoside. Hickinbottom and later Hardegger (ETH Zurich, 1948) found that secondary alcohols of higher molecular weight (menthol, cholesterol) tend to give αβ-mixtures. Regarding a fructofuranose component in the same category, Lemieux reasoned that in a high-temperature condensation with this rather hindered alcohol opening of the oxide ring in the desired direction would involve neighboring group participation of the 6-acetoxy group, as in the alkaline isomerization to levoglucosan. The CH₂OAc group in VIIa, being axial, shields the approach of an external agent but

(IV) was thus expected to attack C₁ of the ion XIII with inversion to the desired configuration. The components were heated in concentrated benzene solution in a sealed tube in the range 80°–120° for periods of 72–168 hrs. The yield, as determined by isotopic dilution analysis, was only 2–9%, but techniques of preparative paper chromatography after deacetylation and of chromatography on

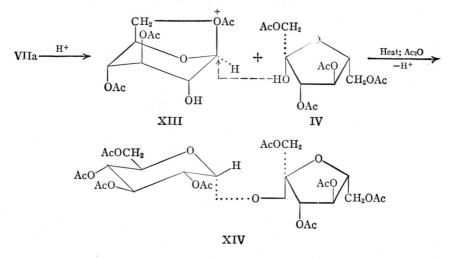

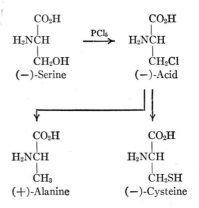

is available for cyclization to the ion **XIII** on diaxial opening of the epoxide ring. The second component 1,3,4,6-tetraacetyl-D-fructofuranoside

Magnesol-Celite after reacetylation enabled successful isolation of an octaacetate identical with that (**XIV**) from sucrose.

II. 11

CORRELATION OF CONFIGURATIONS (*After Chapter 16*)

The statement made without comment in Part I that the natural amino acids derived from proteins all correspond to one another in the configuration of the α-carbon atom and belong to the stereochemical series opposite to that of D-glyceraldehyde is based upon a considerable body of experimental evidence. About half of the acids have been correlated by chemical interconversions, effected mainly in the schools of E. Fischer, P. Karrer,[1] and P. A. Levene[2] (1907–1930). An example is the correlation of levorotatory serine with two other natural acids, one dextro- and the other levorotatory (E. Fischer). Replacement of the hydroxyl group of serine by chlorine and reduction of the resulting α-amino-β-chloropropionic acid gave alanine; replacement of

$$
\begin{array}{ccc}
\text{CO}_2\text{H} & & \text{CO}_2\text{H} \\
| & \xrightarrow{\text{PCl}_5} & | \\
\text{H}_2\text{NCH} & & \text{H}_2\text{NCH} \\
| & & | \\
\text{CH}_2\text{OH} & & \text{CH}_2\text{Cl} \\
(-)\text{-Serine} & & (-)\text{-Acid}
\end{array}
$$

$$
\begin{array}{ccc}
\text{CO}_2\text{H} & & \text{CO}_2\text{H} \\
| & & | \\
\text{H}_2\text{NCH} & & \text{H}_2\text{NCH} \\
| & & | \\
\text{CH}_3 & & \text{CH}_2\text{SH} \\
(+)\text{-Alanine} & & (-)\text{-Cysteine}
\end{array}
$$

[1] Paul Karrer, b. 1889 Moscow; Ph.D. Zurich (Werner); Univ. Zurich; Nobel Prize 1937
[2] Phoebus A. Levene, 1869–1940; b. Russia; Ph.D. St. Petersburg; Rockefeller Inst.; Science, **92**, 392 (1946)

chlorine by sulfhydryl (barium sulfide) gave natural cysteine. Since none of the reactions involve the asymmetric center, the correlations are unambiguous.

In the absence of suitable functional groups, correlation by interconversion usually is not feasible. One approach is a comparison of optical rotations. A difficulty is that most amino acids are weakly rotatory. Some are levorotatory (range: serine, $\alpha_D - 6.8°$; proline, $-85°$), some are dextrorotatory (range: alanine, $+2.7°$; arginine, $+15.5°$); cystine $(-214°)$ alone is strongly rotatory (compare cysteine $(-10.4°)$. Another difficulty is that the specific rotation of these ionic substances varies considerably with solvent, concentration, temperature, and particularly with pH, as first observed by Pasteur (1851). G. W. Glough (1915–18), and later O. Lutz (1929–31), noted that the rotations of all natural amino acids are shifted to more dextrorotatory values in the presence of a mineral acid, as can be seen from the following typical comparisons of specific rotations:

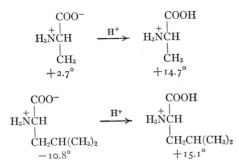

These investigators assumed that the contribution of the carboxyl or carboxylate group to the total rotation is largely independent of other substituents, and although this is now known to have been an oversimplification and the evidence thus is questionable, the conclusion that the natural acids all belong to the same series proved correct. Clough, however, mistakenly concluded that the series is that corresponding to D-lactic and D-malic acid because the latter also shows a positive shift in rotation on addition of acid.

The first substantial evidence correlating natural (+)-alanine with L(+)-lactic acid was adduced by W. Kuhn and K. Freudenberg (1933) from an extensive comparison of the molecular rotations (14.15) of derivatives of the following two types:

CH₃CH(NHR)COOH, CH₃CH(OR)COOH
CH₃CH(NH₂)COOR, CH₃CH(OH)COOR

For example, acetylation and benzoylation produce positive shifts in M_D in both the $(+)\alpha$-amino acid and the L-α-hydroxy acid, an indication that the former belongs to the L-series. However, the relationship is sometimes obscured by solvation effects, and exceptions exist to the relationship noted in the example. Kuhn and Freudenberg therefore investigated a large number of cases, and considered as valid only those in which the change in rotation is large, before drawing the now accepted conclusion that natural alanine belongs to the L-series, the opposite of that of the standard, D-glyceraldehyde.

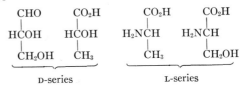

Any doubt that the natural acids from proteins are all configurationally related is dispelled by biochemical evidence. The enzyme D-amino acid oxidase, although it does not catalyze oxidation of unnatural D-amino acids, is stereospecific with respect to those substances on which it acts. The same is true of L-amino acid oxidase. The known enzymes that effect decarboxylation of amino acids (decarboxylases) act only on natural proteinoid amino acids. The method of resolution by selective enzymatic hydrolysis of a DL-acetylamino acid, applied extensively by Greenstein (16.9), provides further evidence of configurational correspondence.

Unambiguous chemical correlation was later accomplished by two groups of investigators. Hughes [3] and Ingold (1950) had established that S_N2 reactions invariably involve Walden inversion, and hence that a reaction at an asymmetric center if rigidly shown to proceed by an S_N2 mechanism provides valid evidence for purposes of correlation. They found that the reaction of a halogen compound with sodium azide can be controlled to assure bi-

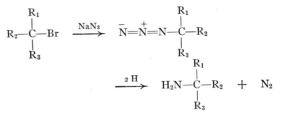

molecular substitution; the reduction of the resulting azide to an amine does not affect the asymmetric center. The conversion of D-lactic acid to α-bromo-

[3] Edward David Hughes, b. 1906 Caernarvonshire, North Wales; Ph.D. Wales (Watson); D.Sc. London (Ingold); Univ. Coll., London

propionic acid had already been shown (Hughes and Ingold, 1937) to proceed, in the reverse direction, with inversion. Hence it remained merely to convert this acid through the azide to the amine to complete the correlation. The product proved to

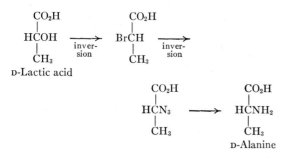

D-Lactic acid

D-Alanine

be unnatural alanine, and hence natural alanine is identified as L.

The second correlation of alanine with glyceraldehyde was achieved by M. L. Wolfrom,[4] R. U. Lemieux, and S. M. Olin (1949) through glucosamine, an amino sugar first obtained in 1878 as a product of hydrolysis of the polysaccharide chitin, of lobster shells. Its constitution as a 2-amino-2-desoxyaldohexose was inferred from its reducing

properties and by reaction with phenylhydrazine to form glucosazone (F. Tiemann,[5] 1887). The structure

$$CH_2OHCHOHCHOHCHOHCH(NH_2)CHO$$

was confirmed by synthesis of the amino sugar from arabinose (E. Fischer and H. Leuchs,[6] 1902). The chemical evidence cited does not establish the configuration at C_2, since it does not distinguish between the two possibilities: glucosamine and mannosamine. The former configuration was inferred from various properties but was not established until 1939 (W. N. Haworth, W. H. G. Lake, and S. Peat). Peat[7] had proved (1938) that a *vic*-oxide group in a sugar derivative is opened by alkaline reagents to give two isomeric sugars by independent rupture of both C—O bonds of the oxide, with Walden inversion at the carbon atom at which rupture occurs (*trans* diaxial cleavage, 13.8). Treatment of the oxide I (an anhydro sugar) with ammonia gave chiefly the 3-amino sugar derivative II. The minor product, which because of the mode of formation must have the structure and configuration of formula III, on methylation gave a product, V, identical with that prepared from glucosamine by acetylation and methylation. Glucosamine

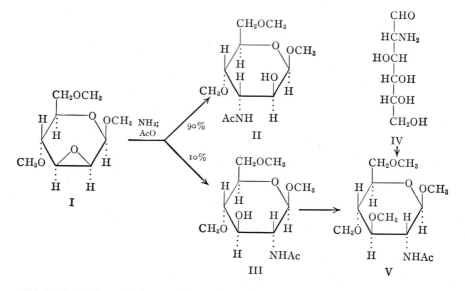

[4] Melville L. Wolfrom, b. 1909 Bellevue, Ohio; Ph.D. Northwestern (W. L. Lewis); Ohio State Univ.

[5] Ferdinand Tiemann, 1848–99; b. Rübeland, Germany; Ph.D. Berlin (Hofmann); Berlin; *Ber.*, **32**, 3239 (1899); **34**, 4403 (1901)

[6] Hermann Leuchs, 1879–1945; b. Nürnberg, Germany; Ph.D. Berlin (E. Fischer); Berlin; *Ber.*, **85**, LV (1952)

[7] Stanley Peat, b. 1902 Newcastle on Tyne; Ph.D. and D.Sc. Birmingham (W. N. Haworth); Univ. Coll. North Wales, Bangor

thus has the configuration at C_2 shown in formula IV and corresponds to glucose.†

The conversion of glucosamine into alanine for the purpose of correlation had been attempted earlier without success. Karrer (1937) had oxidized the derivative VI with lead tetraacetate with the hope that cleavage would occur between carbon atoms 3 and 4; actually the substance is cleaved at the 2,3-position to give VII. A. Neuberger studied the glycol cleavage of various other derivatives of glucosamic acid but found that, in general, excess reagent is consumed with complete destruction of hexose. The desired correlation was achieved by Wolfrom as follows. N-Acetyl-D-glucosamine was converted by reaction with ethyl mercaptan into the diethylthioketal, and the corresponding pentaacetate VIII was desulfurized with Raney nickel to IX. The O-acetyl groups were selectively removed by treatment with ammonia, and the resulting N-acetyl derivative X was oxidized with lead tetraacetate. The aldehyde XI was not isolated but was oxidized directly with bromine water to the acid. The product clearly has the configuration shown in the projection formula XIIa which, when rotated to an angle of 180°, becomes XIIb. Identity with the N-acetyl derivative of natural alanine established that the latter belongs to the L-series.

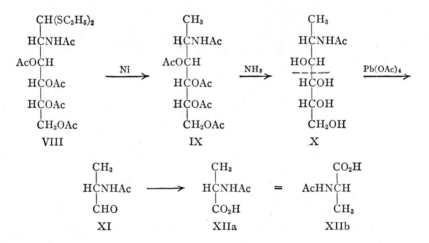

II. 12

BACTERIAL LIPIDS (*After Chapter 15*)

Certain bacteria, including the infectious bacteria of tuberculosis and of leprosy, are called acid-fast because, although they are stained only with some difficulty by rosaniline, a basic triphenylmethane dye, they tenaciously retain dye once applied and, unlike other nonacid-fast bacteria, are not decolorized by vigorous washing with alcoholic acid. Both the slow penetration of dye and the fastness to acid are attributable to the presence of a characteristic fatty envelope. As part of a cooperative project sponsored by the American Tuberculosis Association, which involved culturing of human tubercle bacilli on the huge scale required for chemical investigation of different constituents,

† The enantiomer of D-glucosamine, L-glucosamine, is one of the structural units of the antibiotic streptomycin. The only other natural amino sugar known is chondrosamine, which is 2-amino-2-desoxy-D-galactose.

R. J. Anderson[1] undertook investigation of the lipid components of the fatty capsules (1927). The non-saponifiable fraction contained no sterols. The fatty acids present were found esterified not with glycerol, even though the organisms had been grown on a medium in which glycerol was the chief carbon

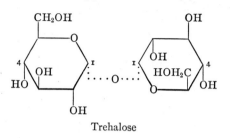

Trehalose

source, but with the nonreducing α,α-disaccharide trehalose, previously isolated from ergot of rye and other fungi.

The fatty acid mixture resulting on saponification was unusual. Relatively large amounts of palmitic

was resolved by reaction with phthalic anhydride and crystallization of the brucine salt of the resulting acid phthalate. Each active form of the alcohol was then put through the synthetic sequence shown: conversion to the bromide, malonic ester synthesis to add a two-carbon chain, Bouveault-Blanc reduction of the ester, condensation of the corresponding CdCl-derivative with an acid chloride ester of a dibasic acid, reduction of the carbonyl group (Clemmensen method, see 19.9), and saponification. The very weakly rotatory active forms melt at 13° and the dl-form at 26°. A mixture of the natural acid with the (−) form melted at 11–12° and a mixture with the (+) form at 25°; tuberculostearic acid is thus identified as the (−)-epimer.

A second novel component isolated by Anderson (1929, 1936) was named phthioic acid and characterized as an acid of the probable formula $C_{26}H_{52}O_2$, m.p. 20°, αD + 12.6°. This substance attracted considerable interest because on interperitoneal injection into normal animals it produced typical tubercular lesions. Cason later (1951) made a care-

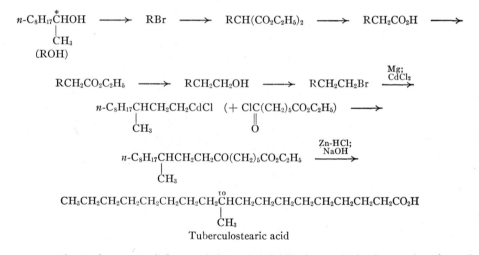

Tuberculostearic acid

acid were present, but only traces of the usual C_{18}-fatty acids. Instead, a number of unique acids are present. One, named tuberculostearic acid, was shown by various degradations to be 10-methyl-stearic acid. It is interesting that the branching methyl substituent lowers the melting point from 70° (stearic) to 10–11°. Although the natural acid seemed to be optically inactive, Cason[2] later suspected that the substance is one of a pair of epimers of very weak rotatory power, an inference established by synthesis of the (+) and (−) forms. Decanol-2

ful distillation analysis of 24 g. of crude methyl ester obtained from Anderson. This was fractionally distilled at 2 mm. pressure through a 4-ft. column and 39 fractions were characterized as to boiling point, refractive index, optical activity, and ultraviolet absorption. The results suggested the presence of at least twelve compounds ranging in molecular weight from C_{23} to C_{31}. Constancy of all properties indicated that fractions 17–20 contained a single, pure ester component. The corresponding acid, named C_{27}-phthienoic acid, was assigned the formula

[1] Rudolph J. Anderson, b. 1879 Harna, Sweden; Ph.D. Cornell; Yale
[2] James Cason, b. 1912 Murfreesboro, Tenn.; Ph.D. Yale (R. J. Anderson); postdoctoral work Harvard (Fieser); de Pauw, Vanderbilt, Univ. Calif., Berkeley

$C_{27}H_{52}O_2$ and had the constants: m.p. 22° and 31° (polymorphic forms), $\alpha D + 17.8°$; $n_D^{25°}$ 1.4666; $\lambda 216$ mμ; 4 methyl groups (Kuhn-Roth); methyl ester, m.p. 14°, 31°; $\alpha D +14.7°$; $n_D^{25°}$ 1.4666; $\lambda 218$ mμ. The ultraviolet absorption is that characteristic of α,β-unsaturated acids, and Cason drew the further inference that the chromophoric system is α-substituted: $—CH{=}C(R)CO_2H$. C_{27}-Phthienoic acid proved comparable to Anderson's phthioic acid in capacity for producing tubercular lesions in test animals. Cason (1956) investigated the fatty acids of an avirulent (noninfectious) strain of tubercle bacilli and did not find C_{27}-phthienoic acid.

A different method of separation was employed in an independent investigation by Polgar [3] (1948–54) of lipid material (145 g.) prepared by the Glaxo Laboratories by extraction of 50 lbs. of steam-killed cells (*B. tuberculosis*, human type) in a Soxhlet

acid. Polgar established that mycolipenic acid has the structure I by the following degradations. Ozonization of the mixture gave pyruvic acid, consistent with the formulation as an α-methyl α,β-unsaturated acid. Permanganate oxidation of the methyl ester mixture left the saturated component unchanged and gave an acid II, characterized as an α-methyl acid by Barbier-Wieland degradation to the methyl ketone V (CHI$_3$ test) by the steps:

$$RCH(CH_3)CO_2CH_3 \;+\; 2\,C_6H_5MgBr \;\longrightarrow\;$$
$$RCH(CH_3)C(OH)(C_6H_5)_2 \;\longrightarrow\;$$
$$RC(CH_3){=}C(C_6H_5)_2 \;\longrightarrow\; RC(CH_3){=}O.$$

The ketone V was isolated as a by-product of oxidation of I to II. The saturated acid II was converted through the α-bromo acid to the α,β-unsaturated acid III, which on oxidation (as ester) gave, in part, the optically inactive methyl ketone IV.

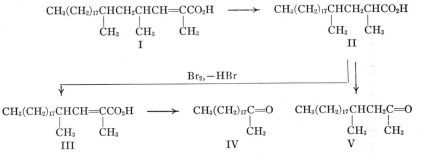

apparatus with acetone (30 l.), and then with isopropyl ether. Since the objective was to characterize the acid components, and since neutral fats, phospholipids, and waxes (RCO_2R') probably contain at least some of the same acid components, the total lipid fraction was hydrolyzed with methanolic potassium hydroxide. Mild hydrolysis liberated a fairly simple dextrorotatory mixture of acids, which could thus be separated from a levorotatory mixture released on more drastic hydrolysis. The dextrorotatory mixture was esterified and distilled; after removal of a considerable amount (23 g.) of material of lower molecular weight, a fraction, b.p. 190–225°/0.2 mm., was collected and chromatographed to give 5.2 g. of ester, $\alpha D + 7.4°$. This was hydrolyzed and the acid converted into the potassium salt, which proved to be separable into two salts differing considerably in their solubility in ether. The more soluble salt yielded a liquid acid, $\alpha D + 10.3°$. The potassium salt of lesser solubility in ether yielded a solid acid (2.6 g.), which was characterized as a mixture of a saturated component and an unsaturated component named mycolipenic

The semicarbazone, m.p. 125°, did not depress the melting point of the semicarbazones of either n-$C_{18}H_{37}COCH_3$ or n-$C_{17}H_{35}COCH_3$, both of which melt at 126°, but X-ray crystallographic comparison established identity with the former. The structure I was later confirmed by synthesis and the synthetic acid shown by infrared comparison to be identical with Cason's C_{27}-phthienoic acid (C. and J. Asselineau, S. Ställberg-Stenhagen, and E. Stenhagen, Göteborg, 1956).

Anderson also investigated (1931–) the constituents of a so-called leprosy bacillus and isolated a polysaccharide, a phosphatide, a wax, two new alcohols of high molecular weight, and a series of saturated and unsaturated fatty acids. However, the organism studied had been isolated from a case of human leprosy in Honolulu in 1909 and cultivated since then in the Mulford Biological Laboratories on a synthetic medium, and in the opinion of bacteriologists H. Zinsser and S. Bayne-Jones it is probably not related etiologically to leprosy.

It is of interest that chaulmoogra oil, a fatty acid glyceride, has been used for centuries in India and

[3] Nicholas Polgar, b. 1904 Budapest; Ph.D. Vienna (Späth); D.Phil. Oxford (Robinson); Oxford

China for treatment of the two diseases caused by fat encapsulated, acid-fast bacteria, leprosy and tuberculosis. The oil is usually administered orally and, since it is irritating in large amounts, treatment must be extended over years. The glycerides are probably converted in the body to the free fatty acids, which are the active agents; the acids themselves are effective when administered in suitably dispersed form (in stearic acid). Chaulmoogra oil is the native name (East Indian) for the seed fat of *Hydnocarpus kurzii*. Investigations by F. B. Power (Wellcome Chem. Res. Lab., London, 1904–07) and by R. L. Shriner[4] and R. Adams (1925) established the structures of the main acid components, hydnocarpic acid and chaulmoogric acid,

$$CH=CH$$
$$| \quad \quad \overset{*}{>}CH(CH_2)_{10}COOH$$
$$CH_2-CH_2$$

Hydnocarpic acid ($C_{16}H_{28}O_2$)
$[\alpha]_D + 68°$; m.p. 59–60°

$$CH=CH$$
$$| \quad \quad \overset{*}{>}CH(CH_2)_{12}COOH$$
$$CH_2-CH_2$$

Chaulmoogric acid ($C_{18}H_{32}O_2$)
$[\alpha]_D + 56°$; m.p. 71°

$$CH=CH$$
$$| \quad \quad \overset{*}{>}CH(CH_2)_6CH=CH(CH_2)_4COOH$$
$$CH_2-CH_2$$

Gorlic acid ($C_{18}H_{30}O_2$)
$[\alpha]_D + 61°$; m.p. 6°

of minor components having shorter side chains (n = 8, 6, 4), and of a dienic acid component, gorlic acid. R. Adams synthesized a large number

of analogous cyclopentane acids and branched chain acids and found that leprocidal activity *in vitro* parallels ability of the acids to depress surface tension; probably the antibacterial activity is a result of impairment of the fatty envelope of the bacilli.

The bacillus of diphtheria is related to those of tuberculosis and leprosy. It is not acid fast, but has the related classification of Gram positive. Hans C. J. Gram, a Danish physician, developed (1884) a technique for staining bacteria with the basic triphenylmethane dye gentian violet and iodine. Cells that retain the dye after washing with alcohol or acetone are Gram positive, those that are decolorized are Gram negative. Lederer[5] (1951–) found the lipids of *Mycobacterium tuberculosis* to contain a series of acid components of the type $RCHOHCHR'CO_2H$, called mycolic acids. Two related acids were isolated from the lipids of *Corynebacterium diphtheria*. One pure component acid, corynomycolenic acid (oil, n_D^{25} 1.4758; methyl ester, $\alpha_D + 9°$), was characterized by degradation as having the structure XII, shown below, which was confirmed by synthesis. The key step required conversion of an acid, RCO_2H, into a β-keto ester of the type $RCOCHR'CO_2Et$ (Et = ethyl), and this was accomplished by use of a neat synthetic method introduced by R. E. Bowman and W. D. Fordham (Birkbeck Coll., London, 1952). An alkyl-substituted malonic ester (I) is saponified with exactly one equivalent of alcoholic potassium hydroxide to produce the half ester (II) and, for protection of the free acid group, this is condensed with dihydropyran in benzene solution with *p*-toluene-sulfonic acid as catalyst to give (III). Condensation of the sodio derivative of (III) with an acid chloride gives (IV), and when this is heated in a

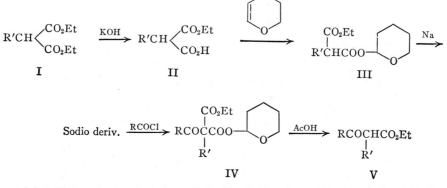

[4] Ralph L. Shriner, b. 1899 Iowa City; Ph.D. Illinois (R. Adams); N. Y. Expt. Sta., Illinois, State Univ. Iowa
[5] Edgar Lederer, b. 1908 Vienna; Ph.D. Vienna (Späth); postdoctoral work Heidelberg (Kuhn), Pasteur Institute; Sorbonne, Paris

medium weakly acidified with acetic acid, dihydropyran is eliminated, the carboxyl group liberated suffers decarboxylation, and the β-keto ester (V) is formed in good yield. For the synthesis of corynomycolenic acid (XII), Lederer and Julio Pudles (1954) employed the acid chloride of natural palmitoleic acid, $CH_3(CH_2)_5CH=CH(CH_2)_7CO_2H$, the

converted on elimination of the protective group into X. Reduction of the keto group of X with sodium borohydride gave the alcohol XI. The product was purified by saponification and chromatography of XII on alumina by elution with ether containing 3% of acetic acid. Reesterification (CH_2N_2) and further chromatography gave the pure

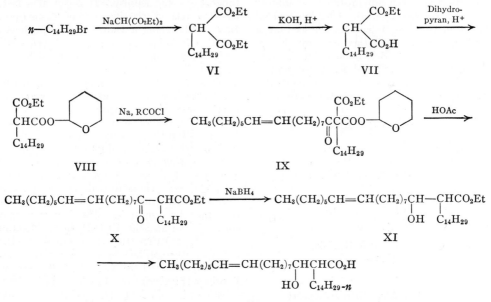

C_{16} analog of oleic acid. Condensation of this acid chloride with the sodio derivative of VIII gave IX,

methyl ester of *dl*-corynomycolenic acid, identical in infrared spectrum with the ester of the natural acid.

II. 13

AZASERINE (*After Chapter 16*)

In the course of a broad search for chemical agents capable of inhibiting tumor growth, a group at the Sloan-Kettering Institute for Cancer Research (C. C. Stock, *et al.*, 1954) found that culture broth produced by a *Streptomyces* contains an antibiotic principle with promising antitumor activity. Initial attempts at isolation were guided by a bioassay method involving inhibition of a virus-induced tumor (Crocker mouse sarcoma 180), but later antitumor activity was correlated with inhibition of growth of the yeast microorganism *Kloekera brevis*, and this more convenient bioassay method was used as a guide to isolation, conducted by S. Fusari,[1] *et al.*, of Parke, Davis and Co. Isolation was complicated by the marked instability of the

active principle to acids and bases; the substance was found reasonably stable in the pH range 6–8, but only at temperatures not higher than 40°. In preliminary processing it was found that both inhibitory biological activities showed excellent correlation with the ultraviolet and infrared absorption spectra of partially purified concentrates. Thus the intensity of a band at 4.66μ (IR) increased with increasing biological potency and could be taken as a guide in evaluation of chromatogram fractions. The broth was slurried with 1% of a filter aid and filtered to remove mycelium. The combined filtrate and washing (46 liters) was flash evaporated in a circulatory still at <35° to 2.3 liters. The concentrate was diluted extensively with ethanol, a pre-

[1] Salvatore A. Fusari, b. 1922 New York; Ph.D. Ohio State Univ. (J. B. Brown); Parke, Davis and Co.

cipitate of inactive material was removed, and the alcoholic filtrate (23 liters) was used as the charge in a first chromatographic step. The column was a four-inch double wall Pyrex pipe containing 4 kg. of alumina, which had been adjusted to pH 5 and then heated at 200° to activate it. The charge was introduced, and after the active material had been adsorbed the column was eluted in succession with 90%, 75%, and 50% ethanol and then with water, at a flow rate of 8 l./hr. The first 93 l. of eluate contained no active material, and the activity was all concentrated in seven terminal fractions totalling 13 l. Further purification was effected by adsorption on carbon-Celite columns and elution with a solution of 1.5% acetone in water. Some of the experiments were done with 10 kg. each of carbon and Celite. Material thus obtained was dried from the frozen state to a yellow-green powder which could be crystallized from 90% ethanol.

Analyses for C, H, N, and O corresponded to the formula $C_5H_7N_3O_4$. Potentiometric titration indicated the molecular weight 175 and a pK_a value of 8.55. The latter observation coupled with the hydrophilic character of the substance and a positive ninhydrin color test strongly suggested the presence of an amino acid function, an inference confirmed by the infrared spectrum, which has several bands

the first three types. An azide structure is consistent with the observation that the nitrogen liberated on acid decomposition corresponds to two thirds of the total nitrogen. However, ninhydrin-carbon dioxide determination gave a value for α-amino acid nitrogen corresponding to the remaining one third of the total. A diazo ketone structure could be discounted because of infrared bands characteristic of an ester carbonyl group rather than of a ketone carbonyl group.

The remaining possibility that the substance contains a diazo ester group was confirmed by the ultraviolet absorption maximum at 250 mμ (E = 19,722), corresponding to that of ethyl diazoacetate, $N_2CHCO_2C_2H_5$, 250 mμ (E = 18,240). The structure I was then proved by hydrolysis of the antibiotic with hot 2M formic acid and identification of the products as glycolic acid (II) and L-serine (III). The former was identified from the Rf value of the p-bromophenacyl derivative, p-BrC$_6$H$_4$CO-CH$_2$OCOCH$_2$OH, and the latter by optical rotation and spectrographic data and as the 2,4-dinitrophenyl derivative. With establishment of the structure as O-diazoacetyl-L-serine (I), the antibiotic was named azaserine. Other reactions are acid decomposition in the cold to IV, hydrogenation to V, and base catalyzed O–N acyl migration to VI.

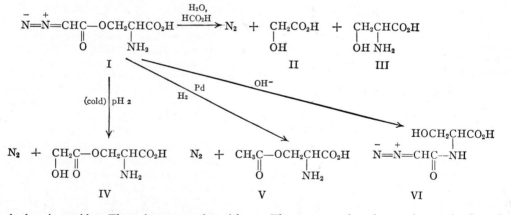

typical of amino acids. The substance melts with decomposition over a wide range (146–162°). It also decomposes with vigorous gas evolution when heated with a mineral acid. The gas evolved was found to be pure nitrogen. This decomposition, coupled with the strong infrared band at 4.66μ characteristic of a cumulative double bond structure occurring in azides (RN=N=N), diazo esters (RO$_2$CCH=N=N), diazo ketones (RC(=O)CH=N=N), and ketenes (R$_2$C=C=O) suggested one of

The D-, L-, and DL-forms of azaserine have been synthesized; only the natural L-form (αD − 0.5°) has biological activity.

L-6-Diazo-5-ketoleucine,

$$\overset{-}{N}=\overset{+}{N}=CHC(=O)CH_2CH_2CH(NH_2)CO_2H,$$

has been isolated from a different *Streptomyces* culture. This antibiotic is 40–80 times more potent than azaserine in antitumor activity in experimental animals, but no substantial therapeutic results have been observed in preliminary clinical studies (Sloan-Kettering Inst., 1956).

537

OXYTOCIN, A PEPTIDE HORMONE (*After Chapter 16*)

The posterior pituitary gland elaborates several hormones, of which two have been isolated in pure form. One, oxytocin, stimulates the smooth muscle of the uterus; the other, vasopressin, is an antidiuretic hormone which exerts a pressor action (increases blood pressure). The two hormones are so similar in physical properties that for a time a single substance was thought to be responsible for both physiological actions. However, techniques of fractional precipitation, chromatography, and electrophoresis were all found to effect partial separation (1928–44). Then, by countercurrent distribution of a commercial extract having oxytocic activity of 20 units/mg., du Vigneaud[1] (1949) obtained essentially pure material of activity of 850 units/mg. Complete hydrolysis and amino acid analysis of the hydrolyzate indicated the presence of eight different amino acids in equimolecular ratio, and the amount of ammonia liberated corresponded to three amide groupings of the type —CONH₂. The molecular weight was that of an octapeptide, and not a higher multiple. One of the eight units identified is cystine. In insulin (16.18), this disulfide unit binds peptide chains together and its severance by performic acid oxidation causes separation of the chains: $RS\text{—}SR' \xrightarrow{+OH} RSO_3H + HO_3SR'$. However, similar oxidation of the cystine unit of oxytocin gives material of molecular weight in the same range as oxytocin, and hence the disulfide unit must be part of a ring system.

The sequence of the eight amino acids in the cyclic peptide was established independently in 1953 by du Vigneaud and by Tuppy.[2] The two investigators arrived at the same conclusion from two sets of experimental evidence, both of which will be summarized. Tuppy first oxidized oxytocin with performic acid and submitted the oxidized peptide to partial hydrolysis with hydrochloric acid. The cystine unit gives rise to two oxidized amino acid units of the formula $HO_3SCH_2CH(NH_2)CO_2H$, named cysteic acid, and designated by the symbol CySO₃H (see 16.4 for symbols of other amino acids). Four dipeptides and two tripeptides were isolated, and most of the amino acid sequences were established by treatment of each peptide with 2,4-dini-

trofluorobenzene, hydrolysis, and chromatographic identification of the amino acid present as the DNF derivative and hence derived from a terminal amino acid residue, conventionally written to the left (side chain = R): H₂NCHRCO—NHCHR'CO—. When the sequence in a peptide is known, the symbols for the components are connected with a dash; use of a comma means that the order is not known. The six peptides initially isolated by Tuppy from oxidized oxytocin are represented as follows:

I Asp—CySO₃H	IV Leu—Gly
II CySO₃H—Tyr	V CySO₃H—(Leu, Pro)
III Ileu—Glu	VI Tyr—(Glu, Ileu)

Since the tripeptide VI was characterized as having an amino-terminal (to the left) tyrosine unit, the structure of the dipeptide III establishes for VI the structure Tyr—Ileu—Glu. The structure of dipeptide II establishes the further sequence CySO₃H—Tyr—Ileu—Glu. The tripeptide V is shown to have the order CySO₃H—Pro—Leu rather than the alternate order CySO₃H—Leu—Pro because in IV the carboxyl group of leucine is shown to be bound to the amino group of glycine, not of proline.

Tuppy then submitted oxidized oxytocin to partial hydrolysis by a crystalline proteinase isolated from *Bacillus subtilis* by Linderstrom-Lang[3] (1949) and obtained a basic product identified as glycine amide, H₂NCH₂CONH₂, symbol Gly(NH₂), and two acidic peptides. Each was hydrolyzed and the amino acids identified by chromatography, and each was treated with DNF and the end group determined. The first tetrapeptide, VII, corresponds

VII CySO₃H—(Glu, Tyr, Ileu)
VIII Asp—(CySO₃H, Leu, Pro)

to the above sequence: CySO₃H—Tyr—Ileu—Glu. The second tetrapeptide, VIII, contains aspartic acid in addition to the acids of the tripeptide V, shown above to be CySO₃H—Pro—Leu, and therefore it is identified as Asp—CySO₃H—Pro—Leu. The glycine amide resulting from enzymatic hydrolysis must be a terminal unit and the structure of dipeptide IV shows it to be linked to leucine. Thus the following carboxy-terminal sequence can be deduced:

—Asp—CySO₃H—Pro—Leu—Gly(NH₂).

[1] Vincent du Vigneaud, b. 1901 Chicago; Ph.D. Rochester; Cornell Med. Coll.; Nobel Prize 1955
[2] Hans Tuppy, b. 1924 Vienna; Ph.D. Vienna (Späth, Wessely); postdoctoral work Cambridge (Sanger), Carlsberg Laboratory, Copenhagen, Stockholm (Theorell); Univ. Vienna
[3] Kaj Linderstrom-Lang, b. 1896 Copenhagen; Ph.D. Copenhagen (S. P. L. Sörensen); Carlsberg Laboratory, Copenhagen

The amino-terminal sequence must be that deduced above for VII, and hence the complete sequence of oxidized oxytocin is that formulated.

of peptides resulted from hydrolysis of desulfurized oxytocin (Raney Ni), in which case an alanyl residue represents an original cysteinyl unit. The se-

$$CySO_3H—Tyr—Ileu—Glu(NH_2)—Asp(NH_2)—CySO_3H—Pro—Leu—Gly(NH_2)$$

$$\underset{\text{proteinase}}{\underline{\quad\quad\quad\quad\quad\quad\quad\quad\quad\quad}}$$

Oxidized oxytocin

The linkages hydrolyzed by bacterial proteinase are indicated. The two additional amide groups are placed in the two available dibasic acid units. The two cysteic acid units in the oxidized peptide evidently arose by cleavage of the disulfide group of a cystine unit in a cyclic system, and hence oxytocin is:

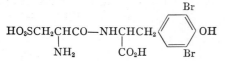

Ileu———Tyr————CyS
| |
Glu(NH₂)—Asp(NH₂)—CyS—Pro—Leu—Gly
Oxytocin

The du Vigneaud group relied less on end-group analysis than on identification of the components of a large number of small peptides. They also investigated the reaction of oxidized oxytocin with bromine water, which cleaves the molecule into a heptapeptide and a brominated dipeptide. The smaller fragment was shown to have the structure formulated, indicative of the sequence CySO₃H—Tyr,

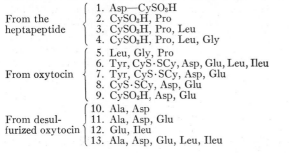

and the free amino group of the heptapeptide to which tyrosine was originally linked was found, on end-group analysis by the DNF method, to be that of an isoleucine residue, whence the sequence CySO₃H—Tyr—Ileu is established.

Of the thirteen peptides listed below, the first four were obtained by hydrolysis of the heptapeptide just mentioned. The next group resulted from hydrolysis of oxytocin. The neutral fraction was separated and treated with bromine water to oxidize cystine units to cysteic acid units and the resulting acidic peptides were separated from residual neutral peptides on an ion-exchange resin. The third group

From the heptapeptide
1. Asp—CySO₃H
2. CySO₃H, Pro
3. CySO₃H, Pro, Leu
4. CySO₃H, Pro, Leu, Gly

From oxytocin
5. Leu, Gly, Pro
6. Tyr, CyS·SCy, Asp, Glu, Leu, Ileu
7. Tyr, CyS·SCy, Asp, Glu
8. CyS·SCy, Asp, Glu
9. CySO₃H, Asp, Glu

From desulfurized oxytocin
10. Ala, Asp
11. Ala, Asp, Glu
12. Glu, Ileu
13. Ala, Asp, Glu, Leu, Ileu

quence was established in only one of the thirteen fragments; peptide 1 was shown by DNF analysis to be Asp—CySO₃H. This peptide is the equivalent of peptide 10 from desulfurized oxytocin. From the overlapping constituents of peptides 1–4, the following sequence can be deduced:

Asp—CySO₃H—Pro—Leu—Gly.

Peptide 5 is consistent with this sequence and evidently is Pro—Leu—Gly. Consideration of peptide 9 extends the sequence to:

Glu—Asp—CySO₃H—Pro—Leu—Gly.

Peptide 12 shows that the Glu unit is preceded by Ileu, and peptide 7 shows that Tyr is linked to the second half of the cystine unit:

Tyr—CyS
|
Ileu—Glu—Asp—CyS—Pro—Leu—Gly.

This sequence, which is supported by the observation that only one of the cysteic acid units in oxidized oxytocin carries a free amino acid group (DNF derivative), contains all eight amino acid units known to be present, and hence the Tyr and Ileu units must be joined together to form a cyclic pentapeptide system, a deduction confirmed by evidence presented above that bromine oxidation cleaves a Tyr—Ileu link. Further evidence was adduced by end-group analysis by the method of Edman[4] (1950). A terminal amino group adds to phenylisothio-

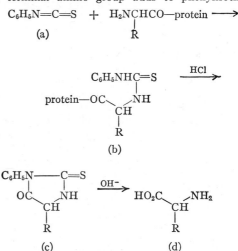

[4] Pehr Edman, b. 1916 Stockholm; M.D. Karolinska Inst. (E. Jorpes); Lund, Sweden

cyanate (a) to give the phenylthiocarbamyl derivative (b), which is cleaved by hydrochloric acid to a phenylthiohydantoin (c). Finally, alkaline hydrolysis gives the free amino acid (d). Oxidized oxytocin was degraded in this way, and after removal of the first amino-terminal unit the residual peptide was hydrolyzed and the component amino acids determined. The degradation was applied four times with the following results: the first Edman reaction removed cysteic acid, the second tyrosine, the third isoleucine, and the fourth glutamic acid.

The structure of the hormone was confirmed by a synthesis (du Vigneaud, 1954) involving coupling of the N-carbobenzoxy-S-benzyl dipeptide I with the heptapeptide triamide II by means of tetraethylpyrophosphite. On removal of the carbobenzoxy and benzyl groups protecting respectively the α-amino group of one cysteine unit and the sulfhydryl groups of both units, the dithiol nonapeptide was produced and this on air oxidation was cyclized to oxytocin. Boissonnas [5] (1955) synthesized the dithiol nonapeptide by a different route and likewise oxidized it to a cyclic octapeptide having the biological activity of oxytocin.

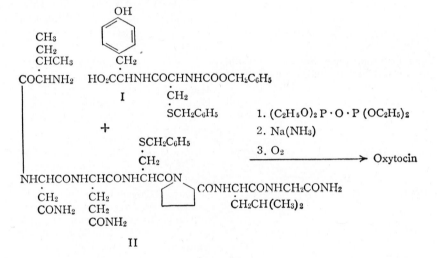

II. 15

SPECIFICITY OF ENZYME ACTION (*After Chapter 17*)

In contrast to inorganic catalysts (noble metals, acids, bases), enzymatic catalysts function only in specific reactions and often only with specific substrates. These proteinoid catalysts are hence usually named by addition of the suffix –ase to the root of the name of the substrate or of a reaction that they accelerate (urease, carbohydratase, deaminase, reductase). Enzymes of one broad group control hydrolysis (and sometimes resynthesis) of esters, carbohydrates, or proteins and appear to be simple proteins. Enzymes of a second group control oxidation-reduction processes and contain a prosthetic group essential for such activity. In pioneering work on the action of proteolytic enzymes on synthetic peptides, Max Bergmann (1937) established that these enzymes have linkage specificity; the various peptidases also require specific amino acid units in the vicinity of a peptide bond

in order to effect its cleavage. Indeed the latter requirement is apparently more exacting than linkage specificity. Thus at least some proteolytic enzymes, which split peptide links (—CONH—), also split ester links (—COO—) in synthetic peptide esters of similar structural environment.

That enzymes possess stereochemical specificity is shown by the classical experiments of Pasteur (1858), who found that the mold microorganism *Penicillium glaucum* utilizes natural L-(+)-tartaric acid much more readily than it utilizes unnatural D-(−)-tartaric acid. Likewise Fischer (1898) found that of the sixteen aldohexoses only the three that occur in nature are fermented by yeast: D-glucose, D-mannose, and, less readily, D-galactose. Degradation of fructose to ethanol and carbon dioxide under the influence of enzymes of yeast involves fission of the hexose to three-carbon components and the

[5] Roger A. Boissonnas, b. 1921 Zurich; D.Sc. Geneva (K. H. Meyer); Geneva

sequence of further transformations discussed in Part I (7.11). If either glucose or mannose is the substrate, it is converted into the 6-phosphate and this is isomerized to fructose-6-phosphate to a point of equilibrium by the enzyme isomerase. The same changes can be brought about nonenzymatically through the common enediol. Under the influence

the mold *Penicillium notatum* (1932–41), certain preparations were found to exert antibiotic activity only in the presence of glucose, whereas pure penicillin is active in the absence of glucose. The substance requiring glucose for antibiotic activity was isolated in nearly pure form in 1941 and named penicillin B, and later notatin. H. Raistrick ob-

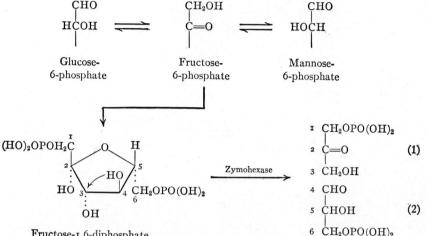

Glucose-6-phosphate   Fructose-6-phosphate   Mannose-6-phosphate

Fructose-1,6-diphosphate

of an enzyme and a phosphate donor, fructose-6-phosphate is transformed into the 1,6-diphosphate, the substance actually participating in the fission, which involves transfer of hydrogen from the C_4-hydroxyl to carbon atom 3 with formation of the fragments (1) and (2). Since the transfer occurs in a *trans*-glycol grouping and involves attack by hydrogen at the unshielded side of carbon 3, it is not surprising that the enzymatic fission is stereospecific. Galactose has the epimeric configuration at C_4, and hence a 3,4-*cis*-glycol grouping, and indeed it is fermented at a substantially slower rate than glucose and mannose. That the fermentation of galactose requires initial inversion at C_4 to give glucose was established by Leloir[1] (1950), who isolated an enzyme which controls the inversion. The prosthetic group is called cogalactowaldenase.

In early work on the production of penicillin by

tained pure material in 1945. Actually notatin is an enzyme having the specific function of catalyzing the oxidation of glucose to gluconic acid and hydrogen peroxide, and the antibacterial action is due to the hydrogen peroxide produced. Notatin was thus recognized as identical with glucose oxidase, first obtained (crude) by D. Müller (1928–36) from *Aspergillis niger*.

$$HOCH_2(CHOH)_4CHO \ + \ O_2 \ + \ H_2O \longrightarrow$$
Glucose

$$HOCH_2(CHOH)_4COOH \ + \ H_2O_2$$
Gluconic acid

Further study, mainly by D. Keilin[2] (1948–52), showed that the enzyme, which is yellow, has an absorption spectrum suggesting that the prosthetic group, or coenzyme, is flavin adenin dinucleotide, FAD. The isoalloxazine unit in this substance

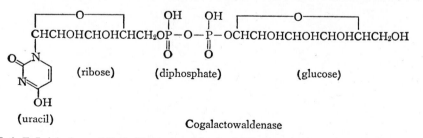

Cogalactowaldenase

[1] Luis F. Leloir, b. 1906 Paris (Argentine citizen); M.D. Buenos Aires; Buenos Aires
[2] David Keilin, b. Poland; Molteno Inst., Cambridge

(lower left) is responsible for the oxidation-reduction function; acceptance of hydrogen by 1,4-addition to the conjugated system —N=C(—)C(—)=N— gives the dihydrocoenzyme FADH₂. Other oxida-

of D-amino acid oxidase. Restoration of ability to oxidize D-amino acids established that FAD is indeed the prosthetic group of both enzymes.

Keilin found that of some fifty sugars investigated,

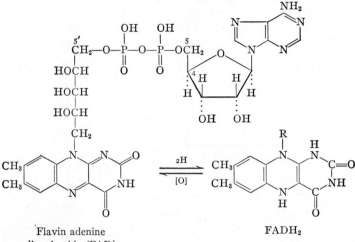

Flavin adenine
dinucleotide (FAD)

FADH₂

tive coenzymes have various other reducible groups in place of isoalloxazine. The simplest proof that FAD is the specific coenzyme of glucose oxidase would be to split off the prosthetic group of the enzyme and obtain the native, inactive protein; restoration of activity on addition to the inactive protein of FAD would identify this as the specific coenzyme. This standard method could not be used in the case at hand because the protein moiety of glucose oxidase was found to be denatured by all procedures that split off the coenzyme. FAD was known to be the prosthetic group of another enzyme, D-amino acid oxidase, the inactive protein of which can be obtained without destruction. Therefore a solution of glucose oxidase was boiled with water to denature the protein and liberate the coenzyme and the solution was added to the native protein

only glucose is attacked by the enzyme to any significant extent, and, more significantly, only the β-form of glucose (I). The product of enzymatic oxidation is δ-gluconolactone (II), which then undergoes spontaneous, nonenzymatic hydrolysis to gluconic acid (III). β-D-Glucopyranose (I) is also more susceptible than the α-form to chemical oxidation (bromine water, hypoiodous acid, mechanism unknown); it is oxidized 25–35 times more rapidly. In the enzymatic oxidation, however, the relative rates are 100:0.64.

This and several related enzymatic dehydrogenations involve direct transfer of hydrogen from substrate to coenzyme. It is not known whether the process involves transfer of hydride ion, or transfer of a hydrogen atom and an electron in separate steps. The transfer, at least in the cases

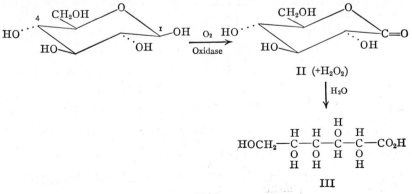

II (+H₂O₂)

III

examined, is stereospecific. An example is the reversible dehydrogenation of ethanol to acetaldehyde by the enzyme alcohol dehydrogenase, studied by B. Vennesland [3] and F. H. Westheimer [4] (1954). The coenzyme of this protein is diphosphopyridine nucleotide, DPN. This substance contains a nicotinamide grouping responsible for the reversible oxidation-reduction function of the enzyme; a positive charge on the ring nitrogen is balanced by a negative charge on one of the two phosphate groups. When the enzyme reacts with dideuterioethanol, CH_3CD_2OH, a deuterium atom abstracted from the α-position of ethanol appears in nonionic form

terium to the front and hydrogen to the rear. Asymmetry would not be possible in the absence of the amide group. Evidently chemical reduction gives nearly equal amounts of the two forms, with only a slight preference for one form because of the principle of asymmetric synthesis; on chemical oxidation of the reduced coenzyme formulated the product carries close to half the deuterium initially present. In contrast, enzymatic reduction gives one specific epimer. Deuterium (or hydrogen in the general case) is transferred onto one specific side of the pyridine ring only, as shown schematically for back-side approach of substrate. In enzymatic

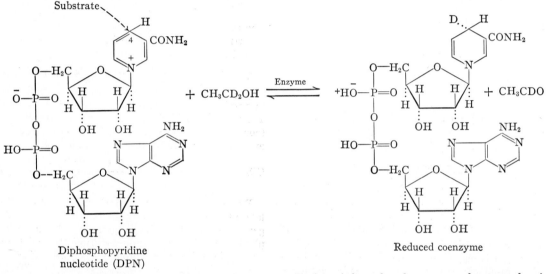

Diphosphopyridine nucleotide (DPN)

Reduced coenzyme

in the pyridine ring of the coenzyme and the hydroxylic hydrogen acquires the positive charge. On reversal of the reaction, that is enzymatic oxidation of the reduced coenzyme with acetaldehyde, the coenzyme produced is completely free from isotopic label. In contrast, on chemical oxidation the product carries about half the deuterium initially present. Position 4 in the reduced coenzyme is asymmetric, and the formula shows one of two possible 4-epimers; the other would be represented with deu-

oxidation of the reduced coenzyme the stereochemical requirements are the same as in the reduction reaction.

The relationship of stereospecificity to the mechanism of enzymatic action was first discussed by Fischer (1894), who said "To use a metaphor, I would say that enzyme and substrate must fit together like a lock and key." In modern terminology this concept is expressed as the idea of an intermediate activated complex between enzyme and substrate.

II. 16

PHOTOSYNTHESIS (*After Chapter 17*)

The green plant synthesizes its complex organic constituents from carbon dioxide, as the only source of carbon, and from water and inorganic salts derived

from the soil. The animal organism cannot initiate syntheses starting with such simple entities, and is dependent upon preformed organic materials sup-

[3] Birgit Vennesland, b. 1913 Kristiansand, Norway; Ph.D. Chicago (Hanke); postdoctoral work Harvard (Hastings); Chicago
[4] Frank H. Westheimer, b. 1912 Baltimore; Ph.D. Harvard (Conant); Nat. Res. Fellow Columbia (Hammett); Chicago, Harvard

plied in the diet. Since fats and proteins of plants are apparently derived from carbohydrate precursors rather than the reverse, carbohydrates are the probable primary products of photosynthesis. The energy required for the overall process shown in the equation is supplied by the sun, but photosynthesis is possible only in plants which contain

$$n\,CO_2 \;+\; n\,H_2O \;\underset{Respiration}{\overset{h\nu}{\rightleftarrows}}\; n\,O_2 \;+\; (CH_2O)_n$$

pigments of a specific type capable of absorbing light. The commonest is the green pigment chlorophyll, which Willstätter showed (1906–14) to consist of the two pigments chlorophyll-a and chlorophyll-b; these differ in that the latter has a formyl group in ring II in place of a methyl group. They

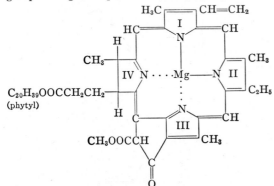

Chlorophyll-a (H Fischer)

are dihydroporphyrins related to hemin (16.22) but the metal is magnesium rather than iron, and one of the propionic acid groups is esterified with phytol (15.6). In the plant the pigments are bound to protein. The mechanism by which they function is not known, but maximal rate of photosynthesis is observed at a wave length corresponding to maximal absorption by chlorophyll.

The once-held belief that green plants alone are able to effect photosynthesis was questioned by Englemann (1883), who suspected that certain bacteria require light in order to assimilate carbon dioxide and thus are photosynthetic. This view was strengthened by isolation from purple bacteria of the pigment bacteriochlorophyll, which differs from chlorophyll-a in having two dihydropyrrole

rings instead of one, and in replacement of the vinyl group in ring I by an aceto group. van Niel [1] (1941) investigated the metabolism of purple bacteria and found that they do require light for growth. Thus *B. thiorhodaceae* can grow on a medium containing an oxidizable inorganic sulfur compound and bicarbonate as the sole carbon source, but only when irradiated. Typical equations that were verified are as follows:

$$2\,CO_2 \;+\; 4\,H_2O \;+\; H_2S \;\overset{h\nu}{\longrightarrow}\; 2\,(CH_2O) \;+\; 2\,H_2O \;+\; H_2SO_4$$

$$CO_2 \;+\; 2\,H_2O \;+\; 2\,H_2SO_3 \;\overset{h\nu}{\longrightarrow}\; (CH_2O) \;+\; H_2O \;+\; 2\,H_2SO_4$$

The essential step in these and similar processes is reduction of carbon dioxide by a hydrogen donor, H_2A, two moles of which are required:

$$CO_2 \;+\; 2\,H_2A \;\overset{h\nu}{\longrightarrow}\; (CH_2O) \;+\; H_2O \;+\; 2\,A$$

This general equation was shown to be applicable to purple bacteria that require an organic substance as substrate (*Athiorhodadaceae*), when a strain was found that reduces one mole of carbon dioxide by oxidation of two moles of isopropyl alcohol:

$$CO_2 \;+\; 2\,(CH_3)_2CHOH \;\overset{h\nu}{\longrightarrow}\; (CH_2O) \;+\; H_2O \;+\; 2\,(CH_3)_2CO$$

Ruben [2] and Kamen [3] (1941), using isotopically labeled water, H_2O^{18}, established that van Niel's general equation applies to photosynthesis in green plants. In this case water functions as hydrogen donor, since the oxygen produced is isotopic:

$$CO_2 \;+\; 2\,H_2O^{18} \;\longrightarrow\; (CH_2O) \;+\; H_2O \;+\; O_2^{18}$$

Ruben also initiated experiments on the fixation of $C^{14}O_2$; the radioactive label has the advantage of ready detection. He ruled out an early postulate that chlorophyll functions as acceptor for CO_2, and found that in the absence of light CO_2 is assimilated but not reduced. Hence the key photochemical reaction is reduction of CO_2 to (CH_2O), followed by conversion of (CH_2O) to specific stable compounds in a sequence of steps not yet fully clarified but under active investigation, mainly by Calvin [4] and by Gaffron [5]. The carbon of assimilated CO_2 is incorporated into a wide variety of cellular constitu-

[1] Cornelius B. van Niel, b. 1897 Haarlem, Netherlands; D.Sc. Delft; Hopkins Marine Station, Stanford Univ.
[2] Samuel Ruben, 1913–43; b. San Francisco; Ph.D. Univ. California, Berkeley (Latimer); Univ. California, Berkeley
[3] Martin D. Kamen, b. 1913 Toronto, Canada; Ph.D. Chicago (Harkins); postdoctoral work Univ. California, Berkeley; Washington Univ., St. Louis
[4] Melvin Calvin, b. 1911 St. Paul; Ph.D. Minnesota (Glockler); postdoctoral work Manchester (Polanyi, Heilbron); Univ. California, Berkeley
[5] Hans Gaffron, b. 1902 Lima, Peru (German parentage); Ph.D. Berlin (Traube); postdoctoral work KWI f. Biologie (Warburg); Chicago

ents, even during a period of exposure of only a few minutes, and hence identification of early products in the sequence is difficult. One expedient is to expose the plant to $C^{14}O_2$ for periods as short as 0.4–15 sec.; another is to conduct the experiments at low temperatures (2°). By these methods, and by extrapolation to zero time, it has been established that the first stable derivative of assimilated $C^{14}O_2$ is phosphoglyceric acid:

$$(HO)_2OPOCH_2CH(OH)C^{14}O_2H.$$

In short-term experiments only the carboxyl group contains the label, but after longer exposure radiocarbon appears in the other two positions of the acid, and to the same extent. Other radiocarbon components detected in short-term experiments are dihydroxyacetone monophosphate,

$$HOCH_2COCH_2OPO(OH)_2,$$

glucose monophosphate, and fructose monophosphate. The two hexose monophosphates evidently arise from combination of two C_3 units related to glyceric acid, because the distribution of radioactivity agrees with that expected on this basis. The technique for experimental determination of distribution is illustrated for the case of glucose (H. G. Wood,[6] 1945). The microorganism *Lacto-*

contain twice as much label as the others and can be represented as C^{++}, in contrast to C^+. The condensation of the three-carbon units is thus as follows:

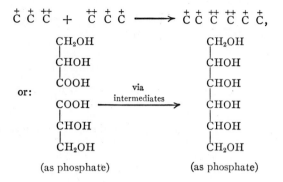

(as phosphate)   (as phosphate)

Other labeled compounds identified in short-term experiments are substances known to be involved in the metabolism of hexoses (Krebs cycle, 17.5): phosphoenolpyruvic acid, phosphoglycolic acid, malic acid, citric acid.

In addition to the two common hexose phosphates, two other sugars have been identified by paper chromatography as early products in photosynthesis. One is the monophosphate of the heptose

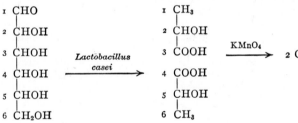

bacillus casei cleaves the 3–4 bond to form two molecules of lactic acid of the origin indicated. Oxidation of this acid gives carbon dioxide derived from C_3 and C_4, and haloform cleavage of the aldehyde gives fragments derived from the combinations C_1–C_6 and C_2–C_5.

The phosphoglyceric acid isolated from barley after exposure to $C^{14}O_2$ for 15 sec. has the following distribution of radiocarbon:

C_1, 49%; C_2, 25%; C_3, 26%

The distribution of radiocarbon in the hexose monophosphates formed in the same experiment is:

$C_1 + C_6$, 24%; $C_2 + C_5$, 26%; $C_3 + C_4$, 52%

Thus the central two carbon atoms of the chain

sedoheptulose, previously known as a general but minor constituent of plants. The other is the 1,5-diphosphate ester of a ketopentose, ribulose, which at the time of identification (1952) had not been known as a natural product. The sugar was later shown to be an oxidative metabolite of glucose in several microorganisms. An identified intermediate in the conversion is 6-phosphogluconic acid. Ribulose is related to the common natural aldopentose ribose in the same way that fructose is related to glucose, and indeed, in the presence of the enzyme phosphopentose isomerase, ribulose-5-phosphate is reversibly isomerized to ribose-5-phosphate. Sedoheptulose is also a 2-ketose, and is related to ribulose and ribose. The enzyme transketolase, isolated

[6] Harland G. Wood, b. 1907 Delavan, Minn.; Ph.D. Iowa State Coll.; Nat. Res. Fell. Wisconsin; Iowa State Coll., Minnesota, Western Reserve

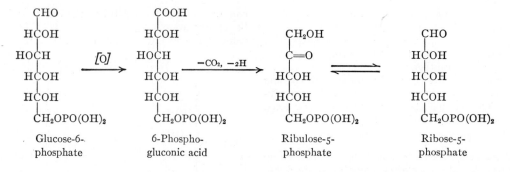

Glucose-6-   6-Phospho-   Ribulose-5-   Ribose-5-

phosphate   gluconic acid   phosphate   phosphate

from plants in essentially pure form, can catalyze the reversible transformations formulated, in which a two-carbon fragment is transferred from a seven-carbon phosphate to a three-carbon phosphate to

(temperature, light, partial pressure of CO_2 and O_2), Calvin found (1955) that formation of ribulose diphosphate and of phosphoglyceric acid are related in a reciprocal manner. Thus factors which suppress

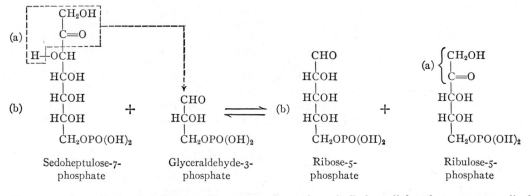

Sedoheptulose-7-   Glyceraldehyde-3-   Ribose-5-   Ribulose-5-

phosphate   phosphate   phosphate   phosphate

produce two five-carbon phosphates. The same enzyme catalyzes interconversion of the phosphates of fructose (6-C) and glyceraldehyde (3-C) to those of erythrose (4-C) and ribulose (5-C).

formation of ribulose diphosphate correspondingly increase production of phosphoglyceric acid, and vice versa. Other investigations have shown that addition of ribulose diphosphate to cell-free extracts

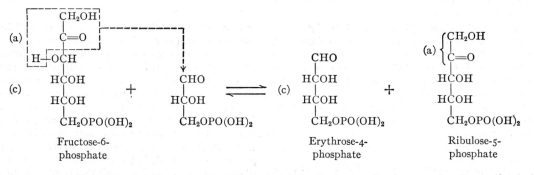

Fructose-6-   Erythrose-4-   Ribulose-5-

phosphate   phosphate   phosphate

That the first recognized product of assimilation of CO_2 is a C_3-compound suggested that the CO_2-acceptor is a C_2-unit, which is continuously regenerated during photosynthesis. However, no evidence to support this hypothesis has been forthcoming. In a study of the effect of various external variables

of *Chlorella* (green algae) causes fixation in the dark of $C^{14}O_2$ into the carboxyl group of phosphoglyceric acid. Ribose-5-phosphate is also active in this respect, but other substrates are inactive. It thus appears that ribulose diphosphate (I) is the CO_2-acceptor. Calvin postulates that conversion to

546

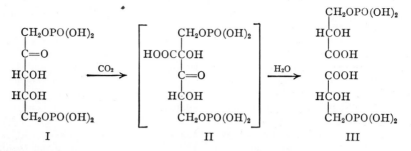

$$I \qquad II \qquad III$$

glycerophosphoric acid (III) proceeds through the branched intermediate II.

The CO_2-acceptor, ribulose diphosphate, must be

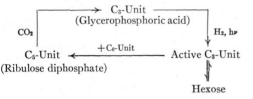

regenerated in a cyclic process such as that outlined in the diagram; the actual pathway undoubtedly is more complex and may well involve the interconversions of C_5, C_3, and C_7 sugars indicated above. The initially formed C_3-unit appears to be glycerophosphoric acid, reduction of which with absorption of radiant energy gives a substance described as an active C_3-unit and defined as the precursor of the C_5-acceptor of CO_2. The photochemical reduction may afford phosphoglyceraldehyde and dihydroxyacetone monophosphate, which are known to condense to fructose diphosphate; combination of hexose with phosphoglyceraldehyde could then regenerate the C_5-unit. Various other pathways are possible and the problem is still under study.

II. 17

CHLORAMPHENICOL, A PROBLEM *

The isolation of the valuable antibiotic streptomycin from several strains of *Streptomyces* (S. Waksman, 1942–44) prompted widespread investigations of other strains. A strain named *S. venezuelae*, because it was isolated by the Yale botanist P. R. Burkholder from a sample of soil obtained from Venezuela, was found to yield another antibiotic, investigated particularly by Parke, Davis and Co. (Q. R. Bartz, J. Controulis, H. M. Crooks, Jr., M. C. Rebstock, *et al.*, 1949). The substance was originally named chloromycetin, but after elucidation of structure the name was changed to the more descriptive chloramphenicol, although the original designation is retained as a trade name. Separation from the crude culture broth was followed by microbiological assay with *Shigella paradysenteriae*. The biologically active material was found to be neutral and relatively stable to acids but unstable to alkalis. The crude broth was first treated with an adsorbent (Super Filtrol) found not to adsorb active material but capable of removing some colored contaminants. Extraction with ethyl acetate removed all activity. The extract was washed in turn with dilute sulfuric acid and with bicarbonate solution to remove basic and acidic contaminants, dried, and evaporated. The residue was partly crystalline and the active substance was obtained pure by digestion with petroleum ether and crystallization from ethylene dichloride.

Physical constants and analytical data for chloramphenicol are as follows: colorless needles, m.p. 150°, $\alpha D + 19°$ (ethanol), $-25.5°$ (ethyl acetate); empirical formula, $C_{11}H_{12}O_5N_2Cl_2$ (both chlorines inert to silver ion); mol. wt. (Rast), 310; inert to carbonyl reagents and to dilute bromine solution; neutral. The substance has an ultraviolet maximum at 278 mμ similar to that of benzene. Infrared absorption characterization would have been useful but instruments were not at the time available. One clue to the functional groups was that chloramphenicol forms a diacetate from which it is regenerated under hydrolytic conditions so mild as to indicate that both acetyl groups are linked to oxygen rather than nitrogen.

Further evidence is that on catalytic hydrogenation of the antibiotic three moles of hydrogen are

* In this section the experimentally determined facts leading to elucidation of structure are presented and left for the reader to interpret, step by step. An analysis of the data is given in the back of the book.

absorbed rapidly without marked alteration of the spectrum. Reduction with tin and hydrochloric acid followed by diazotization and coupling with β-naphthol gives a heavy orange-red precipitate.

Chloramphenicol had been observed to suffer decrease in biological activity in contact with alkali, and hence alkaline hydrolysis was tried and found to give an easily distillable, strongly acidic fragment of the formula $C_2H_2O_2Cl_2$ and a crystalline, optically active base, $C_9H_{12}O_4N_2$, which forms a triacetate. The results of the degradation permit a further significant inference. Although chloramphenicol itself is stable to periodic acid under conditions ordinarily employed for determination of vicinal hydroxyl groups, the base $C_9H_{12}O_4N_2$ readily consumed two oxygen equivalents of the reagent and the following four products were identified: ammonia, formaldehyde, formic acid, and an aldehyde of the formula $C_7H_5O_3N$. The aldehyde was identified readily by the Parke, Davis group, but for the purpose of the present problem it will be described as a substance convertible into p-toluidine.

At this point, the Parke, Davis group regarded the evidence for the structure of the antibiotic as conclusive, took stock of the number of possible stereoisomers, and considered possibilities for synthesis. The reader should do likewise. Synthetic methods will, of course, lead to one or more dl-mixtures which have to be resolved, and if two racemates are possible one can more or less expect to obtain a mixture of both but has no way of predicting whether the desired or undesired racemate will predominate.

The Parke, Davis group (Controulis, Rebstock, Crooks) reported a synthesis of chloramphenicol in 1949. From a broad outline of the chemical reactions involved, the reader may be able to fill in the details; the stereochemistry is summarized in the analysis at the end of the book. The synthesis started with a sodium methoxide-induced aldol-type condensation of benzaldehyde with β-nitroethanol, $HOCH_2CH_2NO_2,$* to give an addition product which on catalytic hydrogenation absorbed 3 moles of hydrogen and gave an amino diol. This afforded a triacetate, actually a mixture of two diastereomeric triacetates. Nitration and deacetylation gave a mixture of two diastereomeric nitrophenyl-aminodiols, which were separated. A levorotatory base from one of the racemates on reaction with methyl dichloroacetate gave a product identical with natural chloramphenicol.

Chloramphenicol is a broad-spectrum antibiotic; it is currently the drug of choice for treatment of typhoid fever and rickettsial infections. Shortly after its isolation it was used with dramatic success in a typhus epidemic in Bolivia (1947). For a time it was used rather widely in therapy of many diseases; by 1950, however, it became apparent that the drug could cause fatal bone marrow injury. Its use is thus restricted to treatment of serious infectious diseases where other antibiotics are relatively ineffective.

II. 18

URUSHIOL (After Chapter 22)

Urushiol, a dark, vesicatory oil occurring in the sap of the Japanese lac tree (*Rhus vernicifera*), was actively investigated by R. Majima[1] in the period 1907–22. Majima characterized the material as a mixture of closely related substances having a phenolic group in combination with a long hydrocarbon side chain containing from one to three double bonds. All techniques of separation available at the time were tried without success. However, Majima found that on catalytic hydrogenation all the components are converted into a single, crystalline substance, hydrourushiol. He characterized hydrourushiol as a derivative of catechol having an $n\text{-}C_{15}H_{31}$ side chain by isolation of cate-chol as a product of pyrolytic degradation and of palmitic acid as a product of permanganate degradation. That the hydrocarbon residue is at the 3- rather than the 4-position was established by synthesis. Condensation of 2,3-dimethoxyphenyl-propionyl chloride (I) with the sodio derivative of dodecyne-1 (II), hydrogenation of the acetylenic ketone II, and Clemmensen reduction of the saturated ketone III, gave a product (IV) identical with hydrourushiol dimethyl ether, m.p. 36°.

The principle of poison ivy (*Rhus toxicodendron radicans*) responsible for the well-known vesicant action can be extracted from leaves and twigs of the plant with ethanol and processed for removal of

---

* Prepared (a) from ethylene chlorohydrin and silver nitrate or (b) as follows: $O{=}CH_2 + CH_3NO_2 \longrightarrow HOCH_2CH_2NO_2$
[1] Rikō Majima, b. 1874 Kyoto, Japan; D.Sci. Tokyo, postdoctoral work Kiel (Harries), Zurich ETH (Willstätter), London; Tokyo, Tohoku, Osaka

fats, waxes, and chlorophyll. The resulting dark, viscous oil resembles Japanese lac urushiol, and G. A. Hill[2] and his students found (1934) that on hydrogenation it yields a single product identical with hydrourushiol. H. S. Mason and L. Schwartz

alumina (heated at 300° for 4 hrs.). In a typical experiment, initial chromatography of 13.5 g. of the dimethyl ether on 1.6 kg. of alumina afforded nine fractions of oils of refractive index increasing from 1.4951 to 1.5150 and of progressively increas-

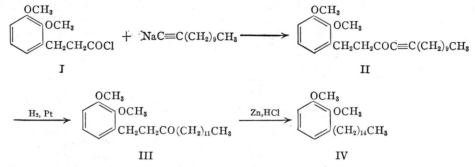

(1942) chromatographed poison ivy oil on alumina and obtained indications of the presence of several components, but were unable to recover the components in form suitable for study, probably because the unsaturated catechol components are highly sensitive to air oxidation. In a fresh attack of the problem (1954), C. R. Dawson[3] circumvented both the autoxidation of the vesicant and its troublesome allergenic properties by working with the nontoxic dimethyl ether. The more highly saturated components proved to be adsorbed only on activated

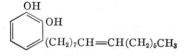

V

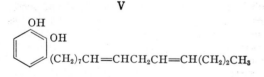

VI

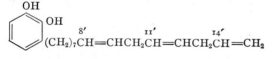

VII

VIII

ing unsaturation. Hydrourushiol dimethyl ether seemed a likely component of the least strongly adsorbed fraction and was isolated after treatment of the fraction with performic acid followed by hydrolysis. Chromatography then afforded hydrourushiol dimethyl ether and a strongly adsorbed diol derived from a monoolefinic component. The diol on periodic acid cleavage yielded heptaldehyde, and hence the monoolefinic vesicant from which it is derived is V. Intermediate and late fractions were rechromatographed and fractions of similar refractive index were pooled and rechromatographed. Finally fractions of constant refractive index were identified as follows: monoolefin, n_D^{25} 1.4932; diolefin, n_D^{25} 1.5030; triolefin, n_D^{25} 1.5160. Ozonization of the diolefin gave n-butyraldehyde and an aldehyde containing the aromatic nucleus and shown to be $Ar(CH_2)_7CHO$ by oxidation to the corresponding acid, available by synthesis. The vesicant precursor was thus identified as VI. Ozonization of the triolefin gave formaldehyde and the above aldehyde $Ar(CH_2)_7CHO$ (identified as the acid amide), which places one double bond at $C_{8'}$ and another at $C_{14'}$. The triolefin showed no ultraviolet absorption indicative of a conjugated diene system and hence the third double bond can only be at $C_{11'}$, as in VII. The pattern of unsaturation thus corresponds to that found in common unsaturated fatty acids (compare V, VI, and VII with oleic, linoleic, and linolenic acids). All the olefinic double bonds have the cis-configuration, since they show no absorption at 10.4μ, characteristic of trans double bonds (Dawson, 1956).

By the same technique, Dawson isolated four components of Japanese lac urushiol (as the di-

[2] G. Albert Hill, b. 1892 Worcester, Mass.; Ph.D. Harvard (Kohler); Wesleyan Univ. (Conn.)

[3] Charles R. Dawson, b. 1911 Peterboro, N. H.; Ph.D. Columbia; Columbia

methyl ethers). A saturated, a monoolefinic, and a diolefinic component were found identical with those from poison ivy. A triolefinic component differs from that in the other series by having a higher refractive index (n_D^{25} 1.5227) and in being sensitive to alumina. Prolonged chromatography on alumina led to formation of a yellow resinous contaminant, but this could be removed by terminal chromatography on Florisil. The triolefin has an ultraviolet absorption band at 227 mμ, and therefore contains a conjugated diene system, as in VIII. Ozonolysis gave the aldehyde $Ar(CH_2)_7CHO$, acetaldehyde, and malondialdehyde. These fragments fit not only the structure shown but that with double bonds at $C_{8'}$, $C_{10'}$, and $C_{13'}$. However, the maleic anhydride adduct gave no acetaldehyde on ozonolysis, which shows that structure VIII is correct.

II. 19

SORBICILLIN (*After Chapter 26*)

In a study of the purification of penicillin being manufactured for clinical use, D. J. Cram[1] and M. Tishler (1948) isolated nine microbiologically inactive by-products. Five were identified as relatively simple known compounds. A sixth was shown to be 2-decendioic acid (I) by hydrogenation to sebacic acid (II) and permanganate oxidation to suberic acid (III). The other three substances were

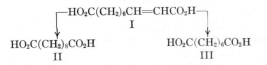

$$-HO_2C(CH_2)_6CH=CHCO_2H-$$
$$I$$

$$HO_2C(CH_2)_8CO_2H \qquad HO_2C(CH_2)_6CO_2H$$
$$II \qquad\qquad III$$

pigments, and the one available in largest amount (4.5 g.), later named sorbicillin, was characterized as follows: formula, $C_{14}H_{16}O_3$; mol. wt. (Rast), 214; orange plates, m.p. 113–114°; optically inactive; 2 active hydrogens (Zerewitinoff); no methoxyl groups (Zeisel); 3 C-methyl groups (Kuhn-Roth); insoluble in bicarbonate but soluble in sodium hydroxide solution (deep orange solution); positive ferric chloride test; no carbonyl reactions; one acylable hydroxyl group; $\lambda_{max}^{C_2H_5OH}$ 320 mμ. The solubility in alkali and positive ferric chloride test show the presence of at least one phenolic hydroxyl group, and since sorbicillin monoacetate and monomethyl ether are also acidic a second, hindered phenolic group is probable. The color and ultraviolet absorption indicate the presence of conjugated unsaturation, an inference verified by catalytic hydrogenation to colorless di- and tetrahydro derivatives.

In the second stage of structure elucidation, Cram (1948) found that oxidation of sorbicillin with hydrogen peroxide in alkaline solution (Dakin reaction) gave as the only isolable pure product sorbic acid: $CH_3CH=CHCH=CHCO_2H$. A sorboyl group in sorbicillin would account for two easily hydrogenable double bonds and for one of the three C-methyl groups. The evidence would allow presence of a carbonyl group if it were hindered; infrared spectroscopy might have detected such a group but was not then available. Alkaline hydrolysis of sorbicillin produced two colorless products: A, $C_{14}H_{18}O_4$; and B, $C_{10}H_{12}O_3$. Compound B proved to be the aceto derivative of a dihydric phenol, and this benzenoid fragment must contain the other two C-methyl groups. The carbonyl group of B must correspond to the carboxyl group of sorbic acid, and the following formula accounts for the production of a C_{10}-fragment (B) in one reaction and a C_6-fragment (sorbic acid) in another:

$$\overbrace{C_6H(CH_3)_2(OH)_2CO}^{C_{10}}\underbrace{CH=CHCH=CHCH_3}_{C_6}$$

Since compound B is phenolic, the ultraviolet spectrum in neutral solution is markedly altered by the addition of alkali (Fig. 1a). 2,4-Dihydroxyacetophenone (IV), studied as a model compound, was found to have almost exactly corresponding spectroscopic characteristics (Fig. 1b), and therefore compound B is probably one of the three isomers corresponding to V. These compounds were syn-

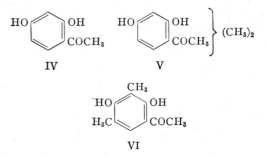

[1] Donald J. Cram, b. 1919 Chester, Vt.; Ph.D. Harvard (Fieser); Nat. Res. Fellow Harvard; Univ. Calif. Los Angeles

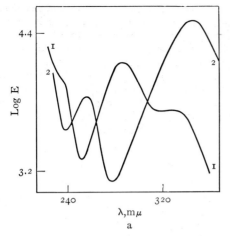

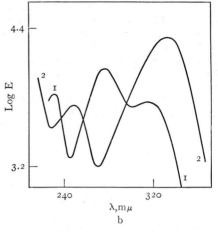

FIG. 1. — a, Compound B; b, 2,4-Dihydroxyacetophenone. Curves 1, in ethanol; 2, in ethanolic sodium hydroxide.

thesized and one of them, VI, proved identical with compound B.

Cram's synthesis of VI started with formylation of resorcinol (VII) by the Adams modification of the Gattermann reaction, methylation of VIII to IX, Wolff-Kishner reduction (X), and demethylation (XI). The dihydroxy aldehyde VIII presumably was methylated prior to reduction to obviate possible cyclization of the intermediate *o*-hydroxyhydrazone. Friedel-Crafts acylation of XI to XII proceeded under mild conditions; nuclear methylation to VI was accomplished by a method discovered by J. Herzig and S. Zeisel (1888) and clarified by R. Robinson and R. C. Shah (1934). It probably proceeds by C-alkylation of the enolate ion XIII and is analogous to the alkylation of acetoacetic ester. Cram found that control of the reaction temperature to 0° obviates secondary O-methylation. The dihydroxydimethylacetophenone VI is also a natural product, known as clavatol, isolated from cultures of the mold *Aspergillis clavatus*. The structure was established by C. H. Hassell and A. R. Todd (1947) by the following synthesis.

Resorcinol (VII) was converted into the known diformyl derivative XIV (2,4-dihydroxyisophthalaldehyde) by the Reimer-Tiemann reaction, and the aldehyde groups were reduced by hydrogenation to give XV. Gattermann acylation then gave clavatol, VI. This substance, like sorbicillin, does not react with carbonyl reagents, and forms only a monoacetate and a monomethyl ether. The masking of the carbonyl function and of one phenolic hydroxyl group seems attributable to existence of the substance in the chelate ring form VIa. Hassell and Todd's observation that clavitol is oxidized by alkaline hydrogen peroxide to the hydroxyquinone XVI suggests that, in the oxidation of sorbicillin under the same conditions to sorbic acid, the unisolated second fragment is XVI.

The foregoing observations permit deduction with reasonable certainty that sorbicillin has structure XVII. The colorless di- and tetrahydrides correspond exactly in absorption spectrum to clavitol (VI) and are entirely different from sorbicillin, which indicates that the double bond attacked first is that adjacent to the carbonyl

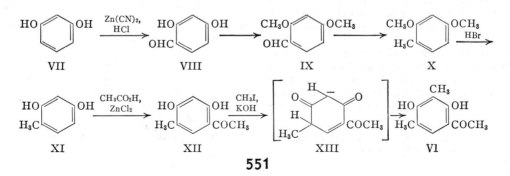

551

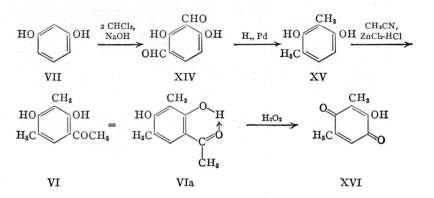

VII   XIV   XV

VI   VIa   XVI

group, as in formula XVIII for the dihydride. The white product of hydrolysis, A, of the formula $C_{14}H_{18}O_4$ is also similar in spectral characteristics

ciated with tautomerism to the *para* and *ortho* quinonemethene forms XVIIa and XVIIb, in which the carbonyl group in the ring is conjugated

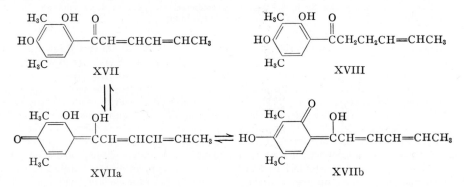

XVII   XVIII

XVIIa   XVIIb

to XVIII and is formulated by Cram as the product of 1,4-addition of water and regarded as an intermediate to compound B:

$$ArCCH=CHCH=CHCH_3 \xrightarrow{HOH}$$

O

XVII

$$ArCCH_2CHCH=CHCH_3 \longrightarrow ArCOCH_3$$

O   OH

A   B

One fact not evident from formula XVII is the color of sorbicillin and the intense color of its anion. The carbonyl group is conjugated with the benzene ring on one side and with the diene system on the other, and hence the system as a whole is described as cross-conjugated. In usual cross-conjugated systems the contributions of the component parts to light absorption are not additive; instead the spectral characteristics are close to those of the more powerful contributor. Possibly the color is asso-

with four and with five double bonds, respectively. The second enolic form (b) also allows for chelate stabilization.

The structure assigned to sorbicillin by Cram was later verified by a synthesis of the methyl ether by R. Kuhn and H. A. Staab (1954). The key step involved a variation of the Reformatsky reaction, previously limited to condensation of carbonyl compounds with α-halo esters: $RCHXCO_2R'$. The German workers noted that, in a study of the rates of reaction of a large number of chloro compounds with potassium iodide in acetone, J. B. Conant [2] (1925) had found ω-chloroacetophenone to react 60 times as fast as chloroacetic ester. In an earlier study of relative reactivities, H. T. Clarke [3] (1916) had found ω-bromoacetophenone to be 7 times as reactive as ω-chloroacetophenone. Kuhn and Staab found, as expected, that ω-bromoacetophenone reacts with crotonaldehyde in the presence of zinc; the intermediate carbinol spontaneously undergoes dehydration to the conjugated

[2] James B. Conant, b. 1893 Boston; Ph.D. Harvard (Kohler); Harvard
[3] Hans T. Clarke, b. 1887 Harrow, England; D.Sc. London; Eastman Kodak Co., Dept. Biochem., Coll. Phys. and Surg. Columbia

dienone, which was named sorbophenone. Application of the reaction to the synthesis of sorbicillin

$$C_6H_5COCH_2Br + Zn + O=CHCH=CHCH_3$$

$$\longrightarrow \left[\begin{array}{c} C_6H_5COCH_2CHCH=CHCH_3 \\ | \\ OH \end{array}\right]$$

$$\longrightarrow C_6H_5COCH=CHCH=CHCH_3$$

Sorbophenone
λ_{max} 297 mμ

required as starting material one of the intermediates mentioned above, 2,4-dihydroxyisophthalalde-

of 3.5%. They found a better process starting with the condensation of resorcinol with N,N'-diphenyl-formamidine (XIX, from formic acid and aniline at 150°). The reagent characteristically condenses with carbanions, and resorcinol evidently reacts to give a diketonic product which enolizes to XX. Hydrolysis of this double Schiff base gives the dialdehyde XIV in 21–24% overall yield. Reduction was accomplished conveniently by the Clemmensen method and methylation gave XXI, which was submitted to Friedel-Crafts reaction with chloroacetyl chloride. One methoxyl group suffered demethylation in the process; this was assumed but

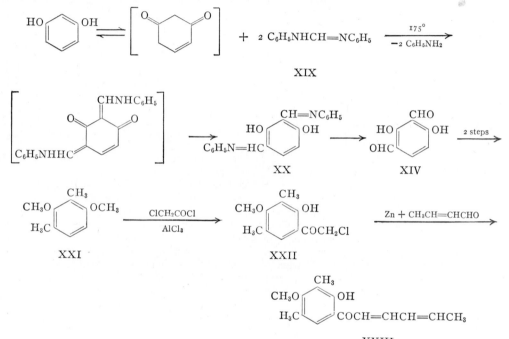

XIX

XX

XIV

2 steps

XXI

XXII

XXIII

hyde (XIV). Kuhn and Staab noted that the Reimer-Tiemann preparation of this dialdehyde, first applied by Tiemann (1877) and reinvestigated in several subsequent studies, gives at best a yield

not proved to be that adjacent to the position substituted, as in XXII. This substance on Reformatsky condensation with crotonaldehyde gave sorbicillin methyl ether, XXIII.

II. 20

STRUCTURAL RELATIONS OF NATURAL PRODUCTS (*After Chapter 26*)

Isotopic tracer techniques have made possible experimental investigation of the pathways of biosynthesis of natural products, and some of the biogenetic sequences established could not have been predicted from knowledge of classical organic

chemistry. Before these techniques had become available, intuitive speculation of possible building units played a significant role in guiding structure elucidation and schemes of synthesis. Such intuitive reasoning remains useful in planning tracer studies deemed most likely to disclose the true pathway of a given biosynthesis. The unquestioned leader in deduction of reasonable schemes of biogenesis of natural products is Sir Robert Robinson,[1] whose first paper on the subject in 1917 still provides fascinating reading. Although Robinson has occupied himself for the most part with problems more complicated than those of the numerous polyisoprenoid compounds, which are $(C_5)_n$ compounds generally built by head-to-tail linking of isoprene

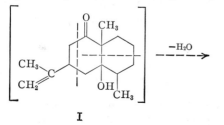

I

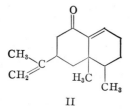

II

units, he did postulate an explanation for the fact that the structure II assigned to eremophilone $(C_{15}H_{22}O)$ does not obey the isoprene rule. He postulated that II arises from the hypothetical isoprenoid precursor I by dehydration with Wagner-Meerwein rearrangement of a methyl group (the symbol - - - - → designates a postulated reaction).

In his first paper, concerned mainly with alkaloids,

Robinson noted that many of these substances can be envisioned as arising from amino acids and from simple units known to be involved in metabolism, such as acetone or an equivalent. He felt that the coincidences were so many that speculation was justified. His speculative schemes, presented with realization that the details were not necessarily correct, led to some remarkably simple syntheses of complex molecules. Whereas others had assumed "that plants have at their command enormously powerful reagents that are able to cause substances . . . to undergo transformations which cannot be induced in the laboratory," Robinson limited himself to reactions known to occur with ease, such as aldol condensation and condensation of a carbinolamine (a), or the equivalent pseudo base (b), with an anion (A^-) to give (c). He sug-

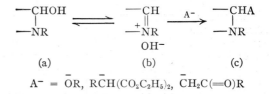

(a)   (b)   (c)

$A^- = \bar{O}R, \ R\bar{C}H(CO_2C_2H_5)_2, \ \bar{C}H_2C(\!\!=\!\!O)R$

gested, for example, that the five-membered pyrrolidine ring of the alkaloid hygrine is derived from glutamic acid, $HO_2CCH_2CH_2CH(NH_2)CO_2H$, or from an amino acid conceivably available to the plant from glutamic acid, such as ornithine. The steps shown involve reasonable chemistry, and indeed hygrine has been synthesized by a scheme similar to that outlined. By an analogous process, the piperidine ring of coniine could be formed from lysine. The more exotic ring system of lupinine, a constituent of seeds of the yellow lupine, conceivably could arise from two molecules of lysine.

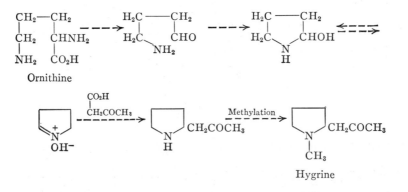

Hygrine

[1] Sir Robert Robinson, b. 1886 Rufford/Chesterfield; Ph.D. Manchester (Perkin); Liverpool, Manchester, Oxford; Nobel Prize 1947; see "The Structural Relations of Natural Products," Weizmann Memorial Lectures, Clarendon Press, 1955

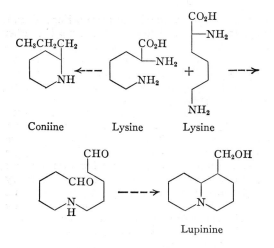

Coniine   Lysine   Lysine

Lupinine

An example of the widespread isoquinoline and tetrahydroisoquinoline alkaloids is salsoline. The pathway of biogenesis postulated by Robinson is

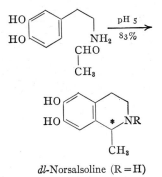

dl-Norsalsoline (R = H)

The ketone tropinone, which is related to the alkaloids cocaine and atropine, had been synthesized by Willstätter in a thirteen-step process starting with cycloheptanone (1901–03). Robinson noted that tropinone, which also contains a pyrrolidine unit, could conceivably arise by a Mannich-type condensation (Part II. 4) of succindialdehyde (a possible product of oxidation of glutamic acid, or perhaps derived from succinic acid), methylamine, and an activated form of acetone, such as acetonedicarboxylic acid. He indeed achieved (1917) chemical synthesis of tropinone on the basis

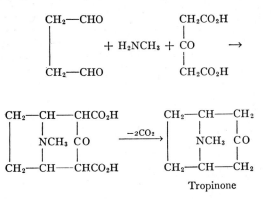

Tropinone

of this hypothesis. The yield was low, but was later improved by C. Schöpf[2] by use of simulated physiological conditions (neutral pH, room temperature, decarboxylation coupled with condensation).

condensation of acetaldehyde with the amine derived from 3,4-dihydroxyphenylalanine by decarboxylation, followed by N-methylation. Indeed Schöpf (1934) effected the condensation shown at 25° and obtained the racemic form of norsalsoline in high yield.

As early as 1907, J. N. Collie noted that many natural aromatic compounds can be envisioned as arising from acetoacetic acid, $CH_3COCH_2CO_2H$, or polyacetic acid, $CH_3CO(CH_2CO)_nOH$, shown later to be involved in the synthesis of fatty acids from acetic acid (17.3). An example cited by Robinson (1955) is the lichen component, orsellinic acid, postulated to arise by self-condensation of

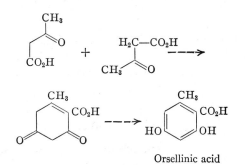

Orsellinic acid

acetoacetic acid. The red quinone endocrocin from a Japanese lichen (Y. Asahina[3]) could arise from the polyacetic acid formulated.

Birch[4] (1953–) has noted further examples of natural products whose structures are divisible into

[2] Clemens Schöpf, b. 1899 Gersfeld/Rhön; Ph.D. Munich (Wieland); Darmstadt
[3] Yasuhiko Asahina, b. 1881 Tokyo; Ph.D. Tokyo (Shimoyama); postdoctoral work Zurich (Willstätter), Berlin (E. Fischer); Tokyo
[4] Arthur John Birch, b. 1915 Sydney, Australia; Ph.D. Oxford (Robinson); Sydney, Manchester

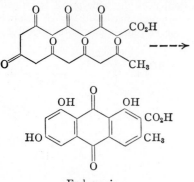

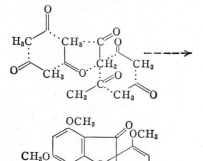

Endocrocin

acetate units linked head-to-tail. An example is griseofulvin, a substance possessing antibiotic activity isolated from cultures of *Penicillium griseofulvum* (A. Oxford and H. Raistrick, 1939),

Griseofulvin

and characterized as a benzofuran of the structure shown; the structure includes the interesting fea-

ture of a carbon atom shared by two rings to form a spiran grouping. The substance is the enol ether of a 1,3-diketone. The formulation shows that condensation of seven acetyl groups in the directions indicated by dotted lines could give the ring system of griseofulvin with oxygen functions and a methyl substituent correctly placed.

The acetate hypothesis, however, must be used with reservation, since acetate in the organism enters into a wide variety of reactions leading to products in which the unit is no longer recognizable as such. Moreover, isolated aromatic rings, as far as available evidence shows, apparently arise by an elaborate sequence involving both hexose and heptose. Even so, Birch has found the acetate hypothesis a useful guide in structural investigations. An example is eleutherinol, isolated from *Eleutherine bulbosa* by H. Schmid (Univ. Zurich, 1952). With but 500 mg. of material, Schmid was able to deduce that the substance is either III or V. One of two methyl groups present (Kuhn-Roth determination) was characterized as reactive by formation of a piperonylidene derivative:

$$-CH_3 \ + \ O{=}CHAr \ \longrightarrow \ -CH{=}CHAr,$$

which establishes the presence of a β-methyl α,β-unsaturated ketone system. The ring system was characterized by conversion to the dimethyl ether (CH_2N_2) and alkaline cleavage. One of two products was shown to be a naphthol, either the 1-naphthol VI or the isomeric 2-naphthol, by oxidation to the naphthoquinones VII and VIII, the former of which was identified by synthesis. Either the 1-naphthol VI derived from III or the β-naphthol derived from V would account satisfactorily for the formation of VII, but Schmid, from a few ex-

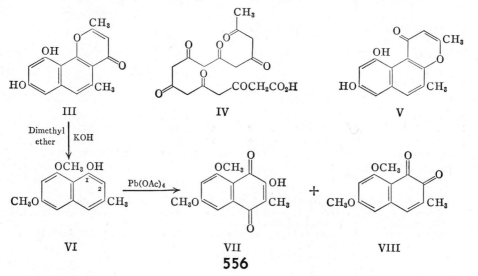

periments with model compounds, thought oxidation of VI by lead tetraacetate to the β-naphthoquinone VIII unlikely, and so concluded that eleutherinol has the structure V. Birch (1953), noting that formula III but not V accords with the acetate

2,5,7-arrangement alone agrees with biogenetic expectations, and Birch (1955) proved this structure correct by synthesis.

The structure of the antibiotic aureomycin, containing four fused rings carrying eight oxygen func-

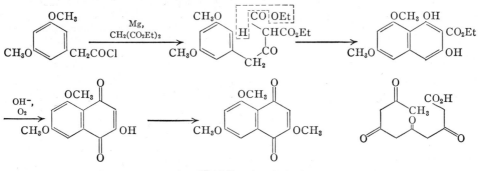

Flaviolin trimethyl ether

hypothesis (see IV), undertook synthesis of 3-methyl-6,8-dimethoxy-1-naphthol (VI). He found that the synthetic substance is identical with Schmid's degradation product and thereby established formula III as correct.

Since many of the anthraquinone mold metabolites conform to the acetate hypothesis, Birch was led to speculate on the structure of the naphthoquinone flaviolin, a metabolite of *Aspergillus citricus* isolated by B. D. Astill and J. C. Roberts (Nottingham, 1953). These investigators showed that the substance is a trihydroxy-1,4-naphthoquinone (spectrum, three acylable hydroxyl groups) and located two hydroxyls by oxidation of the triacetate to 3,5-dihydroxyphthalic acid. The third hydroxyl is thus in the quinone ring, but the choice between the two possible positions was left open. The

tions, suggests that the substance may arise from a polyaceto-α-amino dibasic acid.*

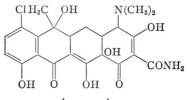

Aureomycin

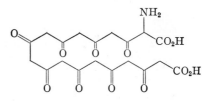

<h1 style="text-align:center">II. 21</h1>

HOOKER OXIDATION † (*After Chapter 26*)

One of eleven papers by Samuel C. Hooker published posthumously in the July issue of the *J. Am. Chem. Soc.* for 1936 begins as follows:

"In the course of my researches on the constitution of lapachol (I), oxidation with alkaline permanganate was studied in anticipation of additional confirmation regarding the structure of the amylene chain in this compound. The results obtained, however, were entirely unexpected. Instead of helping substantiate in a simple way the conclusions

I had reached, they themselves gave rise to a major problem, the solution of which has led to the discovery of a most interesting general reaction by means of which substances of type I can be readily converted in good yield into others of type II with elimination of CH₂ from the body of the chain, a conclusion which would be difficult to accept but for the very conclusive evidence I shall give in this and succeeding papers."

The extensive evidence presented by Hooker was

---

* For a discussion of this and other topics in "theoretical biochemistry," see R. B. Woodward,
   Z. Angew. Chem., **68**, 13 (1956).
   † A personal account by L.F.F.

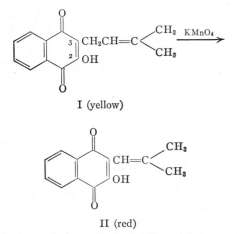

I (yellow)

II (red)

indeed conclusive. Several other quinones with unsaturated side chains gave comparable products, some of which were identified by synthesis. The reaction was shown applicable equally well to the

ported, but the results did not fit into any recognizable pattern. Hooker suspected that members of this series present difficulties in combustion and that the reported analyses might be erroneous. He therefore modified the usual method of operation by burning a small sample in a tube packed with lead chromate, rather than copper oxide. Accurate analyses were secured for many known and some new derivatives, and the results soon fitted into a consistent pattern. In a series of four articles, Bamberger and Hooker presented evidence that retene is a methylisopropylphenanthrene. At the age of 23, and on the basis of a research that had been completed in one year, Hooker was awarded the Ph.D. degree. He immediately came to the United States in the hope of continuing research in a university but, being unsuccessful in this objective, he obtained a position as chemist with the Franklin Sugar Refining Co. in Philadelphia. One project conducted in his leisure moments was a careful investigation of the Philadelphia water supply; his

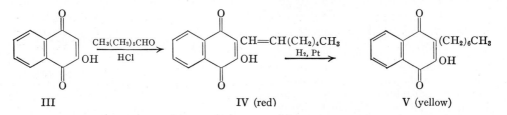

III   IV (red)   V (yellow)

shortening of saturated chains. For example, Hooker synthesized the *n*-heptyl derivative V by aldehyde condensation (IV) and hydrogenation, and by successive oxidations transformed it to all the lower homologs and finally into hydroxynaphthoquinone, III.

Hooker had noted that as an oxidation proceeds the deep red color of the hydroxyquinone anion nearly disappears and is then slowly replaced by color due to the new anion formed. He thought that the reaction must involve opening of the quinone ring and closure in a different manner, but he was more interested in use of the smoothly proceeding reaction than in the exact mechanism. At the time of his death in 1935 his lapachol work was not quite complete and his papers only partly written, but he had bequeathed all his notes and samples to me and I was thus able to prepare his papers for publication.

Samuel Cox Hooker was born in England in 1864, and in 1884 he undertook work for the doctorate under Bamberger at Munich and was assigned the problem of elucidating the structure of the hydrocarbon retene. Retenequinone and several derivatives and oxidation products had been re-

report played an important part in rectifying long-standing sources of pollution. A second project arose when a local manufacturer of fishing rods from Bethabarra wood imported from South America offered Hooker a supply of wood scraps for investigation of a yellow pigment evident in the grain. Hooker identified the pigment as a known but little studied compound which he called lapachol. The chemistry of lapachol, investigated by Hooker in his spare time, became more and more intriguing, and investigations in the period 1889–1896 were reported in eleven papers published in the *J. Chem. Soc.* This period of research was regretfully terminated because of increasing assignments and responsibilities in sugar technology and business. In these fields he demonstrated outstanding capacities. However, he had not forgotten promises expressed in his papers of 1896: "The results of my experiments will form the subject of a future paper"; "I shall hope to return to the consideration of this subject in the future." Consequently, after thirty years of service in the sugar industry and after having acquired a competency, he retired in 1915 in order to devote himself to resumption of his lapachol work and to two other avocations.

I first met Dr. Hooker in 1925 at the beginning of my first teaching assignment at Bryn Mawr College. I wanted to see if the inductive effect of substituents would be transmitted along a carbon side chain to a quinone nucleus sufficiently to influence the oxidation-reduction potential, and the only known quinones of the type needed were derivatives of lapachol. I learned with surprise and pleasure that Dr. Hooker had resumed his lapachol research, and was thrilled at his invitation to visit the private laboratory which he had built in the former stable of his house in Brooklyn. I was greeted by a stately, bearded gentleman who stood six feet six, and who took me on an orienting visit to his orderly laboratory, impressive because of the unusually high benches, to an adjoining study which housed a part of one of the most extensive private chemical libraries in the world (now the Kresge-Hooker library of Wayne University), and, upstairs, to a small theatre for the performance of magic (Hooker was one of the few amateurs ever elected to membership in the American Society of Magicians). My memory is rich with the many inspiring things I learned in ten years of contact with an extraordinary man and a true master of experimental investigation.

In agreement with Dr. Hooker, my students J. L. Hartwell and A. M. Seligman tested his idea that the quinone ring opens and then closes in a different sense by applying the reaction to naphthoquinones labeled with substituents in the benzenoid ring. The hydroxyl and modified alkyl group do indeed change place. No ideas for further elucidation of the mechanism occurred until the spring of 1940, when, in investigating the chemistry of vitamin K_1, I gained experience in the conversion of K_1 into its 2,3-oxide by reaction with alkaline hydrogen peroxide. I thus tried the reaction on lapachol in the hope of obtaining an intermediate in the Hooker oxidation. A colorless product resulted and had a reasonable analysis corresponding to lapachol plus the elements of hydrogen peroxide. I tried oxidation of phthiocol (2-OH-3-CH₃) in the same way and again obtained a colorless product, but in this case the analysis did not fit into the pattern of the other product. I presented the problem to Mary Fieser, who soon identified my product from phthiocol as phthalic acid. She subsequently isolated the product corresponding to that from lapachol and established that these compounds on further oxidation with permanganate yield the products of Hooker oxidation and therefore are true intermediates; she also isolated from a Hooker permanganate oxidation one of the colorless products of hydrogen peroxide oxidation. She characterized several Hooker intermediates as having one carboxyl group, two difficultly acylable hydroxyl groups, and a carbonyl group adjacent to a benzenoid ring, as in formula II (the stereochemistry was established later). This intermediate, in alkaline solution, is in equilibrium with the ketol III, and oxidation to IV activates the adjacent methylene group for aldol condensation to a product (V) which

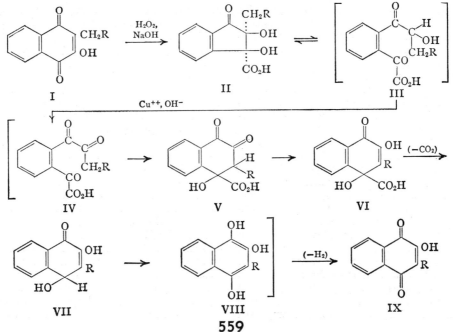

559

can enolize to a structure (VI) subject to ready decarboxylation (vinylog of a β-keto acid); the product VII then enolizes to a hydroquinone (VIII), which is easily oxidized to IX.

In 1943 Dr. A. P. Richardson, directing one of the many projects in antimalarial research sponsored by The Committee on Medical Research, reported that among several hundred random samples from university research collected by Abbott Laboratories he had found three samples from Harvard to possess antimalarial activity. These were hydrolapachol, derived from the Hooker collection of samples, and two related, less active, quinones. For exploitation of this interesting clue to a new type of antimalarial (nitrogen-free), an intensive program of synthesis was launched in our laboratory and by the Abbott group. For assay by the Richardson group at Memphis we prepared about every conceivable variant of the hydrolapachol structure. Of particular interest were a series of 2-hydroxy-1,4-naphthoquinones with 3-substituents of the types:

—(CH₂)ₙCH₃
—(CH₂)ₙCH(CH₃)₂
—(CH₂)ₙ-cyclohexyl

—(CH₂)ₙ-cyclohexyl-4-cyclohexyl
—(CH₂)ₙC₆H₅

In the *n*-alkyl series the number of methylene groups covered the range from 1 to 16. For synthesis of these quinones the Hooker oxidation proved invaluable, for once a higher homolog was available all the lower homologs could be prepared by successive elimination of CH_2 from the chain. The original procedure of oxidation with permanganate in dilute aqueous alkali gave yields of only 30–40% with quinones having unsaturated side chains, and was not applicable to compounds of high molecular weight and sparing solubility. Also, if more than 0.5–1 g. of material is oxidized, the product formed suffers oxidation before the starting material is consumed. However, with knowledge of the mechanism of the reaction, it was possible to develop a two-step Hooker procedure in which oxidation to the intermediate II is done with hydrogen peroxide in dioxane-soda solution and oxidation to IX is done in alkaline solution with copper sulfate, which, unlike permanganate, is incapable of effecting the first step. Pure products are obtainable in yields of 85–90%, and there seems to be no limitations in type of quinone or size of sample.

II. 22

RHODOMYCIN (*After Chapter 28*)

In an extensive study of the antibiotics elaborated by *Actinomyces*, a genus of bacteria, H. Brockmann isolated (1951) an active, water-soluble, red material, rhodomycin, from *Streptomyces purpurascens*. The pigment is amphoteric and is extractable from the aqueous medium and the mycelium only at the isoelectric point, pH 8.5. The basic character proved useful in isolation, since the pigment forms sparingly soluble salts (hydrochloride, picrate, perchlorate). Material which initially appeared homogeneous was later separated by countercurrent distribution (1953–55) into three components: rhodomycin A and B and isorhodomycin A. These water-soluble pigments are glycosides, and on acid hydrolysis are split to an amino sugar, rhodosamine, and a water-insoluble, pigmented aglycone. Chemical characterization of the rhodomycins was hampered by the fact that the glycosides are present in extremely minute amounts (20 mg./l.). However, the neutral aglycones are present in the cultures in larger amounts and can be isolated readily from the mycelium by vigorous hydrolysis with mineral acid and solvent extraction. Aglycones derived from the glycosides rhodomycin A and isorhodomycin A

have been isolated in this way and named β-rhodomycinone and isorhodomycinone; the structure of the former was elucidated in 1955.

The β-rhodomycinone isolated from total broth hydrolyzate formed brown-red needles, m.p. 225°, dec.; it was shown by IR and UV comparison and from the Rf value to be identical with a sample obtained by hydrolysis of the pure glycoside. The color of dilute solutions is too intense for determination of the specific rotation, but the yellow pentaacetate could be characterized as optically active, α_D −34° (2.5% in methanol). Possibly because of difficulties in effecting complete purification and because of analytical difficulties in this series, carbon and hydrogen percentages found with early samples led to consideration of the formulas (and molecular weights): $C_{15}H_{14}O_6$ (290), $C_{16}H_{14}O_6$ (302), and $C_{16}H_{16}O_6$ (304). However Beckmann determination of molecular weight in phenol solution gave the value 320, and isolation of the hydrocarbon naphthacene ($C_{18}H_{12}$) on zinc dust distillation established the presence of at least eighteen carbon atoms. These facts, coupled with new analyses on a purer sample, led to assignment of the formula $C_{18}H_{16}O_7$,

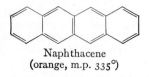

Naphthacene
(orange, m.p. 335°)

sponding hydrocarbons. Thus the reductive hepta-acetate from β-rhodomycinone has a spectrum definitely of the anthracene type.

In view of the presence of a C-methyl group and the C_{18}-formula, β-rhodomycinone evidently is an anthraquinone (C_{14}) with a four-carbon side chain, and since this chain can cyclize during zinc dust distillation to give naphthacene, it must be located at a β-position. The chain was inferred to contain one of the five hydroxyl groups from the observation that on catalytic hydrogenation (Pd-C, acetic acid) the pigment slowly absorbs one mole of hydrogen beyond that required for reduction of the quinone group and gives, after air oxidation in alkaline solution, a desoxyquinone. Since loss of this hydroxyl group does not alter the spectrum, the group could not have come from a nuclear position and hence is in the side chain. This hydroxyl group is also eliminated by dehydration, and the double bond so introduced must be conjugated with the chromophoric system since it produces a shift of ultraviolet absorption to longer wave length. Brockmann interpreted these facts as pointing to the partial formula I. This accounts for the optical activity,

even though the percentages found for carbon and oxygen deviate from the calculated values by an amount beyond the usual tolerance. The percentages found for C-methyl (Kuhn-Roth) and for active hydrogen (Zerewitinoff) agree satisfactorily with

$C_{18}H_{16}O_7$ (344.31)
Calcd.: C, 62.79; H, 4.68; O, 32.53;
    1 C—CH$_3$, 4.4; 5 act. H, 1.46
Found: C, 62.40; H, 4.83; O, 32.92;
    C—CH$_3$, 4.7; act. H, 1.21

the theoretical values for one of the former groups and five of the latter. Acetyl determinations on the product of exhaustive acetylation gave the values: CH$_3$CO, 37.61; 36.70, in reasonable agreement with the value calculated for five acylable hydroxyls (38.81).

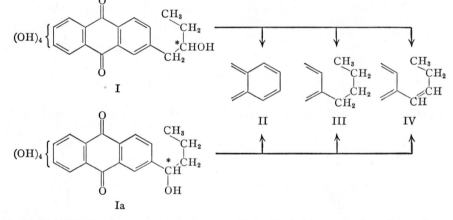

Although all the original carbon atoms are present in the degradation product naphthacene, the pigment itself cannot be a naphthacene derivative because of the analytical evidence of the presence of a C-methyl group. The two oxygen atoms not present as hydroxyl groups were recognized as being in a quinone group because of the color and the change in color on reduction. The absorption characteristics of polynuclear quinones are complicated and difficult to interpret, but reductive acetylation gives substances having characteristic, easily recognized spectra very similar to those of the corre-

Kuhn-Roth determination, formation of a new aromatic ring in conversion to naphthacene, II, and dehydration to an ene group conjugated with the anthraquinone system, IV. Evidence for the structures IV and III is that on permanganate oxidation the former gave a volatile fragment identified as propionic acid and the latter gave valeric, butyric, propionic, and acetic acid.* Formula Ia accounts equally well for the facts cited but seemed to Brockmann less likely because of differences in the behavior of rhodomycinone and alkannin (26.15), a pigment which he had previously characterized as

---

* This behavior is typical of acids higher than propionic and probably involves β-oxidation (K. Nakanishi, 1952).

a naphthoquinone with an α-hydroxyl group in the side chain. This activated group is eliminated on hydrogenolysis much more readily than is the alcoholic hydroxyl group of rhodomycinone. Furthermore, alkannin is readily racemized by acids, and is converted on reaction with methanolic hydrogen chloride into the *dl*-methyl ether, but rhodomycinone does not share these properties. Structure I thus appears to be correct, and the slow hydrogenolysis to III perhaps proceeds through IV.

The positions of the four nuclear hydroxyl groups were deduced by spectroscopic comparison with model compounds. Anthraquinone itself has an IR carbonyl band at 6.0μ, and if one α-hydroxyl is present the band for the adjacent carbonyl group is shifted to 6.2μ as the result of hydrogen bonding and two bands are observed, at 6.0μ and 6.2μ. If an α-hydroxyl is adjacent to each carbonyl group, a single, intensified band appears at 6.2μ. β-Rhodomycinone exhibits the latter behavior and hence contains hydroxyl groups adjacent to each carbonyl group. α-Hydroxyanthraquinones form colored chelated complexes with boroacetic anhydride and undergo further color changes with heating as the result of acetylation. Comparison of β-rhodomycinone with models containing hydroxyls at the 1,4,5-positions revealed similarities indicating the presence of hydroxyls at these positions. 1,4,5-Trihydroxyanthraquinone was found to be indistinguishable from its 7-methyl derivative, which shows that the presence of the alkyl chain in the antibiotic does not influence the spectrum. The fourth nuclear hydroxyl group was shown by special tests to be β, and this left four possibilities, of which

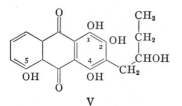

V

V is one. Models for the other three structures were available in the following tetrahydroxyanthraquinones: 1,3,4,5-, 1,4,5,6-, 1,4,5,7-. Spectroscopic and color comparisons with these substances in methanol, concentrated sulfuric acid, piperidine, TiCl₃-methanol, etc. revealed marked differences in each case; hence Brockmann assigned to β-rhodomycinone the 1,2,4,5-arrangement of formula V.

The sugar component of the water-soluble primary antibiotic, rhodosamine, is isolated most readily with use of a cation-exchange resin and was characterized as the crystalline hydrochloride, m.p. 153°, αD − 48°. Analysis established the formula $C_8H_{17}O_3N$, and the nitrogen was shown to be present as the group —N(CH₃)₂ by ready liberation of dimethylamine on alkaline hydrolysis. The presence of two acylable hydroxyl groups was established by application of a procedure developed by C. W. DeWalt, Jr. and R. A. Glenn (Carnegie Inst. Techn., 1952) for functional group analysis of products resulting from mild hydrogenolysis of coal. A sample containing 0.1 to 1.0 milligram equivalent of acylable hydroxyl is heated for 5 min. at 118° with a weighed 1-ml. sample of a mixture of 3 ml. of acetic anhydride with 12 ml. of pyridine. Titration of the amount of unused anhydride under that from a blank gives a measure of the number of easily acylable groups present; a second determination made after a reflux period of 1 hr. gives a measure of partially hindered groups. Rhodosamine reduces Fehling's solution but is stable to oxidation with periodic acid in dilute aqueous solution. It is therefore not a 2-ketose or a 2-hydroxyaldose, and must be a 2-desoxyaldopyranose. Kuhn-Roth determination indicates one C-methyl group, and since the IR spectrum shows no band indicative of a carbonyl group, the methyl group must be present as

>C(OH)CH₃ and not —C(=O)CH₃. Brockmann thus tentatively assigned to rhodosamine the structure VI, which he regards as giving better expression to the ease of hydrolytic elimination of dimethylamine than the alternate structure in which the groups at C₃ and C₄ are interchanged.

The water-soluble antibiotic rhodomycin A corresponds exactly in UV spectrum to the aglycone rhodomycinone, and therefore the sugar residue

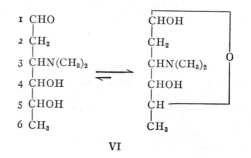

VI

must be linked to the hydroxyl group in the side chain and not to one of the hydroxyls joined to the chromophoric nucleus. Analytical data indicate that the antibiotic glycoside is made up of approximately two equivalents of the quinone to three equivalents of the amino sugar.

CARCINOGENIC HYDROCARBONS (*After Chapter 28*)

A tumor is an abnormal tissue growth arising without obvious cause from pre-existent normal cells. Normal growth proceeds by cell division at a rate adjusted to the needs of the organism and stops when not required. Malignant, cancerous cells lack a control mechanism and give rise to wild growth of a tumor, which may invade a vital organ and cause death. A tumor at an accessible site may be removable by surgery or treated with X-rays, but there is danger that a few malignant cells may be carried in the blood and start a secondary tumor at another site. Since most individuals have adequate resistance to withstand whatever attrition leads others to fall victim to cancer, it would seem possible that means can be found for increasing the resistance of cancer-susceptible subjects. The possibility that cancer can arise through the action of a chemical produced by abnormal metabolism was suggested by the discovery of chemical agents capable of transforming normal cells of test animals into malignant cells.

The discovery was the outcome of the realization, at the early part of the present century, that individuals in specific occupations involving prolonged exposure to coal-tar products tended to show an abnormally high incidence of skin cancer, which sometimes developed only several years after the period of exposure. The inference that "tar cancer" arises from contact of the skin with chemicals in the tar was confirmed in 1915 when Yamagiwa and Ichikawa succeeded in producing tumors by prolonged application of a coal tar distillate to the ear skin of rabbits. The observation was soon confirmed and extended by others, particularly by Kennaway[1] and associates at the Royal Cancer Hospital, London, who sought to identify the causative agent (1925). The mouse was adopted as test animal because tumors, whether spontaneous or induced, appear more rapidly in mice than in other available animals, perhaps because the normal life span is shorter. Even with mice nearly a year may be required to obtain positive results, and a test can be declared negative only when the mice all die free of tumors (about 2 yrs.!). However, the British group eventually characterized the carcinogen as a constituent of the higher-boiling hydrocarbon fractions of coal tar distillates. All known coal tar hydrocarbons of appropriate boiling point were assayed, but with negative results. Then I. Hieger of the London group (1930) discovered that carcinogenic tars differ from noncarcinogenic tars in having a fluorescence spectrum characterized by the presence of bands at 400, 418, and 440 mμ. Examination of a number of polynuclear hydrocarbons disclosed that 1,2-benzanthracene has a fluorescence spectrum rather similar to that of the carcinogenic tars but with the bands displaced to shorter wave length. J. W. Cook,[2] chemist of the group, had

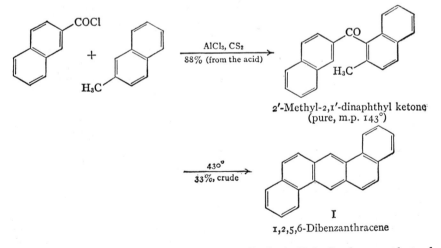

2'-Methyl-2,1'-dinaphthyl ketone
(pure, m.p. 143°)

I
1,2,5,6-Dibenzanthracene

[1] Sir Ernest Lawrence Kennaway, b. 1881, Exeter, England; D.Sc. London; postdoctoral work Lister Inst., Guy's Hosp.; dir. Chester Beatty Res. Inst., Roy. Cancer Hosp.; Dept. Pathol., St. Bartholemew's Hosp.
[2] James Wilfred Cook, b. 1900 London; Ph.D. and D.Sc. London (Barnett); London, Glasgow

undertaken synthesis of a number of derivatives of 1,2-benzanthracene. Biological and optical investigations of the compounds were conducted by Kennaway, Hieger, and W. V. Mayneord. One of the hydrocarbons considered, 1,2,5,6-dibenzanthracene (I), had been made available in 1929 (E. Clar [3]; L. F. Fieser and E. M. Dietz) by application of the previously little used Elbs reaction (1884), by which anthracene derivatives had been formed in about 10% yield by pyrolysis of o-methyl derivatives of benzophenone. The reaction proceeds much better with the more reactive dinaphthyl ketone, and hence I is easily prepared in two steps from β-naphthoyl chloride and β-methylnaphthalene. In 1930 Kennaway and Hieger reported that, when applied to mice by painting a 0.3% solution in benzene onto the skin twice weekly, 1,2,5,6-dibenzanthracene produced epitheliomal tumors in a large proportion of the animals.

The first known carcinogenic hydrocarbon was recognized as different from the carcinogen of coal tar because its fluorescence spectrum did not match the characteristic three-banded spectrum of the tars. In 1933 Cook, C. L. Hewett, and Hieger, using fluorescence spectroscopy as a guide, processed two tons of pitch by distillation, solvent extraction, crystallization, and purification through the picrate and isolated the substance responsible for the fluorescence. The hydrocarbon, unknown at the

time, was identified as 3,4-benzpyrene by synthesis from pyrene by succinoylation at the 3-position, reduction to the γ-arylbutyric acid, cyclization, reduction, and dehydrogenation. This hydrocarbon is also a 1,2-benzanthracene derivative, and it proved to be a considerably more potent carcinogen than dibenzanthracene and is undoubtedly the chief

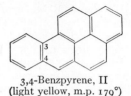

3,4-Benzpyrene, II
(light yellow, m.p. 179°)

agent responsible for the early observed occupational skin cancer. Actually, benzpyrene is much more of a menace than was initially suspected, since it is formed on pyrolysis of various cellulosic and hydrocarbon materials and appears in city soot, in the soot from gasoline engines and woodburning stoves, and in scorched food.

Discovery of a further hydrocarbon carcinogen was an incidental outcome of work done by H. Wieland [4] and Elizabeth Dane in 1933 in completing the evidence of the structure of bile acids. The last point of uncertainty was the position at which the acid side chain is joined to the terminal five-mem-

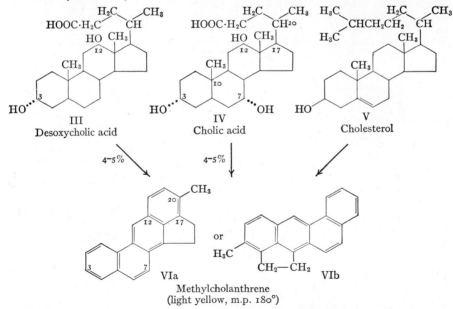

III
Desoxycholic acid

IV
Cholic acid

V
Cholesterol

VIa   or   VIb
Methylcholanthrene
(light yellow, m.p. 180°)

[3] Eric Clar, b. Herrnskretschen/Elbe, Sudetenland; Ph.D. Dresden (Scholl); Dresden, Glasgow
[4] Heinrich Wieland, b. 1877 Pforzheim, Germany; Ph.D. Munich (Thiele); Freiburg, Munich; Nobel Prize 1927

bered ring, and the German investigators settled the issue by showing that an aromatizable, and hence six-membered, ring can be formed between positions 12 and 17 (see formula IV). Desoxycholic acid (III) was oxidized to the 3,12-diketone and the less hindered 3-keto group eliminated by selective Clemmensen reduction. The 12-keto acid when heated at 330° underwent intramolecular Perkin condensation, with simultaneous decarboxylation of the initially formed α,β-unsaturated acid and production of a colorless hydrocarbon, which on selenium dehydrogenation suffered aromatization with elimination of the two angular methyl groups and formation of a yellow hydrocarbon named methylcholanthrene, VIa (cholic acid + anthracene). When the formula is arranged as in VIb, it is seen that methylcholanthrene is a derivative of 1,2-benzanthracene that resembles dibenzanthracene (I) in having carbon substituents at the 5- and 6-positions, and resembles benzpyrene (II) in containing a carbocyclic ring linked to one of the *meso* carbon atoms. Cook and Haslewood[5] repeated the degradation and in 1934 reported the substance to be powerfully carcinogenic to mice.

The hydrocarbon subsequently was obtained by similar degradation of the more abundant cholic acid (IV) and by an unusual pyrolytic degradation of cholesterol (V). The yield in all these degradations is very low, but, in cooperation with a U. S. Public Health Service cancer research group then stationed at the Harvard Medical School (M. J. Shear, N. B. Andervont, *et al.*) and seeking material for biological experimentation, Fieser and Seligman[6] in 1935 worked out a practical synthesis. Friedel-Crafts condensation of *p*-chlorotoluene with β-chloropropionyl chloride gives a mixture of both possible isomers (2), but separation is not required, for after cyclization to a mixture of hydrindones (3), Clemmensen reduction affords a single product, 4-methyl-7-chlorohydrindene (4). This is converted into the nitrile (5), which is condensed with α-naphthyl-magnesium bromide to give the ketone (6); the initial product is a ketimine, readily hydrolyzed to a ketone: ArC(=NH)Ar' ⟶ ArCOAr'. This ketone undergoes unusually smooth Elbs pyrolysis, with condensation of the *o*-methylene group of the five-membered ring into the second aromatic nucleus, and pure methylcholanthrene is obtainable in over-all yield from *p*-chlorotoluene of 23%.

Work on the synthesis and testing of hydrocarbons was actively pursued by many investigators. The chief test methods utilize skin painting and subcutaneous injection in tricaprylin solution. The mice used are of pure strains developed by brother-

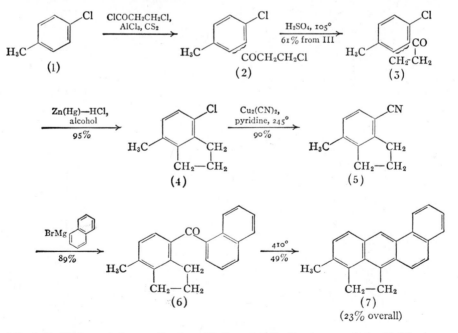

[5] G. A. D. Haslewood, b. 1910 London; Ph.D. and D.Sc. London; worked with Marrian, J. W. Cook, E. J. King; Guy's Hosp. Med. Sch.
[6] Arnold M. Seligman, b. 1912 St. Johnsbury, Vt.; stud. Harvard (Fieser), M.D. Harvard; Beth Israel Hospital, Boston, Sinai Hospital, Baltimore

sister matings for at least twenty generations. The type of tumor produced is dependent upon the nature of the tissue with which the carcinogen is in contact: epitheliomas (skin painting), sarcomas (injection into connective tissue). The order of potency in all comparative tests is: methylcholanthrene > benzpyrene > dibenzanthracene. Thus subcutaneous injection of 1-mg. quantities into C3H mice produced tumors in at least 80% of the mice

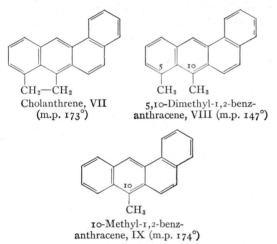

CH₂—CH₂
Cholanthrene, VII
(m.p. 173°)

CH₃ CH₃
5,10-Dimethyl-1,2-benz-
anthracene, VIII (m.p. 147°)

CH₃
10-Methyl-1,2-benz-
anthracene, IX (m.p. 174°)

after the following average latent periods: methylcholanthrene, 9.7 weeks; benzpyrene, 12.4 weeks; dibenzanthracene, 21.7 weeks; methylcholanthrene acts as rapidly at a dosage of 0.25 mg. as at a 2-mg. level. In comparative skin paintings, the latent periods were: methylcholanthrene, 18 weeks; dibenzanthracene, 30 weeks.

One objective was to determine the structural features in methylcholanthrene which contribute to its potency. Systematic studies of synthetic model compounds showed that the methyl group has no importance; that much, if not all, of the efficacy of cholanthrene (VII) is retained in the analogous hydrocarbon 5,10-dimethyl-1,2-benzanthracene (VIII); and that the most significant structural feature of cholanthrene or methylcholanthrene is the 1,2-benzanthracene ring system with a carbon substituent at the *meso* position 10. 10-Methyl-1,2-benzanthracene (IX) evokes sarcomas in mice nearly as rapidly as methylcholanthrene, though it is distinctly less effective in production of skin cancer. The activity falls rapidly in the series methyl, ethyl, propyl. All twelve possible monomethyl derivatives of the inactive 1,2-benzanthracene have been synthesized and tested, and of these the 10-isomer is the most potent. The *meso*-substituted 9-methyl compound is next, followed closely by the 5-methyl derivative, which produces sarcomas in mice with a latent period about twice as long as that observed with 10-methyl-1,2-benzanthracene. Methylcholanthrene and benzpyrene can be regarded as 1,2-benzanthracenes substituted at the *meso* positions 10 and 9, respectively, and in model compounds combination of the two types of substitution is particularly favorable. 9,10-Dimethyl-1,2-benzanthracene produces skin tumors in mice with remarkable rapidity and in this test surpasses methylcholanthrene in speed of action, though it is less effective when administered by subcutaneous injection.

Investigation of the chemical properties of methylcholanthrene and benzpyrene revealed the striking

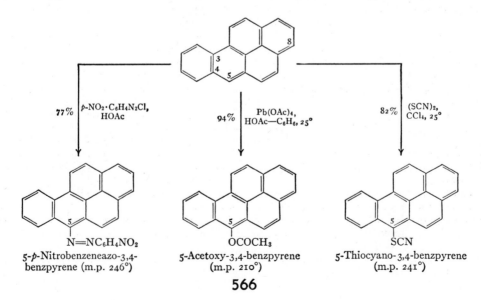

5-*p*-Nitrobenzeneazo-3,4-
benzpyrene (m.p. 246°)

5-Acetoxy-3,4-benzpyrene
(m.p. 210°)

5-Thiocyano-3,4-benzpyrene
(m.p. 241°)

566

fact that these most potent carcinogens are endowed with remarkable susceptibility to substitutions. They surpass all other known aromatic hydrocarbons in this special manifestation of chemical reactivity and resemble phenols. Thus benzpyrene couples with the only moderately reactive *p*-nitrobenzene-diazonium chloride to give an azo compound, it is acetoxylated by lead tetraacetate at room temperature, and it reacts readily with thiocyanogen, a reagent somewhat like a halogen but less reactive.

that the relationship is merely approximate and not without exceptions. However, the likelihood of a causative relationship is strengthened by the fact that the chemical substitutions occur at that part of the molecule which is recognized from the data surveyed in the preceding section as being particularly important for carcinogenic potency. These considerations led to the hypothesis that a carcinogen combines chemically with an enzyme in control of cell division, and indeed investigation of the metabolism of isotopically labeled dibenzan-

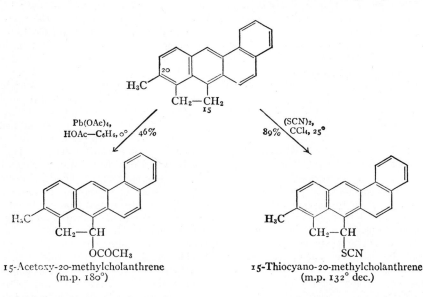

15-Acetoxy-20-methylcholanthrene
(m.p. 180°)

15-Thiocyano-20-methylcholanthrene
(m.p. 132° dec.)

In all three reactions substitution occurs exclusively at a position (C₅) corresponding to the meso position 10 in the 1,2-benzanthracene ring system. Neither related noncarcinogenic hydrocarbons nor less potent carcinogens exhibit comparable reactivity, but methylcholanthrene is substituted readily by the same three reagents. In this case the point of attack is not at a nuclear position, as in benzpyrene, but at the methylene group joined to the 1,2-benzanthracene ring system at the 10-*meso* position. It is remarkable that the two hydrocarbons exhibit comparable susceptibility to the special substitutions even though one is substituted in a benzenoid ring and the other in a methylene group.

The correlation of high carcinogenic potency with unusual sensitivity to specific reagents suggests a possible association between the two phenomena, though comparative results for a series of carcinogenic and noncarcinogenic hydrocarbons indicate

thracene has afforded evidence of combination of the hydrocarbon with protein (Heidelberger,[7] 1955).

Although most of the known hydrocarbon carcinogens are of chief interest for experimental production of cancer and study of the mechanism and possible counteraction of carcinogenesis, it seemed possible for a time that methylcholanthrene may be a causative agent in spontaneous cancer. It can be produced in the laboratory by chemical transformations of two acids normally present in the bile and of cholesterol. However, the pyrolytic degradations of steroids are wholly unlike known metabolic reactions. Trace amounts of the hydrocarbon are readily detectable by absorption spectroscopy, but many attempts to detect the substance in cancerous tissue have yielded negative results. The accumulated evidence thus strongly discounts the possibility of a causative relationship. Possibly a chemical of some other structural type is implicated.

[7] Charles Heidelberger, b. 1920 New York; Ph.D. Harvard (Fieser); McArdle Lab., Med. Sch., Wisconsin

SYNTHETIC ALIZARIN * (*After Chapter 28*)

The art of Turkey red dyeing with the root of the madder plant was known to the ancient world, and for many centuries madder and indigo were the leading dyes of the world. Mummies wrapped in cloth dyed with Turkey red have been found with the color still in excellent condition. Madder (*Rubia tinctorum*), native to Asia, became an article of commerce in Europe as early as 700, and cultivation of the plant was carried into Italy as a result of the Crusades. It appeared in France in the sixteenth century and flourished particularly well in Alsace and Provence. By the end of the seventeenth century madder cultivation had acquired considerable economic importance to France, with annual exportations of the order of 2,500,000 kg. To stimulate production, Louis Philippe equipped his armies with breeches dyed with Turkey red, a practice only abandoned in 1914.

The active dye is alizarin, 1,2-dihydroxyanthraquinone. This occurs in the plant as a glycoside, from which it is liberated by enzymatic hydrolysis. The commercial powder made by grinding dried root contains about 1% of total pigment; alizarin is the chief component but is accompanied by 1,3-di- and 1,2,4-trihydroxyanthraquinone and by methyl and carboxy derivatives of these two substances; the relative proportion of the components varies with the season.

Production of the color Turkey red requires application to cotton of a basic mordant (L. *mordere*, to bite) to form a binding link between cloth and dye. In early formulas cotton was impregnated with rancid olive oil containing lime and then with a solution of aluminum sulfate, and steamed. The alumina-mordanted cloth was then treated with an aqueous suspension of madder. The colloidal metal hydroxide adheres to the cloth and the dye molecule combines with it to form a complex salt, or lake. The initial color is a little dull and must be enlivened in a soap bath containing a tin salt. Early processes involved still further processing and required as much as four months for completion, and the most successful formulas were handed down from father to son. A skilled madder colorist could produce remarkably beautiful color effects, and was not limited to red; for instance violet colors are obtained with an iron mordant, brownish red with a chromium mordant. Wool and silk can be dyed, as well as cotton.

The high opinion of the dye with respect to fastness, beauty, and variety of color is illustrated by the prediction made in 1867 by Schutzenberger in his *Traité des matières colorantes* that the only substance which could possibly dethrone madder would be the artificially produced active principle of madder. The principle had been isolated in a pure state by Robiquet and Colin in 1826 and named alizarin (Arabic, *azara*, to press out). Samples purified by sublimation were analyzed in 1835 by Robiquet, whose results agree well with the percentage composition for the true formula $C_{14}H_8O_4$. However, the value for the atomic weight of carbon accepted at the time was so in error as to lead Robiquet to deduce the formula $C_{37}H_{48}O_{10}$. A number of subsequent investigators reported variable analyses and suggested formulas ranging from C_{14} to C_{60}. In 1848 E. Schunck obtained results agreeing with those of Robiquet and deduced the nearly correct formula $C_{14}H_{10}O_4$. This was rejected, however, in consequence of Schunck's finding that alizarin on oxidation affords a substance which Wolff and Strecker in 1850 found to be identical with phthalic acid. These investigators reasoned that since phthalic acid also results from oxidation of naphthalene, a C_{10} compound, alizarin must be a C_{10} compound derived from naphthalene. The conclusion appeared to be supported by a similarity of alizarin to chloronaphthalenic acid, which Laurent had prepared from naphthalene: both compounds give color reactions with alkalis and acids, both are reducible, and both give phthalic acid on oxidation. The structural similarity is that both compounds are hydroxyquinones; Laurent's compound has the structure I.

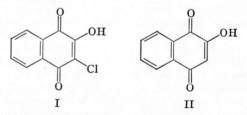

I   II

Wolff and Strecker, however, assigned to alizarin the formula $C_{10}H_6O_3$ in order to express the expected relationship to chloronaphthalenic acid, which they regarded as chloroalizarin. Naphthalenic acid, II, was then unknown. Failure of all efforts to reduce the chloro compound to alizarin was attributed to accidental circumstances and the synthesis of alizarin was believed to be merely a matter of finding an appropriate experimental

* Based on an article by one of us (L.F.F.) in *J. Chem. Ed.*, **7**, 2609 (1930)

method. Despite the fallacious reasoning and the analytical discrepancy (carbon 1% off), these views were accepted and for twenty years alizarin was regarded as a naphthalene derivative. When Martius and Griess discovered naphthalenic acid (II) in 1865 they described it as an isomer of alizarin.

No further facts came to light until Graebe and Liebermann commenced their investigations in 1868. Appreciation of their contribution may be aided by a reconstruction of the chemical world of the day. In 1868 organic chemical theory was in a state of transition. The older ideas were still being advocated in the schools of the masters. But Geheimrat Prof. Dr. Friederich Wöhler of Göttingen, Geheimrat Prof. Dr. Freiherr Justus von Liebig, and Sénateur Jean Baptiste Dumas of Paris had all passed their sixty-fifth year and their influence was decreasing. Though somewhat younger, Geheimrat Prof. Dr. Robert Bunsen of Heidelberg should be classed with this distinguished trio. Of the men in their early fifties, Kolbe had just accepted a call to Leipzig and the days of his experimental work were largely over, Wurtz of Paris had already made his greatest contributions, while Hofmann really belongs to two periods, for this great experimentalist and leader was nearly as active in the years following 1868 as he had been up to that time. Each of the six chemists had exerted a profound influence on the development of the new science, and they numbered among their students practically all the productive investigators of the world; but, with the exception of Hofmann, the day of their greatest creative activity and influence had passed. Even Berthelot, at the age of forty-one, had passed the peak of his activity in organic chemistry and now occupied the post of Minister of Education in France.

The moving spirit of the day was August Kekulé. Kekulé, now in his fortieth year, was at the University of Bonn, having transferred from Geneva in 1858. His classical structural theory had been announced in that same year, and the first volume of his *Lehrbuch* appeared in 1859. His new ideas, which eventually led to a clear conception of valence and to a general adoption of structural formulas, created widespread interest and his views found support which was more than adequate to sustain the attack of some of his older colleagues. His most significant achievement came in 1865 when Kekulé published in a lengthy *Annalen* paper his theory of the structure of benzene. Up to this time aromatic compounds had received little attention and no views regarding their constitution had been advanced. The benzene hexagon is comparable to the carbon tetrahedron of van't Hoff. In each case

a large number of perplexing facts were explained by a theory which can be expressed with a simple diagram. Each theory had to weather the storm of Kolbe's bitter attack, and each received experimental support from modern physics and has been retained in only slightly modified form.

The new theory was received with enthusiasm and by 1868 numerous investigators were busily engaged in working out structural problems according to Kekulé's ideas of valence. A few of Kekulé's contemporaries, men in the early forties, who shared in this work were Erlenmeyer of Heidelberg, Stanislao Cannizzaro, then at Palermo, and Friedel of Paris. On the other hand, the group in London, which consisted of Hofmann's successor Frankland, the industrialist Griess, and Williamson, were busy following programs based upon their recently discovered reactions. It thus remained largely for a still younger group to explore the field suddenly illuminated by Kekulé. Kekulé was a man of delightful personality and his charm and wit were no small factors in causing even some of the Kolbe-trained men to regard themselves before long as belonging to the Kekulé school.

Berlin was the center of this active group of thirty-year-old chemists who plunged with enthusiasm into problems of structural chemistry. Adolf Baeyer was the leader. At the age of thirty-three, Baeyer had completed an important work on uric acid and had commenced his indigo work. In 1860 he had founded an organic laboratory at the *Gewerbe-Akademie*, which later grew into the present *Technische Hochschule*. Since the conditions in Hofmann's laboratory were not very satisfactory for independent work on the part of assistants, many able men were attracted to the laboratory of the successful young experimenter who cordially encouraged them to undertake problems of their own. Baeyer played a leading part in the founding of the *Deutsche Chemische Gesellschaft*, of which the distinguished August Wilhelm von Hofmann was the first president. The organization took place on November 11, 1867, with a membership of one hundred and three.

Among the contemporaries of Baeyer who, in or near their early thirties, were active followers of the new school in Germany during 1868, Karl Alexander von Martius and Carl Graebe were at Berlin, Wislicenus was commencing his lactic acid work at Zurich, Caro was at Heidelberg, Fittig was at Wöhler's laboratory at Göttingen, and Ladenburg was assistant to Bunsen at Heidelberg. (Victor Meyer had just passed his examinations at the latter university at the age of nineteen.) Markownikoff and Beilstein were in Russia, where the latter already was at work on his *Handbuch*. Körner, at

Palermo, was busily engaged in his investigations on orientation.

At the Greenford Green dye works of the firm of Perkin and Sons in England, William Henry Perkin, at the age of thirty, was an accomplished chemist with twelve years of experience in the first synthetic dye plant ever operated. In 1856, on oxidizing crude aniline, he had discovered a method of preparing a dye synthetically. Against the advice of his teacher Hofmann, who was then at the Royal College of Chemistry in London, Perkin resigned his assistantship, set up a factory, and was soon manufacturing his mauve. The new dye, which was the first rival of the natural dyes, soon acquired great popularity and once brought as high a price as platinum. Following Perkin's lead, several other factories sprang up in England, as well as a few in Germany and France. Satisfactory methods of distilling coal tar and of preparing the necessary intermediates were soon developed in England, and the dye producers also had successful alkali and acid industries from which to draw supplies. New processes for the manufacture of mauve were discovered, and new dyes of the mauve and of other types soon made their appearance. It was a veritable wonderland of discovery, fame, and fortune.

No small part in the development of the English dye industry was played by a group of German chemists. Hofmann's discoveries in the field of the aromatic amines formed the basis upon which the industry had been founded, and most of the important English chemists had received their training in Hofmann's laboratory. Though he had not encouraged the attempts to commercialize Perkin's first discovery, he soon gave full support to the new industry and played a leading part in the scientific study of the new products. It was through his influence that his countrymen, Martius and Griess, were in England at this time. Heinrich Caro, after a few years of experience in madder dyeing in Alsace, was attracted by the discoveries in England and secured a position with the firm of Roberts and Dale at Manchester in 1859. His dreams of sharing in the romantic successes were soon realized, for he proved to have a remarkable faculty for unearthing new reactions and compounds. Like Perkin, Martius, and Griess, he kept in close touch with Hofmann's laboratory and investigated the scientific side of the technical problems as fully as time permitted. Among many achievements in this early period, Caro discovered a new method of making mauve and, with Martius, introduced Manchester Brown and Martius Yellow. The list of other dyes which appeared on the market at this time includes Crysaniline, Rosolic Acid, Spirit Blue, Paeonin, Azulin, Regina Violet, Methyl Rosaniline, Aniline Green, Aniline Black, and Diphenylamine Blue.

All these substances had been discovered without reference to a theory of color and without knowledge of the structure of the dyes which occur in nature. The structures of the synthetic products were unknown and, until the benzene problem had been solved, unknowable. Thus about ten years after Perkin's initial discovery of mauve progress of the new industry began to slacken perceptibly. Discoveries based largely upon chance or accident could not continue indefinitely. The announcement of the Kekulé theory in 1865 was the signal that the time had come for a change, for it now seemed possible to work out the structures of the dyes. Rational plans for the advancement of the industry could then be made. Thus Hofmann left the scene of the greatest activity in the dye field and returned to Germany in 1865. Martius followed his former teacher; Caro, bent on scientific investigations at Heidelberg, returned in 1866. This young technologist, however, could not long remain out of contact with the industry and, three years later, Caro became co-director with Glaser of the dye laboratory of the Badische Anilin-und Soda-Fabrik at Ludwigshafen. This company had been formed in 1865, when it employed thirty workmen.

This, then, was the state of affairs when the investigation of alizarin was undertaken by Graebe and Liebermann in 1868. The stage could not have been set more appropriately for the synthesis and the determination of the structure of one of the most beautiful and important of natural dyes. No one was better suited to play the leading role than Carl Graebe. A student of Kolbe, he had spent brief periods in the laboratories of Bunsen and of Erlenmeyer, and he had worked for a year in the Höchster Farbwerke laboratory of the firm of Meister Lucius u. Co. The problem of searching for new dyes interested him, but a case of poisoning by methyl iodide caused him to break this industrial connection. In 1865 he accepted a position as assistant to Baeyer in the *Gewerbe-Akademie*. His relationships here were very pleasant and he found in Baeyer, who was his senior by six years, a warm friend and a stimulating leader. He was introduced to Kekulé one day while carrying out a combustion, and talked with him for several hours. Writing to his parents, Graebe described Kekulé as

. . . an exceptionally amiable person, which pleased me all the more because I hardly expected that Kekulé, who is one of the most influential chemists of the time, would bother much about us young people. Kekulé spoke about everything, about himself, his relationships, his work, as though we had been old friends. . . . That Kekulé knows what he is, is often noticeable in the course of the conversation, but this never appears in an unpleasant or arrogant manner.

In his first attempts to apply the doctrines of his new-found friend, Graebe became interested in the quinones. These fascinating substances had formed a perplexing problem and even Kekulé had been so far in error concerning their constitution that he had regarded them as open-chain compounds. His formula for quinone was:

O=CH—CH=CH—CH=CH—CH=O.

Working with chloranil (tetrachloroquinone) rather than quinone because it was cheaper, Graebe was impressed by the fact that the quinone is easily converted by reduction into a truly aromatic compound. It was hard to believe that ring-closure took place in this simple reaction, and it seemed more probable that both the quinone and the hydroquinone contain the benzene hexagon. He was able to prove this by the conversion of chloranil into hexachlorobenzene. In reasoning about the positions of the oxygen atoms, he took it as a fact that neither resorcinol nor catechol are capable of yielding quinones on oxidation, in the manner characteristic of hydroquinone. The first proposition is still regarded as true, but it is now known that oxidation of catechol to o-benzoquinone can be accomplished under special conditions. Graebe reasoned that if only one of the three dihydroxybenzenes yields a quinone, this must be the one with the two hydroxyls in close proximity, and he thus wrote for quinone the formula:

While his formula was wrong in two respects, Graebe's conceptions and experimental work represented a distinct advance. Graebe had become familiar in this early work with the fact that the quinones are easily reduced, that chloranil, III, can be converted into chloranilic acid, IV, by the action of aqueous alkali, that hydroxyquinones form highly colored solutions in alkali, and that their reduction products are readily oxidized in alkaline solution by the air.

With this experience, Graebe turned to the chemistry of naphthalene and soon became convinced that Laurent's chloronaphthalenic acid and its supposed chloride (2,3-dichloro-1,4-naphthoquinone) as well as the supposed isomer of alizarin discovered by Martius and Griess are all naphtho-

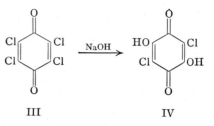

quinones. His only error lay in regarding the parent as an *ortho* derivative. A valuable part of this work was to prove for the first time that naphthalene contains two benzene rings, thus:

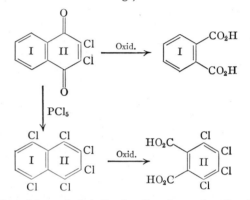

That this work led Graebe directly to the alizarin problem is obvious. Alizarin was generally regarded as an isomer of the substance which Graebe had shown to be a hydroxynaphthoquinone, and a study of the dye was thus the next logical step in his quinone work.

Graebe's collaborator, Carl Liebermann, was one year younger and had had less experience in scientific work. A *Burschenschafter* active in the *Allemania* at Heidelberg, Liebermann had taken his degree at the *Gewerbe-Akademie* in 1863 and then turned to industrial work in accordance with the wishes of his father, a *Geheimer Kommerzienrat*, who owned a prosperous cotton mill near Berlin. The young chemist was sent to a large dye and print works in Alsace for training as colorist. Here he became familiar with the process of dyeing with madder and with the method of preparing extracts of the dyes which it contains, but he soon became dissatisfied. After the exact methods practiced in Baeyer's laboratory it was disappointing to work with a substance of so variable a nature as madder. Samples differed considerably in composition and in the concentration of the active matter, and the control was not exact. A common method of testing consisted in chewing a sample of madder. Sand was detected in an obviously unpleasant manner, and the color of the sputum afforded an indication of the tinctorial qualities. Regarding his attitude, Liebermann says:

> One day I saw at a church festival a group of old peasant women wearing madder-colored scarfs from our factory. These scarfs had cost my friends, the colorists, their positions because the red had turned out a little too bluish. It became clear to me that I could not contemplate a lifework spent in attention to such details.

Thus Liebermann gave up the idea of industrial work and in 1867 returned to the laboratory of the esteemed Baeyer. Here he was to devote fifty years of his life to active scientific work. In looking for a problem it was natural that he should think of working on alizarin, which he had learned to extract from madder. Perhaps through a knowledge of the chemistry of alizarin it would be possible to introduce scientific methods into Turkey red dyeing.

Liebermann soon found a friend in Graebe, and each confided in the other the intention of working on alizarin while walking home. The decision to collaborate followed and, after securing material, they started active work on a Friday, February 21, 1868. Friday, Saturday, Sunday, and Monday were spent in energetic work, and by 7 o'clock on Monday evening they had advanced so far that they were able to communicate an important result at the meeting of the *Chemische Gesellschaft* which took place at seven-thirty. They had applied a reaction which Baeyer had discovered in the previous year in his indigo work. He had succeeded in reducing indigo to indoxyl by ordinary methods, but elimination of the last atom of oxygen required a more vigorous reducing agent. Baeyer had tried passing the vapor of indoxyl over heated zinc dust and had discovered indole, the mother substance of indigo. The reaction, which was also found to afford a means of converting phenol into benzene, was applied by Graebe and Liebermann to the oxygen-containing alizarin. Instead of naphthalene, a hydrocarbon was obtained which was soon identified as anthracene. A review of the published analyses of alizarin revealed the fact that the best results indicated the formula $C_{14}H_8O_4$, and the combined information definitely classed the substance as a derivative of anthracene rather than of naphthalene. This accounted for the failure of all previous attempts to prepare the dye, for they had all started with the latter hydrocarbon.

Some impression of the local interest in the discovery and of the excitement of the event is furnished by a letter from Graebe to his parents, in which he speaks of the celebration of his twenty-seventh birthday on the 24th, and of the report which he made to the *Chemische Gesellschaft* on that day:

> Unprepared as I was, I spoke briefly about the most important results. That was the first celebration. The second was at a dinner at Baeyer's which was just for close friends. When we went in to dinner I found at my place a wreath of madder blossoms. Baeyer proposed a toast to Dr. Liebermann, whose birthday was on the 23rd, to myself, and to our work. I made a reply, and I do not think I am mistaken in believing that I spoke very well.

Even the great Bunsen was impressed by the work of the two young men, for he mentioned it in a letter to Kolbe.

Anthracene had been isolated from coal tar, and Graebe and Liebermann at once speculated on the possibility of preparing the dye from this hydrocarbon. The substance was not easy to obtain, however, and the two investigators were fortunate in securing about 500 grams from Martius, who purchased it for them in England. When they undertook a synthesis, Graebe and Liebermann were still far from a knowledge of the structure of alizarin. They knew only that the carbon skeleton was the same as that of anthracene, but the structure of this hydrocarbon had not been established. Graebe and Liebermann, in fact, were the first to discuss the problem of its structure. Their own observation that alizarin is derived from anthracene, coupled with the fact that the dye yields phthalic acid on oxidation, furnished evidence that eight of the carbon atoms are arranged as in *o*-xylene, for Graebe already had pointed out that the unique ability of phthalic acid to form an anhydride is evidence for the *ortho* structure. On the basis of the Kekulé theory, the above facts, together with the empirical formula, indicated that anthracene must contain three benzene rings joined in either a linear or an angular manner. There was thus a choice between the present formula for anthracene and the formula now assigned to phenanthrene, which was still unknown. The angular formula was preferred by Graebe and Liebermann partly because it seemed to explain more easily Berthelot's synthesis of anthracene from styrene and benzene by passing the vapors of the compounds through a hot tube, and partly because the arrangement of bonds in the *para*-bond formula, with which they represented the linear structure, seemed to them to indicate a more unusual set of properties than are found in the hydrocarbon.

Graebe's knowledge of quinones soon led to recognition that alizarin has properties characteristic of such substances. The color reactions, the ease of reduction, and the air oxidation of the reduction product furnished convincing evidence that alizarin is a quinone. It must be derived from the quinone of anthracene. Anthraquinone had been prepared by several investigators who had called it "para-naphthalose," "anthraceneuse," "oxanthracene," and "oxyphoten," but no one had attempted to assign it a formula. It was found by Graebe and Liebermann to have the properties of a quinone, and they gave it the present name. The question as to whether it is a terminal ring or the central ring which is quinonoid was decided as follows. Naphthalene is oxidized to a quinone more easily than is benzene, they said, and naphthalene has a greater accumulation of carbon atoms. Since anthracene is oxidized with still greater ease, the oxidation must attack the central ring.

That alizarin contains two more atoms of oxygen than anthraquinone and is weakly acidic was interpreted to mean that the dye is a dihydroxyanthraquinone. Since, from the facts available, alizarin could have either the angular or linear structure, it might have any of twenty possible structures. In attempting a synthesis from anthraquinone, Graebe and Liebermann were taking a 1:10 chance of obtaining the desired isomer. Without being aware of the extent of the odds against success they soon attempted synthesis. The method planned was based on knowledge that 2,3-dichloro-1,4-naphthoquinone reacts readily with alkali by replacement of one chlorine by a hydroxyl group to give chloronaphthalenic acid (I). The analogy was fallacious in two respects. The first is that only one of the two chlorine atoms in the quinone ring is replaceable by hydroxyl, and the second is the assumption that halogen atoms in a benzenoid ring would share the reactivity of those in a quinonoid ring. The method of bromination and hydrolysis which they proposed to employ was one for which no parallel existed, since no aryl halide had at the time been converted into a phenol.

Basing their plans upon faulty reasoning and looking for one compound out of a possible ten, Graebe and Liebermann succeeded in synthesizing alizarin. In 1869 they dibrominated anthraquinone and treated the product with aqueous alkali. No reaction took place at first, but they boiled the mixture down and heated the residue to a high temperature and under these conditions a substance was formed which proved to be identical with natural alizarin. For the first time a naturally occurring and a very beautiful and important dye had been produced synthetically.

The discovery was widely acclaimed and the names of Graebe and Liebermann were by-words.

Accounts of the work appeared in the daily papers and the young chemists received the universal praise of their colleagues. They were not slow in realizing the importance of their discovery. When they published their results, Graebe and Liebermann said:

> We need not point out the importance of our discovery for the madder industry if it is possible to make a technical success. The enormous consumption of madder and the large tracts of fertile soil required for its cultivation clearly bespeak the importance which would be obtained by a new branch of industry based on the artificial preparation of alizarin from a constituent of coal tar.

One remarkable aspect of the synthesis came to light only later. When the structure of alizarin became known, it was generally assumed that the dibromo compound employed was the 1,2-derivative. However, it has been shown that the compound actually is 2,3-dibromoanthraquinone. The rearrangement that occurs on alkali fusion of the dibromide is one of several cases now known in which a group introduced by nucleophilic displacement takes a position other than that vacated by the expelled group. Such rearrangements have been shown to proceed by an elimination-addition mechanism involving an unstable neutral "benzyne" intermediate (J. D. Roberts, 1953–56).

The synthesis was reported at a meeting of the *Chemische Gesellschaft* on January 11, 1869, and samples of the synthetic material and of dyeings were exhibited. Having secured patents, Graebe and Liebermann in May signed a contract with the Badische Anilin- und Soda-Fabrik calling for a 3% royalty over a period of fifteen years. Caro undertook to work out the technical production and Graebe went to Mannheim to assist him. It was soon found, however, that the great expense of bromine and the difficulty in carrying out the bromination and the alkali fusion in the reaction vessels then available rendered the process impractical.

A search for a more suitable method was commenced without delay. The diazonium salt procedure had been used in the technical production of α-naphthol, and the simpler method of alkali fusion of an aromatic sulfonate had just been discovered in 1867 by Kekulé, by Wurtz, and, in a sealed note deposited earlier, by Dusart. Graebe, Liebermann, and Caro attempted to sulfonate anthraquinone, but the material was recovered unchanged. Compounds of the stability and the resistance to substitution which characterizes anthraquinone were rare, and a moderate temperature and concentrated acid had been adequate. Fuming acid was not available in Germany. It was only through an accident in Caro's laboratory that conditions required for bringing about the sulfonation were discovered. Phenols had been condensed with oxalic acid in the presence of sulfuric acid to give triphenylmethane dyes of the type of rosolic acid. Caro thought that the oxygen-containing anthraquinone might react in a similar fashion, and he had just started to heat a mixture of this substance with oxalic and sulfuric acid when he was called to another room. The flame had not been adjusted and, when he returned, the laboratory was filled with dense fumes and he found that his mixture had boiled down nearly to dryness. He found, however, that the anthraquinone, at the accidentally high temperature, had been sulfonated. It was soon found that the sulfonated anthraquinone can be converted easily into alizarin by fusion with alkali, and a second method of preparing the dye was thus available.

The new process was found well suited to large-scale production, but disappointment was in store for the three investigators. On applying for a patent in Prussia, they were informed that, since they had merely substituted one anthraquinone derivative for another, a disulfonate for a dibromo compound, there was not sufficient novelty in the method to entitle them to a second patent. On the other hand, the original patent did not prevent competitors from using the sulfonation method. Thus the Badische Company found itself in the awkward position of having patent protection for their unworkable process, but no protection for the process which actually worked. The result was that the manufacture of alizarin was undertaken by eight different German firms.

Better results were expected in England, but the Germans were here denied full success by a coincidence. The patent application of Caro, Graebe, and Liebermann was sent to England early in June, but there was some delay on account of changes in the wording and the application reached the British patent office on June 25th. Here there was further delay and the application was set aside for several weeks. On June 26th an application covering the same process was filed by Perkin. The Englishman's application was examined at once and Perkin was soon granted a patent. Rather than attempt to restrain the Perkin patent by entering into litigation, Caro and Graebe went to England to confer with Perkin and an agreement was effected to divide the market.

Perkin's first research problem under Hofmann at the Royal College of Chemistry was to prepare an amine of anthracene. Though he never achieved this end, he learned how to prepare anthracene from coal tar and studied the oxidation and chlorination of the hydrocarbon. The synthesis of natural products appealed to him; his discovery of mauve was the result of an unsuccessful attempt to synthesize quinine by the oxidation of allyltoluidine. Following publication of Graebe and Liebermann's first alizarin synthesis, Perkin at once set out in search of some means of dispensing with bromine. Use of bromine might be avoided by using the new method of Kekulé, Wurtz, and Dusart, were it not for the difficulty in sulfonating anthraquinone. Perhaps anthracene is sulfonated more easily; it might be sulfonated and then oxidized to an anthraquinone. This is the case, but the reaction appears to be quite complicated. He was thus led to try a derivative of anthracene which he had prepared in Hofmann's laboratory. 9,10-Dichloroanthracene was found to be sulfonated readily, and it was not even necessary to oxidize the product to a quinone, for the sulfonated dichloroanthracene yielded alizarin when fused with alkali:

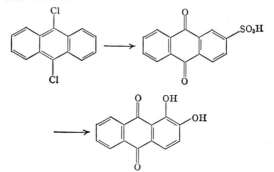

Perkin subsequently found the means of sulfonating anthraquinone itself, so that he was in possession of two satisfactory processes.

A disulfonate of anthraquinone was at first assumed to be the intermediate, but fusion in a closed vessel yielded a considerable amount of 2-hydroxyanthraquinone. Actually it is the β-monosulfonate which produces alizarin; replacement of the sulfon-

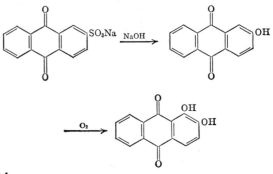

574

ate group is followed by air oxidation. If the discoverers had known the structure of alizarin and the rules of substitution they probably would not have made the discovery. The first sulfonic acid group enters the β-position because this is *meta* to an unsaturated carbonyl group. The second substituent surely does not enter a position *ortho* to two *meta*-directing groups, but attacks both β-positions of the second ring. The structure of alizarin was established a few years after the synthesis had been achieved. The linear structure of anthracene was established by van Dorp in Liebermann's laboratory, while discovery by Baeyer and Caro of the hydroxyanthraquinone synthesis from phthalic anhydride and phenols led to proof of the positions of the hydroxyl groups.

The most immediate effect of the alizarin synthesis was on the young German dye industry. The sulfonation process, unprotected by patents, was studied in the laboratories of several independent firms. Means were found for obtaining anthracene in quantity, and oxidation to anthraquinone was accomplished with dichromate in dilute acid suspension. The demand for fuming sulfuric acid, which gave less of the undesirable disulfonates than concentrated acid, eventually led to discovery of the contact process (1875). The practice of carrying out the alkali fusion in the open (at first in silver vessels) was abandoned in favor of Koch's process, in which the mixture is fused in an autoclave under pressure and oxidation is brought about by potassium chlorate. So rapid was the progress that by January, 1871 the technical production of the dye was in full swing. The product was of excellent quality, and much more easily applied than madder. The color could be varied from red to bluish or yellowish red by making slight changes in the process. When pure anthraquinone-2-sulfonate is employed and the fusion carried out with a minimum amount of chlorate, a very pure alizarin is obtained which furnishes a bluish red dyeing. On fusion at a higher temperature, and with more chlorate, a certain amount of the alizarin is oxidized to purpurin and the dyeing is redder. Alizarin prepared from a mixture of the mono- and disulfonates contains the trihydroxyanthraquinones: flavopurpurin (1,2,6, yellowish), and anthrapurpurin (1,2,7, reddish). In 1877 the yield from 100 parts of anthracene was 100–105 parts of alizarin, or about 79% of the theoretical figure.

Madder could not compete with the manufactured material in price, ease of application, or quality, and cultivation of the plant was given up within a few years. An industry worth about sixteen million dollars per year was wiped out, and this source of revenue largely transferred from France to Germany. Owing to the active competition between the various firms and to technical improvements, the price of alizarin dropped steadily until it was fixed in 1881 at a figure about one-sixth of that ten years earlier. The cost of dyeing with Turkey red dropped to one-twentieth its former figure. The consumption of the dye increased regularly until about 1900, when the annual production of alizarin (dry) amounted to about two million kilograms. With the changes in the chemical industry resulting from the wars and with introduction of cheaper dyes, the production of alizarin has fallen off considerably.

If alizarin has finally relinquished its position as one of the dyes of greatest commercial importance, the manufacture of this substance will always be remembered as one of the chief factors in the development in Germany of a chemical industry which dominated the field. For the successful operation of the alizarin factories, acids, alkalis, and chlorates were required in large quantities. Considerable coal tar had to be distilled in order to furnish the anthracene and uses had to be found for other coal-tar crudes. Thus all branches of the industry were given a great stimulus by the production of a single dye. The English dye industry had developed more rapidly at first, but soon after 1870 was overshadowed by the advances in Germany, particularly by three firms: the Badische Anilin- und Soda-Fabrik, the Höchster Farbwerke vorm. Meister Lucius und Bruning, and the Elberfelder Farbwerke vorm. Fr. Bayer.

Both Graebe and Liebermann acquired fame as teachers and investigators, particularly in the chemistry of quinones and of the more highly condensed hydrocarbons. Houben's *Das Anthracen und die Anthrachinone* contains 382 references to the researches of these two men. In each of forty-seven consecutive years, the *Berichte* contains one or more papers by Liebermann. The friendship which had existed between the two young collaborators was maintained throughout subsequent years when Liebermann remained at Berlin while Graebe moved to Leipzig, to Königsberg, to Geneva for a period of 28 years, and finally to Frankfurt and retirement. In 1911 the president of the *Deutsche Chemische Gesellschaft* sent to a former president a letter of congratulation on the occasion of the latter's seventieth birthday. The recipient of the letter was Carl Graebe. He addressed his reply, in formal fashion, to the *Herr Geheimer Regierungsrat* Prof. Dr. Carl Liebermann, but he employed the intimate form of speech in expressing his thanks for the many compliments of his *Lieber Freund*.

ANSWERS TO PROBLEMS

ANSWERS TO PROBLEMS

Chapter 1. Structures of Carbon Compounds

1. H:C̈:Br̈: with :Br̈: above and :Br̈: below the C   :Ö::C::Ö: H:C:::N:

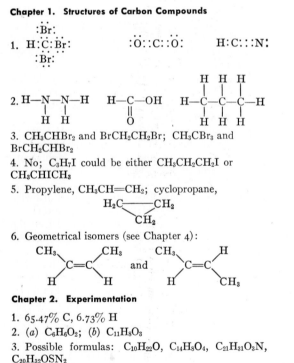

2. H—N—N—H with H below each N   H—C—OH with O double bonded   H—C—C—C—H with H above and below each C

3. CH_3CHBr_2 and $BrCH_2CH_2Br$; CH_3CBr_3 and $BrCH_2CHBr_2$

4. No; C_3H_7I could be either $CH_3CH_2CH_2I$ or CH_3CHICH_3

5. Propylene, $CH_3CH{=}CH_2$; cyclopropane,

$$H_2C\text{———}CH_2$$
$$CH_2$$

6. Geometrical isomers (see Chapter 4):

CH_3 \C=C/ CH_3 with H below each   and   CH_3 \C=C/ H with H below left and CH_3 below right

Chapter 2. Experimentation

1. 65.47% C, 6.73% H

2. (a) $C_6H_6O_2$; (b) $C_{11}H_8O_3$

3. Possible formulas: $C_{10}H_{22}O$, $C_{14}H_8O_4$, $C_{21}H_{31}O_3N$, $C_{20}H_{32}OSN_2$

4. $C_5H_{12} = (CH_3)_4C$, b.p. $9.5°$

5. $C_{15}H_{14}O_3$ (lapachol, II. 21); 74.36% C, 5.82% H

6. $C_{31}H_{46}O_2$ (vitamin K_1, 15.6; analysis at the Merck Research Laboratories of a sample isolated from alfalfa. Fieser)

7. $C_{18}H_{21}O_3N$ (codeine)

Chapter 3. Alkanes

1. Dibromoisobutanes:
$(CH_3)_2CHCHBr_2$ (1,1-), $(CH_3)_2CBrCH_2Br$ (1,2-), $BrCH_2CH(CH_3)CH_2Br$ (1,3-)
Dibromo-*n*-butanes:
$CH_3CH_2CH_2CHBr_2$ (1,1-), $CH_3CH_2CHBrCH_2Br$ (1,2-), $CH_3CHBrCH_2CH_2Br$ (1,3-),
$BrCH_2CH_2CH_2CH_2Br$ (1,4-),
$CH_3CH_2CBr_2CH_3$ (2,2-), $CH_3CHBrCHBrCH_3$ (2,3-)

2. Dimethyl-*n*-butylmethane,
$(CH_3)_2CHCH_2CH_2CH_2CH_3$
Diisopropylmethane, $(CH_3)_2CHCH_2CH(CH_3)_2$
Methylethylisopropylmethane,
$(CH_3)_2CHCH(CH_3)CH_2CH_3$
Methylethyl-*n*-propylmethane,
$CH_3CH_2CH(CH_3)CH_2CH_2CH_3$
Trimethyl-*n*-propylmethane, $(CH_3)_3CCH_2CH_2CH_3$

3. (a) $CH_3CH_2CH_2CH_2CH_2CH_2CH_2CHClCH_2Br$
(b) $CH_3CH_2CH_2CH_2CHClCCl_2CH_3$
(c) $CH_3CH_2C(OH)(CH_3)_2$
(d) $(CH_3)_2CHCH(CH_3)_2$
(e) $(CH_3CH_2)_4C$
(f) $CH_3CH_2CH_2CH_2CH_2CH_2MgI$

4. (a) Dichlorodifluoromethane
(b) Dimethyldiethylmethane
(c) Trimethyl-*n*-butylmethane
(d) Di-(*n*-propyl)-isopropylmethane

5. (a) 2,5-Dimethylheptane
(b) 2-Methylpropane
(c) 3-Methylhexane
(d) 2,5-Dimethyl-3-ethylhexane

6. 2,2-Dimethylhexane, $CH_3CH_2CH_2CH_2C(CH_3)_3$
3,3-Dimethylhexane, $CH_3CH_2CH_2C(CH_3)_2CH_2CH_3$
2,2,3-Trimethylpentane, $CH_3CH_2CH(CH_3)C(CH_3)_3$
2,2,4-Trimethylpentane, $(CH_3)_2CHCH_2C(CH_3)_3$

Chapter 4. Alkenes

2.

$$H:\overset{..}{\underset{..}{O}}:\overset{..}{\underset{..}{S^+}}:\overset{..}{\underset{..}{O}}:H$$ with $:\overset{..}{\underset{..}{O}}:^-$ above and $:\overset{..}{\underset{..}{O}}:$ below

Alternate structure: $H:\overset{..}{\underset{..}{O}}:\overset{..}{\underset{..}{S}}:\overset{..}{\underset{..}{O}}:H$ with $:\overset{..}{\underset{..}{O}}:^{++}$ above and $:\overset{..}{\underset{..}{O}}:^-$ below

3. (a) Propanediol-1,2
(b) 2,3-Dimethylbutane
(c) 3,7-Dimethyloctene-6-ol-1
(d) 2-Methyl-3-isopropylhexene-5-ol-1
(e) 1,2-Dimethyl-4-ethylcyclohexane
(f) 2,5-Dimethylhexadiene-2,4

4. (a) $CH_3CH_2CH(CH_2CH_3)CH(CH_3)CH_2OH$
(b) $C_6H_5CH=CHCH=CHC_6H_5$
(c) $(CH_3)_2C=CHCH_3$
(d) $CH_3CH(OH)CH(OH)CH_3$
(e) $ClCH_2CH(CH_3)CH_2CH=CH_2$
(f) $CH_3CH_2CH\underset{\underset{O}{\diagdown\diagup}}{-}CH_2$

5. 3-Methylhexanol-1
3-Methylhexanol-2
2-Ethylpentanol-1
3-Methylhexanol-3
4-Methylhexanol-3
4-Methylhexanol-2
4-Methylhexanol-1

6. (a) Wash with concentrated sulfuric acid and dis-
card the lower layer of acid containing $ROSO_2OH$
formed by addition to the olefin.
(b) Same as in (a).
(c) Prepare the dibromide, separate it from n-hexane
by fractionation, debrominate with zinc.

7. On drastic oxidation the first hydrocarbon gives
a C_3-acid and a C_3-ketone and the second gives a C_2-acid
and a C_4-ketone.

8. 1,4-Dimethylcyclopentadiene-1,3

9. Hexene-2

10. Dehydration to cyclohexene and oxidation;
actually adipic acid is formed on direct oxidation of
cyclohexanol with nitric acid.

11. $CH_3CH_2C(CH_3)=CHCH_2CH_2CH=CHCH_2CH_3$

12. (a) 2 rings; (b) 4 rings

13. $\underset{CH_2CH_2CCH_2CH_2}{\overset{CH_2CH_2CCH_2CH_2}{| \quad \| \quad |}}$

Chapter 5. Alkynes

1. (a) Reaction with PBr_3 to give $CH_3CBr_2CH_3$; dehydrohalogenation with alcoholic potassium hydroxide.
(b) Dehydration, addition of bromine, dehydrobromination.
(c) Reaction of the sodio derivative with methyl iodide.
(d) Dimerization of acetylene to vinylacetylene; exhaustive catalytic hydrogenation.

2. $CH_2=CHCOCH_3$ (the triple bond has greater nucleophilic additive power than the double bond).

3. $CH_3C\equiv CCH(CH_3)_2$

4. Addition of bromine, dehydrohalogenation to di-
phenylacetylene, selective hydrogenation (2 H).

Chapter 7. Alcohols

1. (a) 3-Methylpentene-2
(b) $(CH_3)_2C=CHCH_2CH(CH_3)_2$
(c) $(CH_3)_2C=CHCH_2CH_2OH$
(d) $CH_3CH_2CO_2H$ + $O=C(CH_3)_2$ [initial dehydration to $CH_3CH_2CH=C(CH_3)_2$]
(e) Adipic aldehyde, $OHC(CH_2)_4CHO$
(f) n-$C_5H_{11}OCH_2CH_2OH$
(g) Ethanolamine, $HOCH_2CH_2NH_2$

2. (a) $CH_3CH_2CH_2MgBr$ + $(CH_3)_2CO$
(b) 2 $CH_3CH_2CH_2MgBr$ + $CH_3CO_2C_2H_5$
(c) $CH_3CH_2CH_2MgBr$ + CH_2O
(d) $CH_3CH_2CH_2MgBr$ + ethylene oxide
(e) $CH_3CH_2CH_2MgBr$ + $CH_3COCH_2CH_3$

3. (a) $(CH_3)_2CHMgBr$ + CH_2O
(b) $(CH_3)_2CO$ + $BrMgCH_2CH_3$
(c) $CH_3CH_2CO_2CH_3$ + 2 CH_3CH_2MgI
(d) $CH_3CH_2CH_2MgBr$ + ethylene oxide
(e) CH_3CH_2MgCl + $OC(CH_3)_2$; dehydration
(f) $(CH_3)_2CHMgBr$ + ethylene oxide $\longrightarrow$
$(CH_3)_2CHCH_2CH_2OH$;
$(CH_3)_2CHCH_2CH_2MgBr$ + CH_2O; dehydration
(g) $(CH_3)_2CHMgI$ + $OC(CH_3)_2$; dehydration
(h) $(CH_3)_2CO$ + CH_3MgCl; dehydration; hydrogenation
(i) $CH_3CH_2CH_2MgBr$ + $OC(CH_3)_2$; dehydration;
hydrogenation
(j) 2 $(CH_3)_2CHMgBr$ + $CH_3CO_2C_2H_5$; dehydration; hydrogenation

4. (a) 2 $CH_3CH_2CH_2MgBr$ + $CH_3CH_2CO_2CH_3$;
dehydration; hydrogenation
(b) $CH_2=CHCH_2MgBr$ + $OC(CH_3)_2$; dehydration
(c) $(CH_3)_2CO$ + CH_3MgI $\longrightarrow$ $(CH_3)_3COH$;
$(CH_3)_3COH$ $\longrightarrow$ $(CH_3)_3CBr$ $\longrightarrow$
$(CH_3)_3CMgBr$;
$(CH_3)_3CMgBr$ + CH_2O $\longrightarrow$ $(CH_3)_3CCH_2OH$

5. (a) $(CH_3)_2CHCH_2MgCl$ + $OC(CH_3)_2$; dehydration
(b) $CH_3CH_2CH(OH)CH_3$ $\longrightarrow$ $CH_3CH_2COCH_3$;
reaction with $CH_3CH_2CH_2MgBr$
(c) $(CH_3)_2CO$ + $CH_3CH_2CH_2CH_2MgCl$; dehydration; hydrogenation
(d) $(CH_3)_3CMgCl$ + CH_3CH_2CHO; conversion to
$(CH_3)_3CCHBrCH_2CH_3$; formation of $RMgBr$; decomposition with water

6. $(CH_3)_2CHCH{=}CH_2$

7. $(CH_3)_2CHCHOHCH_3$

8. Cyclohexene $+ H_2O_2 \longrightarrow$ cyclohexanediol-1,2; glycol cleavage with HIO_4 gives the dialdehyde, $OHCCH_2CH_2CH_2CH_2CHO$, which on condensation with CH_3MgCl yields $CH_3CHOHCH_2CH_2CH_2CH_2CHOHCH_3$; dehydration affords $CH_3CH{=}CHCH_2CH_2CH{=}CHCH_3$.

9. On dehydration to a diene, followed by chromic acid oxidation, the first diol would give a C_6-diketone and the second would give a C_6-diacid.

Chapter 8. Halogen Compounds

1. (a) Treat stearyl alcohol with thionyl chloride and remove excess by evaporation in vacuum; or use PCl_5 and remove $POCl_3$ by distillation.
(b) Shake t-amyl alcohol with 36% hydrochloric acid in a separatory funnel; separate and wash the upper layer, dry, and distil.
(c) Treat the alcohol with PBr_3; decant the bromide from phosphorous acid.
(d) Heat the alcohol with constant-boiling hydriodic acid.

2. $d > b > a > c$

3.
$$\overset{\displaystyle :\overset{..}{Br}:}{H:C::C:C:H} \quad \xrightarrow{\quad -:\overset{..}{Br}:^{-}\quad}$$
$$\underset{H\ HH}{H:C::C:\overset{+}{C}:H} \quad \longleftrightarrow \quad \underset{HH\ H}{H:C:\overset{+}{C}::C:H}$$

(Note that the departing bromide ion takes along one electron that originally belonged to carbon, with the result that carbon is left with a positive charge.)

4. (a) $\underset{H\ H}{H:\overset{\frown}{C}:\overset{\frown}{C}:\overset{..}{Br}:} \quad \longleftrightarrow \quad \underset{H\ H}{H:\overset{..}{C}:C::\overset{+}{Br}:}$

(b) The initially uncharged bromine atom shares an additional pair of electrons with the adjacent carbon atom, and this atom in turn donates to the terminal carbon atom a pair of shared electrons in which each atom originally had an equal stake of one electron. Hence bromine, in effect, has donated one electron to the terminal carbon atom.

(c) The electronic formulation of $\overset{+}{CH_2}{-}CH{=}Br^{-}$ represents more electrons (10)

$$\underset{H\ H}{H:\overset{+}{C}:C::\overset{..}{Br}:^{-}}$$

than bromine can accommodate.

5. Positive: b, e, g

6. (a) $(CH_3)_2CHMgBr + BrCH_2CH{=}CH_2$
(b) $CH_2{=}CHCH_2Br + Br_2$
(c) $CH_2{=}CHCH_2Br + HBr$
(d) $CH_2BrCHBrCH_2Br$ (b) $+$ alcoholic KOH

Chapter 9. Carboxylic Acids

1. Acidic strength increases in the order $CH_3CH_2CO_2H$, $HOCH_2CO_2H$, ICH_2CO_2H, $ClCH_2CO_2H$. The order of relative electronegativity, as indicated by the position in the periodic table, is: $C < O < I < Cl$.

2. Malonic acid is the more strongly acidic; the electron-attracting inductive effect of the second carboxylic acid group decreases with increasing distance from the first group.

3. (a) $(CH_3)_2CHCH_2CO_2H$
(b) $CH_3CHBrCHBrCO_2H$
(c) $(CH_3CH_2)_3CCOOH$
(d) $CH_3CH_2CH_2CH_2CH_2CH_2CH_2CO_2H$

4. (a) Grignard (KCN probably would eliminate HBr).
(b) Nitrile synthesis (the hydroxyl group would prevent formation of a Grignard reagent).

5. $CH_3CH_2OH \longrightarrow CH_2{=}CH_2 \longrightarrow$
$BrCH_2CH_2Br \longrightarrow NCCH_2CH_2CN \longrightarrow$
$HO_2CCH_2CH_2CO_2H$

6. By sodium hypochlorite oxidation.

7. Dissolve the mixture in ether, extract the acidic component with sodium bicarbonate solution, acidify the extract, extract with ether, dry the solution and evaporate the solvent.

8. On chlorination in the presence of iodine as catalyst, (a) would give a monochloro derivative, (b) would give a dichloro derivative, and (c) would remain unchanged. Rates of esterification would also distinguish between the three acids.

9.
$$:\overset{..}{O}:\ :\overset{+}{N}:\ :\overset{..}{O}:^{-} \longleftrightarrow \ ^{-}:\overset{..}{O}:\ \overset{+}{N}::\overset{..}{O}:$$
$$\quad\ :\overset{..}{O}: \qquad\qquad\qquad :\overset{..}{O}:$$

10. No; a requirement for resonance is that the structures involved do not differ in the position of the atomic nuclei.

11. $\underset{H}{H:\overset{-}{\overset{..}{C}}:N:::N:} \longleftrightarrow \underset{H}{H:\overset{..}{C}::\overset{+}{N}::\overset{-}{\overset{..}{N}}:}$

12. (a) Fischer esterification with HCl, H_2SO_4, or BF_3 as catalyst.
(b) Diazomethane or silver salt method.
(c) Fischer esterification with BF_3 as catalyst (HCl or H_2SO_4 might add to the double bond).
(d) Reflux the n-propyl ester with excess methanol containing 3% sulfuric acid.

13.

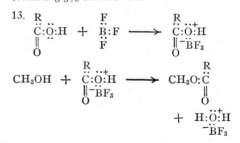

14. $(CH_3)_2CHCO_2H \longrightarrow (CH_3)_2CHCOCl$ (reaction with $SOCl_2$); $(CH_3)_2CHCOCl + CH_3CdCl$

15. $CH_3COOH + Br_2$ (I_2 catalyst) $\longrightarrow$ $CH_2BrCOOH$; $CH_2BrCOOH + PCl_3 \longrightarrow$ $CH_2BrCOCl$

16. Acetic acid and ethyl acetate.

17. Dehydration with acetic anhydride to succinic anhydride; action of boiling methanol on the anhydride to produce the half ester; reaction with thionyl chloride.

18. Replacement of hydrogen by acetyl involves a net gain of C_2H_2O, hence four hydroxyl groups must have been acetylated. The substance contains only four carbon atoms and each can carry only one hydroxyl group (*gem*-diols are unstable), hence the structure must be $HOCH_2CHOHCHOHCH_2OH$. Note that the structure $(HOCH_2)_3COH$ is ruled out because the tertiary alcoholic group would not be acylated on treatment with acetic anhydride.

19. Prepare the diester, $CH_3OCOCH_2CH_2COOCH_3$, and treat it with four moles of CH_3MgCl; dehydrate the diol, $(CH_3)_2C(OH)CH_2CH_2C(OH)(CH_3)_2$.

20. $RCOCl > (RCO)_2O > RCOOCH_3 > ROR$

Chapter 10. Aldehydes and Ketones

1. (a) Pentanol-2-one-3
(b) 3,7-Dimethyloctene-2-ol-1
(c) 2,6-Dimethyloctatriene-2,4,6-dial-1,8

2. (a) Oxidation with chromic acid
(b) Oxidation with chromic acid
(c) Grignard reaction of allylmagnesium bromide with acetaldehyde to give $CH_2{=}CHCH_2CH(OH)CH_3$; Oppenauer oxidation (chromic acid would attack the double bond).
(d) Hydroxylation of the double bond with H_2O_2 in acetic acid and cleavage of the glycol, $HOCH_2CHOH(CH_2)_8COOH$, with lead tetraacetate.
(e) Conversion to the acid chloride (e.g. with $SOCl_2$); Rosenmund reduction.

3. Cyclohexanone on nitric acid oxidation gives adipic acid, $HO_2C(CH_2)_4CO_2H$; pyrolysis of the calcium salt of this acid affords cyclopentanone. To effect the reverse transformation, oxidize cyclopentanone with nitric acid to glutaric acid, $HO_2C(CH_2)_3CO_2H$, reduce the diethyl ester with sodium and alcohol (Bouveault-Blanc method) to produce pentamethylene glycol, $HO(CH_2)_5OH$, replace both hydroxyl groups by bromine, replace the bromine atoms by nitrile groups (aqueous-alcoholic KCN), hydrolyze to $HO_2C(CH_2)_5CO_2H$, pyrolyze the calcium salt of the diacid.

4. Aldehydes, but not ketones: give the Ag-mirror test and reduce Fehling's solution, polymerize under acid catalysis or in aqueous solution, give a positive Schiff test; aldehydes with no α-hydrogen atom undergo the Cannizzaro reaction. Aldehydes react to a greater extent than ketones: with $NaHSO_3$, with HCN, in aldol condensations, and with alcohols (acetal formation).

5. Chloral is the most reactive of the compounds because it alone forms stable addition products with water and with hydroxylamine. The bisulfite reaction (Table I) establishes the order acetaldehyde > acetone > diethyl ketone. The failure of diisopropyl ketone to add isopropylmagnesium bromide (10.12) shows it to be the least reactive compound listed.

6. By reduction with aluminium isopropoxide and isopropyl alcohol (Meerwein-Ponndorf method).

7. $(CH_3)_2CHCH(OH)C(CH_3)_2CHO$

8. $(CH_3)_3CCH_2OH + (CH_3)_3CCO_2H$

9. Preparation of diacetone alcohol by aldol condensation; oxidation with sodium hypochlorite.

10. $CH_3COCH_2CH_2CHO + 2\ C_2H_5OH$ (dry HCl) $\longrightarrow CH_3COCH_2CH_2CH(OC_2H_5)_2$; oxidation with alkaline hypochlorite to $HO_2CCH_2CH_2CH(OC_2H_5)_2$; hydrolysis of the acetal with dilute aqueous hydrochloric acid.

11. $2\ CH_3CHO \longrightarrow CH_3CH(OH)CH_2CHO \longrightarrow$ $CH_3CH{=}CHCHO \longrightarrow CH_3CH_2CH_2CH_2OH$

12. Methyl ketones add $NaHSO_3$ and HCN; none of the esters add these reagents. Ketones react with hydrazine with replacement of the carbonyl oxygen, whereas an ester reacts with hydrazine to form a hydrazide ($RCONHNH_2$, (9.20)), in which the carbonyl group is still intact.

13. $(CH_3)_2CHCH(OH)CH_3$

14. $CH_3COCH_2CH_2CHO$

15. (a) $HOCH_2CH_2CN$ (compare action of RMgX on ethylene oxide and on carbonyl compounds).
(b) $(CH_3)_3CCH(OH)CH_2COCH_3$ (trimethylacetaldehyde cannot undergo self-condensation but has a more reactive carbonyl group than acetone).

16. (a) Pyrolysis of $(CH_3CH_2COO)_2Ca$
(b) $CH_3CH_2CH_2MgBr + CH_3CH_2CHO$; oxidation of the resulting secondary alcohol
(c) Acetone $\longrightarrow$ diacetone alcohol $\longrightarrow$ mesityl oxide $\longrightarrow (CH_3)_2C{=}CHCO_2H$ (NaOCl) $\longrightarrow$ $(CH_3)_2CHCH_2CO_2H$ (hydrogenation)

17. Vinylcyclopentane

18. The formation of a monoacetate indicates the presence of a primary or secondary alcoholic group; resistance to phenylhydrazine shows that the second oxygen atom is not present as a carbonyl group. The reaction with lead tetraacetate is evidently a glycol cleavage producing two carbonyl groups; since these are in the same molecule, III, the glycol group must be part of a ring. The positive Fehling's test indicates that at least one carbonyl must be present as an aldehydic group, and the formation of iodoform reveals the presence of a methyl ketone group. The acid $HOOC(CH_2)_4COOH$ must, then, have come from the keto aldehyde $CH_3CO(CH_2)_4CHO$, and the glycol I must have the structure:

$$\begin{array}{c} CH_3 \\ | \\ CH_2CH_2COH \\ |\qquad\quad| \\ CH_2CH_2CHOH \end{array}$$

19. Reaction of ethyl acetate with ethoxide ion to form $\bar{C}H_2CO_2C_2H_5$, addition of this anion to the carbonyl group of another molecule of ethyl acetate to form the anion (a), and expulsion of ethoxide ion to form (b).

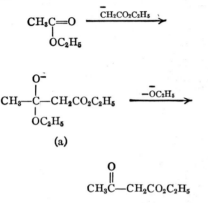

(a)

$$CH_3C\!\!-\!\!CH_2CO_2C_2H_5$$

(b)

20. (a) $(CH_3)_2CHBr + Na^+[CH(CO_2C_2H_5)_2]^- \longrightarrow$ $(CH_3)_2CHCH(CO_2C_2H_5)_2$; hydrolysis and decarboxylation

(b) $CH_3I + Na^+[CH(CO_2C_2H_5)_2]^- \longrightarrow$ $CH_3CH(CO_2C_2H_5)_2$; conversion to sodio derivative; reaction with CH_3CH_2I; hydrolysis and decarboxylation.

(c) Condensation of $Br(CH_2)_4Br$ with two moles of sodiomalonic ester, etc.

21. The second compound, the C-acetyl derivative, has three carbonyl groups in a position to activate the central hydrogen atom and hence this substance exists to the greater extent in the enolic form.

22. Both forms are enolic; they are the hydroxy derivatives of maleic and fumaric acid:

$$HO\!\!-\!\!C\!\!-\!\!CO_2H \qquad HO\!\!-\!\!C\!\!-\!\!CO_2H$$
$$H\!\!-\!\!C\!\!-\!\!CO_2H \qquad HO_2C\!\!-\!\!C\!\!-\!\!H$$
m.p. 152° \qquad m.p. 184°

Chapter 11. Amines

1. (a) sec-Butylamine (primary)
(b) Diethylisopropylamine (tertiary)
(c) t-Amylamine (primary)
(d) Methylisobutylamine (secondary)
(e) Methyldi-n-propylamine hydrochloride (salt of tertiary amine)
(f) Tetraisopropylammonium bromide (quaternary ammonium salt)
(g) N-Nitrosoethyl-n-propylamine (nitroso derivative of a secondary amine)
(h) N-Ethylacetamide (secondary amide)
(i) Trimethylacetamide (primary amide)

2. Weakly acidic: phthalimide (pK$_a$ 8.3), succinimide (pK$_a$ 10.5). Substantially neutral: acetamide, acetylmethylamine; inner salt: β-alanine. Feebly basic:

urea. Basic: methylamine (pK$_b$ 3.4), tetramethylammonium hydroxide (pK$_b$ nearly zero).

3. (a) Treat with a little acetic anhydride, extract an ethereal solution of the resulting mixture with portions of dilute hydrochloric acid until no more amine is removed, neutralize the acid solution, extract with ether, distil the ether and then the triethylamine.

(b) Treat with $NaNO_2$ + HCl, extract an ethereal solution of the resulting mixture with dilute HCl to remove the triethylamine, heat the neutral fraction with HCl to hydrolyze the $(CH_3CH_2)_2NNO$, extract the acidic solution with ether, recover the diethylamine from the acid liquor by neutralization and ether extraction.

(c) Treat with benzenesulfonyl chloride, separate the alkali-soluble $CH_3CH_2NHSO_2C_6H_5$ from the alkali-insoluble $(CH_3CH_2)_2NSO_2C_6H_5$ and $(CH_3CH_2)_3N$, hydrolyze the alkali-soluble derivative.

4. (a) $CH_3CH_2CH_2CH_2OH \longrightarrow$ $CH_3CH_2CH_2CO_2H \longrightarrow$ chloride $\longrightarrow$ amide $\longrightarrow CH_3CH_2CH_2NH_2$ (NaOBr).

(b) $CH_3CH_2CH_2CH_2OH \longrightarrow$ bromide $\longrightarrow$ nitrile $\longrightarrow CH_3CH_2CH_2CH_2CH_2NH_2$ (LiAlH$_4$).

5. $CH_3CH_3CHOHCH_3 \longrightarrow CH_3CH_2COCH_3$ $\longrightarrow$ oxime $\longrightarrow CH_3CH_2CHNH_2CH_3$ (H$_2$, Pt).

6. The Gabriel synthesis would give a pure product, whereas reaction with ammonia would give some secondary amine. The route through the aldehyde and oxime suffers from some difficulty in avoiding overoxidation in the preparation of the aldehyde.

7. RCN $\longrightarrow$ RCONH$_2$ $\longrightarrow$ RCOOH. RCOOH $\longrightarrow$ RCOCl $\longrightarrow$ RCONH$_2$ $\longrightarrow$ RCN (Ac$_2$O). Yes, the reaction RCH=NOH $\longrightarrow$ RC≡N is realizable (action of Ac$_2$O).

8. Exhaustive methylation, conversion to the quaternary ammonium hydroxide, and pyrolysis affords cyclohexene.

9. Exhaustive methylation, conversion to the quaternary ammonium hydroxide, and pyrolysis opens the ring and gives a vinyl derivative. A second degradation eliminates nitrogen as $(CH_3)_3N$ and gives a divinyl derivative. The latter could be oxidized to $(CH_3)_2C(COOH)_2$.

10. Yes, they both contain an electron sextet (they are described as isoelectronic):

$$R:\ddot{B} \qquad R:\ddot{C}^+$$

11.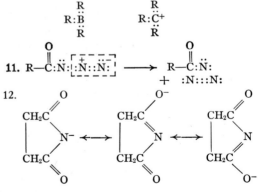

12.

13. In an alkyl bromide (a) the bromine atom is described as negative because it separates with the pair of shared electrons and accepts a proton.

(a) R⌐:Br: ⌐ + H:O:H ⟶

R:O:H + H:Br:

In N-bromosuccinimide (b) the two electron-attracting carbonyl groups prevent separation of the electron

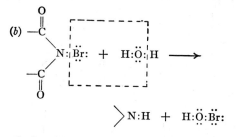

(b)

>N:H + H:O:Br:

pair shared between nitrogen and bromine, and hence bromine departs with only an electron sextet and combines with hydroxide ion to form HOBr.

14. Cracking: methane ($CH_4 \longrightarrow HC\equiv CH$); alkanes ($CH_3CH_3 \longrightarrow CH_2=CH_2$); alkenes ($CH_3CH_2CH=CH_2 \longrightarrow CH_2=CHCH=CH_2$); aromatization (n-heptane $\longrightarrow$ toluene). Thermal dehydration of alcohols over alumina. Alkenes from alkylsulfuric acids. Formation of calcium carbide (electric furnace). Pyrolysis of castor oil to n-heptaldehyde and undecylenic acid. Decarboxylation of formic acid at 160°. Thermal chlorination of propylene to allyl chloride (formed instead of the saturated addition product). Pyrolysis of acetone to ketene. Catalytic dehydrogenation of secondary alcohols to ketones. Thermal depolymerization of aldehyde polymers. Aldol $\longrightarrow$ crotonaldehyde. Thermal decomposition of quaternary ammonium hydroxides.

15.
CH_3
|
$HCNHCH_3$
|
$HOCH$
|
C_6H_5
Ephedrine

Synthesis.
(a) $C_6H_5COCH_2CH_3$ $\xrightarrow{Br_2}$ $C_6H_5COCHBrCH_3$ $\xrightarrow{CH_3NH_2}$ $C_6H_5COCH(NHCH_3)CH_3$; reduction.
(b) $C_6H_5CHO + CH_3CH_2NO_2$ $\longrightarrow C_6H_5CHOHCH(NO_2)CH_3$ $\longrightarrow C_6H_5CHOAcCH(NO_2)CH_3$ $\longrightarrow C_6H_5CHOAcCH(NH_2)CH_3 \longrightarrow$ $C_6H_5CHOAcCH(NHCH_3)CH_3$; hydrolysis.

ANSWERS TO REVIEW PROBLEMS

1. Dimerization (5.11) and hydrogenation.

2. $R_2C=O + R'MgBr$; dehydration (7.20).

3. Allylic bromination and dehydrobromination (8.10).

4. Prepare the ethyleneketal (10.18), reduce the ester group (7.8), and regenerate the carbonyl group by hydrolysis with dil. HCl.

5. Prepare the ethylenethioketal and desulfurize with Raney nickel (10.18).

6. Condense $HC\equiv CMgBr$ (5.5) with acetone, selectively hydrogenate (2 H, see 5.10), and dehydrate; isoprene is formed in preference to an allene because of resonance stabilization of the conjugated system.

7. Make the α-bromo acid (9.10) and treat it with excess ammonia (11.4).

8. Dehydrohalogenate the α-bromo acid (4.8).

9. Aldol condensation (10.14), Meerwein-Pondorff reduction (10.13).

10. Conversion to the oxime (10.16) and reduction (11.5).

11. Prepare the cyanohydrin (10.11), hydrolyze, and reduce the carboxyl group (7.8).

12. Dimerization (5.11) and selective hydrogenation (5.10).

13. Treat diethyl malonate with sodium to form the sodio derivative, let this react with the bromide, hydrolyze and decarboxylate (10.22).

14. See acetoacetic ester synthesis (10.20). Condense the bromide with sodio acetoacetic ester, convert the product into its sodio derivative and repeat the alkylation; hydrolyze to the β-keto acid and decarboxylate.

15. From ethylene via the dibromide (5.2) or from acetaldehyde (5.3).

16. From ethylene via the chlorohydrin (4.21).

17. Allyl alcohol, obtainable in two steps from propylene (7.17), reacts with HBr the way it reacts with HCl (8.2).

18. Allyl alcohol to glycerol (Shell process, 7.17) and dehydration (10.7).

19. Cracking of acetone (9.27).

20. Ketene + acetic acid (9.27).

21. $CH\equiv CH + HCN$ (5.8).

22. $ClCH_2CO_2Na + KCN$; $C_2H_5OH + H_2SO_4$ (10.22).

23. $2\ CH_3CO_2C_2H_5 + NaCO_2H_5$ (10.20).

24. The structure is divisible into two 3-carbon units, one of which is an allyl group; hence Grignard coupling (8.9) is applicable.

25. The structure is divisible at the double bond into two 4-carbon units and is an αβ-unsaturated aldehyde (see 10.14).

26. The structure is divisible into two equivalent alkyl groups (see 3.10).

27. This is a t-alcohol of the type RR′R′COH, hence reaction of a Grignard reagent with an ester is applicable (7.9).

28. Acid-catalyzed dimerization of isobutene and hydrogenation (6.10); alkylation of isobutane with isobutene (6.11).

29. (a) Bromination of *n*-butyric acid and dehydro-halogenation (9.10); (b) $CH_3CHO \longrightarrow$ $CH_3CH=CHCHO$ (10.14); oxidation with Fehling's solution (10.8).

30. The structure is divisible into two 4-carbon units, which suggests synthesis from $RCdCl + R'COCl$ (9.24).

31. This symmetrical ketone is available from two moles of the appropriate acid (10.5).

32. The structure is similar to that of pinacolone (7.21), a methyl ketone susceptible to haloform cleavage (8.13).

33. From the acid of 32 with diazomethane (9.15).

34. From the acid of 32 by Arndt-Eistert reaction of the acid chloride (9.25).

35. From the acid of 34 through the acid chloride and amide by the Hofmann reaction (11.6).

36. This has a 6-carbon chain with two terminal functional groups, like the product of oxidation of cyclohexanone (10.8); see 9.17.

37. (a) Couple methylmagnesium bromide with allyl bromide (8.9) and hydroxylate the double bond (4.22); (b) cyanohydrin synthesis of $CH_3CH_2CH_2CH(OH)COOH$ and reduction (7.8).

Chapter 12. Stereochemistry

1. No, the expected product is
dl-$CH_3(CH_3CH_2)C(OH)C_6H_5$

2.

COOH	COOH
HCCH₃	CH₃CH
HCBr	BrCH
COOH	COOH
I	II

COOH	COOH
HCCH₃	CH₃CH
BrCH	HCBr
COOH	COOH
III	IV

I is the enantiomer of II and is diastereoisomeric with III and IV; III and IV are enantiomers.

3. (a) 4; (b) 2; (c) 8; (d) 16

4. $CH_3CH_2CH(CH_3)COOH$

5. Monomethyl ester of mesotartaric acid

6. (a) *d*-, *l*-, *dl*-
(b) No stereoisomers
(c) *cis* and *trans*
(d) *d*-, *l*-, *dl*-
(e) *d*-, *l*-, *dl*-, *d'*-, *l'*-, *d'l'*-
(f) No stereoisomers
(g) *d*-, *l*-, *dl*-, *meso*-
(h) Eight optically active isomers; four *dl*-forms

7. Partial epimerization at the asymmetric carbon atom adjacent to the carbonyl group (through enol form).

8. Hydrogenation to *n*-butyric acid would establish the nature of the carbon chain; isolation of acetic acid as a product of permanganate oxidation would establish the position of the double bond.

9. The 1,2-acid can exist in an optically inactive *cis* form and in *d*- and *l*-*trans* forms; the 1,3-acid can exist only in one *cis* and one *trans* form.

10. Butene-2: *cis* and *trans* forms. Ricinoleic acid: *d*- and *l*-*cis* and *d*- and *l*-*trans* forms. Menthol: 3 dissimilar asymmetric carbon atoms, 8 optically active forms possible.

11. It must be tetrahedral.

12. Since the two double bonds lie in planes perpendicular to each other, an allene with four different substituents should exhibit molecular asymmetry and hence be resolvable into optically active components. Even an allene of the type $R_1R_2C=C=CR_1R_2$ should be resolvable. Allenes are very reactive and very easily isomerized to acetylenes, and it was not until 1935 (Mills, England; Kohler, U.S.A.) that the predictions were verified.

13. The fluorescent agent originally has the *trans* configuration but on absorption of light it may change in part to the *cis* form, which probably is less powerfully fluorescent.

14. Pairs a, c, and d are epimers. Pairs a and c, but not d, should be interconvertible through the common enols.

15. a, Diastereoisomers, the first is optically active, the second inactive (*meso*); b, identical; c, structural isomers; d, enantiomers, optically active; e, geometrical isomers; f, diastereoisomers, optically active.

16. The chemical evidence does not distinguish between the structure shown and the alternate structure

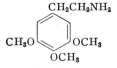

Mescaline

with the amino group at the α- rather than the β-position in the side chain, but a naturally occurring base of the latter structure would contain an asymmetric carbon atom and should be optically active. Synthesis: $(CH_3O)_3C_6H_2CHO + CH_3NO_2$ (OH⁻, heat) $\longrightarrow (CH_3O)_3C_6H_2CH=CHNO_2 \longrightarrow (CH_3O)_3C_6H_2CH_2CH_2NH_2$.

Chapter 13. Ring Formation and Stability

1. Pentene-2 and 1,2-dimethylcyclopropane would decolorize bromine solution whereas cyclopentane would not. Pentene-2, but not 1,2-dimethylcyclopropane, would give a test for unsaturation with permanganate.

2. In muscone the carbon atom carrying the methyl group is asymmetric because the part of the ring joined to it on one side contains a β-keto group and the part joined on the other side does not; reduction of the carbonyl group destroys the asymmetry.

3. trans-2-Methylcyclohexanol-1; conformation: 1α-OH, 2β-CH$_3$ (both groups equatorial). In the alternate conformation (1β-OH, 2α-CH$_3$) both large groups are axial. In each conformation of the cis isomer one large group is axial.

4. cis-Isomer (diequatorial)

5. In 9β-methyl-trans-decalin the methyl group is axial to both rings and hence its hydrogen atoms are repelled by 1,3-interactions with the two axial hydrogens in each ring; the increase in strain energy, estimated as equivalent to four skew interactions, is 2.8 kg.-cal. In the cis isomer the angular methyl is axial to one ring but equatorial to the other and hence the increase in energy is only half as great. The energy difference is thus reduced from 2.1 to 0.7 kg.-cal.

6. Condensation of butadiene with maleic anhydride; saturation of the double bond by catalytic hydrogenation; hydrolysis of the anhydride group. (Note that the Diels-Alder reaction gives cis addition products.)

8. CH$_2$=O + 2 CH$_2$(CO$_2$C$_2$H$_5$)$_2$ $\longrightarrow$
CH$_2$[CH(CO$_2$C$_2$H$_5$)$_2$]$_2$ (elimination of H$_2$O); hydrolysis to CH$_2$[CH(CO$_2$H)$_2$]$_2$; decarboxylation to CH$_2$(CH$_2$CO$_2$H)$_2$.

9. (a) O=C=C=C=O + 2 H$_2$O $\longrightarrow$
(HO)$_2$C=C=C(OH)$_2$ $\longrightarrow$ HOOCCH$_2$COOH
(b) Malonamide: H$_2$NCOCH$_2$CONH$_2$

Chapter 14. Carbohydrates

1. 2-Ketopentose

2. On oxidation with nitric acid (a) would give a C$_6$-monobasic acid and (b) would give a C$_6$-dibasic acid.

3. On reaction with excess phenylhydrazine (a) would give a phenylhydrazone and (b) would give an osazone.

4. Isomer (a) would not react with phenylhydrazine until after it had been hydrolyzed with dilute acid and then it would give an osazone; (b) would react directly to give a methoxyl-containing phenylhydrazone; isomer (c) would react directly to give a methoxyl-containing osazone.

5. A D-4-ketohexose corresponding in configuration to glucose and galactose at C$_2$, C$_3$, and C$_5$.

6. A is D-threose and B is D-erythrose (14.8).

7. (a) Galactose yields an inactive C$_6$-diacid, talose an active acid; (b) galactose alone is fermentable.

Chapter 18. Aromatic Structure and Substitution

1. The 1,3-dicarboxylic acid could be obtained by condensation of trimethylene bromide with methylene-bismalonic ester, CH$_2$[CH(CO$_2$C$_2$H$_5$)$_2$]$_2$, followed by hydrolysis and decarboxylation of the tetrabasic acid. The ester (C$_2$H$_5$O$_2$C)$_2$CHCH$_2$CH$_2$CH(CO$_2$C$_2$H$_5$)$_2$, re-quired for the synthesis of the 1,4-isomer, is obtainable by condensation of BrCH$_2$CH$_2$Br with two moles of sodiomalonic ester; the preparation of methylenebis-malonic ester by condensation of formaldehyde with diethyl malonate is mentioned in question 8, Chapter 13.

2. The molecular ratio of glyoxal to diacetyl to methyl-glyoxal should be 1:1:4.

3. Yes; 1,2,3-trimethylbenzene can afford two mono-substitution products, three are derivable from 1,2,4-trimethylbenzene, and one from the 1,3,5-isomer.

4. The answer will be obvious from the formulas.

5. (a) 4-Nitro-1,3-dimethoxybenzene
(b) Substitution ortho to the acetylamino group (more potent)
(c) Substitution ortho to the methyl group (smaller)
(d) Substitution ortho to the methyl group and meta to —COCH$_3$
(e) Mild conditions: 2-nitrophenol-4-sulfonic acid; more drastic conditions: 2,4-dinitrophenol, picric acid
(f) 2,4,5-Trimethylacetophenone
(g) 2,4-Dichloronitrobenzene
(h) C$_6$H$_5$COCH$_2$C$_6$H$_4$(p)-COCH$_2$CH$_2$CO$_2$H
(i) o- and p-NO$_2$C$_6$H$_4$CH$_2$C$_6$H$_4$CO$_2$H(p)
(j) 4-ClC$_6$H$_4$CH$_2$C$_6$H$_4$CH$_3$-4'
(k) 4-Methyl-3'-nitro-4'-hydroxydiphenyl

Chapter 19. Aromatic Hydrocarbons

1. (a) Benzene, t-butyl chloride, with 0.4 mole AlCl$_3$.
(b) Condensation of t-butyl chloride with t-butyl-benzene in the presence of BF$_3$ at 25°.

2. (CH$_3$)$_3$CCl + C$_6$H$_5$CH$_3$ (+ BF$_3$) $\longrightarrow$
p-(CH$_3$)$_3$CC$_6$H$_4$CH$_3$; the t-butyl group is resistant to oxidation, and hence the hydrocarbon can be oxidized to the acid desired.

3. Isopropylbenzene could be obtained by Friedel-Crafts condensation of benzene with (CH$_3$)$_2$CHCl, CH$_3$CH$_2$CHCl, CH$_3$CH=CH$_2$, or (CH$_3$)$_2$CHOH; condensation of (CH$_3$)$_2$CHC$_6$H$_5$ with CH$_3$COCl in the presence of AlCl$_3$ would give p-(CH$_3$)$_2$CHC$_6$H$_4$COCH$_3$, which could be converted by the haloform reaction with NaOCl into p-(CH$_3$)$_2$CHC$_6$H$_4$CO$_2$H (the usual oxidizing agents would attack the isopropyl group).

4. (a) C$_6$H$_5$C(CH$_3$)$_3$
(b) p-(CH$_3$)$_2$CHC$_6$H$_4$CH$_2$CH$_3$
(c) 1,3,5-Triethylbenzene
(d) p-CH$_3$C$_6$H$_4$COCH$_3$

5. (a) CH$_3$CH$_2$CH$_2$COCl + C$_6$H$_6$ (AlCl$_3$) $\longrightarrow$
CH$_3$CH$_2$CH$_2$COC$_6$H$_5$; Clemmensen or Wolff-Kishner reduction.
(b) CH$_3$CH$_2$CH$_2$CH$_2$Br + C$_6$H$_5$Br + 2 Na
(c) C$_6$H$_5$CH=O + BrMgCH$_2$CH$_2$CH$_3$ (decompose reaction mixture with H$_2$O) $\longrightarrow$
C$_6$H$_5$CH(OH)CH$_2$CH$_2$CH$_3$; dehydrate to C$_6$H$_5$CH=CHCH$_2$CH$_3$; hydrogenate.

6. Friedel-Crafts succinoylation of benzene
$\longrightarrow$ C$_6$H$_5$COCH$_2$CH$_2$CO$_2$H; Clemmensen reduction to C$_6$H$_5$CH$_2$CH$_2$CH$_2$CO$_2$H; cyclization to α-tetralone

with HF (or by the action of AlCl₃ on the acid chloride); reaction with C₆H₅MgBr; dehydration of the resulting carbinol; dehydrogenation with Se (or S, or Pd—C).

7. Friedel-Crafts condensation to p-CH₃C₆H₄COCH₂CH₂CO₂H; Clemmensen or Wolff-Kishner reduction; cyclization with HF to the tetralone; reduction to the tetralin; dehydrogenation.

8. (a) Wurtz-Fittig reaction of α-bromonaphthalene with methyl bromide (+ 2 Na);
(b) conversion to α-naphthylmagnesium bromide and reaction of the latter with (CH₃)₂SO₄.

9. Condensation of cyclohexanone with C₆H₅MgBr to give 1-phenylcyclohexanol-1; dehydration to 1-phenylcyclohexene-1; permanganate oxidation to cleave the hydrocarbon at the position of the double bond to give C₆H₅CO(CH₂)₄CO₂H; Clemmensen or Wolff-Kishner reduction to C₆H₅(CH₂)₅CO₂H (see 24.11 for a shorter method).

Chapter 20. Nitro Compounds and Sulfonic Acids

1. The nitro group *meta* to methyl in each isomer is *ortho* or *para* to two other nitro groups and hence labile. Separation can be accomplished by treatment of the crude material with alkali to hydrolyze the labile nitro groups and convert the contaminants into alkali-extractable phenols. In another process the crude TNT is warmed with aqueous sodium sulfite, when the labile nitro groups are replaced by sodium sulfonate groups (—SO₃Na) to give water-soluble products.

2. Dinitration of chlorobenzene gives 2,4-dinitrochlorobenzene, in which the halogen is labile; condensation with methylamine and reduction gives the product desired.

3. (a) Disproportionation of nitrobenzene in the presence of alkali to give a reduction product (azoxybenzene) and products of hydroxylation in the o- and p-positions (o- and p-nitrophenol). Attack by the negative ion occurs at centers rendered relatively positive by resonance in nitrobenzene; the nitro group is *meta* directing only for electrophilic substitution.
(b) Action of KOH or alkaline ferricyanide on m-dinitrobenzene with hydroxylation o- or p- to both nitro groups.

4. (a) Reaction of o- or p-dinitrobenzene with OH⁻, CH₃O⁻, or NH₃ with displacement of one nitro group by OH, OCH₃, or NH₂.
(b) Similar displacement of chlorine in o-chloronitrobenzene.
(c) Low temperature reactions of 2,4-dinitrochlorobenzene with aniline, with ammonia, and with sodium carbonate (preparation of picric acid).

Chapter 21. Aryl Amines

2. Oxidation of a primary amine can abstract a hydrogen atom from the amino group (transient free radical) and can also result in attack at the reactive p-position (formation of quinone). Stabilization is achieved by salt formation (e.g. nitration in a solution

in concentrated sulfuric acid), when the nitrogen function becomes ionic and weakly *meta* directing. Stabilization by formation of the N-acetyl derivative decreases the substitution-facilitating effect and makes possible the preparation of mono o- or p-derivatives.

3. Aniline sulfate ⟶ phenylsulfamic acid ⟶ orthanilic acid ⟶ sulfanilic acid. N-Methylaniline ⟶ N-nitroso derivative ⟶ p-nitroso-N-methylaniline. Benzenediazonium chloride + aniline ⟶ diazoaminobenzene ⟶ p-aminoazobenzene. Similar rearrangements (20.11): phenylhydroxylamine ⟶ p-aminophenol; hydrazobenzene ⟶ benzidine.

4. Brominate, hydrolyze to p-bromoaniline, diazotize, hydrolyze the diazonium salt.

5. Diazotize, run Sandmeyer with Cu₂(CN)₂, hydrolyze the nitrile to 2-methylbenzoic acid, oxidize with permanganate in alkaline solution.

6. (a) Diazotize, Sandmeyer to give p-bromotoluene, oxidize.
(b) Diazotize, reduce with sodium sulfite.
(c) Brominate (e.g. with bromine water), with introduction of Br at both positions *ortho* to the amino group, diazotize, deaminate by reduction with H₃PO₂.
(d) Diazotize, run Gattermann condensation with toluene in the presence of copper powder.
(e) Acetylate, nitrate adjacent to the acetylamino group, deacetylate, diazotize, hydrolyze —N₂Cl to —OH, reduce the nitro group.
(f) Treat with benzenesulfonyl chloride to produce the Hinsberg derivative, methylate this in alkaline solution, and remove the benzenesulfonyl group by hydrolysis.

7. Make the N-nitroso derivative, rearrange to 4-nitroso-N-methylaniline, reduce.

8. (a) Diazotize m-nitroaniline, run a Sandmeyer reaction to form m-chloronitrobenzene, reduce.
(b) From m-toluidine (available from p-toluidine, 21.22) by diazotization and hydrolysis.
(c) Convert m-nitroaniline into m-chloronitrobenzene as in (a), reduce, replace NH₂ by Br by the Sandmeyer method.

9. (a) From mesitylene by mononitration, reduction, diazotization, and hydrolysis.
(b) From p-xylene by nitration, reduction, diazotization, and Sandmeyer reaction with Cu₂(CN)₂. Another route: reaction of p-xylene with CH₃COCl + AlCl₃, hypochlorite oxidation to p-xylenecarboxylic acid, conversion through the acid chloride to the amide, dehydration with acetic anhydride. The route from p-xylene through the sulfonate to the nitrile would be limited by a poor yield.
(c) Monochlorination of m-xylene (or nitration, reduction, replacement of NH₂ by Cl) and oxidation.
(d) From p-xylene by sulfonation, alkali fusion, coupling with diazotized sulfanilic acid, and reduction.
(e) From toluene by Friedel-Crafts acetylation in the 4-position, nitration, and reduction.

1. A *meta* nitro group decreases pK_a of phenol by 2.0 units and increases pK_b of aniline by 2.1 units; for a *para* group the effects are -2.8 and $+2.7$ units. The *ortho* series is irregular: -2.8 units for phenol and $+4.5$ units for aniline.

2. Instances in this chapter: steam-volatility of *o*-nitrophenol; greater steam-volatility, lower boiling points, greater solubility in ligroin of *o*-hydroxyacetophenones as compared with *p*-isomers. Instances cited earlier: separation of *o*-(chelated) from *p*-nitroaniline by steam distillation; chelation of *o*-hydroxy azo compounds accounts for insolubility in alkali, steam volatility and low m.p. as compared with *p*-isomers.

3. Saligenin is not soluble in bicarbonate solution but dissolves in aqueous alkali and, unless the solution is very dilute, precipitates on acidification; hence at least one phenolic hydroxyl group is present. On treatment with HBr one hydroxyl group is replaced by bromine, and hence this must be an alcoholic and not a phenolic group.

4. Prepare the dimethyl ether (dimethyl sulfate and alkali) and condense it with $CH_3COCl + AlCl_3$. Reflux the product in benzene with $AlCl_3$ to remove the methoxyl groups, and reduce the ketonic group with amalgamated zinc and HCl.

5. (*a*) $C_6H_6 \longrightarrow C_6H_5SO_3H \longrightarrow C_6H_5SO_3Na \longrightarrow C_6H_5OH \longrightarrow C_6H_5OCH_3$ (dimethyl sulfate and alkali)
(*b*) $C_6H_5OH \longrightarrow$ 2,4-disulfonate $\longrightarrow$ catechol-4-sulfonate $\longrightarrow$ catechol
(*c*) $C_6H_5OH \longrightarrow$ *o*-*p*-$NO_2C_6H_4OH$; separate *o*-nitrophenol by steam distillation; reduce
(*d*) $C_6H_5OH + N_2^+C_6H_5SO_3^-(p) +$ alkali $\longrightarrow$ $NaO_3SC_6H_4N=HC_6H_4OH(p) \longrightarrow$ sulfanilic acid Na salt $+$ *p*-aminophenol. (Alternates: $C_6H_5OH \longrightarrow$ *p*-nitrosophenol; reduction; $C_6H_5NO_2 \longrightarrow$ $C_6H_5NHOH \longrightarrow$ *p*-aminophenol.)
(*e*) Preparation and alkali fusion of *m*-benzenedisulfonic acid to give resorcinol; condensation with caproic acid $(ZnCl_2)$; Clemmensen reduction.

6. The acid is soluble in bicarbonate solution; the phenol is insoluble in bicarbonate but soluble in alkali solution; the ester is insoluble in cold alkali but dissolves when the mixture is warmed or allowed to stand; the last compound, a ketal, is neutral and nonhydrolyzable and it could be identified by formation of an osazone.

7. α-Naphthol: $C_6H_6 +$ succinic anhydride $(+ AlCl_3)$ $\longrightarrow C_6H_5COCH_2CH_2CO_2H$; reduce to $C_6H_5CH_2CH_2CH_2CO_2H$; cyclize with HF to α-tetralone, dehydrogenate. β-Naphthol: $CH_3OC_6H_5 \longrightarrow$ $CH_3OC_6H_4COCH_2CH_2CO_2H \longrightarrow$ 7-methoxy-1-tetralone (with HF); Clemmensen reduction of keto group; dehydrogenate; demethylation.

8. In either *p*-aminophenol or its diacetate the N-function has a stronger directive influence than the O-function. However, acetylation in aqueous solution gives *p*-$HOC_6H_4NHCOCH_3$, in which a free hydroxyl group competes for a substituting agent with the weaker acetylamino group. Hence controlled bromination gives 2-bromo-4-acetylaminophenol, which affords the desired product on hydrolysis.

9.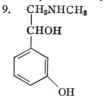

Chapter 23. Aryl Halides

1. $C_6H_5NH_2 \longrightarrow C_6H_5NHCOCH_3 \longrightarrow$ *p*-$BrC_6H_4NHCOCH_3 \longrightarrow$ *p*-$BrC_6H_4NH_2 \longrightarrow$ *p*-$BrC_6H_4N_2^+Cl^-$ $(+ KI) \longrightarrow$ *p*-BrC_6H_4I.

2. $C_6H_5CH_2Cl \longrightarrow C_6H_5CH_2OH$.
$C_6H_5CHCl_2 \longrightarrow [C_6H_5CH(OH)_2] \longrightarrow C_6H_5CHO$.
$C_6H_5CCl_3 \longrightarrow [C_6H_5C(OH)Cl_2 \longrightarrow C_6H_5COCl] \longrightarrow C_6H_5COOH$.

3. (*a*) $CH_3C_6H_5 + CH_2O + HCl(ZnCl_2)$ $\longrightarrow$ *p*-$CH_3C_6H_4CH_2Cl$; hydrolysis (expect mixture in which *p*-isomer predominates).
(*b*) *p*-$ClC_6H_4Br \longrightarrow$ *p*-ClC_6H_4MgBr $[+ (CH_3)_2SO_4]$ $\longrightarrow$ *p*-$ClC_6H_4CH_3$ $(+ 2$ Li$) \longrightarrow$ *p*-$LiC_6H_4CH_3$ $(+ CH_2=O) \longrightarrow$ *p*-$HOCH_2C_6H_4CH_3$.

4. Chloromethylation of *p*-xylene.

5. $C_6H_5OCH_3 + Br_2 \longrightarrow$ *p*-$BrC_6H_4OCH_3$ $\longrightarrow$ 2-nitro-4-bromoanisole $\longrightarrow$ 2-amino-4-bromoanisole.

6. Conversion to the nitrile, hydrolysis, decarboxylation. Catalytic hydrogenation is also applicable.

7. Preparation of the 4-bromo derivative, formation and carbonation of the Grignard reagent; chlorination, formation, and carbonation of the lithium derivative; conversion of either the bromide or chloride to the nitrile (cuprous cyanide in pyridine) and hydrolysis.

Chapter 24. Aromatic Carboxylic Acids

1. From *m*- and *p*-xylene by Friedel-Crafts acetylation and hypohalite oxidation.

2. Naphthalene $\longrightarrow$ phthalic anhydride $\longrightarrow$ phthalimide $\longrightarrow$ phthalamidic acid $\longrightarrow$ anthranilic acid.

3. Toluene nitrated and *o*- and *p*-isomers separated by fractionation; *p*-nitrotoluene $\longrightarrow$ *p*-toluidine $\longrightarrow$ N-acetyl-*p*-toluidine; bromination *ortho* to acetylamino group, hydrolysis, diazotization, deamination to *m*-bromotoluene (see 23.1); preparation and carbonation of the Grignard reagent.

4. The esters melt at much lower temperatures and more sharply than the acids; a high melting acid often suffers decarboxylation or dehydration to an anhydride when heated.

5. In analogy with the behavior of acetanilide, the N-acetyl derivative of anthranilic acid would be ex-

pected on bromination to yield 2-acetylamino-5-bromo-benzoic acid. This could be deacetylated, diazotized, and the diazonium salt treated with $Cu(NH_3)_2OH$ (compare 24.10).

6. (a) Friedel-Crafts succinoylation of toluene and Clemmensen reduction.
(b) $C_6H_5(CH_2)_4COCl$ + $C_6H_6(AlCl_3)$ $\longrightarrow$ $C_6H_5(CH_2)_4COC_6H_5$; Clemmensen reduction $\longrightarrow$ $C_6H_5(CH_2)_5C_6H_5$. The required δ-phenylvaleric acid is available from cinnamaldehyde and malonic acid or from phenylmagnesium bromide and cyclopentanone (24.11).
(c) Pyrolysis of the calcium salt of the diacid o-HOOCCH_2C_6H_4CH_2CH_2COOH or Dieckmann condensation (10.21) of the diester.

Chapter 25. Aromatic Aldehydes and Ketones

1. (a) Oxidation of p-bromotoluene (available from p-toluidine) with MnO_2—H_2SO_4.
(b) p-Xylene + CO; HCl, $ZnCl_2$—Cu_2Cl_2 (Gattermann-Koch).
(c) Resorcinol dimethyl ether + HCl, $Zn(CN)_2$ in ether (Gattermann-Adams).
(d) Side-chain bromination of p-xylene to p-$Br_2CHC_6H_4CHBr_2$ and hydrolysis.

2. The chart should include all methods specifically covered.

3. The groups CH_3, CN, CHO, and $COCH_3$ are ordinarily convertible to COOH, which can be eliminated by decarboxylation. The nitro group is convertible to NH_2, which can be eliminated by the deamination reaction. The SO_3H group can be removed by hydrolysis. The only general method of eliminating OH, zinc dust distillation, is subject to limitations. A halo substituent can be replaced by CN, the nitrile hydrolyzed, and the acid decarboxylated; an iodide can be reduced directly with HI; a bromo substituent is removable by catalytic hydrogenation.

4. (a) $C_6H_5CH=C(C_2H_5)CHO$ (10% alkali)
(b) $C_6H_5CH=CHCH=CHCOC_6H_5$ (10% alkali)
(c) $C_6H_5CH=CHCH=CHCHO$ (condensation in 70% alcohol with piperidine acetate as catalyst affords the phenylpentadienal in 50% yield).

5. Oxidation with MnO_2—H_2SO_4 to o-bromobenzaldehyde; condensation of the aldehyde with $(CH_3CO)_2O$ + CH_3CO_2Na or with $CH_2(CO_2H)_2$ in pyridine-piperidine.

6. $C_6H_5COCH_3$ + $BrCH_2CO_2C_2H_5$ + Zn $\longrightarrow$ $C_6H_5C(OH)(CH_3)CH_2CO_2C_2H_5$; dehydration to $C_6H_5C(CH_3)=CHCO_2C_2H_5$ (or bond isomer); hydrogenation; hydrolysis.

7. Reimer-Tiemann synthesis of aldehydic phenols; Fries synthesis of ketonic phenols; acylation of resorcinol-type phenols (very reactive) with RCOOH + $ZnCl_2$; condensation of dimethylaniline with phosgene to give Michler's ketone.

8. β-Acetonaphthalene.

Chapter 26. Quinones

1. (a) p-Xylene $\longrightarrow$ sulfonate $\longrightarrow$ p-xylenol; couple with diazotized sulfanilic acid, reduce to 2,5-dimethyl-4-aminophenol, oxidize.
(b) The naphthols can be converted by the process formulated (26.5) into α- and β-naphthoquinone, both of which react with acetic anhydride in the presence of sulfuric acid (better catalyst: boron fluoride etherate) to give 1,2,4-trihydroxynaphthalene triacetate. Hydrolysis of the triacetate and oxidation gives 2-hydroxy-1,4-naphthoquinone (lawsone) in excellent overall yield.
(c) Alkylation of lawsone with the peroxide from $(CH_3)_2CHCH_2CH_2CO_2H$.
(d) Thiele reaction, hydrolysis, oxidation.
(e) Alkylation with the peroxide from n-dodecylic acid.
(f) Conversion to the 2,3-oxide with H_2O_2—Na_2CO_3; hydrolysis with H_2SO_4.

Chapter 27. Naphthalene

1. (a) β-Acetonaphthalene $\longrightarrow$ β-COOH $\longrightarrow$ β-COCl; Friedel-Crafts condensation with benzene.
(b) α-Bromonaphthalene $\longrightarrow$ α-MgBr $\longrightarrow$ α-COOH $\longrightarrow$ α-COCl $\longrightarrow$ α-CHO (Rosenmund reaction).
(c) Naphthalene-β-sulfonic acid $\longrightarrow$ β-naphthol $\longrightarrow$ β-naphthylamine $\longrightarrow$ diazonium salt $\longrightarrow$ β-iodonaphthalene (Sandmeyer).
(d) β-Acetonaphthalene + CH_3MgBr $\longrightarrow$ β-C(OH)(CH_3)_2 $\longrightarrow$ β-C(=CH_2)CH_3 $\longrightarrow$ β-CH(CH_3)_2.

2. (a) Sulfonation to the 6-sulfonic acid (Schaeffer acid) and alkali fusion.
(b) See 26.5.
(c) Nitrosation.
(d) Methyl ether + CH_3COCl ($AlCl_3$ in $C_6H_5NO_2$) $\longrightarrow$ 6-aceto-2-methoxynaphthalene; Clemmensen reduction and demethylation.
(e) Claisen rearrangement of β-naphthol allyl ether and hydrogenation of the double bond in the side chain.

3. (a) Nitration and reduction.
(b) Friedel-Crafts reaction with acetyl chloride in nitrobenzene solution and hypochlorite oxidation of the 6-aceto derivative.
(c) Sulfonation to 2-methylnaphthalene-6-sulfonic acid, alkali fusion to the naphthol, Bucherer reaction with ammonium bisulfite.
(d) Oxidation to 2-methyl-1,4-naphthoquinone, conversion to the 2,3-oxide, hydrolysis with H_2SO_4.

4. (a) Nitration of α-nitronaphthalene gives a mixture from which the high-melting 1,5-dinitro compound is easily separated; this on reduction gives the 1,5-diamine.
(b) Dibromination of α-naphthylamine gives the 2,4-dibromo compound (compare dinitration of α-naphthol); this on diazotization and deamination gives 1,3-dibromonaphthalene.
(c) α-Naphthylamine $\longrightarrow$ α-naphthol $\longrightarrow$ 2,4-disulfonic acid $\longrightarrow$ 2,4-dinitro-1-naphthol (Martius Yellow) $\longrightarrow$ 2,4-diamino-1-naphthol.

5. The reaction affords 78% of β-3-acenaphthoylpropionic acid (substitution *para* to the methylene group) and 15% of β-1-acenaphthoylpropionic acid (*ortho* to methylene group).

6. Succinoylation of naphthalene gives a mixture of 1- and 2-naphthoylpropionic acids that need not be separated. Clemmensen reduction gives a mixture of two naphthylbutyric acids, each of which on cyclization with liquid HF yields a ketotetrahydrophenanthrene. Both isomers on reduction afford tetrahydrophenanthrene, and phenanthrene is obtained on dehydrogenation (Se or Pd—C).

Chapter 28. Polynuclear Hydrocarbons

1. (*a*) Bromination to the 9-bromo compound; RMgBr + (CH₃)₂SO₄. (*b*) Cyclization, condensation with CH₃MgI, dehydration, dehydrogenation.

2. 2-Retenol (2-hydroxyretene).

3. (*a*) The dibasic acid obtained as a degradation product is 5,5′-dimethoxydiphenic acid (for synthetic method, see 24.10), and the sulfonation product is phenanthrene-3,6-disulfonic acid.
(*b*) Nitration of *p*-toluidine in sulfuric acid solution results in substitution *meta* to the amino group. Diazotization, hydrolysis, and methylation gives 4-methoxy-2-nitrotoluene, and permanganate oxidation of the methyl group and reduction of the nitro group gives the required intermediate.

4. Friedel-Crafts condensation ⟶ *o*-(4-chlorobenzoyl)-benzoic acid; cyclization to β-chloroanthraquinone; reaction with ammonia.

5. Condensation of phthalic anhydride with α-methylnaphthalene effects substitution in the 4-position and cyclization of the product with H₂SO₄ gives 3-methyl-1,2-benzanthraquinone, which affords the desired hydrocarbon on reduction with zinc and ammonia.

6. Monosulfonation in the presence of mercuric sulfate reduction with zinc and ammonia, alkali fusion.

7. Reaction of anthrone with CH₃MgI and dehydration of the resulting carbinol (1,4-elimination of water).

Part 2, Section 17

It is evident from the absorption spectrum that six of the eleven carbon atoms are present in a phenyl group. The formation of an evident O-diacetate shows that two hydroxyl groups are present. Reduction to a substance capable of being diazotized and coupled with a phenol indicates the presence of a nitro substituent in the phenyl group. Absorption of three moles of hydrogen confirms this conclusion, for unsaturated nitrogen compounds other than nitro compounds do not require this much hydrogen for reduction.

One of the two products of alkaline hydrolysis, $C_2H_2O_2Cl_2$, is acidic and hence the only possible formula is $CHCl_2COOH$. The other product is basic, whereas chloramphenicol is not. Thus hydrolysis liberates an amino group and dichloroacetic acid, and hence chloramphenicol must contain the group —NHCOCHCl₂.

This amide group, which would be inert to carbonyl reagents, accounts for one of the five oxygens, and one nitro and two hydroxyl groups account for the remainder. Oxidation with periodic acid to an aromatic aldehyde, ArCHO, formaldehyde, formic acid, and ammonia indicates the presence of a three carbon chain, Ar—C—C—C, containing two hydroxyl and one amino group, and these have to be distributed one to a carbon atom to account for the cleavage. Since chloramphenicol, which contains one —NHCOCHCl₂ and two free hydroxyl groups, is stable to periodic acid the distribution cannot be ArCHOHCHOHCH₂NH₂ or ArCHNH₂CHOHCH₂OH and can only be:

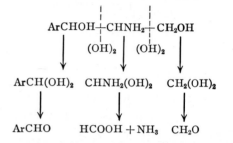

The aldehyde, $C_7H_5O_3N$, must still carry the nitro group and hence is a nitrobenzaldehyde, NO₂C₆H₄CHO, identified as the *para* derivative. Chloramphenicol thus has the structure
p-NO₂C₆H₄CH(OH)CH(NHCOCHCl₂)CH₂OH.

Chloramphenicol contains two asymmetric carbon atoms and could have the threo configuration I or the erythro configuration II. That I is probably correct

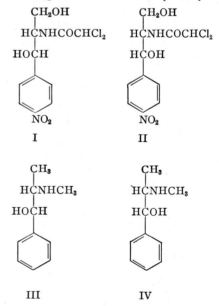

was deduced by comparison of the antibiotic with ephedrine (IV), a plant product, and pseudoephedrine (III), and the corresponding nor derivatives (lacking the N-methyl group). Configurations in the ephedrine series were deduced by Freudenberg (1934) through correlation to mandelic acid and to alanine. Various salts of the C$_9$ base desacylchloramphenicol show shifts in molecular rotation corresponding to those of nor-pseudoephedrine, of threo configuration. The Geneva name for the antibiotic is D(−)threo-2-dichloroacet-amido-1-*p*-nitrophenylpropane-1,3-diol.

The first synthesis involved the steps shown in the formulation.

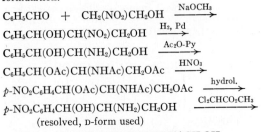

C$_6$H$_5$CHO + CH$_2$(NO$_2$)CH$_2$OH $\xrightarrow{\text{NaOCH}_3}$

C$_6$H$_5$CH(OH)CH(NO$_2$)CH$_2$OH $\xrightarrow{\text{H}_2,\ \text{Pd}}$

C$_6$H$_5$CH(OH)CH(NH$_2$)CH$_2$OH $\xrightarrow{\text{Ac}_2\text{O-Py}}$

C$_6$H$_5$CH(OAc)CH(NHAc)CH$_2$OAc $\xrightarrow{\text{HNO}_3}$

p-NO$_2$C$_6$H$_4$CH(OAc)CH(NHAc)CH$_2$OAc $\xrightarrow{\text{hydrol.}}$

p-NO$_2$C$_6$H$_4$CH(OH)CH(NH$_2$)CH$_2$OH $\xrightarrow{\text{Cl}_2\text{CHCO}_2\text{CH}_3}$
(resolved, D-form used)

p-NO$_2$C$_6$H$_4$CH(OH)CH(NHCOCHCl$_2$)CH$_2$OH

A second synthesis (L. L. Bambas, H. D. Troutman, and L. M. Long, 1950) from *p*-nitroacetophenone involved conversion to *p*-nitrophenacyl bromide (V), reaction with hexamethylenetetramine and hydrolysis of the product to the amino derivative VI. The

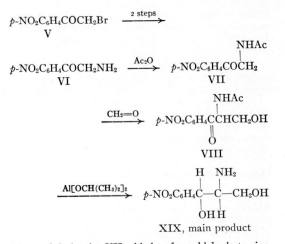

p-NO$_2$C$_6$H$_4$COCH$_2$Br $\xrightarrow{\text{2 steps}}$
V

p-NO$_2$C$_6$H$_4$COCH$_2$NH$_2$ $\xrightarrow{\text{Ac}_2\text{O}}$ *p*-NO$_2$C$_6$H$_4$COCH$_2$NHAc
VI   VII

$\xrightarrow{\text{CH}_2=\text{O}}$ *p*-NO$_2$C$_6$H$_4$C(=O)CH(NHAc)CH$_2$OH
VIII

$\xrightarrow{\text{Al[OCH(CH}_3)_2]_3}$ *p*-NO$_2$C$_6$H$_4$C(OH)(H)—C(NH$_2$)(H)—CH$_2$OH

XIX, main product

N-acetyl derivative VII added to formaldehyde to give VIII. Usual methods for reduction of the carbonyl group would also reduce the nitro group, but the Meer-wein-Ponndorf method has just the specificity required (20.11) and afforded XIX. The preponderant reduction product proved to be the DL-threo base, the D-form of which could be resolved and converted into chlor-amphenicol.

INDEXES

AUTHOR INDEX

Biographies are indicated by bold-face type and literature citations by parentheses.

Hewett, C. L., 564
Hey, D. H., (37)
Hickinbottom, W. J., 528
Hieger, I., 563, 564
Hilditch, T. P., (297)
Hill, G. A., **549**
Hinsberg, O., 187
Hirst, E. L., **271**, (285)
Hoff, J. H. van't, **6**, 204, 205, 222, 226, (234), 275
Hofmann, A. W. von, **178**, 181, 183, 188–189, 332, 402, 569, 570
Holleman, A. F., **346**, (353)
Homolka, B., 516
Honeyman, J., (285)
Hooker, S. C., 469, 557–559
Houben, J., (498)
Huang-Minlon, 169
Huber, G., 526
Hückel, W., **238**
Hudson, C. S., **209**, (234), 276, (285)
Huggins, M. L., (114)
Hughes, E. D., (127), 341, **530**, 531
Huntress, E. H., (127)

Ichikawa, K., 563
Iljinsky, M., 492
Ingold, C. K., **117**–119, 341, 530, 531
Ipatieff, V. N., **58**
Irvine, J. C., 526

Jacobs, T. L., **501**–502
Japp, F. R., (7), (353)
Johnson, A. W., (429)
Johnson, E. A., 512
Johnson, J. R., **145**, (151), 368, (457)
Johnson, W. S., **247**
Jones, E. R. H., 512, 513

Kamen, M. D., **544**
Karrer, P., 528, **529**, 532
Keilin, D., **541**–542
Kekulé, A., **3**, 64, 225, 333, 569, 573
Kennaway, E. L., **563**, 564
Kenyon, R. L., (297)
Khan, N. A., 512
Kharasch, M. S., **34**, 52
Kidder, C. W., 509
Kiliani, H., **259**, 263
Kishner, N. M., **169**
Kjeldahl, J., **18**
Kloetzel, M. C., (257)
Klyne, W., (257)
Knoevenagel, E., **451**
Koch, J. A., 446
Kohler, E. P., **162**
Kolbe, H., **32**, 205, 440, 569
Kornblum, N., 183
Körner, W., **338**, 339, 569–570
Krebs, H. A., **327**–328
Kremers, E., 513
Krockow, E. W., 518
Kuhn, R., 134–135, **336**, 467, 502, 503, 552, 553

Kuhn, W., 530
Küster, W., 317

Ladenburg, A., 337–**338**, 569
Lake, W. H. G., 531
Lauer, W. M., **163**
Laurent, A., 332, 381, 568
Le Bel, J. A., **6**, 204–205
Lederer, E., **535**–536
Leloir, L. F., **541**
Lemieux, R. U., **526**, 528, 529, 531
Leonard, N. J., **524**
Leuchs, H., **531**
Levene, P. A., **529**
Lewis, G. N., (7), **108**
Liebermann, C., 569, 570, 571, 572, 573, 575
Liebig, J. von, **13**, 16, 62, 202, 332, 452, 503, 504, 505, 569
Lindberg, B., 528
Linderstrøm-Lang, K., **538**
Lipmann, F., **321**
Loon, J. van, 512
Lothrop, W. C., (391), 473
Loudon, J. D., (429)
Lumb, P. B., 511
Lutz, O., 530
Lynen, F., **321**, (331)

Macleod, J. J. R., **315**
Mai, J., 408
Majima, R., **548**
Malus, E. L., 196
Marckwald, W., 471
Marker, R. E., (37)
Markownikoff, V. W., **51**, 569
Martin, A. J. P., **308**
Martin, E. L., 364, (374)
Martius, K. A. von, 569
Marvel, C. S., (234)
Mason, H. S., 549
Mayer, F., (469)
Mayneord, W. V., 564
Mayo, F. R., (68)
McElvain, S. M., **172**, 513, 514, 515
McKay, A. F., **140**
McKeever, C. H., (436)
McKenzie, A., **219**
Medicus, L., 504
Meerwein, H., **98**, 163–164
Meinwald, J., 514
Meisenheimer, J., **507**
Mering, J. von, 505
Meyer, K. H., **170**, 172, (285)
Meyer, M., 513
Meyer, V., 183, **338**, 444, 569
Michael, A., **227**, 454
Midgley, T., **80**, 125
Mitscherlich, E. A., **199**, 200, 332
Mohr, E., **237**–238
Moore, F. J., (7)
Moore, S., **309**
Morton, W. T. G., 105
Müller, D., 541

594

SUBJECT INDEX

Hydrolapachol, 560
Hydrolases, 320
Hydronium ion, 3, 109
Hydroperoxides, 293, 418
Hydroquinone, 416, 420–421, 459–460
Hydrourushiol, 548, 549
Hydroxyacetophenone, o- and p-, 424
o-Hydroxyazobenzene, 410
p-Hydroxyazobenzene, 409, 411–412
o-Hydroxybenzaldehyde, see Salicylaldehyde
p-Hydroxybenzaldehyde, 447–448
α-Hydroxybutyric acid, 208
β-Hydroxybutyric acid, 326
Hydroxylamine, 167
2-Hydroxy-3-methoxybenzaldehyde, 449
2-Hydroxy-1,4-naphthohydroquinone triacetate, 465
2-Hydroxy-1,4-naphthoquinone, 462, 464, 465, 467
Hydroxyproline, 304
β-Hydroxypropionic acid, 133, 329
Hygrine, 554
Hyperconjugation, 346
Hypochlorous acid, 388
Hypohalite, additions, 53–54
    oxidation, 122–124, 132, 264, 437–438, 450, 514
    reaction with RCONH₂, 183–184
Hypophosphorous acid, 408

Idose, 267
Imides, 191–192
Indane, 364
Indanthrene, 496
Indanthrone, see Indanthrene
Indanthrone dyes, 496
Indican, 494–495
Indigo, 381, 392, 494, 495
Indoxyl, 494, 495
Inductive effects, 51–52, 129–130, 139, 179, 250–251, 343–346
Insulin, 314–315, 538
Inulin triacetate, 526, 527
Invert sugar, 258
Iodine monobromide, 291–292
Iodine monochloride, 291
Iodine value, 291–292
Iodoacetic acid, 130
Iodobenzene, 405, 430
o-Iodobenzoic acid, 441
Iodoform, 122–123
Iodoform test, 123–124
Iodomercuric chloride, 292
o-Iodophenol, 424
Ion-exchange resins, 190
Isoalloxazine, 320, 541–542
Isobutane, 26, 81, 82
Isobutene (isobutylene), 43, 81–83
Isobutyl alcohol, 85
Isocaryophyllene, 523–524
Isocitric acid, 328
Isocrotonic acid, 224
Isocyanates, 184, 185
Isoelectric point, 300, 301
Isoeugenol, 449

L-Isoleucine, 301, 302
Isomerase, 541
Isomerism, geometrical, 222–230
    optical, 196–222
Isomerization, cis–trans, 223–224, 225, 404
Isomycomycin, 512, 513
Isonepetic acid, 515
Isooctane, 79, 81
Isooctene, 81–82
Isopelletierine, 506, 507, 508
Isopentane (2-methylbutane), 78
Isophthalic acid, 338, 437, 442
Isoprene, 62
Isoprenoids, 62, 281–282, 288–289, 500, 514, 516, 554
Isopropyl alcohol, 53, 85, 94, 100
Isopropylbenzene, see Cumene
Isopropyl bromide, 29
Isopropyl iodide, 29, 43
Isoquinoline, 355
Isorhodomycin, 560
Isorhodomycinone, 560
Isosucrose, 526
Isotope dilution method, 309

Juglone, 467

Keratin, 298
Ketals, 169–170
Ketene, 147
Keto-enol systems, see Tautomerism
α-Ketoglutaric acid, 327, 328, 329
Ketones, see Carbonyl compounds
Ketonic hydrolysis, 173
Ketonuria, 326
1-Ketotetrahydrophenanthrene, 417
Kjeldahl determination, 18
Knoevenagel reaction, 451
Kolbe reaction, 440–441
    synthesis, 32–33
Körner's absolute method, 338–339
Krebs cycle, 327–329, 545
Kuhn-Roth determination, 134–135, 512–513, 514

Lactic acid, 202–203, 205–206, 207–208, 210–211, 327, 530–531
Lactones, 255, 264
Lactose, 277, 278–279, 324
Lapachol, 557–558
Lauric acid, 290, 511
Lawsone, 467
Lead azide, 103, 382
Lead dioxide, 515
Lead tetraacetate, 101, 369, 466, 566, 567
Lecithins, 286–287, 325
Leucine, 300, 301, 302, 311, 329
Leucoindigo, 494, 495
Leucylglycylglycine, 311
Leucyltriglycylleucyltriglycylleucyloctaglycylglycine, 311
Levoglucosan, 528
Lewis acids, bases, 108–109, 179
Licanic acid, 293
Lignin, 91

Phoenicin, 466, 467
Phosgene, 184, 192, 312
Phosphocholine, 286
Phosphoenolpyruvic acid, 545
Phosphoglucomutase, 526
6-Phosphogluconic acid, 545, 546
Phosphoglyceric acid, 545
Phosphoglycolic acid, 545
Phosphohomoserine, 330
Phospholipids, 286–287, 325
Phosphorus diiodide, 503
   trichloride, 143, 144
   triiodide, 116
   pentachloride, 116, 143–144
Phosphorylase, 526
Photosynthesis, 267, 543–547
Phthalamidic acid, 439, 440
Phthalhydrazide, 313, 314
Phthalic acid, 338, 369, 439
Phthalic anhydride, 439
Phthalic anhydride synthesis, 362
Phthalide, 439, 440
Phthalimide, 185–186, 439, 440
Phthalylglycyl chloride, 313, 314
Phthalyl synthesis, 313–314
C$_{27}$-Phthienoic acid, 533–534
Phthiocol, 465, 467
Phthioic acid, 533, 534
Phyllopyrrole, 318
Phytol, 289
Picolines, 355, 356
Picramide, 394
Picrates, 384–385
Picric acid, 380–381, 382, 383, 416
Pimelic acid, 250, 251, 252, 253
Pinacol, 41, 99, 163
Pinacolone, 99, 132
Pinacol rearrangement, 99, 454
Pinacol reduction, 163
Pinenes, 282
Piperylene, 249
Plasma proteins, 298–299
Plumbagin, 467
Poison ivy principle, see Urushiol
Polarimeter, 197–198
Polyacetic acid, 555, 556, 557
Polyglycolide, 254
Polyisoprene, see Rubber
Polymer gasoline, 81
Polymerization, acetylene, 75
  aldehydes, 157–158
  dienes, 62–63
  enes, 81–82, 125
Polysaccharides, 258, 279–283, 324
Porphyrins, 317–319
Prileschajew reaction, 57
Primacord, 104
Progesterone, 287, 288
Proline, 301, 302, 304, 311, 330
Propane, 8, 22, 77
Propanol-1, 85
Propargyl alcohol, 75

Propargyl bromide, 501–502
Propionamide, 190
Propionic acid, 129, 130
Propionitrile, 133
Propiophenone, 169
1-n-Propoxy-2-amino-4-nitrobenzene, 388
n-Propyl alcohol, 53
n-Propylbenzene, 169
Propylene, 38, 43, 81, 95
  chlorohydrin, 54
n-Propyl halides, 29, 43, 115, 361
Proteins, 298–322
  metabolism, 329–330
Prothrombin, 299
Protopine, 524
Pseudocumene, 442
Pseudopelletierine, 506
Pyran, 271
Pyranoside, 271
Pyrene, 354
Pyridine, 78, 148–149, 355, 356, 434–435
Pyrogallol, 421
  1,3-dimethyl ether, 421
Pyroligneous acid, 91–92, 131, 154
Pyroxylin, 281, 282
Pyruvic acid, 92, 326–327, 328, 329, 509

Quasi-racemates, 515
Quaternary ammonium compounds, 180–181
  decomposition, 188–189
Quaterphenyl, 407
Quinhydrone, 459
Quinic acid, 458
Quinoline, 78, 355
Quinone, see o- and p-Benzoquinone
p-Quinonediimine, 462
Quinones, 458–469
p-Quinonimine, 462
Quinquiphenyl, 407

Racemic acid, 199
Racemization, 218–219, 508
Radicals, acyl, 466
  hydrocarbon, 370–371
  nitrogen, 401
  phenoxyl, 425–426
Raney nickel catalyst, 58–59
Rearrangements, alkyl halides, 360, 361
  allylic, see α,γ-Shifts
  Beckmann, 455
  benzilic acid, 455–456
  bromoamides, 184
  Curtius, 185
  diazoamino compounds, 411
  hydrazobenzene, 384
  N-nitroso compounds, 401
  phenylhydroxylamine, 384
  pinacol, 454
  Wagner-Meerwein, 97–99, 146, 554
Reduction, bimolecular, 163
  Bouveault-Blanc, 140–141
  by LiAlH$_4$, 88–89, 140, 163, 182–183, 500–501, 502

Bond Distances (* designates hybrid bond)

Bond	Type	Distance, Å	Bond	Type	Distance, Å
C—C	R—R	1.54	C—N	$(CH_3)_3N$	1.47
C—C	Ar—R	1.54	C—N	$CH_3—NO_2$	1.46
C—C	Cyclopropane	1.53	C—N*	Trinitrobenzene	1.4
C—C	$CH_3CH{=}CHCH_3$	1.54	C—N	$H_2N—CHRCO_2H$	1.47
C—C*	$CH_3C{\equiv}N$	1.49	C≡N	$HC{\equiv}N$	1.15
C—C*	$CH_3C{\equiv}CCH_3$	1.47	$C\overset{\cdots}{-}\overset{+}{N}$*	Diazomethane	1.34
C—C*	$C_6H_5—C_6H_5$	1.48			
C—C*	$CH_2{=}CH—CH{=}CH_2$	1.46	$C\overset{\cdots}{-}\overset{+}{N}$*	Urea	1.37
	(2,3-bond)		$C\overset{\cdots}{-}N$*	Pyridine	1.37
C—C*	Furan (β,β-bond)	1.46	C—S	CH_3SCH_3	1.82
C—C*	Thiophene (β,β-bond)	1.44	C=S*	CS_2	1.54
C—C*	O=CH—CH=O	1.47	C—F	CH_3F	1.42
C—C*	N≡C—C≡N	1.37	C—F	CCl_2F_2	1.35
C—C*	HC≡C—C≡CH	1.36	C—Cl	CH_3Cl	1.77
C=C	$R_2C{=}CR_2$	1.33	C—Cl	$(CH_3)_3CCl$	1.78
C=C	$CH_2{=}C{=}CH_2$	1.33	C—Cl*	$CH_2{=}CHCl$	1.69
$C\overset{\cdots}{-}C$*	Benzene	1.40	C—Cl*	C_6H_5Cl	1.70
$C\overset{\cdots}{-}C$*	Naphthalene	1.36, 1.39	C—Cl	$HC{\equiv}CCl$	1.68
C≡C	RC≡CR	1.20	C—Cl	$N{\equiv}CCl$	1.67
C≡C	$C_6H_5C{\equiv}CC_6H_5$	1.19	C—Br	CH_3Br	1.91
C—H	CH_4	1.09	C—Br*	$CH_2{=}CHBr$	1.86
C—H	$CH_2{=}CH_2$	1.09	C—I	CHI_3	2.12
C—H*	HC≡CH	1.06	C—I*	$CH_2{=}CHI$	2.03
C—H*	HC≡N	1.06	O—H	H_2O	0.96
C—O	CH_3OCH_3	1.42	N—H	NH_3	1.01
C—O	$CH_3—ONO_2$	1.43	N—O	$CH_3O—NO_2$	1.36
C—O	Dioxane	1.46	N—N	Calculated	1.40
C=O	$CH_2{=}O$	1.21	N=N	$C_6H_5N{=}NC_6H_5$	1.23
C=O*	CCl_3CHO	1.15		(*cis* and *trans*)	
C=O*	Carbon dioxide	1.16	$\overset{+}{N}\overset{\cdots}{\equiv}N$*	Diazomethane	1.13
$C\overset{\cdots}{-}O^-$*	Carbonate ion	1.30	S—H	H_2S	1.35
:C=O:*	Carbon monoxide	1.13	S—S	CH_3SSCH_3	2.04
C=O*	Carbon suboxide	1.20			

BOND ENERGIES (kg.-cal./mole)

BOND	ENERGY	BOND	ENERGY	BOND	ENERGY
C—H	87.3	C—F	107.0	N—N	20.0
C—C	58.6	C—Cl	66.5	N≡N	170.0
C=C	100.0	C—Br	54.0	N—Cl	38.4
C≡C	123.0	C—I	45.5	S—H	87.5
C—O	70.0	H—H	103.4	S—S	63.8
C=O (CH₂O)	142.0	H-bond	5.0	F—F	63.5
C=O (RCHO)	149.0	H—F	147.5	Cl—Cl	57.8
C=O (R₂CO)	152.0	H—Cl	102.7	Br—Br	46.1
C—N	48.6	H—Br	87.3	I—I	36.2
C=N	94.0	H—I	71.4	Cl—F	86.4
C≡N (HCN)	144.0	O—H	110.2	Br—Cl	52.7
C≡N (RCN)	150.0	O—O	34.9	I—Cl	51.0
C—S	54.5	O=O	96.0	I—Br	42.9
C=S	103.0	N—H	83.7	Na—Na	18.5

RESONANCE ENERGIES (kg.-cal./mole)

COMPOUND	ENERGY	COMPOUND	ENERGY
Acetamide	25	Furan	23
Acetic acid	25	Indole	54
Acetic anhydride	41	Naphthalene	75
Acetophenone	46	Phenanthrene	110
Aniline	45	Phenol	46
Anthracene	105	Phenylacetylene	49
Benzene	39	Pyridine	43
Butadiene-1,3	3.5	Pyrrole	31
Carbon dioxide	33	Quinoline	69
Crotonaldehyde	2.4	Stilbene	93
Cyclohexadiene-1,3	1.8	Styrene	46
Cyclopentadiene-1,3	2.9	Thiophene	31
2,3-Dimethylbutadiene-1,3	2.9	Toluene	39
Diphenyl	86[a]	1,3,5-Triphenylbenzene	64
Ethyl acetate	25	Urea	41

[a] 2 × 39 (benzene) + 8

PROPERTIES OF SOLVENTS

SOLVENT	DIELECTRIC CONSTANT	SOLY. IN $H_2O^{20°}$, %	SOLVENT	DIELECTRIC CONSTANT	SOLY. IN $H_2O^{20°}$, %
HCN (liq.)	95	∝	Pyridine	12.5	∝
Water	81.1		Aniline	7.2	3.49
Formic acid	47.9	∝	Acetic acid	7.1	∝
Nitromethane	39.4	sl. sol.	Ethylamine	6.3	∝
Acetonitrile	38.8	∝	Chlorobenzene	5.9	insol.
Nitrobenzene	36.1	0.19	Chloroform	5.0	0.82
Methanol	33.7	∝	Ether	4.3	7.5
Ethanol	25.7	∝	Triethylamine	3.1	∝ < 19°
Ammonia (liq.)	21	∝	Dioxane	2.3	∝
Acetone	21.4	∝	Benzene	2.3	0.06
Acetic anhydride	20.5	12	Carbon tetrachloride	2.2	0.1
n-Butanol	17.8	8.3	Pentane	1.8	insol.

INDUCTIVE EFFECTS (ALIPHATIC SERIES)

Electron-attracting groups: $Cl > Br > I > OCH_3 > OH > C_6H_5 > CH{=}CH_2 > H$

Electron-releasing groups: $(CH_3)_3C > (CH_3)_2CH > CH_3CH_2 > CH_3 > H$

ELECTRONEGATIVITY VALUES

F	4.0	S	2.5	B	2.0
O	3.5	C	2.5	Sn	1.7
N	3.0	I	2.4	Al	1.5
Cl	3.0	P	2.1	Mg	1.2
Br	2.8	H	2.1	Na	0.9